ECONOMIC
GEOGRAPHY:

Selected Readings

ECONOMIC

GEOGRAPHY:

Selected Readings

edited by FRED E. DOHRS
Wayne State University

and LAWRENCE M. SOMMERS
Michigan State University

THOMAS Y. CROWELL COMPANY
New York
Established 1834

PREFACE

In compiling this as well as the previous three volumes of readings in the series, we have sought materials from the wide variety of literature available that would be especially suitable for introductory geography courses. We have endeavored to cover each of the main topics discussed in the majority of introductory texts, and although our organization is systematic, we have included articles pertaining to most of the major regions of the earth, thus making the collection suitable for courses of the regional type. And although economic geography is increasingly offered as an introductory geography course at many colleges and universities, the geography of economic activity forms an important part of other introductory courses as well.

Drawing upon the rich and varied geographical and economic literature that is available, *Economic Geography: Selected Readings* is concerned with the nature and pattern of economic activities on the surface of the earth. The first section introduces economic geography as an important field of geography in general, emphasizing contemporary concepts and ideas. Following this introduction are three sections organized to conform to the fundamental concept of primary, secondary, and tertiary economic activities. This organization facilitates the presentation of theoretical, methodological, and substantive materials for each of these areas of economic activity. Furthermore, such organization makes for effective correlation with the wide variety of economic geography textbooks. An additional advantage is the opportunity to examine in some depth the very important tertiary activities of retail trade and the broad spectrum of services that have frequently been neglected in some otherwise excellent courses and texts.

The final section is concerned with the economic region, both theoretically and empirically. The importance of the process of regionalization is also stressed, and examples of economic regions are examined.

Selections for this volume were made to provide (1) examples of the various approaches to economic geography, (2) illustrations of important ideas and concepts in economic geography, (3) methods of approaching challenging spatial problems, and (4) a sampling of material on diverse regions of the world, their differing economies, economic activities, and processes. In geography it is often impossible to separate economic activity from the physical and cultural environments; thus some of the articles do contribute to earlier volumes in this series—*Physical Geography: Selected Readings,* and *Cultural Geography: Selected Readings* —just as parts of those volumes supplement this one. The impact of man and his economic activities on the character of the earth's surface should be studied along with, as well as in relation to, the natural environment.

To make this volume as useful as possible for teacher and student alike, several distinctive features have been included. Each section is preceded by a brief introduction that suggests the breadth and scope of the subject covered within the section, and its place within the field of geography as a whole. In addition, preceding each selection, there are headnotes that place each article in relation to the topic being covered, as well as to the other articles in that section. We have also provided brief bibliographical notes on the opening page of each selection, which serve to identify the author and the source from which the selection was taken. Finally, to aid the instructor in making assignments, a table has been included that correlates chapters in selected introductory geography texts with the articles in this book.

Economic Geography: Selected Readings is the fourth volume in the series. The earlier volumes, *Introduction to Geography: Selected Readings, Physical Geography: Selected Readings,* and *Cultural Geography: Selected Readings,* will, when used with this collection, provide instructors of basic courses with an abundance of materials from which to choose, thus adding depth and interest to introductory geography. It is hoped that the inherent flexibility of this volume, as well as the coverage of the series as a whole, will allow the teacher to select articles and volumes consistent with his own emphasis and notions of how the course should be taught.

Deep appreciation is expressed to the authors and publishers of the articles included, and to colleagues and others who gave valuable suggestions and assistance.

F.E.D.
L.M.S.

CONTENTS

I. INTRODUCTION

From the time of the Greeks to present-day United States and Europe, economic activity has long been a major focus of geographic study. The great variety of ways in which people make a living in different parts of the world and the impact of these activities upon the spatial character of the physical and cultural landscape result in a highly complex configuration. The objective of most past writing in the field of economic geography has been to describe the unique conditions involved in understanding the spatial variations and interrelationships of an economic activity, such as wheat or steel production, in a single area or in different parts of a country, a continent, or the entire world. More recent efforts by some scholars have been concentrated on higher levels of generalization with the purpose of arriving at useful theories or at least a conceptual structure that will permit a better analysis of real world regions and problems.

The two articles in this first section are intended to introduce the reader to the place of economic geography in the total discipline of geography, as described by Webb, and to some of the more recent developments, as indicated by King in his survey of approaches to location analysis. Certain economic phenomena lend themselves to exact measurement and quantification. Statistical methods and computer analyses have been increasingly utilized to aid the researcher in reaching meaningful generalizations with complex data. Theory and concepts have been borrowed and adapted from other disciplines, as is emphasized by King.

The three sections that follow are based on the classification of economic activity. The last part illustrates theoretical and empirical methods leading to the formulation or delineation of economic geographic regions.

The organization of the major sections is topical, or systematic, rather than regional, except for the last section on economic regions. The selections illustrate concepts, generalizations, and theories important to the field of economic geography. Some selections are more factual and descriptive than others; these were included to provide variety and also because certain areas of study are more highly developed theoretically (such as locational analysis) than others.

With room on the earth's surface becoming an increasingly critical factor in our daily lives, the study and understanding of the spatial structure of economic activity is becoming more and more relevant to the student, citizen, and businessman. The rapidly exploding world population and resultant pressure upon natural and human resources will create an even more complex pattern of economic geographic phenomena in the future.

1. Economic Geography: A Framework for a Disciplinary Definition

Martyn J. Webb

Scholars have always sought precise definitions of their subject. Economic geography, a major systematic sub-discipline of geography, deals with the spatial character of man's production, trading, and consuming activities. Different individuals will vary the emphasis somewhat in their treatment of the subject but the core deals with the spatial structure of economic activity. In this article Webb is concerned with the necessity to establish the proper framework for defining the scope of economic geography. The relationship of other segments of the discipline to economic geography is illustrated in Webb's diagram as well as the related fields that contribute to the subject matter of general economic geography.
The central column of the framework diagram is also similar to the scheme of organization utilized in this volume of readings. It is an organization that fits in well with most textbooks that are systematic in approach. The primary, secondary, and tertiary classification of economic activity results in a more complete coverage, particularly in the retail and service categories, which are becoming more and more important in most parts of the world. This type of organization is in harmony with much current substantive, as well as theoretical, research in the field. Thus both substantive and theoretical articles are included in the main subdivisions following this introductory section. Webb concludes with economic regions; this book also concludes with economic regions. As economic geography deals with the spatial structure of

> *economic activity, each article in this volume develops*
> *generalizations concerning the real world or theoretical*
> *concentrations or patterns of economic geographic*
> *phenomena that help us to understand economic*
> *or production regions.*

. . . Current developments within the subject [of economic geography] and the impact of more clearly formulated concepts concerning space relations have encouraged economic geographers to think anew upon the nature and scope of their subject. Whatever the outcome of these deliberations, it will become increasingly necessary at some stage to formulate a disciplinary definition of the field and scope of economic geography. The value of disciplinary definitions has been questioned, but there is a need, as McCarty has suggested, "for developments of new and more useful systems of classification in economic geography." Systems of this type need not of necessity be sterile. In precise terms, a good disciplinary definition of the subject should:

1. Clearly identify the main avenues of work and their relation to economic geography and to geography as a whole.
2. Allow a more precise knowledge of the position and potential of any particular problem or aspect within the scope of economic geography to be secured.
3. Encourage and stimulate specialization of a kind which in the long run will provide better opportunities for synthetic studies in general and regional economic geography.

In this process, *classification* of existing material must be regarded as a foundation. Definitions *de novo* tend to favor novelty at the expense of what is already known, tried, and accepted. A classification approach, on the other hand, is better able to maintain the most enduring element of all definitions of geography: cosmos.

The framework about to be discussed (Fig. 1) was drawn up according to a number of principles, of which one must be made clear at the outset. This is that economic geography can properly be defined only in terms of the parent subject, geography; and in a classificatory scheme, this principle implies structural isomorphism. In addition, while precision demands a taxonomic approach, the number of coined terms must be reduced to an absolute minimum; albeit at the risk of giving new meanings and interpretations to existing terms.

SOURCE: *Economic Geography*, XXXVII (July, 1961), 254–57. Reprinted with permission of the author and the editor. The author is professor of geography at the University of Western Australia.

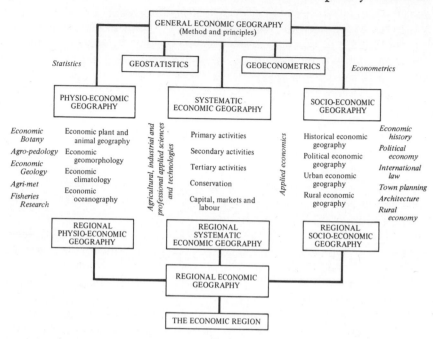

FIGURE 1: A framework for economic geography. The box headings refer to the main structure, the lower case titles to its subdivisions, and the italics to other disciplines to which these subdivisions are related. Only the more obvious and the most direct of these relationships are here depicted.

I

General economic geography is an abstraction; reality only exists in its parts. The basis of general economic geography lies in principles and methods, for which the keystone is a proper understanding of the history of the development of economic geography. To be effective, this history must be written by trained economic geographers. Only in this manner may economic geography the more easily absorb past and present contributions to discussions concerning the aims, scope, and methods of the subject.

Principles and methods may be divided into those which are general to economic geography as a whole, and those particular to each of its subbranches. General methods concern statistics and econometrics, or, more exactly, *geo*statistics and *geo*econometrics. Economic geographers have long been aware of the importance of statistics, and, in their portrayal of data by cartographic, diagrammatic, and tabular means, have developed many specific geostatistical techniques. Other branches of geography have developed similar special techniques, geomorphology and climatology for example, and it is perhaps time that some thought was given to the need to redefine the field of mathematical geography, the one branch of the subject whose scope has remained substantially unchanged since Ptolomaic times. A grouping of all geostatistical techniques employed by geographers under the heading of mathematical geography would do a great deal to focus attention upon the common interest of all branches of geography in statistical and mathematical methods of description and analysis. Geostatistics gives precision to methods, logic to forms of analysis, and quantitative values to conclusions. Geoeconometrics, stemming from econometric studies of socioeconomic distributions in space, by stimulating theoretical and empirical studies by geographers of space relations, has done much to encourage the formulation of generalizations and to provide new insight into age-old problems.

General economic geography proper is, therefore, concerned with methods and principles common to its parts. Because of its abstract quality it is justifiable to speak of it as representing the theoretical branch of the subject. Applied economic geography, because it deals more directly with terrestrial realities, is best conceived in relation to specific points of view. Broadly these may be classified under three heads: the *geo*centric, the *anthropo*centric, and the *econo*centric viewpoints. Each viewpoint may be given a precise classificatory heading.

Physio-economic geography represents the *geocentric* viewpoint, and, in contradistinction to views expressed elsewhere, is a meaningful aspect of the study of economic geography. As a consequence of its particular approach, its subdivisions are comparable to the branches of physical geography. *Socio*-economic geography, on the other hand, personifies the *anthropocentric* standpoint, and its structure is analogous to that of human geography. Consequently, socio-and physioeconomic geography are to economic geography as human and physical geography are to geography itself.

The significance of these two aspects of economic geography is manifold, but the importance of a two-way relationship must be stressed. Physio-economic geography, for example, is not simply a study of the influences of the physical environment upon economic activity, for it is equally a part of its function to observe the effect which economic activity has upon the physical environment. Similarly, in socioeconomic geography, concepts formulated by economic geographers have already contributed a great deal: for example, in *urban* economic geography.

Historical economic geography is of particular importance to the development of economic geography. Historical geography, as H. C. Darby remarked, is a foundation "meant for greater things to be built on." The techniques of economic geography are of considerable importance to evolutionary and time cross-section studies in economic geography. Contemporary studies cannot ignore the past, and the incorporation of an historical base gives to economic geography an element without which no discipline can ever be complete.

The third subdivision, *systematic* economic geography, because it classifies the *econocentric* outlook, is particular to economic geography. Its subdivisions, corresponding to a functional classification of economic activity, are therefore the core areas of applied economic geography. Nevertheless, it cannot be separated from either physio- or socioeconomic geography; and to assume, as even some economic geographers have done, that systematic economic geography is the whole of economic geography is to mislead. Yet well-known specialist library classifications, for example, continue to restrict economic geography to little more than this.

There are thus three divisions within the field of applied economic geography and each division is further subdivided. Reintegration can only be achieved through the region. Hence, as the diagram shows, each of the three branches is linked to regional studies of a type particular to its central viewpoint. Regional economic geography, like general economic geography, is concerned with methods and principles. The realities correspond to regions derived from applied general economic geography and culminate in *The Economic Region*, which for economic geography fulfills the same role as does *The Geographic Region* for geography as a whole.

II

The relations of economic geography only appear to be complex in the absence of orderliness. Within economic geography itself, relations are effectively osmotic; the various cells or compartments within the subject are so constructed, or should be so constructed, that a constant stream of material passes into and out of the subdivisions carried on a plasma of methods and principles. The relations of economic geography to the rest of geography are very similar, but here movement can be hindered because of a lack of an intermediary process of digestion. For economic geography, the existence of physio- and socio-economic geography provide one way of overcoming this difficulty.

The relations of economic geography to all other disciplines are of a third order and in principle are endosmotic rather than exosmotic. This is an important qualification, because so far as economic geography is concerned, the exosmotic ideal presupposes not only a utilitarian role for economic geography, but all too frequently premature claims by geographers as to what are these utilities or relationships. The endosmotic viewpoint on the other hand stresses only that which is of utility to economic geography itself. When this is considered in relation to the disciplinary definition now proposed, it is immediately apparent that these endo-dynamic relations are mainly of one kind—to the applied arts, sciences, and technologies. The more important of these have been sketched in.

Conclusion

This disciplinary definition is essentially conservative and therefore professional economic geographers should have no difficulty in classifying works and materials already known to them according to this scheme. As an essay in geographical taxology it will have served its purpose if, as a result of classification, avenues for future work might become more apparent.

2. Approaches to Location Analysis: An Overview
Leslie J. King

Recent developments in economic geography have placed emphasis upon location analysis. Empirical research on the spatial aspects of the economy has concentrated on the development of valid generalizing concepts that would advance the field. Scholars have attempted to build theoretical models or adapt those developed in other fields to help solve the problems of economic geography. King summarizes the types of models and their relevance in the study of the geography of economic activity.

This article and Webb's previous statement set the stage for the articles that follow. In selection 4, for example, Harvey treats many of the same theoretical ideas and models as they apply to agricultural problems. The footnotes in this article by King lead the reader to many valuable empirical and theoretical studies available in the literature. Location analysis research is in its infancy in the field of geography, but the approach has already demonstrated that it will add to the understanding of agricultural, manufacturing, and other patterns found in space and changing over time. As economic geography

*evolves, less emphasis is being placed on factual
coverage and more on a higher level of conceptualization or generalization. King summarizes some of the ac-
complishments to date in this direction and points the way
to the work that needs to be done.*

The study of the spatial organization of economic activity encompasses
a wide range of contemporary research interests, as is evidenced by
the increasing number of studies to be found in the literature of economics, business logistics, and planning, in addition to the continuing
work of geographers and regional scientists.[1] Is is impossible to attempt
here an exhaustive review of all of the contributions which have been
made to this field of study. What is intended in this paper is a brief
survey of the literature of economic geography with the aim of discussing the extent to which model-building and empirical research
have complemented one another in the geographer's quest for understanding.

The methods of science, more particularly of social science, provide
the backdrop against which the ensuing discussion is staged. This is
not to overlook the fact that a complete identification of the goals of
economic geography with the formal aims of science, albeit social
science, is held by many to be unnecessarily restrictive, perhaps even
misleading. One argument along these lines is that the historical geographer has much to contribute to an understanding of the spatial organization of economic activity, and such a contention is not easily
dismissed in view of the number of good historical studies which are
to be found in the literature of economic geography. However, an extended discussion of this theme lies outside the scope of this paper and
only one general comment is entered at this point. There appears to be
a rather vaguely defined boundary between the work of the social
scientist, particularly as it relates to dynamic situations, and the work
of many historians. Indeed, the nature of the boundary between the
two approaches often is a matter of philosophical debate, witness the
lengthy discussion of the issue in the works of Brown and Nagel.[2]

SOURCE: *The East Lakes Geographer,* II (August, 1966), 1–16. Reprinted with permission of the author and the editor. The author is associate professor of geography
at Ohio State University.
[1] Consider, for example, such statements as J. L. Heskett, R. M. Ivie, and N. A. Glas-
kowsky, *Business Logistics* (New York: The Ronald Press, 1964), pp. 120–51; J. R.
Meyer, "Regional Economics: A Survey," *American Economic Review,* Vol. 53
(1963), pp. 19–54; J. Friedman and W. Alonso (ed.), *Regional Development and
Planning* (Cambridge: M.I.T. Press, 1964), Pt. II; and P. Haggett, *Locational
Analysis in Human Geography* (New York: St. Martin's Press, 1966).
[2] R. Brown, *Explanation in Social Science* (Chicago: Aldine Publishing Company,
1963), pp. 25–39, 47–57, and E. Nagel, *The Structure of Science* (New York:
Harcourt, Brace and World, Inc., 1961), Chapter 15.

The role of models in the pursuit of scientific inquiry has been viewed in a number of different ways by diferent scholars. The philosophers of science, for example, have stressed the formal epistemological contrasts between a model and the theory which it represents and have sought to emphasize the dangers inherent in the careless use of analogies or analogue models.[3] Social scientists generally have taken a broader view of the use of models in their research. Ackoff, for example, has said of models that they ". . . are utilized to accumulate and relate the knowledge we have about different aspects of reality. . . . They are our descriptions and explanations of reality." [4] As such, models are categorized by Ackoff into "iconic," "analogue," and "symbolic" types. In terms of this classification, the models referred to in this paper are symbolic ones, although some analogue type models have been proposed for studying the location of economic activity.[5]

An alternative grouping of models into three categories has been suggested in a recent paper by Lowry.[6] He emphasizes the differences between *descriptive models*, which ". . . replicate the relevant features of an existing . . . environment or of an already-observed process of . . . change"; *predictive models*, which incorporate relationships between form and process and allow for the prediction of future values on certain variables; and finally, *planning models*, which permit the evaluation of outcomes in the light of certain goals and constraints. Coleman also has discussed the distinction between descriptive and planning or normative models.[7]

In the present context, the descriptive model has obvious application and, indeed, most of the models to be discussed here are of this type. Although normative models seem more appropriate for the realm of planning and policy-making rather than economic geography, some recent studies in this field prompt the conclusion that these same models may yield considerable insight into the structure of existing locational systems. The analysis, for example, of the deviations observable in reality from the completely rational economic situations postulated by the model often suggests new hypotheses for testing.

Another distinction drawn in discussions of models, and one which is emphasized throughout this paper, is between *deterministic* and

[3] See, for example, R. B. Braithwaite, *Scientific Explanation* (Cambridge: University Press, 1955), pp. 88–96; P. Achinstein, "Models, Analogies and Theories," *Philosophy of Science*, Vol. 31 (1964), pp. 328–350.
[4] R. L. Ackoff, *Scientific Method. Optimizing Applied Research Decisions* (New York: John Wiley & Sons, Inc., 1962), pp. 108 ff.
[5] For example, S. Enke, "Equilibrium Among Spatially Separated Markets: Solution by Electric Analogue," *Econometrica*, Vol. 19 (1951), pp. 40–47.
[6] I. S. Lowry, "A Short Course in Model Design," *Journal of the American Institute of Planners*, Vol. 31, No. 2 (1965), pp. 158–166.
[7] J. S. Coleman, *Introduction to Mathematical Sociology* (New York: The Free Press, 1964), pp. 524–25.

indeterministic models.[8] This distinction is clearer if the model is re-garded as the representation of an approach to scientific inquiry. The deterministic approach assumes that the world is comprehensibly law-ful, and that for any observable system there is an underlying order which can be discovered by science. It assumes, further, that all of the relevant variables affecting the system can be known and their interre-lationships specified by mathematical equations. In this sense, the sys-tem is considered to be a closed one, although this does not imply that outside forces are unimportant. Closure simply demands that all of the relevant variables, both endogenous and exogenous, be known and their significance understood. The unfolding of the system through time is described by the process law, embodied in a set of differential equa-tions which explicitly represent changes in the variables as functions of time. For this set of equations or models, there exists an analytic so-lution. Given a description of the system at any one time, then it is possible to predict or describe the system at any other time either in the past or future.[9]

By contrast, the indeterministic approach in science denies that exact and invariable relationships hold for many systems. Rather, the contention is that the description and prediction of the state of any one of these systems can be given only in statistical or probabilistic terms. In the context of this approach, there is repeated reference made to *random phenomena* whose observations under given sets of circumstances do not always lead to the same outcomes, but to differ-ent outcomes in such a way that only statistical regularities can be ex-pected. For any random phenomenon that arises through a dynamic process, ". . . in a manner controlled by probabilistic laws" the term *stochastic process* is used and the corresponding models are called *stochastic models*.

The distinction between deterministic and indeterministic models is useful, but as with any categorization of models it is not always clear-cut. For example, the model $Y = a + bX$ might be interpreted as a de-terministic one, and there are examples in the literature of economic geography of such a formulation.[10] On the other hand, the model $Y = a + bX + e$, where e is an error term, might be regarded as an indeterministic model and, again there are many examples of this

[8] See, for example, J. G. Kemeny and J. L. Snell, *Mathematical Models in the Social Sciences* (Boston: Ginn and Co., 1962), pp. 5–6, and Coleman, *op. cit.*, pp. 526–28.
[9] The classical deterministic syllogism is that of Newtonian mechanics. For a dis-cussion of this schema see Nagel, *op. cit.*, Chapters 7–10, and G. Bergmann. *The Philosophy of Science* (Madison: University of Wisconsin Press, 1957), pp. 84–100.
[10] For example, see B. J. L. Berry and H. G. Barnum, "Aggregate Relations and Ele-mental Components of Central Place Systems," *Journal of Regional Science*, Vol. 4, No. 1 (1962), pp. 35–68.

type of formulation which may be cited.[11] But it is noteworthy that Blalock, for example, does not accept the identification of an indeterministic approach simply with the introduction of error terms into the model.[12] He argues that if the error of variation in Y can be attributed to outside variables that have not been considered then the model is still a deterministic one, and only if the error reflects chance or random process is the formulation indeterministic. However, he notes that "we shall never be in a position to resolve the determinism-indeterminism controversy by empirical means." A similar insistence upon the distinction between determinism and indeterminism as one of conceptualization in the model-building is put forward by Neyman.[13]

As will be noted below, the models which have been developed to date for the spatial organization of economic activity typically have been deterministic. The fact that the empirical testing of these models has not proven very fruitful in terms of increased understanding lends weight to the contention that the spatial organization of economic activity is subject to random or stochastic influences which generally have been ignored by the model-builders; that as a result, their models have provided but poor descriptions and explanations of the geographer's empirical observations.

The foregoing comments on the nature of models provide the backdrop against which some selected problem areas of economic geography now are reviewed.

Much of the early geographic research on this problem is devoid of any serious discussion of models. The oft-quoted empirical studies concerned with identifying agricultural types and associated regions were not structured around any models or even hypotheses,[14] nor did they provide much feedback for the future model-builders in the form of inductive generalizations.

Admittedly, prior to the 1950's there had been few serious attempts at constructing models of the spatial organization of agriculture which could be calibrated by way of empirical investigations. The well-known Von Thunen model of agricultural land-use, with its important location-rent postulate, is a rather loosely structured set of generally qualitative

[11] For example, W. L. Garrison, "The Benefits of Rural Roads to Rural Property," Pt. IV, *Allocation of Road and Street Costs* (Seattle: Washington State Council for Highway Research, 1956), pp. 47–48.

[12] H. M. Blalock, *Causal Inferences in Non-experimental Research* (Chapel Hill: University of North Carolina Press, 1961), pp. 15–18.

[13] J. Neyman, "Indeterminism in Science and New Demands on Statisticians," *Journal of the American Statistical Association,* Vol. 55 (1960), pp. 625–639.

[14] See H. H. McCarty, "Agricultural Geography," *American Geography: Inventory and Prospect,* ed. P. E. James and C. F. Jones (Syracuse: Syracuse University Press, 1954), pp. 258–277. In this review statement there is no reference made to any models or theoretical constructs.

statements,[15] and as a consequence, the rigorous empirical testing of the structure has not been facilitated.

This point about the testing of models will reappear in the course of the subsequent discussion and it is perhaps desirable to elaborate briefly on it. In a strictly logical sense, a model itself is never tested against reality. For as ". . . a logico-mathematical construct of inter-related variables" a model can stand by itself independent of reality. But to the extent that models are used in interpreting real-world situations, it is usually desirable to fit or calibrate the model to a set of empirical observations. Lowry points out that this fitting involves at least two important steps. First, "the variables mentioned in the model must be given precise empirical definition," and secondly, ". . . numerical values must be provided for the model's parameters." Lowry's own illustration of the first point is relevant to the present discussion. He notes that "location rents," such as are postulated by Von Thunen, are not directly measurable and the question arises, ". . . can contract rents be statistically standardized to serve as a reliable proxy for location rents?"

The limitations of the Von Thunen model as regards its possible calibration may account for its comparative neglect by empirical workers in economic geography. This is not to overlook the fact that some researchers, for example, Grotewold and Chisholm, have found the model useful in providing a general reference framework for their interpretations of the spatial structure of the economy.[16] However, the patterns with which these studies dealt were fairly aggregative ones and the contribution of the model to an understanding of these patterns appears to have been marginal.

Two other empirical studies might be cited in this context. Lewthwaite in a study of the Wisconsin cheese industry examined some of the broad locational hypotheses which are implicit in the Von Thunen structure. His conclusion was that the factors of relative market location and freight-absorption differentials have governed the location pattern of cheese production only in the sense of ". . . a broad and permissive framework rather than as a locally effective determinant."[17] Harvey, in his study of the Kentish hop industry, noted ". . . a persistent tendency throughout the century (1800-1900) for the distribution of the hop acreage to be related to distance from the center of pro-

[15] J. H. Von Thunen, *Der Isolierte Staat in Beziehung auf Landwirtschaft und Nationalokonomie* (Rostock: 1826). For a discussion of the model see M. Chisholm; *Rural Settlement and Land Use* (London: Hutchinson University Library, 1962), pp. 21–35.

[16] Grotewold, "Von Thunen in Retrospect," *Economic Geography*, Vol. 35, No. 4 (1959), pp. 346–355, and Chisholm *op. cit.*

[17] G. R. Lewthwaite "Wisconsin Cheese and Farm Type: A Locational Hypothesis," *Economic Geography*, Vol. 40, No. 2 (1964), pp. 95–112.

duction," and he sought to explain this tendency in terms of agglomeration economies, factors of cumulative change, and cost-levels.[18]

The Von Thunen model is deterministic, and the more recent work on agricultural location patterns generally has been in the same vein. This is especially true of Dunn's work on the problem.[19] He outlines a simple model of the space-price equilibrium for an agricultural system involving n commodities, in which there are the following unknowns: prices ($P_1 \ldots P_n$), demand ($D_1 \ldots D_n$), boundary ($k_{10} \ldots k_{1n}$), and supply ($S_1 \ldots S_n$). For this set of 4_n equations there is a unique solution which ". . . will provide the price of every commodity, the quantity of each commodity that will be produced and consumed, and at the same time will explicitly determine the spatial orientation of production." An equally deterministic approach is characteristic of Garrison and Marble's contribution to this same problem.[20] By use of an axiomatic method they seek to show that for every location there is an optimum combination of crops, intensities, and markets. The recent work of Alonso and Wingo or urban land-use theory, while involving somewhat different postulates from those in Dunn's model, also is couched in a deterministic framework.[21]

Significantly, one of the few empirical tests made of the Von Thunen-Dunn postulates, namely Garrison's study on *The Verification of a Location Model*,[22] is couched in terms of a regression model, a form of statistical analysis. A regression model also was employed by Yeates in his study of the spatial pattern of land-values in Chicago.[23] But aside from these studies, there has been little consideration shown by geographers for the rigorous testing of the agricultural and urban rent-models. In large part, this is a reflection of the difficulty mentioned earlier concerning the empirical definition of model constructs. However, seemingly a great deal could still be accomplished by the use of proxy variables.

Attention now is focused on the structuring of normative models of

[18] D. Harvey, "Locational Change in the Kentish Hop Industry and the Analysis of Land Use Patterns," *Transaction and Papers of the Institute of British Geographers,* No. 33 (1963), pp. 123–44.

[19] E. S. Dunn, *The Equilibrium of Land-Use Patterns in Agriculture* (Gainesville: University of Florida Press, 1954); also in *Southern Economic Journal,* Vol. 21, No. 2 (1955), pp. 173–187.

[20] D. F. Marble and W. L. Garrison, "The Spatial Structure of Agricultural Activities," *Annals of the Association of American Geographers,* Vol. 47, No. 2 (1957), pp. 137–144.

[21] W. Alonso, *Location and Land Use* (Cambridge: Harvard University Press, 1964), and L. Wingo, *Transportation and Urban Land* (Baltimore: Johns Hopkins Press, 1961).

[22] W. L. Garrison, "Verification of a Location Model," *Northwestern University Studies in Geography,* II, 1957, pp. 133–140.

[23] M. H. Yeates, "Some Factors Affecting the Spatial Distribution of Chicago Land Values, 1910–1960," *Economic Geography,* Vol. 41, No. 1 (1965), pp. 57–70.

the regional allocation of agricultural production. This work has been initiated by agricultural economists,[24] and for the most part it has emphasized linear, and only more recently non-linear, programming solutions.[25] These normative solutions yield spatial patterns of agricultural production which are consistent with the minimization or maximization of an objective function subject to a number of constraints. In his recent study of farming patterns in central Sweden, Wolpert presented a provocative illustration of how the normative model might be used by the geographer to provide not only a partial explanation of reality but also a norm from which deviations are to be explained in terms of other social science models.[26] To the extent that Wolpert's study therefore raises questions concerning the farmers' perception of goals and risk-situations, it directs attention to the realm of behavorial analysis. Here, the models and theories which the geographer might draw upon for the purposes of his research appear to be quite numerous.[27] These models are typically couched in the language of probability theory, and their "solutions," in terms of obtaining results from some input data, often demand computer simulation.

Unfortunately, to date there have been but few excursions by economic geographers into the field of behavioral analysis. Gould's discussion of a game-theory approach to questions of agricultural land-use is worthy of note, although here the model is more clearly normative and not probabilistic.[28] Curry's discussion of the programming of livestock farms in New Zealand provides a better example of an indeterministic approach to questions of farmer behavior.[29] This study attempts to treat of some of the different elements affecting a farmer's decisions

[24] See for example, R. A. King (ed.), *Interregional Competition* (Raleigh, N.C.: Agricultural Policy Institute, 1963); E. O. Heady and A. C. Egbert, "Regional Programming of Efficient Agricultural Production Patterns," *Econometrica*, Vol. 32, No. 3 (1964), pp. 374–386; and the set of papers on "Spatial Economics," *Journal of Farm Economics*, Vol. 46, No. 5 (1964), pp. 1365–1390.

[25] It is convenient to reference here some studies which relate to this non-linear formulation not only of agriculture models but also, of more general location models. The studies are by T. Takayama and G. G. Judge and include, "Spatial Equilibrium and Quadratic Programming," *Journal of Farm Economics*, Vol. 46, No. 1 (1964), pp. 67–93: "An Interregional Activity Analysis Model for the Agricultural Sector," *Journal of Farm Economics*, Vol. 46, No. 2 (1964), pp. 349–365; "An Intertemporal Price Equilibrium Model," *Ibid.*, pp. 477–86; "Equilibrium Among Spatially Separated Markets: A Reformation," *Econometrica*, Vol. 32, No. 4 (1964), pp. 510–524.

[26] J. Wolpert, "The Decision Process in Spatial Context," *Annals of the Association of American Geographers*, Vol. 54, No. 4 (1964), pp. 537–558.

[27] See F. Massarik and P. Ratoosh, *Mathematical Explorations in Behavioral Science* (Homewood, Illinois: Richard D. Irwin Inc. and Dorsey Press, 1965).

[28] P. Gould, "Man Against His Environment: A Game Theoretic Framework," *Annals of the Association of American Geographers*, Vol. 53, No. 3 (1963), pp. 290–297.

[29] L. Curry, "Regional Variation in the Seasonal Programming of Livestock Farms in New Zealand," *Economic Geography*, Vol. 39, No. 2 (1963), pp. 95–118.

within a probability framework; to accord recognition to the fact that pastoralists ". . . subject to various capacity restraints . . . must schedule the timing of operations and the storage and transfer of atmospheric resources between different periods, while weighing the probabilities of gains and losses."

Two promising avenues of behavioral research which are relevant to the problem of the spatial organization of agriculture are those of the spatial diffusion studies and the perception of environment analyses. The former is, in part, concerned with the spread and adoption of agricultural practices throughout an area.[30] The perception studies seek to discover the different ways that men perceive of their environment and how these perceptions condition their responses in realms such as economic activity.[31] In both lines of research, the behavioral questions are emphasized clearly and, in the diffusion studies particularly, there is explicit consideration of the dynamics of the situations. It will be surprising if the work being done at present in both of these areas does not suggest at least some new insight to the geographer concerned with the spatial organization of agriculture.

What of the position as regards the geographers' analysis of the spatial organization of manufacturing? At first sight it may appear as though model-building and empirical research have come together much closer in this area than has been the case in the study of agriculture. For in a number of empirical studies, the Weberian location model particularly has been tested and referenced. Kennelly's study of the Mexican iron and steel industry and Lindberg's analysis of the Swedish paper industry are but two of the studies which might be cited in this regard.[32] Again, the problem of providing suitable empirical or operational definitions for some of the model constructs has proven to be troublesome. Furthermore, the gap between the "ideal"

---

[30] See, for example, T. Hägerstrand, "A Monte Carlo Approach to Diffusion," *Archives Européenes de Sociologie*, Tome VI, No. 1 (1965), pp. 43–67; L. W. Bowden, *Diffusion of the Decision to Irrigate: Simulation of the Spread of a New Resource Management Practice in the Colorado Northern High Plains*, Research Paper 97 (Chicago: Department of Geography, University of Chicago, 1965); see also, E. M. Rogers, *Bibliography of Research on the Diffusion of Innovations* (East Lansing: Department of Communication, Michigan State University, 1964).

[31] See, for example, R. W. Kates, *Hazard and Choice Perception in Flood Plain Management*, Research Paper 78 (Chicago: Department of Geography, University of Chicago, 1962); R. C. Lucas, "Wilderness Perception and Use: The Example of the Boundary Waters Canoe Area," *Natural Resources Journal*, Vol. 3 (1964), pp. 391–411.

[32] R. A. Kennelly, "The Location of the Mexican Steel Industry," *Revista Geografica*, Tome 14, No. 40 (1954), pp. 51–80; Tome 15, No. 41 (1954), pp. 105–129; Tome 16, No. 42 (1955), pp. 199–213; Tome 17, No. 43 (1955), pp. 60–82. O. Lindberg, "An Economic-Geographical Study of the Localization of the Swedish Paper Industry," *Geografiska Annaler*, Vol. 35 (1953), 28–40.

conditions postulated in the model and the actual nonexperimental situations with which the geographer has to deal has been difficult to bridge.[33] These difficulties notwithstanding, Kennelly found that the Weberian model afforded considerable insight into the location pattern of the Mexican steel industry. Lindberg's analysis, on the other hand, served to underline the difficulties inherent in the application of models to situations for which they were never intended. Since lumber in Sweden is virtually a "ubiquitous" material, its "localizing effect" as postulated in the Weberian model has been small. Hence, Lindberg concluded that "Weber's ideas are not entirely applicable" to this industry.[34]

The restructuring of a deterministic location model for manufacturing has been spearheaded by the work of Isard. In the book *Location and Space Economy*, there is an attempt made to handle the location problem within the framework of substitution analysis and to present a mathematical formulation of a continuous space-economy.[35] Unfortunately, the Isardian model does not lend itself easily to calibration by way of empirical analysis. For one thing, satisfactory operational definitions have still to be suggested for many of the model-constructs, such as transport-inputs and agglomeration economies. Furthermore, the model in its spatial aspects is very abstract; Lefeber, for example, has criticized it in this respect for its dependence on the notion of a "continuous transport plane." [36]

In recent years, empirical research into the spatial organizations of manufacturing has tended to focus upon three themes. The first of these is "comparative cost" analysis. A number of studies of specific industries have sought to explain existing locational patterns in terms of the comparative cost advantage which different locations and areas could offer. Craig's study of the U.S. iron and steel industry and Lindsay's analysis of the oil-refining industry are two such studies.[37] Isard and Cumberland had shown earlier how this comparative-cost approach

[33] Both Nagel and Blalock in discussing this gap conclude that statistical formulations may be all that social scientists can hope for, given that experimental situations cannot be achieved. See Nagel, *op. cit.*, pp. 503–509 and Blalock, *op. cit.*, p. 18.

[34] In a recent paper, Lindberg has questioned the "ubiquity" concept as it appears in the Weberian model. See O. Lindberg, "Ubiquity and Areal Transport Costs," *Geographical Reports*, Umea University, No. 1 (1965).

[35] W. Isard, *Location and Space-Economy* (New York: M.I.T. Press and John Wiley & Sons, Inc., 1956).

[36] L. Lefeber, *Allocation in Space* (Amsterdam: North-Holland Publishing Company, 1958), pp. 3–5.

[37] P. Craig, "Location Factors in the Development of Steel Centers," *Papers, The Regional Science Association*, Vol. 3 (1957), pp. 249–265; R. Lindsay, "Regional Advantage in Oil-Refining," *Papers, The Regional Science Association*, Vol. 2 (1956), pp. 304–317.

might be used to analyze possible alternatives to the existing location pattern.[38] This empirical analysis has not been divorced completely from theory, in the sense that it has relied in part upon theory to suggest relevant cost factors, while providing in turn, partial verification of some theoretical constructs.

A second line of inquiry has been suggested by the development of normative models of manufacturing location. The transportation model, a form of the more general linear programming algorithm, has provided the basic framework for a number of spatial allocation models. Reference to the work along these lines by Beckman and Marschak, Goldman, and Lefeber will suffice at this point.[39] In comparison to the spatial allocation models of agriculture, these normative models for manufacturing production appear disappointing. To a large extent, this is a reflection of the greater complexity of the manufacturing location problem. For in contrast to the agricultural problem, there is now a set of discrete production points to be located, in itself a mathematically vexing question, and in addition there is the problem of how to handle the agglomeration economies, which virtually may be ignored in agriculture. The industrial-complex analysis, which Isard and Schooler developed in conjunction with their Puerto Rican studies, does afford a specific solution to the problem of dealing with the agglomeration economies, but it seems feasible only for the case of a very small number of highly technical related activities.[40] Empirical studies related to these normative models are few in the geography literature. A forthcoming study by Casetti applies a Goldman-type model to the location pattern of the Canadian iron and steel industry with emphasis on the question of where additional production capacity might best be located.[41] The Morrill-Garrison study of wheat movements might be men-

[38] W. Isard and J. H. Cumberland, "New England as a Possible Location for an Integrated Iron and Steel Works," *Economic Geographer,* Vol. 26, No. 4 (1950), pp. 245–259.

[39] M. Beckman and T. Marschak, "An Activity Analysis Approach to Location Theory," *Kyklos,* Vol. 8 (1955), pp. 125–143; T. A. Goldman, "Efficient Transportation and Industrial Location," *Papers, The Regional Science Association,* Vol. 4 (1958), pp. 91–109; Lefeber, *op. cit.,* most of the models cited here are reviewed excellently in W. L. Garrison, "Spatial Structure of the Economy, I, II, III," *Annals of the Association of American Geographers,* Vol. 49 (1959), pp. 232–239, 471–482, and Vol. 50 (1960), pp. 357–373. A more formal review in terms of the economic constructs is available in R. E. Kuenne, *The Theory of General Economic Equilibrium* (Princeton: Princeton University Press, 1963), Ch. 7, "Spatial Models," pp. 395–454.

[40] W. Isard and E. W. Schooler, "Industrial Complex Analysis, Agglomeration Economies, and Regional Development," *Journal of Regional Science,* Vol. 1, No. 2 (1959), pp. 19–33.

[41] E. Casetti, "Optimal Location of Steel Mills Serving the Quebec and Southern Ontario Steel Market," Vol. X, No. 1 (1966), *The Canadian Geographer,* pp. 27–39.

tioned, although the location of production is considered fixed in this analysis.[42]

A third line of empirical research in geography has been the analysis of spatial associations in the location pattern of manufacturing. The emphasis here has been upon the testing of theoretical constructs within the framework of correlation and regression analysis.[43] Unfortunately, these studies appear to suffer from weaknesses in design particularly as regards the choice and inclusion of variables and in the nature of the statistical analysis. The fact that there is no concern with questions of multicollinearity, identification, and spatial contiguity, for example,[44] raises serious doubts as to the interpretations which may be drawn from many of these spatial association studies.

It appears as though something of an impasse exists as regards analysis of the spatial organization of manufacturing. On the one hand, as Alonso notes ". . . significant contributions to location theory have become rare." [45] This is not to imply that the models or theories already are refined sufficiently, but that new insights are lacking. The normative approach has not yielded the results that early expectations might have promised, although there have been some worthwhile gains, witness the interpretations of location rent in terms of the "dual" solutions.[46] A start has been made towards incorporating elements of behavior into the location models, for example in Stevens' simple two-person location game, and in Isard and Dacey's recently published studies.[47] Mention should be made also of Greenhut's work on *Microeconomics and the Space Economy*,[48] in which he attempts to develop a maximum profit theory allowing for questions of uncertainty and subjective probabilities on the part of a decision maker in an oligopoly situation, and to incorporate this formulation into a general theory of the space economy.

[42] R. L. Morrill and W. L. Garrison, "Projections of Interregional Patterns of Trade in Wheat and Flour," *Economic Geography*, Vol. 36, No. 2 (1960), pp. 116–126.
[43] See, for example, H. H. McCarty, *et al.*, *The Measurement of Association in Industrial Geography* (Iowa City: Department of Geography, 1956); H. A. Stafford, "Factors in the Location of the Paperboard Container Industry," *Economic Geography*, Vol. 36, No. 3 (1960), pp. 260–266.
[44] The first two of these questions are treated at length in the econometrics literature but have still to command the geographer's attention. See, for example, J. Johnson, *Econometric Methods* (New York: McGraw-Hill, 1963). For a discussion of spatial contiguity, see R. Geary, "The Contiguity Ratio and Statistical Mapping," *Incorporated Statistician*, Vol. 5 (1954), pp. 115–145.
[45] Friedmann and Alonso, *op. cit.*, p. 78.
[46] B. H. Stevens, "Linear Programming and Location Rent," *Journal of Regional Science*, Vol. 3, No. 2 (1961), pp. 15–26.
[47] B. H. Stevens, "An Application of Game Theory to a Problem in Location Strategy," *Papers, The Regional Science Association*, Vol. 7 (1961), pp. 143–157; W. Isard and M. Dacey, "On the Projection of Individual Behavior in Regional Analysis I, II," *Journal of Regional Science*, Vol. 4, Nos. 1, 2 (1962), pp. 1–34, 51–83.
[48] M. L. Greenhut, *Microeconomics and the Space Economy* (Chicago: Scott Foresman and Company, 1963).

But again, these new models are extremely abstract in their treatment of space. To the extent that they deal with questions of human behavior, they also are restricted in their emphasis largely to oligopoly situations, and there remains the question of how aggregated and more competitive-type industrial situations are to be handled.[49] On the empirical side also, with but few exceptions, there has been a dearth of good research which has significant implications for the improvement and further development of models and theory relating to the spatial organization of manufacturing.

Only a few comments will be made on this topic of geographic research since the trends and recent developments in this field have been more than adequately documented in recent years.[50] Model building and empirical research seemingly have combined here to good effect. The deterministic models of Christaller and Lösch, for example, have been tested rigorously in numerous empirical studies, and there have been many restatements and reformulations of theoretical constructs, often prompted in part by the empirical findings.[51] Some of these new statements have been couched in probabilistic terms,[52] and, in a few simulation studies, a start has been made towards developing dynamic indeterministic models of an urban system.[53]

One note of caution might be injected. The array of results from the calibration of these models of tertiary activity is an impressive one, and there are many examples of almost perfect "fits" of the models to sets of empirical data. But a model is only a way of looking at reality; it is not reality itself, and it is quite possible that more than one model will fit the same set of empirical observations. Therefore, there should be special concern for the conceptualization of the model and for the correspondence rules between the model constructs and reality. When

[49] For some comments relevant to this point see J. S. Minas and R. L. Ackoff, "Individual and Collective Value Judgments," in M. W. Shelly and G. L. Bryan (editors), *Human Judgments and Optimality* (New York: J. Wiley and Sons, Inc., 1964), pp. 351–359.

[50] See, for example, B. J. L. Berry and A. Pred, "Central Place Studies: A Bibliography of Theory and Applications," *Regional Science Bibliography Series*, No. 1 (with supp.) (1965); also, B. J. L. Berry, "Cities as Systems within Systems of Cities," *Papers, The Regional Science Association*, Vol. 13 (1964), pp. 147–163.

[51] For example, B. J. L. Berry and W. L. Garrison, "Recent Developments of Central Place Theory," *Papers, The Regional Science Association*, Vol. 4 (1958), pp. 107–120; Berry and Barnum, *op. cit.;* E. S. Mills and M. R. Lav, "A Model of Market Areas with Free Entry," *Journal of Political Economy*, Vol. LXXII, No. 3 (1964), pp. 278–288.

[52] See L. Curry, "The Random Spatial Economy; An Exploration in Settlement Theory," *Annals A.A.G.*, Vol. 54, No. 1 (1964), pp. 138–146; M. F. Dacey, "Modified Poisson Probability Law for Point Pattern More Regular Than Random," *Annals A.A.G.*, Vol. 54, No. 4 (1964), pp. 559–565.

[53] R. L. Morrill, "Simulation of Central Place Patterns Over Time," *Lund Studies in Geography*, Ser. B, No. 24 (1962), pp. 109–120; ———, "Migration and the Spread and Growth of Urban Settlement," *Lund Studies in Geography*, Ser. B, No. 26 (1965).

viewed in this light, the current findings concerning the spatial organization of tertiary activity appear somewhat less impressive. There is a noticeable lack of emphasis on any economic mechanisms or behavioral concepts which might serve to explain the statistical relationships which are observed. Stated another way, there has been little concern with the drawing of causal inferences from the models in the sense that Blalock suggests.

What point may be made in summarizing and concluding this review statement? The first is to note that there is an increasing amount of empirical research in economic geography which is related to model constructs. While this development is most apparent in the study of tertiary activity, it is not without support in the study of agriculture and manufacturing. This trend is regarded as encouraging for it is on the basis of the interaction and feedback between model-building and empirical research that the development of theories will procede. Ultimately, the validity of any claim that economic geography is a meaningful social science must be assessed in terms of the contributions made by its practitioners to a body of theory relating to the spatial organization of economic activity.

That much remains to be done by way of empirical testing and verification of existing models is all too apparent. While admitting that much of the data may not be obtained easily, the rent models, for example, warrant greater attention than has been accorded them in the past. Some normative models also might be tested out in different empirical situations with a view to generalizing the constructs while obtaining insight into particular problem situations. The analysis of behavorial aspects has been stressed already as another topic demanding of more empirical work, and mention of this possibility prompts a more general comment concerning research design. To the extent that economic geographers have made use of inferential statistical procedures, they have been largely hidebound by classical approaches. But if indeed a greater research emphasis is to be placed upon the analysis of behavioral situations, particularly as they may have arisen in the past, then it may behoove the geographer to consider an alternative approach in testing some of his hypotheses. One such approach, involving questions of subjective probability and Bayesian statistics, continues to provoke lively debate in the field of statistics.[54] It is unfortunate that geographers, on the whole, have remained largely indifferent to the issues involved in this debate.

So much for empirical research; what of the models? If on the one hand, there is an insistence that empirical research be directed towards the testing, verification, or even initiation of theory, so must there be

[54] For a general statement on this topic see F. J. Anscombe, "Some Remarks on Bayesian Statistics," in M. W. Shelly and G. L. Bryan (editors), *Human Judgments and Optimality* (New York: John Wiley & Sons, Inc., 1964), pp. 155–177.

equal demands that the models be as realistic as possible and incorporate meaningful constructs. One of the implications throughout this discussion has been that the models will prove more useful only when they are structured in the language of probability theory. Now there is no denying the point which Coleman makes in his recent survey of mathematical sociology, that ". . . stochastic processes tend to be the vogue these days. . . ." Nor is it infrequently that one hears the criticism which Coleman notes, to the effect that ". . . one of the tendencies in the use of probabilistic models is to develop a kind of 'know-nothing' approach toward the behavior that the model is intended to reflect. That is, some probabilistic models do little more than formalize our ignorance." But two points may be made in answering this criticism. The one is that the criticism reflects a naive conception of probability analysis and errs in identifying it simply with curve-fitting. In fact, a good stochastic model will incorporate structural relationships, and in its conceptualization will be no less demanding of insight on the part of the researcher than its deterministic counterpart. An insistence that this be so was implicit in the earlier comments on the models of tertiary activity. The second point is more philosophical and has to do with the structure of explanation. Critics of the indeterministic approach point to the fact that explanations cannot be derived deductively from statistical generalizations. This observation is correct but it does not provide any basis for denying that statistical explanations, which assert that if certain specified conditions are realized, then an occurrence of such and such a kind will come about with such and such a probability, are any less genuine than the deductive forms.

A final comment relates to the essentially static nature of many of the location models developed to date. This reflects, in large part, their emphasis upon equilibrium situations rather than upon the unstable conditions leading up to or away from these positions. In empirical research, however, there has been greater concern for the nature of change in the systems, and the literature is replete with studies of comparative statics—in other words, cross-sectional analyses of data for selected points in time. Now, however, there is apparently an increasing concern on the part of the model-builders with the incorporation of time as a variable in their models. Models of agricultural and urban land-use development, for example, are formulated as recursive models in which parameter values for one time are related to those for a previous time.[55]

[55] See "Urban Development Models: New Tools for Planning," a special issue of the *Journal of American Institute of Planners* (edited by B. Harris), Vol. 31, No. 2 (1965); also, K. J. Schlager, "A Recursive Programming Theory of the Residential Land Development Process," unpublished paper, Annual Meeting Highway Research Board, Washington, D.C., 1966; also, W. N. Schaller and G. W. Dean, "Predicting Regional Crop Production," *U.S. Department of Agriculture Technical Bulletin*, No. 1329 (1965).

It is certain that to the extent that indeterministic approaches are emphasized in the future, then progress in the development of dynamic models will be slow. The mathematics of stochastic processes is not a realm in which the self-taught enthusiast may venture safely very far. Besides it is unlikely, given the present state of the art, that tightly logical structures can be developed which will allow for analytic solutions of, say, the limiting probability distributions as functions of time.[56] In this context then, simulations may be the optimum research strategy for some time to come. Mention already has been made of some spatial simulation studies in urban and cultural geography,[57] and the approach could well be extended to the study of agricultural and manufacturing location patterns developing over space and through time. It is toward an understanding of these problems, that the economic geographer will continue to strive.

[56] See, for example, the difficulties posed in J. S. de Cani, "On the Construction of Stochastic Models of Population Growth and Migration," *Journal of Regional Science*, Vol. 3, No. 2 (1961), pp. 1–13.
[57] Hägerstrand, *op. cit.*, and Morrill, *op. cit.*

II. PRIMARY ECONOMIC ACTIVITY

Primary production includes those activities involved in extracting items of value from their natural state, and numbers such diverse activities as mining, forestry, fishing, and agriculture that uses the natural environment to produce more of special natural items, that is, plants and animals, for man's use. More often than not, the locations of these activities are relatively fixed by the fundamental distributions on the physical earth—climate, soils, water, and minerals—although the intensity of the activity may and does vary widely from place to place.

Agricultural production is not only the most widespread of all economic activities, it is also an activity that involves more people and larger areas than any other occupation of mankind. In many areas agriculture has been and may remain the only activity economically possible. Nevertheless, the nature of farming practices varies widely because of diverse natural, social, and economic factors—from the labor-intensive plantations or the capital-intensive dairy farms of Wisconsin to the bare subsistence agriculture in West Africa. Increasingly, world agriculture is being challenged to meet the food demands of a burgeoning world population. Because of the great importance of agriculture, this section begins with an article that examines agriculture on a world scale. It is followed by a theoretical and quantitative approach to agricultural land use and several additional articles that cover a broad spectrum of agricultural types and areal specializations, ranging from "Agricultural Developments in Nigeria" to "Wisconsin Cheese and Farm Type."

Cutting trees for timber has traditionally been and to a great extent remains an extractive industry—using the natural forests as the resource. Recently, however, the production of logs and lumber from trees has become more of an agricultural activity, one in which trees are planted —reforestation or afforestation—or replanted regularly, carefully maintained, cultivated, and harvested as a crop. Problems facing these activities are examined in "Taming Trees." Of substantially less importance, but of economic significance in some areas, is the extraction of particular parts of certain trees—sap, bark, juice, seeds—as raw materials for special manufactured goods.

"Harvesting the sea" has almost become a cliché, suggesting that the food need for billions may be more readily obtained from the sea than by increasing agricultural productivity. As yet, however, our knowledge of the food producing capability of the sea is quite limited, although many nations have highly developed fishing fleets and seafood production. Much more must be learned about the vast world ocean if we are to be able to increase and maintain a high level harvest from the sea. "New Methods of Appraising the Role of Fisheries in World Nutrition" is a detailed examination of the problem.

The term "mining" applies to all activities through which minerals, solid or liquid, are extracted from the earth by a variety of techniques: through shafts, open pits, pipes, quarries, or other methods. Mining is entirely an extractive primary industry as the development and concentration of economically valuable minerals is, by man's timetable, extremely slow. This, however, adds to the problem, because replacement is hardly possible and, for many uses, substitution is difficult. Furthermore, if minerals are to be used, they must be extracted where they are found, and frequently conditions of access and costs of transportation are of considerably greater economic significance than the quality and quantity of the deposit. Regional differences in mining methods, however, are few, because the nature of the mineral and the character of the deposit rather than the locational factors usually determine the technology. Two selections evaluate the location and the economic and political problems involved in exploiting mineral deposits in two widely separated world areas.

3. The World Outlook for Conventional Agriculture

Lester R. Brown

When we recognize that conventional agriculture provides an adequate and assured supply of food for only one-third of the human beings on earth today, and that population is rising most rapidly among the underfed peoples, the crucial role of agriculture as the most important primary production activity becomes obvious. Coupled with rapid population growth and the constantly pressing de-

Lester R. Brown

> mands for more food is the rising income level of many
> nations and peoples, a factor which, in some instances, gene-
> rates even greater demands for food than the increase of
> population. Furthermore, the possibilities for greater pro-
> duction by expanding agricultural areas appear to be
> quite limited. The prospects for the future are carefully
> evaluated in this selection, which includes production projec-
> tions for several major food crops to the end of the cen-
> tury.

The problem of obtaining enough food has plagued man since his be-
ginnings. Despite the innumerable scientific advances of the 20th century, the problem becomes increasingly serious. Accelerating rates of
population growth, on the one hand, and the continuing reduction in
the area of new land that can be put under the plow, on the other, are
postponing a satisfactory solution to this problem for at least another
decade and perhaps much longer.

Conventional agriculture now provides an adequate and assured supply of food for one-third of the human race. But assuring an adequate
supply of food for the remaining two-thirds, in parts of the world where
population is increasing at the rate of 1 million weekly, poses one of
the most nearly insoluble problems confronting man.

Dimensions of the Problem

Two major forces are responsible for expanding food needs: population growth and rising per capita incomes.

Populations in many developing countries are increasing at the rate of
3 percent or more per year. In some instances the rate of increase appears to be approaching the biological maximum. Populations growing
by 3 percent per year double within a generation and multiply 18-fold
in a century.

According to projections, world population, now just over 3 billion,
will increase by another 3 billion over the remaining one-third of this
century (Fig. 1). Even with the most optimistic assumptions concerning the effect of newly initiated family-planning programs in developing countries, we must still plan to feed an additional 1 billion people
by 1980. The world has never before added 1 billion people in 15 years.
More significantly, four-fifths of these will be added to the less-developed countries, where food is already in short supply.

SOURCE: Science, CLVIII (November, 1967), 604–11. Copyright 1967 by the
American Association for the Advancement of Science. Reprinted by permission of
the author and the publisher. The author is administrator of the International Agriculture Development Service, U.S. Department of Agriculture.

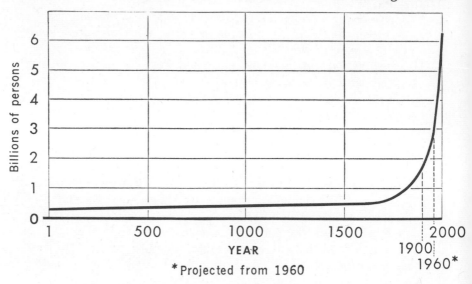

FIGURE 1: Twenty centuries of world population growth. (U. S. Department of Agriculture.)

Rising income levels throughout the world are generating additional demand on the world's food-producing resources. Virtually every country in the world today has plans for raising income levels among its people. In some of the more advanced countries the rise in incomes generates far more demand for food than the growth of population does.

Japan illustrates this well. There, population is increasing by only 1 percent per year but per capita incomes are rising by 7 percent per year. Most of the rapid increase in the demand for food now being experienced in Japan is due to rising incomes. The same may be true for several countries in western Europe, such as West Germany and Italy, where population growth is slow and economic growth is rapid.

Comparisons between population growth and increases in food production, seemingly in vogue today, often completely ignore the effect of rapidly rising incomes, in some instances an even more important demand-creating force than population growth.

The relationships between increases in per capita income and the consumption of grain are illustrated in Fig. 2, The direct consumption of grain, as food, rises with income per person throughout the low-income brackets; at higher incomes it declines, eventually leveling off at about 150 pounds per year.

The more significant relationship, however, is that between total grain use and income. Historically, as incomes have risen, the use of grain, both that consumed directly and that consumed indirectly in the form of meat, milk, and eggs, has risen also. The upper curve in Fig. 2 indicates that every $2 gain in annual per capita income requires one pound of additional grain.

The rapid increases in both population and income are recent phenomena, in historical terms. Both have occurred since the war, and both are gaining momentum on a worldwide scale.

The effect of the resulting explosive increase in the demand for food is greater pressure on the world's food supplies. This rapid expansion of demand, together with the reduction of surplus grain stocks in North

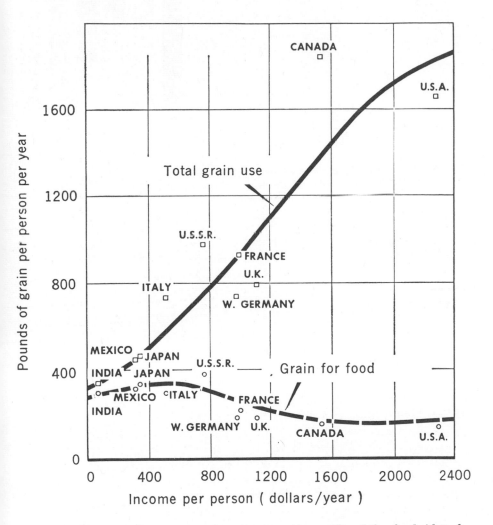

FIGURE 2: Income and per-capita grain consumption, total and for food (data for 1959–61). (U. S. Department of Agriculture.)

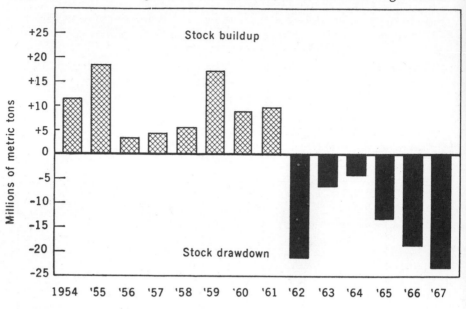

Figure 3: Changes in world grain stocks. (U. S. Department of Agriculture.)

America, contributed to a rapid decline in world grain stocks during the 1960's (see Fig. 3).

Between 1953 and 1961, world grain "carryover" stocks increased each year. The size of the annual buildup varied from a few million tons to nearly 20 million tons. After 1961, however, stocks began to decline, with the reduction or "drawdown" averaging 14 million tons per year.

A stock buildup, by definition, means that production is exceeding consumption; the converse is also true. The trend in grain stocks indicates clearly that 1961 marked a worldwide turning point; as population and income increases gained momentum, food consumption moved ahead of production. Since 1961, the ever-widening excess of consumption over production has been compensated by "drawing down" stocks. But there is little opportunity for further reductions.

This means that the two lines in Fig. 4 cannot remain apart much longer. The question is: How will the lines be brought together? Will the production line go up, or will the consumption line come down? What are the implications of recent trends for world food price levels? Rising prices, a possible result, would act both to reduce consumption, particularly among the world's low-income peoples, and to stimulate production. At a time when hunger and, in some cases, severe malnutrition are commonplace in much of the world, reducing consumption

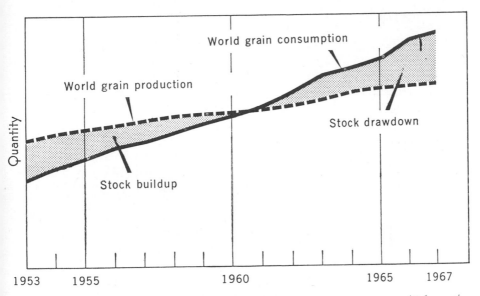

FIGURE 4: World grain production now lagging behind consumption. (Schematic representation is not drawn to scale.) (U. S. Department of Agriculture.)

is obviously not a desirable alternative. The effect would be to widen the food gap between the world's "haves" and "have-nots."

Meeting future food needs will require immense increases in output. The expected increase of 1 billion in world population over the next 15 years will require expansion of world grain production, now totaling about 1 billion tons, by about one-third, or 335 million tons. Additional demand generated by rising per capita incomes, even if only half as large as the population-generated component, could push the total needed increase toward 500 million tons.

What are the prospects of meeting these future increases in world food needs through conventional agriculture? There are two methods of increasing food production: expanding the cultivated area or raising the productivity (output per unit) of land already under cultivation. Throughout most of history, increases in food production have come largely from expanding the area under cultivation. Only quite recently, in historical terms, have some regions begun to rely on raising output per acre for most of the increases in their food supply.

Over the past 30 years, all of the increases in agricultural production in North America and western Europe have come from raising the productivity of land. Food output has about doubled in both regions, while the area cultivated has actually declined somewhat. Available technology has made it more profitable to raise output per acre than to increase the area under cultivation.

Expanding the Cropland Area

The world's present cultivated land area totals some 3 billion acres (1.2 billion hectares). Estimates of the possibilities for expanding this area vary from a few hundred million acres to several billion. However, any such estimate of the area of new land likely to be brought under cultivation must, to be meaningful, specify at what cost this is to be accomplished.

Some land which was farmed a few decades ago has now been abandoned because it is no longer profitable. Much of the abandoned farmland in New England and Appalachia in the United States, or in other countries, such as portions of the Anatolian Plateau in Turkey, falls into this category.

In several countries of the world the area of cultivated land is actually declining. Japan, where the area of cultivated land reached a peak in 1920 and has declined substantially since, is a prominent example. Other countries in this category are Ireland, Sweden, and Switzerland.

Most of the world's larger countries are finding it difficult to further expand the area under cultivation. India plans to expand the cultivated-land area by less than 2 percent over its Fourth Plan period, from 1966 to 1971; yet the demand for food is expected to expand by some 20 percent over this 5-year span. Mainland China, which has been suffering from severe population pressure for several decades, has plowed nearly all of its readily cultivable land.

Most of the countries in the Middle East and North Africa, which depend on irrigation or on dry-land farming, cannot significantly expand the area under cultivation without developing new sources of water for irrigation. The Soviet Union is reportedly abandoning some of the land brought under cultivation during the expansion into the "virgin-lands" area in the late 1950's.

The only two major regions where there are prospects for further significant expansion of the cultivated area in the near future are sub-Saharan Africa and the Amazon Basin of Brazil. Any substantial expansion in these two areas awaits further improvements in our ability to manage tropical soils—to maintain their fertility once the lush natural vegetation is removed.

Aside from this possibility, no further opportunities are likely to arise until the cost of desalinization is reduced to the point where it is profitable to use seawater for large-scale irrigation. This will probably not occur before the late 1970's or early 1980's at best.

The only country in the world which in recent years has had a ready reserve of idled cropland has been the United States. As recently as 1966, some 50 million acres were idled, as compared with a harvested acreage of 300 million acres. The growing need for imported food and feed in western Europe, the Communist countries, Japan, and particularly India is bringing much of this land back into production. Decisions made in 1966 and early 1967 to expand the acreage of wheat, feed grains, and soybeans brought some one-third of the idled U.S cropland back into production in 1967.

Even while idled cropland is being returned to production in the United States and efforts are being made to expand the area of cultivated land in other parts of the world, farmland is being lost because of expanding urban areas, the construction of highways, and other developments. On balance, it appears that increases in world food production over the next 15 years or so will, because of technical and economic factors, depend heavily on our ability to raise the productivity of land already under cultivation.

Increasing Land Productivity

Crop yield per acre in much of the world has changed little over the centuries. Rates of increase in output per acre have, in historical terms, been so low as to be scarcely perceptible within any given generation. Only quite recently—that is, during the 20th century—have certain countries succeeded in achieving rapid, continuing increases in output per acre—a yield "takeoff." Most of the economically advanced countries—particularly those in North America, western Europe, and Japan—have achieved this yield-per-acre take-off.

The first yield-per-acre takeoff, at least the first documented by available data, occurred for rice in Japan during the early years of this century (see Fig. 5). Yield takeoffs occurred at about the same time, or shortly thereafter, in several countries in northwestern Europe, such as Denmark, the Netherlands, and Sweden. Several other countries, such as the United Kingdom and the United States, achieved yield-per-acre takeoffs in the late 1930's and early 1940's.

Increasing food output per acre of land requires either a change in cultural practices or an increase in inputs, or both. Nearly all increases in inputs or improvements in cultural practices involve the use of more capital. Many (mechanization itself is an exception) require more labor as well.

A review of the yield trends shown in Figs. 5 and 6, or of any of several others for the agriculturally advanced countries, raises the obvious question of how long upward trends may be expected to continue. Will there come a time when the rate of increase will slow down or cease altogether? Hopefully, technological considerations, resulting from new research breakthroughs, will continue to postpone that date.

DIFFERING SOURCES OF PRODUCTIVITY / One way of evaluating future prospects for continuing expansion in yields is to divide the known

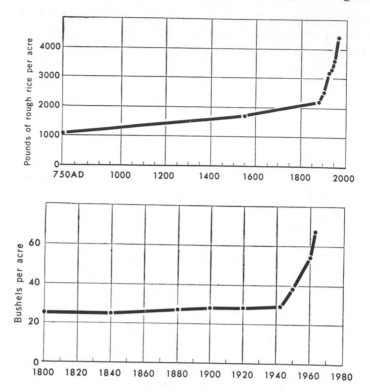

FIGURE 5: (top) Rice yields in Japan from A.D. 750 to 1960. Historical estimates from Japanese ministry of agriculture. (U. S. Department of Agriculture.) FIGURE 6: (bottom) Corn yields in the United States. (U. S. Department of Agriculture.)

sources of increased productivity into two broad categories: "nonrecurring" and "recurring" sources of increased productivity. Nonrecurring inputs are essentially of a one-shot nature; once they are fully adopted, further increases in yields are limited. Recurring inputs, even when fully adopted, offer further annual increases in output through more intensive application.

Corn provides a good illustration. Yields have expanded sharply in the United States (see Fig. 6). Total production now exceeds 100 million tons of grain annually, or about half the total U.S. grain crop. Much of the increase in corn yields, however, was due to two nonrecurring sources of productivity: the replacement of open-pollinated or traditional varieties with hybrids and, to a lesser extent, the use of herbicides.

Hybrid corn has now replaced open-pollinated varieties on more than 97 percent of the corn acreage in the United States (see Fig. 7).

Further improvements in hybrid varieties are to be expected. (Hybrids in use today are superior to hybrids developed in the mid-1930's.) The big spurt in yields, however, is usually associated with the initial transi-

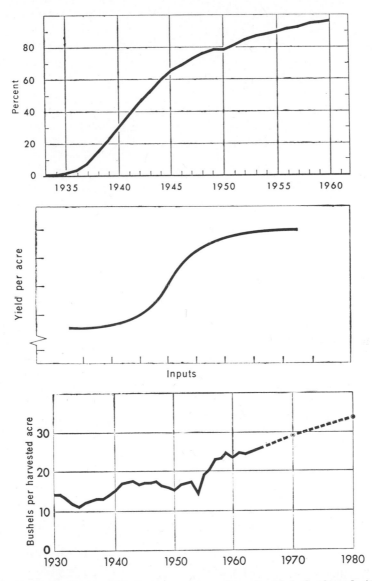

FIGURE 7: (top) Share of U. S. corn acreage planted with hybrid seed. (U. S. Department of Agriculture.) FIGURE 8: (middle) S-shaped yield curve (schematic representation). (U. S. Department of Agriculture.) FIGURE 9: (bottom) Wheat yields in the United States, with projections. Plotted as a 3-year sliding average. (U. S. Department of Agriculture.)

tion from open-pollinated or traditional varieties to hybrids. Consequently, the big thrust in corn yields in the United States resulting from
the adoption of hybrids is probably a thing of the past. Likewise, once
herbicides are widely used and virtually all weeds are controlled, there
is little, if any, prospect of future gains in productivity from this source.

Some sources of increased yields are of a recurring nature. Among
these, there is still ample opportunity for further yield increases as a
result of the use of additional fertilizer. As plant populations increase,
provided moisture is not a limiting factor, corn yields will rise further
as more fertilizer is used.

Just how far the yield increase will go in the United States, however,
is not clear. Paul Mangelsdorf of Harvard University, speaking recently
at the National Academy of Sciences, asked this vital question:

With more than 95 percent of the corn acreage already planted to hybrid
corn, with the genetic potentials of the hybrids having reached a plateau,
with 87 percent of the acreage in the Corn Belt and Lake States already
using fertilizer, and with many farmers already employing herbicides, from
where will come the future improvements that will allow us to continue our
present rate of improvement?

The same question may be asked of other crops in some of the other
agriculturally advanced countries.

THE S-SHAPED YIELD CURVE / As the nonrecurring sources of productivity are exhausted, the sources of increased productivity are reduced
until eventually the rate of increase in yield per acre begins to slow.
This might be depicted by that familiar biologic function the S-shaped
growth curve (Fig. 8). John R. Platt of the University of Chicago recently explained the curve this way:

Many of our important indices of technical achievement have been shooting
up exponentially for many years, very much like the numbers in the biolo-
gists' colonies of bacteria that double in every generation as each cell divides
into two again. But such a curve of growth obviously cannot continue indefinitely in any field. The growth of the bacterial colony slows up as it
begins to exhaust its nutrient. The exponential curve bends over and flattens
out into the more general "S-curve" or "logistic curve" of growth.

We do not know with any certainty when the rate of yield increase
for the major food crops on which man depends for sustenance will
begin to slow, but we do know that ultimately it will.

The key questions are: Is the slow-down near for some of the major
food crops in some of the agriculturally advanced countries? Will the
slowdown come gradually, or will it occur abruptly and with little
warning? Finally, to what extent can the level at which the final turn

of the S-shaped yield curve occurs be influenced? Can the level be raised by increasing the prices received by farmers, by adopting technological innovations, and by stepping up investment in crop research?

Most of those countries which have achieved takeoffs in yield per acre are continuing to raise yields at a rapid rate. But there are indications that the rate of gain may be slowing for some crops in some of the more agriculturally advanced countries.

Projected per-acre yield levels for the major grains in the United States show a substantial slowing of the rate of yield increase over the next 15 years as compared with the last 15. The rate of yield increase for wheat, averaging 3.5 percent yearly from 1950 to 1965, is projected to drop to less than 2 percent per year between 1965 and 1980 (Fig. 9). Sorghum yields, recently increasing at a rate of nearly 6 percent annually, are projected to increase at just over 2 percent per year be-

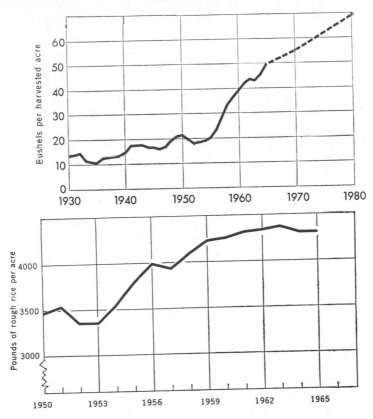

FIGURE 10: (top) Grain sorghum yields in the United States, with projections. Plotted as a 3-year sliding average. (U. S. Department of Agriculture.)
FIGURE 11: (bottom) Rice yields in Japan, 1950–1965. Plotted as a 3-year sliding average. (U. S. Department of Agriculture.)

tween now and 1980 (Fig. 10). For corn, the projected slowdown is less dramatic, with yield increases dropping from about 4 percent to 3 percent. Per-acre yields of wheat and grain sorghum have apparently achieved their more rapid gains as the use of nonrecurring technologies becomes almost universal. In Platt's words, they may already be "past the middle of the S-curve."

The rate of increase could also be slowing down for certain crops elsewhere in the world. Rice yields in Japan may be a case in point. Yields were relatively static before 1900 but began to rise steadily shortly after the turn of the century. This rise continued until about 1959 (except for a brief period around World War II, and a period from 1949 to 1953, when production was disrupted by land reform). Since 1959, U.S. Department of Agriculture estimates indicate, the rate of increase has slowed appreciably and, in fact, has recently nearly leveled off (Fig. 11). Whether or not this is a temporary plateau or a more permanent one remains to be seen. Interestingly, projections of per-acre rice yields made by the Japanese Institute of Agricultural Economic Research, using a 1958–1960 base period, did not anticipate the recent slowdown in the rate of increase in rice yields.

This recent leveling off of yields, however, may be caused by economic as well as technological factors. One key factor contributing to the very high yields obtained in Japan has been the intensive use of what was once low-cost labor. In recent years there has been a withdrawal of labor from rice production as rural workers have found more remunerative urban jobs. If economic development continues, it is unlikely that recent trends in labor costs will ever be reversed. Thus, it may well be that per-acre rice yields in Japan are approaching what is, in the immediately forseeable future at least, a plateau.

A slowdown in the rate of yield increase seems also to be occurring for some of the grain crops in the Netherlands. This is not particularly surprising since yields there are already among the highest in the world. Further yield responses of some grains to the use of additional inputs, such as fertilizer, now seem limited by genetic constraints—the inherent ability of the plant to effectively use additional plant nutrients.

There are, on the other hand, some crops in the agriculturally developed countries which have not yet begun their upward advance on the growth curve. One of the major U.S. crops, the soybean, has thus far stubbornly resisted efforts to generate a yield-per-acre takeoff. The combination of near-static yields, on the one hand, and the very rapid growth in demand for soybeans, on the other, means that the necessary increases in the soybean supply are obtainable only through a rapid continuing expansion in the area planted to soybeans—an expansion which is steadily reducing the area available for other crops.

During the two decades since World War II, projections of increases in per-acre yields in the United States have invariably underestimated the increases actually achieved. This may be due in part to the yield-raising effect of idling large areas of marginal cropland during this period. There is now a risk that our faith in technology will cause us to overestimate future increases in yields if, in fact, the rate of yield increase ultimately slows as the sources of further gains in productivity diminish.

It is significant that the major sources of increased agricultural productivity—the use of chemical fertilizer; the use of improved varieties, including hybrids; the use of pesticides and irrigation—have all been known for decades, if not longer. The key question now is: Are there any sources of increased productivity in existence or in the process of development comparable to the traditional ones listed above?

The concept of the S-shaped curve is not new, but its implications for future agricultural production have not been fully explored. Although the S-shaped yield curve for crops is, at this point, still an untested hypothesis, it is, in Platt's words, "at least as plausible as the uncritical assumption that changes like those of the twentieth century will go on forever."

PHOTOSYNTHETIC EFFICIENCY AND RESEARCH / The ultimate factor limiting crop output per acre is the crop's photosynthetic efficiency. Defined as the percentage of solar energy used relative to that which is available on a given area occupied by a particular crop, photosynthetic efficiency is always quite low, usually less than 3 percent. Density of plant population, actual position of the leaves on the plant, and temperature are key factors accounting for variations within this range.

In 1962, James Bonner of the California Institute of Technology stated:

. . . the upper limit of crop yield, as determined by the factors that regulate photosynthetic efficiency, is already being approached today in those regions with the highest level of agricultural practice—in parts of Japan, of Western Europe, and of the United States.

Obviously, research into ways of increasing the upper limit of yield is needed. This increase could be achieved by developing plants which have greater photosynthetic efficiency or by improving present cultural practices so as to increase efficiency per acre, or by both means. The development of smaller and more efficient corn plants, along with reduction in the need for cultivation during the growing season, makes it possible to reduce the width between corn rows—a width that was initially determined by the width of a horse, in the age of the horse-drawn cultivator. The result is a dramatic gain in the number of corn plants per acre and increased output.

More productive hybrid wheats have been developed, but they are still in the experimental stage and are not yet being grown commercially. Work on breeding new varieties with higher nutritive value—a potentially promising activity—is also under way. The adoption of a new technology takes time, even in an agriculturally advanced country. It took a quarter of a century for U.S. farmers to adopt hybrid corn (see Fig. 7). Hybrid grain sorghum, introduced in the early 1950's, required about a decade to become widely disseminated.

Both corn and wheat have been the subject of many years of research in the United States and other developed nations. Much less work has been done in rice. To help rectify this situation, the Rockefeller and Ford foundations established the International Rice Institute in the Philippines several years ago. The Institute devotes its efforts not only to the development of new varieties but to the whole range of cultural practices as well.

The need for such research is further emphasized by a recent statement by Harvey Brooks, chairman of the Committee on Science and Public Policy of the National Academy of Sciences:

Future food production, even for domestic purposes, will be strongly dependent on the equality and direction of both the basic and applied research undertaken within the next few years. Most of the potential of past basic research has already been realized, and new knowledge will be needed even to maintain present levels of productivity.

Clearly, much more research is essential if we are to (i) get the underdeveloped nations to the yield takeoff point, and (ii) maintain the upward thrust of yields in the developed countries by postponing the final turn on the S-shaped curve.

Research and Reality

Two groups of factors should be kept in mind in evaluating the real potential of research results for significantly increasing food output on a worldwide basis. The first group centers about the pronounced variations in natural resources and managerial abilities, which can lead to wide differences between record yields and average national yields obtained by individual farmers under localized conditions. The second group concerns the matter of costs and returns, which spells the difference between technical potential and economic reality.

RECORD YIELDS VERSUS AVERAGE YIELDS / It is often assumed that record yields attained on experimental plots can be easily and quickly translated into national average yields. Such is not, however, the case. Maximum yields obtained on experimental plots under closely controlled conditions usually far exceed those generally obtained in practice. Average yields of wheat in this country, for example, are far below those attained on experimental plots during the latter part of the last century. The same is true for many other crops.

Equally common and equally unwarranted is the assumption that all countries will eventually attain the average yield prevailing in the nation which now has the highest yield. Potential yield levels attainable by individual countries vary widely with variations in rainfall, temperature, soil types and topography, production costs, managerial abilities of farmers, and other factors.

Wheat yields in the United Kingdom now average about 60 bushels per acre (52 hectoliters per hectare) as contrasted with only 18 bushels per acre in Australia. This does not mean that wheat-production technology is less advanced in Australia than in the United Kingdom. The yield differences do reflect the difference between growing conditions in Australia, where rainfall in the wheat-growing regions averages 12 to 15 inches (30 to 38 centimeters) annually, and those in the United Kingdom, where rainfall may average 40 to 50 inches. Although wheat yields in both the United Kingdom and Australia may continue to rise, there is no reason to assume that the differences in yields between the two countries will narrow appreciably in the foreseeable future.

The average national rice yield in Japan is nearly four times that in India. A large part of this difference is accounted for by a much greater volume of inputs, including labor as well as modern practices and management. Not to be overlooked, however, is the fact that virtually all of the rice crop produced in Japan is irrigated, whereas only part of India's rice crop is irrigated. A large share of India's rice fields are rainfed, thus the yield levels attained depend greatly on the vagaries of the monsoon.

There are also very wide variations in yield within individual countries. Variations in corn yields within various corn-producing states in the United States are almost as pronounced as variations in corn yields between the various corn-producing countries of the world. Average yields in principal U.S. corn-producing states in 1965, for instance, varied from more than 90 bushels per acre in some states in the Midwest to less than 40 bushels in some states in the southern Mississippi Valley.

It is significant that the leveling off of rice yields in Japan has occurred at a time when average rice yields in the more productive and the less productive prefectures vary widely. Some individual villages in Japan obtain rice yields at least double the national average.

Per-acre yields obtained by individual farmers in the same area may vary even more than do those for various states or prefectures. It is often assumed that the performance of the best farmers can be emulated by all. There are and will continue to be some very basic differences in the innate capacities or motivations of farmers. There is no more reason for assuming that all farmers can or really want to attain a record yield of corn or wheat than to assume that all students can or want to become Harvard Phi Beta Kappas. The distribution of talent and motivation is probably at least as wide within the world's rural communities as in any other area.

TECHNICAL POTENTIAL VERSUS ECONOMIC REALITY / The failure to distinguish between the technical potential for expanding food production and the economically profitable possibilities for doing so has resulted in confusing variations in estimates of future food production. The difference between estimates based on these two criteria is often very great. The earlier discussion of the experience in Japan—where rice yields seem to have leveled off in recent years—suggests the importance of economic relationships.

A recent reduction in milk production in the United States closely parallels the Japanese experience with rice yields. Through the early months of 1966, milk production in the United States was 3 to 5 percent below production in comparable months of the preceding year. At prevailing prices it was not profitable for dairy farmers to use some of the existing resources. During 1966, dairy farmers in New York State received scarcely 40 cents an hour for their labor (when allowance is made for interest on their investment), and farmers in Wisconsin received only 50 cents an hour. At a time when slaughter prices were high and there were many job opportunities to choose from—with a 5-day, 40-hour week in industry and a minimum wage of $1.25 per hour—it comes as no surprise to learn that many dairy farmers liquidated their holdings and took other jobs. In order to help increase returns to farmers and expand milk production, the Department of Agriculture raised milk support prices twice during 1966, for a total increase of 23 percent.

Both prices received by farmers and costs of production must be taken into consideration in assessing potential increases in production. As farmers move up the per-acre yield curve, the point of diminishing returns is eventually reached. Additional costs begin to exceed additional returns. Thus it is unrealistic to expect farmers to produce up to the full technical potential.

Therefore, while many farmers can produce much more under a given technology, it is sometimes uneconomic, at existing prices and costs, for them to do so. If society is willing to pay higher prices—and it may have to someday—much greater production may be expected.

Conclusions

1. The worldwide demand for food will continue to be strong in the coming decades. Two forces—rapidly growing population and, in much

of the world, rapidly rising incomes—are expected to result in increases in the demand for food even more rapid than those that have occurred during the past.

2. Conventional agriculture has assured an adequate food supply for the economically advanced one-third of the world. The challenge now is to assure an adequate food supply for the remaining two-thirds, where population is now increasing at the rate of 1 million people per week and where malnutrition is already widespread.

3. Economically feasible prospects for significantly expanding the world's area of cultivated land in the 1960's and 1970's are limited and largely confined to sub-Saharan Africa and the Amazon Basin. Even here, agronomic problems will limit the rate of expansion. When the cost of desalting seawater is substantially reduced—probably not before the late 1970's or early 1980's at best—it may become feasible to irrigate large areas of desert.

4. Given the limited possibilities for expanding the area of land under cultivation, most of the increases in world food needs must be met, for the foreseeable future, by raising the productivity of land already under cultivation. Food output per acre, rather static throughout most of history, has begun to increase rapidly in some of the more advanced countries in recent decades. All of the increases in food production over the past quarter century in North America, western Europe, and Japan have come from increasing the productivity of land already under cultivation. The area under cultivation has actually declined.

5. Achieving dramatic gains in land productivity requires a massive investment of capital and the widespread adoption of new technology. A similar effort must now be made in the less-developed nations if these nations are to feed their people. The most important single factor influencing this rate of investment is food prices, more particularly the relationship between the price farmers receive for their food products and the cost of modern inputs such as fertilizer.

6. In some of the more-developed countries where per-acre yields have been rising for a long time, there is now evidence that the rate of yield increase may be slowing. Nonrecurring inputs may have made their maximum contribution to output in the case of some crops, pushing yield levels past the middle of the S-shaped logistic curve. Although this cannot be determined with any certainty, the possibility that the middle of the curve has been passed in some instances should be taken into account in viewing the long-term future.

7. If the rate of increase in yield per acre does in fact begin to slow in some of the agriculturally advanced countries, additional pressure will be put on the less-developed countries—which have much of the world's unrealized food-production potential—to meet the continuing future increases in world food needs.

8. Man has not yet been able to bypass the process of photosynthesis

in the production of food. This dependence on photosynthesis plays a significant role in determining the upper levels of the S-shaped yield curve. Additional research is urgently needed to increase the photosynthetic efficiency of crops and to raise the upper levels of economically feasible yields.

4. Theoretical Concepts and the Analysis of Agricultural Land-Use Patterns in Geography
David W. Harvey

The search for new theory or the refinement of existing conceptual generalizations have become increasingly important in economic geographic research. Harvey reviews the ways other disciplines have studied agricultural land use by constructing models expressing the normative performance of some aspect of functional activity. He indicates the nature of various models—the von Thünen, the static or partial equilibrium, the dynamic economic function, the decision-making, and the behavioral—and their application to the entire field of economic geography either in explaining various kinds of distribution or in providing broad generalizations from which further research and understanding in the discipline will come. Some useful contributions to model building in geography have been made by some geographers, such as Hägerstrand and Chorley, but, as Harvey states, "We are just at the beginning of this quest."

The analysis of land-use patterns has long been one of the basic concerns of the geographer. Pioneer works on agricultural land use by Baker, Jonasson, and Whittlesey have been followed by numerous empirical studies of agricultural land-use patterns. Apart from the pioneer

SOURCE: *Annals* of the Association of American Geographers, LVI (June, 1967), 361–74. Reprinted by permission. The author is on the staff of the Department of Geography, University of Bristol, England.

works, these studies have mostly been micro-analytical in the sense that they have attempted to examine the unique causes of patterns within specific areas. Broader attempts at generalization have been rare, partly because geographers have not regarded it as their function to provide broad generalizations, and partly because other disciplines have been concerned with theories of land use to which geographers could refer when necessary. But generally speaking we have tended to ignore theoretical notions developed in other disciplines, mainly on the grounds that they prove too "abstract" to help in the search for unique causes of specific events. Recently some opinion has tended to shift to the view that we should be more concerned with searching for broad generalizations and "laws" which will help to elucidate spatial structures. Bunge, for example, has attacked the notion of "uniqueness" and has suggested a more theoretical approach to the analysis of geographic distributions. It may also be argued that even if we are still basically concerned with unique explanations, it is still important to have some broad generalizations against which to match such explanations.

Whichever approach we adopt to "explanation" in geography, it is still, therefore, useful to have some general understanding of theories developed in other disciplines. Such an understanding can have a dual purpose. It can act as a guide to those seeking unique explanations and indicate the kind of explanation that may be appropriate in any specific case. It may also lay the foundation for the development of a general theory of land use in geography. This review article is concerned entirely with agricultural land use. The aim is to outline theories developed in other disciplines and to evaluate their utility for geographers. Clearly other kinds of land use could be considered (recent developments in the analysis of urban land-use systems, for example), but for the purposes of this article, land use means agricultural land use.

Characteristically, the analyses of land use developed in other disciplines have taken the form of "models" of agricultural activity. Chorley has recently summarized the different types of model approach that may be adopted, and the present paper attempts to follow up his summary with reference to one field of interest only. It would be useful, however, to begin with some kind of summary of how a model operates.

A model should specify three groups of variables, together with a set of operating characteristics (or functions) which link these variables. The *input* variables are independent of the model, and their values or attributes are determined by external circumstances. The model should be designed to show how different outputs will result from different combinations of values or attributes given to the input variables. We thus have a class of *output* variables which are entirely dependent upon what happens within the model. The model may also contain *status* variables which specify certain conditions that are important within the model, but that remain constant. If we wish to formulate a simple model explaining how a land-use pattern is decided upon for a particular farm, we might specify the variables as follows:

I. *Input Variables (external to the farm).*
 1) Demand for different products at specified markets over a specified time period,
 2) Transport costs for different products to each of the specified markets over the specified time period,
 3) Costs of different factor inputs (labor, fertilizer, and so on).
II. *Status Variables (internal characteristics of the farm).*
 1) Capital stocks and financial assets on the farm,
 2) Yield of different products under different combinations of factor input,
 3) Total land available on the farm.
III. *Output Variable(s).*
 1) Decision on production system.

Clearly such a model (only hypothetically demonstrated here) requires a set of relationships to be established if it is to become operational. These relationships must link the input, status, and output variables in a specific way. In the model outlined above, for example, we would have to specify that the decision was made in order to maximize income and then show how different decisions would yield different incomes under different combinations of input variable. If the model is to function, therefore, these relationships must be quantified in some way (at least they must be given an order, although not necessarily an absolute value). The relationships specified may be of three distinctive types:

1. *Deterministic* relationships which specify cause and effect sequences.

2. *Probabilistic* relationships which specify the likelihood of a particular cause leading to a particular effect.

3. *Functional* relationships which specify how two variables are related (or correlated) without necessarily indicating any cause and effect relationship at all.

The operating characteristics are crucial to the operation of the model. They may be derived either deductively, as for instance, when we assume rationality on the part of "economic" man, or they may be derived inductively from empirical observations, or from a combination of both procedures.

Of course, any model has only a limited correspondence to the real world. Basically a model examines a set of relationships within a "closed" system, and the applicability of the model will depend upon the way in which the model has been "closed," *i.e.*, the specifications and assumptions made in the model. The development of general systems theory indicates, however, that it is important to try to link rather limited models into a broader analytical frame of reference. At the present time there are many different models which are of use in the analysis of agricultural land-use systems. The variety of them is in no way a disadvantage, provided we do not treat one model as automatically excluding another. At the same time it seems worthwhile to explore some of the links and relationships among these models, for only in this way can we expect any general theory of land-use systems to be developed.

Models in Agriculture

We may roughly group models of agricultural activity according to whether they place emphasis upon the economic aspects of the problem, or upon the behavioral aspects. We may further subdivide each group according to whether the framework is normative (describing what ought to be under certain assumptions) or descriptive (describing what is actually existing). In practice the economic models so far developed tend to be normative, whereas the behavioral models tend to be descriptive. But these are only tendencies, and the framework of the model is not necessarily governed by its content.

Economic Models of the Spatial Distribution of Agriculture

THE VON THÜNEN MODEL / The classic model of agricultural location developed by von Thünen amounts to an econometric analysis of his estates in Mecklenburg, from which many of the variables affecting the determination of land-use systems can be derived. Von Thünen's analysis is basically descriptive rather than normative, and concepts such as the "isolated state" are introduced more for expository purposes than as assumptions for formal theory. As Chisholm has pointed out, von Thünen's notions do not constitute a theory as such. But later writers, particularly Hoover, Lösch, Dunn, and Isard, have used the framework outlined by von Thünen as the basis for a normative model. This model will not be described in detail, since there are several accounts already available, and discussion of its main features will refer only to the normative versions of it.

The normative model explains how a land-use pattern will develop over a flat plain surface of uniform fertility and equal transport facility, given that only one market exists. The major input variable in the model is transport cost, which is assumed to increase with distance from the market and which is assumed, therefore, to determine a pattern of "local price" for each commodity. This will mean that the economic return (or economic rent as it is sometimes called) associated with any one commodity will decline with distance from the market. If only one product is cultivated, then clearly the intensity of production of that product will decline with distance from the market. When several products are introduced into the scheme, we have to recognize that different commodities will have differently shaped rent functions over space, since the impact of transport cost will vary according to the bulk and perishability of the commodity. The normative relationship assumed in the model is the supposed wish to maximize economic rent. This relationship is used to show how concentric zones of land use will emerge under the given assumptions.

The simplest demonstration of the theory has been given by Hoover. Suppose that dairy production from a given acre of land can be sent to market as twenty-five pounds of milk, ten pounds of cream, or one pound of butter. It can quickly be shown that with unit transport cost per pound, the produce will be sent as milk close to the market and as butter furthest from the market, with cream sent from a zone between the two. Using this type of analysis, the agricultural location theorists have demonstrated how a regional differentiation in land use will occur over space according to distance from the central market.

Deviations from this simple "expected" pattern can then be considered. Von Thünen showed the importance of such factors as crop combinations, differentials in transport facility, the existence of multiple markets, variations in the cost of production (particularly differences due to variations in natural fertility and differences due to variations in the cost of factor inputs other than land), as well as external factors that might interfere with the spatial structure of prices (such as tariffs). All of these features have been considered and elaborated on in the subsequent work of Brinkmann, Hoover, Lösch, and Dunn.

The normative basis of the von Thünen model lies in its application of marginal economics to the problem of substitution of costs over distance. But in spite of the introduction of many other variables into the model, it contains several "built-in" assumptions which limit its applicability to real-life situations. It assumes the complete availability of information, or at best assumes that lack of information is only a short-term problem with no long-term effects. It assumes completely rational "economic" behavior on the part of individuals who must be prepared to change their land-use system to reap even a very small net gain in economic rent. These assumptions are not defects in the model as such, but their nature does indicate where we might look to understand differences between the model and reality. To reject the model for these reasons would miss the whole point of normative economics. But there are two points where extensions of the model without a careful examination of the implicit assumptions could lead to substantial errors of prediction about land-use systems.

First, the model is a partial equilibrium one (Garrison and Marble provide a specification of the model which can be solved by a system of simultaneous equations). Von Thünen was not concerned with "the confusing phenomena of transition" and later writers have also tended to ignore the problems of change over time. Most have assumed that any change in technology, demand, transport cost, and so on, will be accompanied by an automatic adjustment in the land-use system. The point here is not that this is unlikely to happen in reality, but that it may well be bad normative economic thinking. The transition from a static equilibrium model in economics to a dynamic growth model is by no means easy, and it is, therefore, with some justification that Garrison criticizes the presentation of Dunn on the grounds that it:

. . . does not extend very far beyond an analysis of static equilibrium at the industry level. Discussions at the level of the firm and the discussion of dynamic factors are cursory although provocative in places.

At the present time the question of how the theoretical model would look under assumptions of continuous technological change and changing demand remains not only unanswered but largely unconsidered.

Second, the extension of the technique of marginal analysis to a situation of multiple markets fails to make the point that production systems may have their costs altered according to their extent of development. We assume, for example, that the production system developed around a vast metropolitan market has no scale advantages over a production system developed around the tiniest settlement. Clearly this is unlikely. We may find that economies of scale around a large market will mean substantially lower production costs relative to the small market. If this cost advantage more than offsets the transport cost of reaching the smaller market, then we would logically expect the production system around the smaller market to be obliterated. This may well explain why towns of intermediate size often do not develop a special production system around them.

In these two respects the von Thünen model appears in need of some theoretical revision, and undoubtedly revisions along these lines will make the model far more realistic.

Interregional Equilibrium Models of Agricultural Location

The von Thünen model has the advantage that it can be seen to operate continuously over space, and through the use of marginal analysis it shows how land-use systems will grade into one another over a continuum. There are other approaches to the analysis of spatial equilibrium which are derived by conceptualizing areas as points. This approach has its roots in classical international-trade theory. Producers, factors of production, products, and consumers are treated as if they are located at a series of discrete points with zero transport cost separating them. An analysis of comparative advantage then "explains" differences in the type of production at the different points (provided trade takes place). Later work by Ohlin and the location theorists extended this framework towards a general spatial equilibrium model in which transport costs were specifically included. In the post-World War II period new computational techniques (in particular those associated with activity analysis) led to a more precisely defined model of spatial equilibrium, and Enke, Samuelson, and Beckmann attempted to make the model operational. The general problem is formulated by Enke in the following way:

There are three regions trading a homogeneous good. Each region constitutes a single and distinct market. The regions of each possible pair of regions are separated—but not isolated—by a transportation cost. . . . For each region the functions which relate local production and local use to local price are known, and consequently the magnitude of the difference which will be exported or imported at each local price is also known. Given these trade functions and transportation costs, we wish to ascertain: (1) the net price in each region, (2) the quantity of exports or imports for each region, (3) which regions export, import, or do neither, (4) the aggregate trade in the commodity, (5) the volume and direction of trade between each possible pair of regions.

Enke demonstrated how the problem might be treated by means of electric analogue, but subsequently Samuelson dealt with it mathematically. The problem is, of course, a very limited one. It takes no account, for example, of the tendency for the mobile factors of production to move in response to regional differentials in factor cost. Capital, labor, entrepreneurial skill, and so on, are all partially mobile, and it must be one of the basic assumptions of a spatial equilibrium model that either there are no geographic differences in the returns to resources or that such differences are present but entirely stable over time. At this point, however, the relatively limited problem posed by Enke becomes embedded in the far more complicated problem of regional equilibrium in economic growth as a whole.

But out of these early theoretical studies various operational models have been developed. These models are basically of two types: (1) input-output models, and (2) spatial equilibrium models.

INPUT-OUTPUT MODELS / These models were initially developed by

Leontieff as a device for examining the structural interrelationships within a national economy, but the technique has subsequently been developed at the regional level by Isard, Moses, Chenery, and others. In the analysis of agricultural production, Peterson and Heady, Schnittkar and Heady, and Carter and Heady have used the model to:

quantify the interrelationships and degree of interdependence among various regional and commodity sectors of agriculture, as well as between these sectors and industrial sectors of the economy.

The model is primarily descriptive of existing interrelationships, but assuming the stability of the technological coefficients it can be used to project the impact of overall economic changes (or policy changes) on the production pattern of different sectors of production within different regions. These models are very generalized and are closely related to other spatial equilibrium models, but they are difficult to operate because of the many regions and commodities that have to be specified if the model is to have any meaning. They will not, therefore, be discussed further here.

SPATIAL EQUILIBRIUM MODELS / Undoubtedly the most operational technique for examining spatial equilibrium in agricultural production is through the application of linear programming to determine the optimal pattern of production of one, or perhaps several, crops. Provided certain information is known, or can be reasonably estimated, it is possible to determine where production should be located if certain goals are to be achieved. The goal to be achieved may be the highest average profit among all producers, or some other measure of "utility." Early studies by Fox, Fox and Taeuber, Judge and Wallace, Henderson, and others have been followed up by intensive studies by Heady and his colleagues at Iowa State and other studies at Illinois. It would be difficult to summarize this work here, for each model developed varies according to the problem to be solved and the data available. But it seems worthwhile to describe one contribution in some detail.

Egbert, Heady, and Brokken have recently described three models of grain production in the United States from which optimal regional patterns of grain production can be derived under certain assumptions. The basic objective of the study was

. . . to determine how production to meet national demand for grains could be best distributed among regions to maximize net returns to farmers in aggregate or to minimize the cost of food requirements to consumers.

To do this the United States was divided into 104 grain-producing regions (accounting for ninety percent of the total U.S. output), and for each one of these regions data were collected concerning production costs and yield per acre. The total acreage under grain in 1953 was treated as the maximum possible acreage available for production in each region. The three models then diverge. The first two models both assume that regional prices are an accurate reflection of transport cost to market (a similar reasoning to the von Thünen form may be applied here), and the problem becomes one of estimating how farmers should allocate their production to maximize profit with respect to regional prices. The production-distribution model, however, attempted to specify

. . . not only where wheat and feed grains would be produced . . . but to which destination they would flow. . . . Both primary production costs and distribution costs make up the objective to be minimized in the model.

In order to do this, national demand for grain was allocated to ten consumption regions, and transport cost was measured as freight charge from the center of each producing region to the center of each consumption region. Using linear programming, an optimal pattern of transport flow and an optimal pattern of production was then determined.

The interest of the third model is not so much in the empirical results (although these are interesting in themselves), as in the way it "explains" agricultural location patterns by examining the interaction between regional production costs, distribution costs between regions, and regional demand. Of course there are many well-recognized defects in the model. It assumes homogeneity of product between regions, constant production coefficients within regions, and there are problems of simultaneously examining competition among several crops at the same time. These problems are all outlined in the literature. But there are two interesting points about this model.

First, the method of assessing production-cost variations between regions is useful. In the above-mentioned paper, inputs of labor, machinery, fertilizer, seed, pesticides, and other miscellaneous items are listed. By taking this empirical approach, the impact of environment upon production-cost patterns is subsumed. The method can thus be best applied to the problem of interregional specialization without considering the direct impact of the physical factor. But for specific purposes the model can be a powerful tool, as Wolpert and others have shown.

Second, the problem of returns to scale at the interregional level is not specifically dealt with. Variations in production cost with quantity produced are difficult to introduce directly into the model for technical reasons and, as with the von Thünen model, dynamic conditions can only be examined by *ad hoc* adjustments to the input data of the model over time.

In general, however, this kind of spatial equilibrium method has distinctive advantages over the von Thünen approach as an operational procedure. By using empirical data on prices, or transport cost to market, regional demand estimates, and estimates of regional production cost, the model introduces a strong empirical descriptive foundation. The use of linear programming to determine an optimal solution places the model as a normative one, but many of the disadvantages of completely normative models are eliminated by resorting to empirical data. One of the greatest difficulties here, of course, is obtaining the right empirical data to feed into the model.

Dynamic Economic Models

The models so far discussed have been partial equilibrium models, and the question naturally arises as to how satisfactory these models are in interpreting location patterns subject to rapid and often jerky change in technology and demand over time. The difficulty of incorporating returns to scale in partial equilibrium models has already been noted, and only *ad hoc* solutions to this problem seem feasible. From the point of view of economic theory the argument must depend on how far the conclusions drawn from partial equilibrium analysis can be applied to dynamic situations. Myrdal has forcibly argued that the significant factors in a dynamic situation are so radically different from the determining factors in a static situation, that it is best not to associate the two types of model. Borts and Stein, on the other hand, disagree with Myrdal's views insofar as they apply to economic equilibrium within countries.

This argument concerning the achievement or nonachievement of equilibrium in returns to resources within a country, given the free interplay of economic forces, has relevance to geography. The factors of production, labor and capital, are mobile, and the spatial equilibrium models so far developed cannot incorporate within them any long-run adjustments in the deployment of these factors of production. Similarly, returns to scale may result in cumulative changes within the agricultural system which may only become unimportant after a long period of time. And under modern conditions it is extremely unlikely that technological change will leave relationships stable over a decade or so. This simply means that equilibrium is unlikely, if ever, to be achieved, and given the importance of these rapid external changes in both demand and technology, it remains to show how important the tendency to equilibrium as posited in the models considered so far is for explaining even the main elements in any agricultural location pattern.

Notions of dynamic economic equilibrium create all kinds of conceptual difficulties if and when we attempt to demonstrate their operation over space. It is perhaps worthwhile pointing out that this difficulty extends to all other forms of location theory and is not simply confined to agriculture. Economic growth will almost invariably involve spatial adjustments in agricultural systems, and these adjustments will, in turn, lead to changes in the rate and direction of economic growth. The von Thünen model, containing as it does explicit notions of behavior at the margin (even though these notions seem unrealistic), has some applicability to the advance and improvement of frontiers of agricultural activity in newly-developing countries. There is a broad analogy between the idea of the frontier of settlement sweeping across a country and a dynamic von Thünen model where, for example, the seaboard region is regarded as the central market. In countries such as Argentina, Brazil, Australia, and the United States in the nineteenth century, a dynamic von Thünen model may be an appropriate generalization for a very complicated process of settlement expansion.

The spatial equilibrium models may also be adapted to take account of the very real costs of change from one agricultural system to another. Thus Henderson treated land-use system in any one year as a function of land-use system in the previous year plus some component of change determined by a linear-programming solution to interregional equilibrium. In this way some of the friction involved in transferring resources from one kind of production system to another was built into the model. Nevertheless, the difficulty of developing adequate normative dynamic models lies mainly in the assumptions one is forced to make about decision-making behavior. This may be partly overcome by developing dynamic models which use stochastic relationships rather than deterministic ones. But we really need to define these relationships in terms of decision-making behavior on the part of entrepreneurs, for only then will a dynamic model which describes the evolution of a land-use system be based on realistic notions of the processes governing that evolution. Such models are bound to be complex and will almost certainly involve simulation procedures if they are to be tested.

Decision-Making Models

Both the von Thünen model and the interregional equilibrium model tend to aggregate individual units and analyze land-use patterns at the "industry" level. But when dealing with regional structures, this treatment becomes less and less appropriate the smaller the region is, unless it can be assumed that what is "optimal" at the individual farm level is also "optimal" at the industry level. Most texts on agricultural economics treat of the problem of the individual farming unit, and it remains to show how this treatment can be built up to the aggregative analyses of the location theorists. Ultimately an agricultural location pattern is the result of a large number of individual decisions. An examination of theories of decision-making brings to light some interesting problems in relation to agricultural patterns.

One of the assumptions of the normative models so far discussed is that complete information is available to the farmer. But the farmer has to make a "rational" decision without prior knowledge of yields or, in most cases, prices. Decision-making theory has developed to deal with this problem of optimizing decisions in the face of risk or uncertainty, and it is perhaps worthwhile to take a closer look at "Game Theory" as it relates to farmers' decision-making.

The basic text on Game Theory by von Neumann and Morgenstern only appeared in 1944, but since this date the theory has come to have wide applications. As an operational procedure the application of the theory to real-life situations requires sophisticated computational techniques. But the basic notions contained within the theory can be demonstrated very simply. Suppose that a farmer has to choose between three different cropping systems, and that he can only choose one of the three systems (mixed choices are excluded). And suppose that the income derived from each cropping system depends upon weather conditions and that only four different types of weather conditions can occur. We can then construct a matrix (called a pay-off matrix) which shows the potential returns:

| | WEATHER CONDITIONS | | | |
| | 1 | 2 | 3 | 4 |
Crop System		*(Income level in £)*		
A	450	550	600	500
B	700	300	900	340
C	0	1,000	0	3,000

The problem is to determine the "best" solution. There are a variety of criteria which can be used. We could, for example, take the "maximum-minimum" solution where we adopt the cropping system which maximizes the minimum income. Crop System A in the above example gives the highest minimum income of £450. On the other hand, if we can assume that each set of weather conditions will occur with the same relative frequency over a period of time, then the overall average return from Crop System C would be £1,000 per annum, which is far greater than the average return from the other system (£525 and £560, respectively). These two divergent solutions present a difficulty, since the kind of criteria used to evaluate the pay-off matrix will affect the decision on cropping system. And the question arises as to which criteria are compatible with the von Thünen and spatial equilibrium models of agriculture. Von Thünen regarded fluctuations in prices and yields as being short-term disturbances which had no basic impact upon the ultimate achievement of equilibrium. But from Game Theory it is evident that this may not be the case, even if we attempt normative solutions.

Both of the solutions to the pay-off matrix presented above are normative in the sense that the farmer is expected to optimize his income, although the first is concerned with a short-term optimization and the latter with a long-term optimization.

But there are disadvantages of regarding decision-making from simply a normative point of view. And in the same way that there is a conflict between the normative theories of spatial equilibrium and normative models of decision-making, so there is a conflict between the normative decision-making models and theories of behavior. It is assumed, for example, that a farmer will have sufficient information to be able to set out a Game Theory matrix in the form above. Only if this assumption is valid can we use normative decision-making models with any precision. And it is at this point that we have to consider theories of behavior and information in relation to decision-making.

Behavioral Models and Agricultural Pattern

Perhaps one of the major criticisms which geographers have of the use of normative economic models in geography is that they fail to account for the multiplicity of factors which determine a land-use pattern. These factors when studied in unique setting, range from chance events in some remote historical period to current decisions made for understandable but noneconomic reasons. Normative economic theories are often thought of as too broad to be useful in understanding patterns resulting from such unique sets of events.

This view ignores the tremendous strides that have been made in the behavorial sciences over the last few years and the links developing among economics, sociology, and psychology. These links are tenuous at present, but they hold out the exciting prospect of building models of agricultural systems which take account of sociological and psychological realities. Land-use patterns are, after all, the end product (or geographical expression) of a large number of individual decisions made at different times for often very different reasons (or perhaps for no adequate reasons at all). The only way we can understand regional variations in agriculture will thus be through an understanding of decision-making processes; and decisions are never simply economic ones. The evaluation of a pay-off matrix provides an interesting example.

If a pay-off matrix is to be evaluated, this can only be done provided certain criteria have been defined. Dillon and Heady list seven sets of criteria, which range from the maximum-minimum solution, through a solution which is designed to take account of the degree of optimism or pessimism on the part of the farmer, to the solution of the "satisficer" proposed by Simon, in which the farmer only seeks for a solution which is "good enough" The criteria thus vary from economic to behavioral. Simon has raised this issue on many occasions and has proposed that we should use the notion of "bounded rationality" as a substitute for the supposedly omniscient rationality of "economic man."

Economists have not been deaf to these pleas, and recently there has been a tendency to move away "from the crude notion of economic decision-making as a process in which the entrepreneur instantly perceives and adopts the best line of action in any given situation." Economics has always been faced with the problem of defining the "best line of action." In most cases this is viewed as a problem of optimizing "utility" or "social welfare," both rather difficult concepts to define with precision. But from the point of view of the individual decision-maker it is often regarded as a simple matter of maximizing profits and/or minimizing costs. But a farmer may wish to optimize in several different directions at the same time (income, comfort, pleasure, leisure, and so on), and it is difficult to find some common scale of measurement for such disparate items. It may well make more sense, when trying to understand the development of land-use patterns, to use Simon's notion of "satisfaction" as a substitute for rational economic decision-making. The utility of this notion for geographic research has been interestingly demonstrated by Wolpert in his study of farming in central Sweden.

But in real life the decision-maker is also a "learner who seeks to improve his choices," an entrepreneur who is "perpetually groping in a mist of uncertainty, gradually and imperfectly learning his way on the basis of experience accruing to him." Faced with the problem of uncertainty, an entrepreneur has to learn to assess his chances. He will only be able to begin to assess a Game Theory problem after some experience. It is thus probably more accurate to think of Game Theory in association with learning theory, a point which several psychologists have made. It may, therefore, be useful to think of a farmer as "groping his way" towards a satisfactory land-use system over time. Once a satisfactory system has been found, there may be no attempt to move towards an optimal solution partly because the farmer has not the knowledge to estimate what that solution is, partly because he will have little incentive to learn, and partly because a specific cost is contained in the process of searching for a "better" solution. A change from a relatively profitable solution may lead toward a less profitable solution, and the farmer will only run this risk if he has the necessary motivation to do so, a point which will be examined later.

The literature on learning and search theory is now considerable and has obvious implications for the analysis of geographic pattern. Thus:

Simon and others have argued that information is not given to the firm but must be obtained, that alternatives are searched for and discovered sequentially and that the order in which the environment is searched determines to a substantial extent the decisions that will be made.

In most real-life situations this process of search has a strong component of chance, and some would suggest that it may be regarded as "searching 'at random' in a given population of alternatives." Yet one of the unwritten assumptions in much of the geographic literature regarding the adjustment of land-use systems to environment is that all systems have been tried and that only the best have survived. This is obviously untrue both as a general rule and as a guide to what happens in specific instances. It may well be that whole regional patterns of land use are suboptimal simply because the optimal solution, given current technology, environment, and demand has never been found. Bearing this in mind, it would be useful to treat of the relationship between cropping pattern and environment. In times of depression in agriculture formerly satisfactory solutions often become unsatisfactory and provide an economic incentive to learn. Undoubtedly the rate of regional change in land use in Britain since 1800 has been very much faster during periods of depression than during periods of prosperity.

Any model of the evolution of land-use systems over time ought to incorporate notions from learning and search theory. Implicit in such theories "is a motivational assumption—*i.e.*, that learning consists in the acquisition of a pattern of behavior appropriate to 'goal achievement,' 'need reduction,' or the like." At this point learning theory must be firmly embedded in an understanding of the broader process associated with "motivation," "communication," and "information."

McClelland's broad survey of the 'need for achievement' in different societies pinpoints a connection between the whole complex of social values accepted by a society and the individual attitude to economic activity, and, hence, the rate and type of economic development. On a worldwide scale his analysis is of tremendous relevance for understanding the world pattern of agricultural activity. But these notions may be applied within countries, for there may be regional variations in the "goals" which farmers wish to achieve. Barzini has argued, for example, that the differences in social values between North and South Italy explain much of the difference in standard of living, and by implication, these social attitudes mean fundamentally different attitudes to learning and to productivity and change. Geographers have long been aware of these kinds of differences, but the significant point here is that such differences are not incapable of being treated theoretically. And they may eventually be blended with economic theory to provide a powerful model of agricultural location.

But learning does not simply depend upon social values. It also depends upon the availability of information. Meier has already pointed out how urban growth must be accompanied by a growth in information flow, and the concept is just as relevant to agriculture. Information is spread throughout a population via the channels of communication which that population has developed. If these channels are constricted, development is bound to be slower than if there is a free flow of information. The communications system is partly a function of technology and partly a function of the degree of human contact (and hence sociological). Again, regional variations in the communications system could be measured and related to the kinds of decisions which farmers make about land use. But the importance of communication lies in its relationship to the information which is available to a farmer. And there are three ways in which information may be considered important.

1. In general terms a farmer's social aspirations and motives may be affected by the information available to him. The spread of "western" values around the coasts of Asia relative to the interior is a case in point.

2. Information on market opportunity may be restricted in one area relative to another. This is particularly important where prices fluctuate in a speculative commodity market, since profits will depend upon an immediate response to short-term rises in price.

3. Information regarding technological possibility or the "satisfaction" to be gained from a land-use system can also spread over space.

The spread of information, in an age of mass communication, may rightly be regarded as less of a spatial constraint today than in the past (although it is worth pointing out that in underdeveloped countries it is still very important). But various studies on "diffusion" have shown a difference between information availability and the acceptance of the information. Thus, although it is reasonable to suppose that information regarding new agricultural practices will be available to all United States farmers at approximately the same time, it can still be shown that the acceptance of this new technique will vary over space. Again, United States studies have shown that whereas mass communications provide the information, it is usually personal contact which effects the acceptance of an idea.

Hägerstrand developed a model which describes the diffusion of an innovation over space. He studied the acceptance of various new agricultural practices throughout an area of central Sweden and showed how the innovation spread outwards from an initial center. Hägerstrand then designed three models to "explain" this diffusion, and his third model fitted the actual pattern of diffusion of a number of indicators relatively well. The model contains six working assumptions:

1. Only one person possesses the information at the start,
2. The probability of the information being accepted varies through

five classes of "resistance," these classes being established entirely arbitrarily,

3. The information is spread only by telling at pairwise meetings,

4. The telling takes place only at certain times, with constant time intervals,

5. At each of these times every knower tells one other person, knower or nonknower,

6. The probability of being paired with a knower depends upon geographical distance between teller and receiver of the information. An empirical estimate of the probability of contact between two persons was derived from a study of migration contact and telephone contacts over distance.

Because of its complexity the model requires Monte Carlo methods for its solution. It is a statistical model and relies upon a simulation of real-world conditions rather than upon the logical development of a set of interrelated deterministic statements about what "ought to be." Any critique of the Hägerstrand model must be largely concerned with testing its applicability to the data and with evaluating the empirical data used in the model to specify the operational characteristics. In this respect the relationships used to define the probability of contact between teller and receiver seem particularly strong, whereas those used to define the probability of acceptance or nonacceptance seem arbitrary and weak. Further testing of the model must necessarily depend upon the availability of similar empirical data in other areas, and the development of adequate testing techniques.

But the model shows how technical information may be taken up at different locations at different times. The spatial time lag in the adoption of new ideas and practices will undoubtedly result in short-term regional variations in production pattern and economic efficiency, and with a rapid rate of technological change it may well be that some regions remain backward in technology relative to other regions over a long period of time. It has been shown, for example, that the rate of adoption of an innovation varies in the United States with such features as age and ethnic group. Pockets of strong resistance to innovations will result in a variation in regional efficiency which will affect the agricultural landscape.

Hägerstrand applied his model to the diffusion of technical innovations, but there is no reason why a similar model should not be applied to the spread of a particular type of cropping system. If we assume, for example, that all farmers start off in an area with only enough knowledge to cultivate at a subsistence level (even though they are market oriented), that they are anxious to "learn" of a new system, and that considerable information is available regarding alternative cropping systems, then the only way that a satisfactory system can be discovered is by experiment. If one farmer discovers a satisfactory cropping system, the less successful farmers close by may well adopt the same solution and a whole regional cropping system may evolve as an innovation dispersing over space. But in this case the extent of dispersion is bound to be limited by the extent of market demand, because as more and more farmers take up the innovation so the crop system will become less and less satisfactory. In two different areas two different solutions may be hit upon by chance experiments so that two distinctive regional patterns of agriculture emerge as part of the diffusion process. It follows that neither pattern need be optimal with respect to environment or rate of economic return. Learning processes taken together with information theories and diffusion processes may adequately account for specialization of agricultural production between regions. Environment and demand may only enter into the problem when the range of cropping systems which yield a return above the "satisfaction" level has to be determined.

An understanding of the processes that determine human decision-making involves an awareness of research currently being carried out in the behavioral sciences. If we recognize the all-important fact that geographical patterns are the result of human decisions, then it clearly follows that any theoretical model developed to "explain" agricultural location patterns must take account of psychological and sociological realities, and this can only be accomplished if the normative theories of agricultural location are made more flexible and blended with the insights provided by models of behavior.

Concluding Remarks

A model may be thought of as a simplified conceptualized representation of reality. In its simplest form, a model may be considered a classification system, and Braithwaite has argued that such a system in itself asserts a set of "primitive" laws about the structure of reality. Scientific investigation, however, usually requires the use of more elaborate model concepts, the aim of which is to develop a structural representation of reality of sufficient accuracy to allow experimentation and a more penetrating analysis of the relevant variables in any real-life situation. In human geography it is exceptionally difficult to experiment with real spatial patterns and, for this reason alone, any study of the spatial system will at some stage involve the building and testing of fairly elaborate models of spatial activity. The models developed so far only partly fulfill this function. They are partial models and to the geographer they are often not intuitively satisfying. Thus, although they may provide useful conceptual notions and in some cases useful operational techniques for analyzing restricted kinds of problems, they scarcely add up to a general theory of agricultural location.

First-stage hypotheses are, of course, usually too crude and too abstract to be useful. Testing against reality and subsequent refinement of the initial model should eventually yield a model which approximates reality fairly well. But testing such models requires that they be specified in an operational form, and unfortunately many of the models discussed above are either just a system of conceptual notions, or they are specified to be operational in a nonspatial context. The von Thünen, spatial equilibrium, and Hägerstrand models are exceptions. Learning theory, communications theory, and most of the behavioral models show how decision-making on the part of individuals and groups can be studied scientifically, but models which specify these processes as operating over space are rare.

If this gap between the spatial models developed by economists and geographers, and the behavioral models of the sociologist and psychologist can be bridged, then one crucial step forward will have been taken. But this is not the only problem. We also require to bridge the gap between models which operate over *time* and those which operate over *space*, for ultimately we need models of evolution of spatial pattern rather than static equilibrium models. Consideration of the various forms of stochastic model seems essential here. If both of these problems can be tackled and overcome, then a general theory of agricultural location which is both operational *and* intuitively satisfying seems a distinct possibility. Such a general theory would be of tremendous utility to geographers, both as a stimulating background for idiographic studies, and as a central pivot in the search for a general theory of spatial interaction. But clearly we are just at the beginning of this quest.

5. Agricultural Developments in Nigeria

J. T. Coppock

One of the major problems of the less-developed countries of the world, and especially of those in the tropical areas, is the transition from essentially subsistence and traditional farming to commercial production. This study of Nigeria, which has the largest population of the new African states, exemplifies the diverse problems of development, and the variety of means and methods being adopted to solve them. Development in the new states of Africa must begin with agriculture for two reasons: first, agriculture is the chief

occupation of most of the population; second, development
of other segments of the economy and the nation can only
be successful if there is a balance between agriculture
and other production activities.

The first four decades of the twentieth century saw considerable changes in the agricultural geography of Nigeria. In 1900 there was little pressure on land resources and there were hardly any export crops other than the produce of wild palms. But by the 1930s, improbable as it might have seemed to an observer forty years before, Nigeria exported substantial quantities of cocoa, groundnuts and cotton, as well as palm kernels and palm oil. The volume of exports has increased since the Second World War and even more marked developments, whose foundations are being laid at the present time, are likely in the next decades. The purpose of this paper is to describe and assess the changes which are taking place in the agricultural scene, with particular reference to those that are concerned with the transformation of traditional agriculture.

Traditional Agriculture and the Stimulus to Change

Although Nigeria, especially the Western Region, is atypical among African countries in its degree of urbanization, the great majority of its people are peasant cultivators and many of those who live in towns are in fact farmers, at least for part of the year. While there are considerable regional differences in the size of farm and in the kind of agriculture practised, the typical farmer is still a hand cultivator, growing crops on scattered parcels of land with the help of his family, and following some system of bush fallowing, where land is cropped for a number of years, allowed to revert to bush to recover its fertility and then cleared again for a further period of cultivation. Over most of Nigeria the growing of subsistence crops is still the main aim of farming. The hoe and cutlass are the standard tools. Intercropping and succession cropping are widely practised and livestock play a minor role. In the southern half of the country, where the tsetse fly excludes large stock numbers and where there is little grazing, livestock are rarely integrated with farming. Sheep, goats, pigs and poultry roam freely about the villages, keeping themselves alive as best they can by scavenging, while a few dwarf Muturu cattle, which have a considerable degree of resistance to trypanosomiasis, are reared for sacrificial purposes. Even in the tsetse-free areas of the north, cattle are largely in

Source: *Journal of Tropical Geography*, XXIII (December, 1966), 1–18. Reprinted by permission of the author and the publisher. The author is on the staff, Department of Geography, University of Edinburgh, Scotland.

the hands of the nomadic Fulani, and the settled Hausa and other farmers are mainly cultivators, keeping few livestock and differing from their southern counterparts chiefly in their larger farms, the predominantly grassy character of their fallows, the relatively minor place given to tree crops and their concern with cereals rather than root crops.

This universal concern with crop production and the marked seasonality of climate over most of the country give rise to very uneven labour requirements throughout the year, especially in the north where the growing season is shortest. The dry season is a period of little activity on farms and seasonal migration, either to the towns or to other farming areas, is widespread; conversely, there are times when labour demands are very heavy and these severely restrict the area which can be cultivated by the individual farmer and his family.

In the main, this agricultural system has been able to supply the needs of the population, for although there are often seasonal or local shortages of food and marked qualitative deficiencies in diet, the quantity of food available, measured in total calories, has generally been fairly adequate. It is true that the per capita intake of milk and meat is very small, the latter being only one seventh that of British consumption, and that children are often undernourished, but deficiencies of diet are due as much to dietetic preferences and to ignorance, as to lack of suitable food. The farming system has also been able to maintain soil fertility, provided that sufficient time elapses between one period of cultivation and the next.

For most of this century, and increasingly in the postwar period, agriculture has come under a variety of pressures encouraging change. The total population has grown from an estimated sixteen million in 1911 to some fifty-five million at the 1963 census and is increasing rapidly; this has created intense local pressures on land resources. The population is also becoming increasingly urbanised through widespread migration from rural areas, especially of young people, and this in turn creates an expanding home market for foodstuffs. The great improvements in communications have both facilitated the marketing of crops and created some awareness of the goods which might be bought with the proceeds of crop sales. Before the Second World War, the railways provided the main channel for crop movements, but in recent years they have been rapidly overtaken in importance by road transport (especially in Western Nigeria), as seen in the increase in the total length of tarred roads from 937 miles in 1949 to 5,404 miles in 1962, and in the five-fold increase in the number of commercial vehicles registered. Export crops have come to be widely cultivated and, while some, such as cotton, have long been grown and fitted in well with established systems of agriculture, others, such as cocoa, have profoundly affected the nature of farming. Rising standards and expectations have created new demands for foodstuffs, as is shown by the ubiquity of bread and other foods of convenience in towns and villages of the south. Perhaps of more immediate importance is the fact that governments (in the plural, since agriculture is now a regional responsibility) have become increasingly concerned with the promotion of agricultural production, particularly since independence. In part this has been due to the desire to improve the lot of the farmer and so discourage urban migration. Other reasons are the desire to increase the sales of export crops and provide foreign exchange for necessary imports, particularly of capital goods; to replace imported foods, notably sugar and wheat flour, by home-grown produce; to provide internal funds for economic development; to improve diets generally; and to promote regional self-sufficiency. Governments have always played a major role in agricultural development in a country where colonial policy virtually excluded foreign-financed systems of agriculture, but larger government revenues, postwar inter-governmental and international aid to tropical countries and a changed climate of opinion about their development, as well as the interests of politicians in promoting the advancement of their constituencies have all contributed to an enlargement of their role.

In the past, official interest was concerned chiefly with acquiring knowledge of the agronomy and botany of the different crops, improving the traditional system and, more especially, facilitating the production of export crops of good quality. The Second World War led, as elsewhere, to major developments, particularly the creation, in the late 1940s, of marketing boards which were intended to provide a more orderly outlet for export crops, but which have since become important as a source of government capital for development in general. The postwar period has also seen both an intensification of attempts to improve traditional systems of agriculture and an increasing interest in the adoption of non-traditional systems, whether small- or large-scale.

Obstacles to Change

Assuming that markets can be found, the essential problem facing governments is how to increase the quantity and quality of marketable agricultural produce in a conservative peasant economy where capital is scarce, labour abundant and land resources, although locally severely restricted, adequate; for despite agricultural improvements, it is thought that agricultural production has only just kept pace with population growth. The improvement of agriculture faces a number of obstacles, of which the most important are the attitudes and ignorance of the peasant farmer himself. There is little doubt that the application of existing knowledge and techniques could produce dramatic changes in both the quantity and quality of crops. For example, the average yield of cocoa is only a quarter of what is easily possible with improved varieties, while that of cotton could be increased tenfold if the best practices were followed. In part the failure to adopt new methods is due either to lack of knowledge of their existence or lack of appreciation of their value. Even in developed countries, where numerous channels of communication to farmers exist, the adoption of new methods is not easily achieved. In developing countries such as Nigeria most of the channels are denied by the illiteracy and poverty of the farmers and by the lack of adequate numbers of extension workers; for example, the ratio of graduate extension workers to farmers is probably less than a fiftieth of that in the United Kingdom, although the need for them is far greater. In these circumstances it is understandably difficult to make farmers aware of new practices, let alone to convince them that these are both desirable and profitable, for the visible effects of improved methods are not always striking. The belief is widespread that what is possible on government farms has little relevance to farmers' achievements, while the pressure to conform to traditional practices is strong and the consequences of failure tragic. Even where the farmer is both aware and convinced of the desirability of a change, he may be unable to make it through poverty, lack of credit or even inadequate supplies of the requisite inputs. Alternatively, he may be unwilling to make the greater effort that better methods often demand, not because he is lazy, but because he values leisure and social activities more highly than additional income, or because, as Galletti and his associates (1956) have shown, he is concerned to achieve an acceptable rather than a maximum income. These attitudes are particularly important where schemes are being promoted by governments whose desires may not coincide with those of the farmers themselves.

Land tenure is also a major obstacle to change, for while per capita land resources are adequate for the country as a whole, they are very unevenly distributed, largely because land is held communally for the benefit of each family or kinship group (although there are great regional variations, particularly as between north and south). At the one extreme, rural densities exceed 1,000 per square mile in parts of Eastern Nigeria, despite the generally poor soils, and bush fallows have been shortened to the point where soil fertility and crop yields are declining; at the other, there are areas of high potential, as in Calabar, which are thinly peopled and little developed. While it is uncertain how far farmers in crowded areas would wish to move, the obvious marriage of surplus population and empty spaces cannot easily be made because land rights are so jealously regarded. Thus, in the Niger Project, settlers could not be brought from the densely settled areas of the north, but had to be found among the inhabitants of the sparsely-peopled Middle Belt who had little incentive to move. The difficulties presented by a communal land tenure should not be exaggerated for land has been acquired on a considerable scale for government projects, often on long lease at minimal cost (although sometimes in the face of local hostility). It is clear that both the planting of tree cash crops, especially cocoa and kola, and the pressure on land resources around the larger towns, have made for some individualisation of land tenure, in practice if not in theory. Generally, however, some kind of communal land tenure prevails, discouraging change, handicapping the provision of credit and preventing the optimum adjustment of land and population resources. It is evident that some modification of land tenure is a necessary preliminary for the full development of agriculture.

There are, of course, many other obstacles which have hindered and still hinder agricultural development: they include the tsetse fly, which discourages the keeping of cattle over large parts of the country; poor communications in many of the remoter areas; the lack of satisfactory marketing arrangements for food crops; and the absence of an adequate infra-structure, especially of technical services, which limits the application of more sophisticated methods. Nonetheless, they have not prevented remarkable strides being made in this century, notably through the introduction of peasant cash crops.

Modifications of Peasant Agriculture

In recent years there have been changes in the pattern of Nigerian agriculture which have been brought about by the spread of peasant cash cropping to new areas and the introduction of new crops, new varieties and new methods to existing peasant farming; by modifications in the scale and character of peasant production; and by the development of large-scale production in estates and plantations. The greatest changes within the framework of existing peasant agriculture have come from the adoption of established cash crops in new areas and the adoption of improved varieties in existing areas, and only to a minor extent from the introduction of new crops. The lack of major cash crops has certainly inhibited agricultural development in some areas, notably in parts of the Middle Belt, and although there have been no major changes in the geography of the principal cash crops, new areas of production have come into being in the postwar period and the growing of crops for sale has become more widespread.

The pattern of cocoa production has been modified both by losses through disease and old age in the long-established areas and by new planting (although the Cocoa Belt remains the principal area and total production there has increased). Millions of cocoa trees have been destroyed in the areas affected by the swollen shoot disease, especially the area of mass infection near Ibadan. Moreover, many of the older trees are now past their prime. It has been estimated that some 30,000 acres are going out of production each year in the Western Region (two-thirds of them through disease), as against an annual planting of 10-16,000 acres. The planting of improved Amazon varieties is being encouraged in all regions and roadside nurseries are a common feature, especially in the Cocoa Belt. Millions of seeds and seedlings have been distributed to farmers, either at no cost or at heavily subsidised prices. More than eight million are bought by Western Region farmers each year. New areas have come into production at the eastern extremity of the Cocoa Belt, in the Eastern Region, especially around Umuahia and Bende, and on a smaller scale in the riverain provinces of the Northern Region.

Seedlings of improved rubber clones and of improved varieties of oil palm have also been made available to farmers at subsidised prices, but no marked change in the principal areas of production has resulted, although the Northern Region Government has been encouraging the planting of oil palms in its southern provinces. The distribution of rubber will be substantially modified if Eastern Nigeria achieves its planned expansion of 150,000 acres by 1968. In comparison, the acreage in Western and Mid-Western Nigeria will only increase to 18,000. There has been a considerable extension of the cotton growing areas of Northern Nigeria, especially in Bauchi Province, and the rapid adoption of improved varieties has been made possible through the control of seed used for planting. Some development of cotton growing has also occurred in the Western Region, where commercial growing of the crop was first established, but where disease has been a major obstacle. The acreage under groundnuts has expanded and a much larger tonnage is now marketed, but there seems to have been little change in the distribution of this crop, Kano remaining by far the most important province.

Attempts have also been made to promote the production of citrus fruits, especially in areas where large numbers of cocoa trees have been felled and replanting is discouraged, but the lack of any certain market for the produce has been a major handicap. *Robusta* coffee has also been encouraged and is grown on a small scale, especially in Abeokuta, Ondo and Kabba Provinces. In the Eastern Region little interest has been shown owing to the lack of marketing facilities. There have also been experiments in the growing of *arabica* coffee on the Mambilla Plateau, but the area under coffee remains small. Probably the most successful development of a minor cash crop has been in tobacco growing, for tobacco has become an important source of income for some 60,000 farmers in Western and Northern Nigeria. It is particularly interesting in that it is not an export crop and its production has been promoted mainly by a commercial firm, with little direct government help.

Other cash crops have been promoted with varying success. In the interests of regional self-sufficiency, the planting of kola, an important item of interregional trade which is produced largely in the Western Region, has been encouraged in both the riverain provinces of Northern

Nigeria and in Eastern Nigeria. However, the area planted so far has been small. Attempts have been made, with little success, to promote the growing of fibre crops, such as jute and kenaf, which could save imports. On the other hand, the considerable expansion of both local and interregional trade in foodstuffs has tended to break down the distinction between cash and subsistence crops (although some crops have long been sold on a small scale for domestic consumption), and to provide a valuable source of income in areas formerly without a staple cash crop. There has been growing interest in the production of yams for sale in the southern parts of the Middle Belt while maize has become an important crop in Western Nigeria. The output of rice trebled between 1950 and 1959 in Eastern Nigeria, particularly on the inland swamps. Production in the Abakaliki area, now an important centre, provides an interesting case study in the introduction of a new and profitable crop. Rice was greeted with suspicion when it was first introduced and much of the early development was associated with migrants from other areas; but after six years half the local farmers were growing the crop and the proportion has since increased.

The encouragement of crop production through the provision of seeds or seedlings is not a new feature. Rubber seedlings, for example, were given to the farmers in the 1920s. Yet cheap or free supplies of improved varieties are not in themselves sufficient: conditions must be suitable, a market available and the crop profitable. It seems clear from experience in tobacco and cotton growing that farmers will respond to price incentives to adopt a crop. Quality can similarly be improved, as has been shown with cocoa in Western Nigeria, where the proportions of first grade cocoa rose from 15 to 93 per cent in three years, and with groundnuts in Northern Nigeria, where the percentage of special grade nuts rose from 2 to 100 in the same period. Improved seeds also require improved methods of cultivation if their full benefits are to be obtained. Yields obtained from improved varieties of cotton are far below what is possible (although their introduction has increased average yields), because seeds are often planted too late in the season, largely owing to the priority understandably given to the care and harvesting of the staple cereal crop, and because cotton is sometimes planted as a catch crop from which any production is regarded as a bonus. Even so, the improvement of annual crops can be achieved much more swiftly than that of tree crops, especially where, as with cotton, the supply of seed is controlled. Replanting the existing acreage of oil palms would take over a century at the 1960 rate of supply of improved seeds.

Attempts have been made, with varying success, to encourage the adoption of desirable farming practices. To control cocoa pests and diseases, more than half a million farmers have been trained in spraying, and subsidised equipment has been provided. Farmers have similarly been trained in rubber tapping, the need for which is made clear by the fact that less than a quarter of the rubber trees in the Western and Mid-West Regions were thought to be in good tappable condition in 1961, largely as a result of bad tapping in the past. The promotion of fertilizers has had only limited success and farmers have often been either unwilling or unable to pay even subsidised prices, for payment is required at the very time when they have least money. Yet cash cropping represents a continuous drain on soil fertility which must be made good in some way, and fertilizers, if they can be adopted, provide the surest way of increasing production from traditional agriculture: fortunately, a recent F.A.O. scheme appears to be having greater success.

The Transformation of Peasant Agriculture

These attempts to improve agriculture within its existing framework represent a considerable and widely-spread investment in agriculture: for example, the production of cocoa seeds in Eastern Nigeria has been estimated to be worth £13 an acre. They have also benefited the greatest number of farmers and been the most important in terms of production. Yet it is the more highly localised and proportionately more costly attempts to modify the agricultural framework which have attracted most attention and which may ultimately prove the more beneficial. These seek both to raise farmers' incomes and to increase production by enlarging the scale and improving the efficiency of production. They imply both the stabilisation of shifting cultivation and some rationalisation of land holding.

To the politician concerned with the transformation of traditional agriculture, the tractor has often seemed a panacea, but it has brought little benefit to Nigeria where its costings are said to make sorry reading. The small plots and the emphasis on roots and tree crops limit its usefulness in the south, and even in Northern Nigeria the high cost of equipment, the lack of trained staff and adequate facilities for maintenance and repair and the limited range of tasks on which it can be employed are disincentives to its widespread use. So far mechanization has largely been confined to ploughing, which is a markedly seasonal activity, representing a small part of total labour input even with hand cultivation. Consequently the equipment lies idle for much of the year, even when it is maintained in working order. Tractors can bring considerable benefits, especially on heavy swamp soils which are difficult to cultivate, and in northern areas where the growing season is short and the land cannot be prepared until the first rains arrive. But attempts to plough more land than can be weeded or harvested can only end in disaster, as in the Niger Project, where ploughing represented less than a tenth of all labour required. Tractor cultivation of peasant holdings has been most widely used for the production of wheat and rice on both seasonally flooded and irrigated land: in Northern Nigeria,

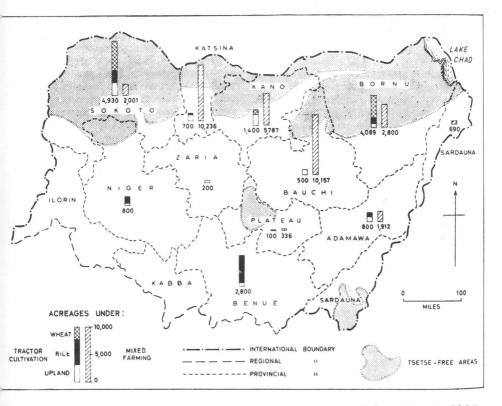

FIGURE 1: *Area under tractor cultivation and mixed farming in Northern Nigeria, 1964, by Provinces.* (There were no mixed farmers in Benue, Ilorin or Kabba Provinces, only twenty six in Niger and twenty four in Zaria. No land was cultivated under tractor schemes in Kabba, only three acres in Ilorin and thirty in Sardauna Province.)

where 13,060 acres were ploughed by tractor in 1964 (out of a cropped area estimated at sixteen million acres in the region in 1957/58), these crops accounted for 39 and 24 per cent of the ploughed area (Fig. 1). Tractors have been readily accepted by farmers where their services have been free, but attempts to secure prepayment have led to a fall in demand, as in the Gwandu Rice Scheme, and tractor hire has been heavily subsidised in Northern Nigeria since 1961. While mechanization has chiefly been a feature of agriculture in Northern Nigeria, cultivation of peasant farms by tractor has also been attempted in other regions, especially for rice cultivation, and has been successfully used in the tobacco-growing areas of Oyo Province, where abundant land permits farmers to pool their tobacco lands in large 'fields' of up to sixty acres and some 15 per cent of the land is mechanically cultivated, in part by tractors belonging to the tobacco cooperatives. Apart from such uses, tractor cultivation is virtually confined to government farms and farm settlements and to a few large private farms, such as that of the Sultan of Sokoto.

Whatever its limitations, the tractor has two merits: it requires no land for its support and it is immune to disease. Cultivation by work oxen, the alternative method of enlarging the area that can be cultivated by a single farmer, is handicapped on both counts. Oxen must be fed throughout the year and this implies a doubling of the farm area, or at least access to communal grazing, and hence a density of less than 100 persons per square mile. Similarly, the risk of trypanosomiasis virtually excludes work oxen from the tsetse-infested areas (Fig. 1). The term 'mixed farming' for this use of work oxen is somewhat misleading, for it involves no integration of crops and stock. It was first encouraged as early as 1928, when there were three mixed farmers, and has been promoted by means of loans for ploughs and oxen. There has been a considerable expansion since the Second World War, for there were 35,261 mixed farmers in Northern Nigeria in 1964 (compared with 4,068 in 1947), most of them distributed in the three provinces of Bauchi, Kano and Katsina. The operation of the scheme has been limited both by finance available for loans and by difficulties in securing sufficient animals of a suitable type, but there are also many cultivators employing work oxen outside the official scheme, and the total number of mixed farms in Northern Nigeria has been estimated at 80,000, or perhaps one out of every hundred farmers in the region.

The development of agriculture in the north has also been promoted by irrigation schemes. As well as small-scale irrigation by *shaduf*, there are already several hundred thousand acres of naturally irrigated rice, sugar cane, tobacco and other crops, notably in the Sokoto-Rima valley, in the Niger valley (where, before the construction of the Niger Dam, some 10,000 acres were thought to be cultivated annually), and on the inland swamps of southern Nigeria. But the floods are very variable and large quantities of water (the lack of which is a limiting factor to agriculture in Northern Nigeria) flow to waste. Unfortunately, the topography of Northern Nigeria outside the Niger trough is not generally favourable for the storage of water and most schemes are consequently small. They are mainly designed to be used in conjunction with mechanical cultivation for the benefit of peasant cultivators who will retain their 'upland' farms elsewhere. The first project of the Irrigation Division of the Ministry of Agriculture (established in 1949) was a rice cultivation scheme on the Kaduna River, and much of the early development was concerned with rice. The rising imports of wheat flour have provided a powerful stimulus to the expansion of irrigation facilities and many of the later projects outside the Niger trough have been designed for the cultivation of winter wheat. About 3,000 acres were already being grown and it was thought that the average might be increased to 35,000. In all, some 8,200 acres were being irrigated on

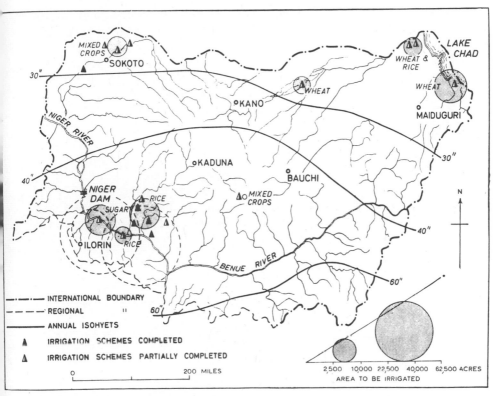

FIGURE 2: *Irrigation schemes in Northern Nigeria,* 1963. (The broken circles in the Niger trough show the area of land thought irrigable.)

official projects in Northern Nigeria in 1963 and the 1962-8 Development Plan forecasts an acreage of 50,000 (Fig. 2). The principal areas are (1) in the Sokoto-Rima valleys, where there are some 750,000 acres of fertile land and where a United Nations Special Fund team is making a comprehensive hydrological investigation; (2) on the Hadeija river; (3) on the alluvial flats around Lake Chad where a million acres might ultimately be irrigated; and (4) on the lower reaches of the Kaduna river. Pending the report of the Special Fund team, the greatest concentration of possible future irrigation schemes is in the Niger trough, where ultimately 500,000 acres might be irrigated. Owing to the capital required and to the difficulty of water storage, the extent of irrigated land is unlikely to be high in the foreseeable future and developments such as these, costing some £30–60 an acre, are an expensive way of growing a crop which may yield only half a ton per acre. Nevertheless, irrigation does help to stabilize agriculture and allows the growing of crops which would not otherwise be produced, as well as providing valuable lessons in cooperation.

In southern Nigeria, the approaches adopted in transforming traditional agriculture include measures to encourage larger and more compact holdings, and the creation of cooperative farm settlements. The Palm Grove Rehabilitation Scheme of Eastern Nigeria, begun in 1962, is one of the best examples of the former approach (Fig. 3). Its purpose is to secure both an improvement in palm produce and some land consolidation, by replacing the low yielding semi-wild palms by small 'plantations' of properly spaced improved varieties, to be achieved by imposing a minimum qualifying acreage. Grants totalling some £ 18 per acre, phased over a number of years to ensure proper care, are payable for the felling, planting and maintenance of at least five acres of oil palm covering not more than two blocks. In the first three years of the scheme, 16,045 acres were planted, mainly in provinces in the forest belt, a figure which contrasts with the 10,551 acres planted between the

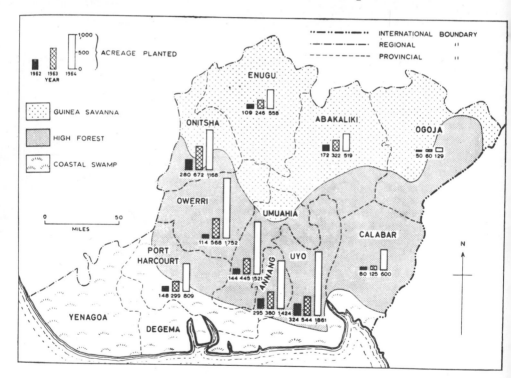

FIGURE 3: *The Palm Grove Rehabilitation Scheme, Eastern Nigeria, 1962–1964, by Provinces.* (The acreages planted in Degema Province were respectively 0, 26, and 37, while those in Yenagoa were 25, 36, and 32. The total acreages planted in Eastern Nigeria were 1,741 in 1962, 3,724 in 1963 and 10,580 in 1964. The vegetation zones on all the maps in this article are based on Rosevear's 1:3,000,000 Vegetation Map of Nigeria, Lagos, 1953.)

wars in the whole of southern Nigeria under an earlier palm grove improvement scheme. A similar approach has been adopted with other crops and in other regions, as for example, a rubber planting scheme in Western Nigeria for which a minimum of 6 acres of rubber was prescribed. The resulting groves of well-spaced trees certainly contrast with the irregularly scattered wild palms and often tightly packed stands of rubber trees which they replace. However, it is too early to judge the success of these projects.

The farm settlements, which owe much to Israeli experience, represent a much more radical departure from traditional agriculture, although there is a long history of attempts to create planned settlements, ranging in size from single farms to the vast Niger Project, which envisaged, in its first stage, the clearing of some 32,000 acres and the creation of 800 individual holdings using mechanical cultivation, but which eventually failed. Attempts in the 1950s to develop group farms and settlements in both the Eastern and Western Regions were also largely abandoned, although a few relics remain. The farm settlement idea has

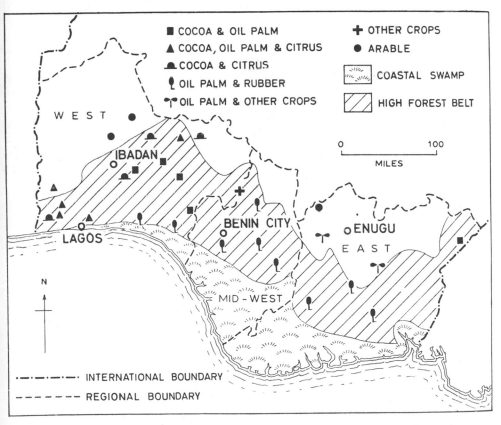

FIGURE 4: Farm settlements in the southern regions of Nigeria, 1964.

received a strong stimulus from the growing problem of urban unemployment, particularly among school leavers, and it is hoped that farm settlements will demonstrate that peasant agriculture, using modern methods, can provide living standards equal to those of clerical workers or artisans in the towns. The settlements also provide a means of bringing uncultivated land into production, although those in the Eastern Region have been deliberately placed in densely populated areas so that they can have the maximum impact on the farming community.

The approach adopted has varied with the environment and with the region. In the savannah areas the farm settlements have been based on the mechanized cultivation of annual crops such as maize and rice, but the great majority depend on tree crops, with oil palm as the most important single crop (Fig. 4). In the Eastern Region the number of settlements has been limited to seven and it is hoped that their success will encourage local communities to start similar settlements of their own. In the Western Region many more have been created. Between 1960 and 1964 thirteen had been established throughout the Region, with as far as possible, one in each division. In 1964 it was decided to create a large number of less ambitious settlements, of which the first was opened at Eruwa, and it is hoped that ultimately one and a quarter million people will be settled on the land.

The procedure adopted and the general appearance of the settlements have been broadly similar. Land was acquired from local communities, generally as a gift or on long lease. After survey, a master plan was prepared, settlers recruited, villages built (usually with temporary accommodation at first), roads made, nurseries for tree crops established, tthe land cleared and holdings laid out. The size of the settlements has varied. In the Eastern Region, the aim has been settlements of 12,000 acres, with six villages of 120 settlers each and a nucleus where communal services and a processing plant would be located. However, owing to difficulties over land acquisition, settlements in fact range from 3,200 acres to 14,929 acres, though the smaller ones may later be enlarged. In the Western Region the range is from 396 to 6,100 acres of cultivated land. The settlers' houses are grouped in open villages, with food plots of two to three acres within easy reach, but experience in the Eastern Region has led to the development of more compact settlements to reduce the cost of providing services. The aim has been to provide a consolidated holding which can be worked by the settler and his family and which will yield a net income of some £300 a year (or £120 on Type B settlements in Western Nigeria). Various combinations of crops have been adopted (Fig. 4), and the size of the holdings varies with crop and region, generally ranging between thirteen and twenty acres, including the homestead and the food plot. The three largest settlements are those on arable land—that at Uzo Uwani in the Eastern Region, based on irrigated rice, being twenty

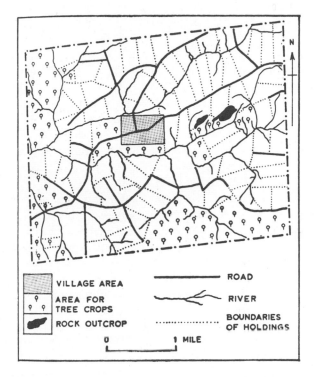

FIGURE 5: Master plan for the Ilora Farm Settlement, Oyo, Western Nigeria.

acres, and those at Ilora and Ogbomosho, based on maize, being seventy acres (although part of this is uncultivated). To provide additional income settlers are encouraged to keep poultry as well as cultivate food and cash crops. Figure 5 shows the master plan of the Ilora settlement; the contrast with the traditional dispersed and fragmented holdings is even greater than the map suggests, for the land is contour-ploughed and bunded.

These settlements are envisaged as cooperative enterprises and membership of a cooperative is a condition of entry. They allow the services of extension workers to be more efficiently provided, tractors and processing equipment can be centrally located and an environment created in which new ideas can be put in to practice away from the conservative influence of the older farmers. The cost is high, although the original estimates of some £3,000 per settler has been reduced to about £1,700, and most of this is provided as a loan to the settler, who acquires his holding on long lease and must begin repayment when his crops start yielding. It was originally intended that settlers should be school leavers who would first receive a period of training at farm in-

stitutes, but many of the youths recruited had entirely wrong concep--
tions of the purpose of the scheme and somewhat older settlers are now
being recruited.

Inevitably there have been mistakes. Not all settlements are well sited,
for the choice of locations has partly been governed by political considerations and by the willingness of communities to provide land.
There has not always been sufficient time for proper surveys. No settlement is more than five years old and many are still on the drawing
board, but there are powerful political incentives for their success,
which should prevent their experiencing the same fate as the Niger
Project and other abortive settlement schemes of the 1950s.

Farm settlements similar to those in the south have not been established in Northern Nigeria, where it was thought that communal settlements would not be acceptable, but there have been several resettlement schemes, notably for the pagan peoples of the Jos Plateau and the
Cameroon Highlands. Like the group farming schemes of southern
Nigeria, most of these resettlement schemes have been abandoned, but
that at Shendam (Plateau Province) has, within the limits set, been
both highly successful and on a larger scale than any in the south, while
another scheme has recently been started at Gwoza, to the south of
Maiduguri. The Shendam scheme began in 1948 and now caters for
more than 8,500 families, a total which is increasing by some 150 a year
and involved the cultivation of some 16,400 acres in 1961-62, 13 per cent
of which was under cash crops. This project is both considerably
cheaper and less ambitious than the farm settlement schemes. Much
more is left to the initiative of the settlers, who build their own houses
on traditional lines and clear and cultivate their holdings by hand.
These holdings, measuring some thirty-two acres, are narrow rectangles
divided into four acre blocks and cultivated on a system of regular bush
fallowing, with successive plots being cleared, cropped and abandoned.
The contrast with traditional farming is less marked and the cash returns to farmers much smaller than those envisaged for the farm settlements, although the farming system still represents a very considerable
change from the former agriculture of the pagan peoples.

Cooperative settlement schemes are comparatively new, but cooperative farming is an old established practice in certain parts of the
country where communal clearing of land is undertaken. Nevertheless,
modern agricultural cooperation, particularly in production and marketing, has been little developed, though a notable exception is again
to be found in the tobacco-growing areas of Oyo Province, where cooperatives own curing barns and cure tobacco.

Livestock and crop husbandry still remain largely separate activities,
although there has been some attempt to relieve grazing pressure in the
more densely settled parts of Kano and Katsina Provinces by reseeding
communal pastures, and a total of some 5,000 acres had been sown by

1961. The greatest advances have been in the encouragement of poultry farming, for poultry have been adopted as a source of cash income on the farm settlements, and poultry centers at Fashola, near Oyo, and Abakaliki have provided farmers with day-old chicks. Many poultry farms have been established, some on a considerable scale, though the operators of these have often been businessmen rather than farmers. Modern poultry farmers in the Western Region were producing some one and a half million eggs in 1963 and this figure was thought likely to double within two years. Pigs for fattening have also been supplied on a smaller scale, but developments in integrated cattle farming have been less successful, although there have been pilot fattening schemes around Shaki. The tsetse problem and the unfamiliarity of southern farmers with cattle have been major obstacles in southern Nigeria, while the reluctance of the Fulani to provide stock for commercial purposes, and the separation of crop and livestock husbandry in different ministries are major difficulties in the way of any developments in Northern Nigeria.

Large-Scale Enterprises

The farm settlements and most of the irrigation schemes, while they cover large areas, are essentially schemes of cooperative peasant farming. The true large-scale enterprises in Nigeria are the estates, plantations and ranches, the development of which represents a marked change of policy from the colonial period when the plantation was generally excluded. Although several plantations, covering some 20,000 acres, were established before the Second World War, chiefly to provide experience of modern agriculture under Nigerian conditions, they were atypical. Since self-government, the regional development corporations have established a considerable number of new plantations, chiefly of oil palm and rubber, but also of cashew, citrus, cocoa, coconuts, coffee and pineapples. Most of these plantations have been established in thinly populated areas of the forest belt where suitable land could more easily be acquired. The major development has occurred in the Eastern Region where there were twenty-two plantations in 1963, covering nearly 134,000 acres, while a further sixteen have been established in the Western Region, occupying some 43,000 acres (compared with over one million acres under tree crops) (Fig. 6). They range in size from 395 to 15,000 acres and most of them cultivate a single crop, the chief exception being the Ijebu Farm Project, where oil palm, cocoa and citrus are grown. Few are yet at a stage where they can make any major contribution to production, and there have inevitably been teething troubles, in part resulting from lack of continuity in management and of sufficient delegation of managerial powers and in part from natural hazards, such as the rodent infestation at Elele. The benefits of higher yields and better quality produce have yet to be fully demonstrated, but the plantation is likely to prove most suitable for those crops, such as rubber and oil palm, where careful handling and relatively elaborate processing are required. In their regular layout and homogeneous cropping, the plantations provide a marked contrast with the high forest or thick bush and scattered farm plots which they replace. A good example is the cocoa plantation at Akure, in the Western Region (Fig. 7).

The development corporation plantation has not been the only form of large scale enterprise to appear. In Western Nigeria the corporation entered into partnership with local communities, but these joint projects generally proved unsuccessful. Joint enterprises with foreign in-

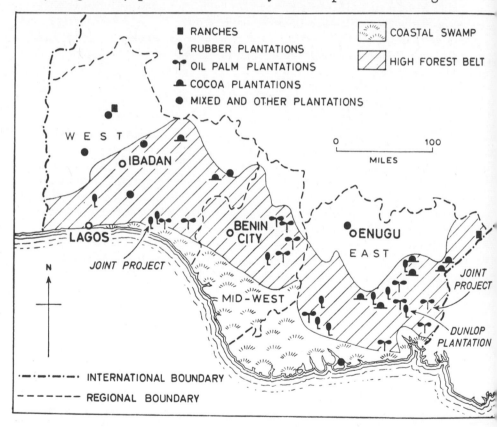

FIGURE 6: *Large-scale agricultural enterprises established after 1945 in Southern Nigeria and still in existence in 1963–64.* (The joint projects are partnerships with expatriate capital. The other enterprises, with the exception of the Dunlop plantations, are wholly government-financed. There are also some private Nigerian-owned plantations and estates, but there are no comprehensive data on them (*see* Udo, 1965).)

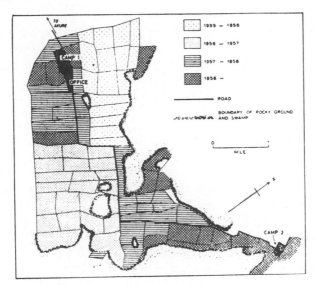

FIGURE 7: *Western Nigeria Development Corporation Cocoa Plantation,*
1958. (The plantation is located near Akure. There has been further planting
since 1958, but this has not made any substantial changes in the layout of
the plantation.)

terests have also been started, as with the Oban oil palm plantation
(Calabar) and the Ilushin rubber estate (Ijebu), where the Colonial
Development Corporation is a third partner. One commercial rubber
plantation has also been established, in Calabar, although it is improbable that it will be followed by others, at least in the Eastern Region.
A more likely form for future developments in the nucleus plantation,
where a commercial plantation will provide the processing equipment
and expert guidance for small holders growing the same crop in the
area around the plantation. Although there had been exploratory talks,
no nucleus plantation had been established by the end of 1964.

Most of the large-scale projects have been concerned with tree crops.
There have been several attempts to establish large mechanized arable-
crop farms, as at Fashola and on the Upper Ogun estate, but these have
proved abortive. Recently, however, a large sugar estate was established by a commercial firm, the Nigerian Sugar Company, with the
Nigerian governments as major shareholders. Located at Bacita, on the
south bank of the Niger near Jebba, the estate covers some 15,000 acres
of largely swamp forest. The land was acquired on a ninety-nine year
lease, and 6,400 acres are being developed in the first instance. The
crop is grown under irrigation, made necessary by the long dry season,
and the first crop was successfully harvested in 1964. In its general lay-

out it is little different from commercial sugar estates established in other parts of Africa, and is considered to be commercially viable and to be capable of supplying much of Nigeria's needs, for although chewing cane is widely grown and brown sugar was produced on a considerable scale during the Second World War, refined sugar is a major and expanding import.

Several large-scale livestock enterprises have also been developed. The Western Nigeria Development Corporation has established a ranch of some 26,000 acres in the derived savannah of the Upper Ogun to provide cattle for slaughter. Approximately 6,000 acres have been cleared and the area divided by fences into 250-acre paddocks in which more than 3,000 Ketaku and N'dama cattle are being raised. Both of these breeds have shown some resistance to trypanosomiasis. A similar ranch has been established by the Eastern Nigeria Development Corporation near Obudu, at an altitude of 5,000 feet on the tsetse-free grassland of the Bamenda highlands. (Unfortunately, the loss of the Southern Cameroons has left Nigeria with little land of this kind). This ranch covers some 20,000 acres and supports more than 2,000 red Fulani cattle, although some South Devons have also been imported for experimental breeding. Both ranches are now in production, though both have experienced some difficulty in marketing livestock. Two ranches are also being established at Mokwa (Niger) and Manchok (Zaria) in Northern Nigeria, in which Fulani cattle intended for slaughter in southern Nigeria will be fattened on natural pastures on cleared savannah. There is also a large-scale pig farm at Minna.

Other large-scale enterprises established by governments include research stations, training schools and livestock investigation centres: examples are the livestock investigation centre at Fashola, which is concerned among other things with producing breeding cattle and weaners for farmers, the Federal Veterinary Centre at Vom, the Cocoa Research Institute near Ibadan and the Institute for Oil Palm Research near Benin. Some of these are only research stations, but most have some commercial function through the supply of seeds or stock, or, as with the dairy units at Vom and Agege, the sale of produce. Increasing numbers of large private agricultural units are also appearing, often run by prominent politicians and businessmen. In southern Nigeria, for example, some individuals have succeeded in acquiring estates covering several hundred or more acres of cocoa, oil palm and rubber. There are also some large rice and other crop farms. At Kano one of the largest pig farms in Africa is being run by private enterprise.

Figure 8 represents in summary form the main features of non-traditional agricultural developments which have appeared in Nigeria in the postwar period. It shows clearly both the concentration of such activities in southern Nigeria and the contrast between Western Nigeria, where the main emphasis has been on farm settlements, and Eastern Nigeria, where plantations have been the distinctive feature. This dichotomy is likely to become more marked. It also shows the large area where little development has taken place, especially the Middle Belt away from the Niger trough, and those localities where special investigations are in hand: the Sokoto-Rima valleys, where the United Nations Special Fund Survey is in progress; the Niger delta where a statutory board, the Niger Delta Development Board, is studying possible developments, including fish and rice farming; and the Cross River, where a joint U.S.A.I.D./Ford Foundation team is conducting a survey of potential developments. Large, relatively empty spaces of varying fertility and potential remain and, while many of these present considerable problems, postwar developments have done little to alter the major imbalance in the distribution of agricultural population and land resources.

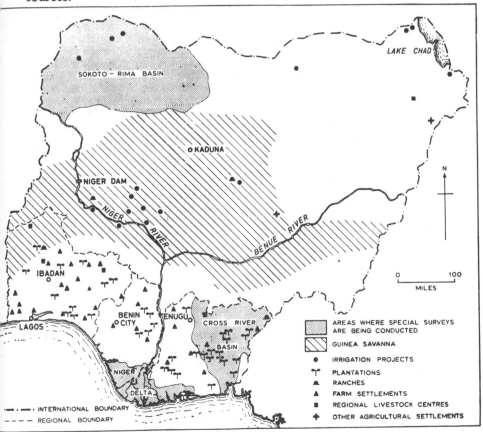

FIGURE 8: Non-traditional agricultural projects in Nigeria, 1963–64.

Conclusions

Most of the schemes of agricultural improvement which have been briefly described in this paper are as yet too recently established for valid judgments to be passed upon them and the unfortunate history of many earlier projects must make any observer chary of predicting their viability. Few of the projects described by K. M. Buchanan have survived in their original form; indeed, it is ironical that several of the more recent schemes are in the same locality as those, often of a different kind, which were abandoned earlier, as for example, the Mokwa ranch on the site of the Niger Project and the Upper Ogun ranch in part on a former mechanized crop farm. Much will depend on the extent to which the projects are regarded primarily as agricultural development schemes rather than measures to alleviate local problems at whatever cost in efficiency, a danger which is particularly acute in large-scale enterprises. In small-scale projects, too, there are hazards and some resources have been misapplied or have failed to benefit those for whom they were intended: thus many of the farm loans in Western Nigeria have gone to 'adventures' rather than farmers and a disproportionate number of those participating in irrigation and mixed farming schemes have been local officials, schoolmasters and the like.

Large-scale developments and radical measures to transform peasant agriculture are attractive because they produce visible results and they may well have important catalytic effects. If plans are fulfilled by the end of this decade these projects should occupy something like three quarters of a million acres. Nevertheless, their importance should not be exaggerated, at least in terms of present achievements. Between 1949 and 1960 agricultural investment by the regional development corporations and their predecessors in agricultural projects (not all of them large-scale) totalled some £7 million and are not now much more than £20, compared with the annual investment of £8 million in land in the 1950s and the £100 million invested in peasant cocoa, that is the value of standing trees. In the short run at least the major contributions to agricultural production must come from improvements in peasant agriculture, where quite small but widespread advances can produce large gains: thus better crop storage alone could increase food supplies by up to 10 per cent by reducing losses of stored crop through pests. In the longer run the improvement of peasant agriculture depends on the discovery of solutions, applicable at the farm level, to the problems posed by communal land tenure, tsetse infestation and the maintenance of soil fertility. The last is of critical importance, especially in the densely populated areas on poor soils in southern Nigeria, where the best solution (in the absence of adequate supplies of fertilizers) seems to be a controlled bush fallow based on the deep-rooting shrub *Acioa Barteri*. Soil exhaustion is no less critical in parts of the close-settled lands of northern Nigeria. Over most of the country the devising of a system of true mixed farming, in the sense of the integration of crops and livestock on the same holding, must clearly await the solution of the tsetse problem, although it will also depend on success in teaching conservative farmers how to handle livestock in the almost instinctive manner of those with long traditions of cattle farming. Some solution must also be found to the problem posed by the migratory Fulani, who have these skills, but whose cattle contribute far less than they could to the economy and whose traditional grazing, over which they have no land rights, is increasingly threatened by the growth of the settled population.

What is not clear is how far there is a will to agricultural improvement among farmers themselves, for most are motivated by economic considerations only to a limited extent and have little idea of costs. On the other hand, there is no reason to suppose that Nigerian farmers are any less conscious of self-interest than farmers elsewhere and more attention could be paid to the possibilities of providing stronger financial incentives, although market demands limit what can be done in this respect. Export crops must generally compete on the world market with other produce, sometimes of better quality, and the downward trend of cocoa prices in recent years provides a warning against unlimited expansion of production of export crops. When world prices are low the practice of using marketing boards as a source of development capital carries a serious risk of discouraging agricultural improvement and even production. Low producer prices for palm oil may be partly responsible for the fall in the quantity exported and have certainly affected the economies of development corporation and commercial plantations, on one of which oil palm is being replaced by rubber. If rubber were in turn to be made a marketing board crop, the probable level of prices to producers would soon kill commercial interest in rubber and also make its production on corporation plantations uneconomic.

The domestic market is no less important and it is useless to encourage the production of commodities of a kind or quality which the market does not require. If Nigeria consumers are unwilling to pay more for beef from cattle fattened on ranches than for that from the surplus cattle of Fulani herds which are in poor condition at the end of a six hundred mile trek from northern Nigeria and if butchers still prefer a thin beast because it is cheap, there is little point in using scarce capital for further ranch development. Nevertheless, improvements in the arrangements for marketing produce for internal consumption could provide a more certain and more remunerative market for farmers and so result in improved agricultural production. The production of export crops, which account for only a fifth of agricultural output, was encouraged by the creation of marketing boards. Some similar organization for marketing domestic produce might be equally beneficial, provided no attempt was made to use it as a source of development funds. Tobacco-growing again provides convincing proof that assured markets and returns can effectively promote crop production. In the immediate future such developments might result in the wisest use of scarce resources, for whatever the long-term benefits of farm settlements, plantations, ranches and irrigation schemes, they will occupy only a small part of the land devoted to agriculture and make only a minor contribution to total agricultural output for some time to come.

6. Irrigation and Land Problems in the Central Plain of Luzon
D. J. Dwyer

Intensification and increased productivity of agriculture in many parts of the world is by no means simply the application of greater amounts of capital and labor to the land. Even irrigation does not necessarily mean higher income from increased yields. Its benefits are often offset by the much greater costs of bringing water to the land. In addition, there are many other economic as well as political and social problems that greatly complicate matters even on small semi-subsistence farms. In this selection, Dwyer presents a study of two Filipino farmers, one able to irrigate part of his rice crop, the other working in the traditional manner of coordinating his farming activities with seasonal rainfall.

Most current discussions of the agricultural problems of the countries of southeast Asia spring from the fact that two basic considerations—rates of population growth and yields of rice and other important food crops—together form a disquieting picture. This is certainly true of the Philippines. There has been a rapid increase in the population of the Philippines during this century. In the first scientific census to be held there, in 1903, the population was returned as 7.6 millions: the latest census, that of 1960, showed a total of 27.4 millions. The growth of

SOURCE: *Geography*, XLIX (July, 1964), 236–46. Reprinted by permission of the author and the Geographical Association. The author is professor of geography and head of the Department of Geography and Geology at the University of Hong Kong.

population between 1958 and 1961 is estimated to have been at the high rate of 3.3 per cent, which should mean a doubling of population within the next 20 years. Yields of rice and maize, the main food crops in the Philippines, are some of the lowest in eastern Asia, as Table I shows, and it is customary for rice to be imported on a substantial scale after poor harvests.

Fortunately there are still prospects in the Philippines (awaiting detailed evaluation, but probably limited) for further agricultural colonization, especially on the island of Mindanao. Such prospects are, however, being so actively canvassed within the country, that at present it can fairly be said that the potentialities of further land colonization are diverting full attention from the problem of low yields of food grains within those areas already farmed. In sharp contrast to schemes for developing the more remote areas stand the low yield of rice and the low intensity of dry season (November-May) land use in the so-called "rice-bowl" of the Philippines, the Central Plain of Luzon. The latter is apparent even to the most casual observer. Travelling out from Manila towards the end of this season, one is surrounded by unkempt, grassed-over rice fields, grazed only by the few *carabao* (water buffalo) required to work them during the summer rainy season. The farm year in the rice-growing areas of central Luzon is clearly divided into the wet season, when for the most part only one crop of rice and perhaps some vegetables are grown, and the idle dry season. In southeast China, in contrast, in a broadly similar climate, the crop year extends well into the dry season. In Hong Kong, for example, much of the paddy land now yields two crops of rice and often an additional crop of vegetables following the rice. Population pressure admittedly accounts for the present extremely intensive pattern of Hong Kong's land use, but the very existence of such a pattern indicates what is probably the most productive use of crop land in such climates. A major difference between agriculture in south China and that in central Luzon lies in the use made of irrigation. Spencer has pointed out that in only a very small area of the Philippines, in the mountain valleys of northern Luzon, have the ancient large-scale, hand-built irrigation systems been constructed that are such a feature of the agriculture of southern China. Elsewhere, as will be shown, the application of irrigation is quite modern.

Two Filipino Farmers in Luzon

Lest comparisons with south China be pushed too far, it will be useful at this point to turn to a recent case study of two Filipino farmers, one with and one without irrigation facilities. As this study will be referred to again and in more detail in a later part of the paper, it must be stressed at the outset that the farmers are typical of those growing rice as their principal crop on the Central Plain of Luzon and that their living standards are identical. The details have been taken from recently published work by Diaz and Von Oppenfeld. The conclusions drawn from them are, of course, those of the present writer.

Miguel and Juan are the two farmers. They live in *barrio* (village) Halang in the municipality of Biñan, about 20 miles south of Manila, near the shores of the lake Laguna de Bay. Miguel rents 2.3 hectares of land and, as he has no means of irrigation, can grow only one crop of rice a year. He also tills a small vegetable patch on a steep hillside nearby. He plants the seedbed for his rice in July and transplants into his prepared fields in August. Some replanting is done in October and the crop is ready for harvesting towards the end of December. Both transplanting and harvesting are carried out with the help of hired labour as is customary in Luzon. For most of the year, therefore, apart from tending his small vegetable patch there is relatively little work for him on the farm. He sells neither chickens nor pigs, his only income coming from his rice crop and from helping other farmers transplant and harvest their rice. During the year his farm was studied his 2.3 hectares yielded 2112 kg. of rice; in addition he earned another 880 kg. from other farmers.

Just across the village lane from Miguel's house stands that of Juan, a relative. Juan rents 2.78 hectares and shares in the use of a 3-h.p. irrigation pump provided by his landlord. His land is divided into three parts. On two of them, totalling 2.08 hectares, he raises one crop of rice a year, largely dependent upon rain. In the middle section (0.7 hectare) he is able to raise two crops of rice through the use of

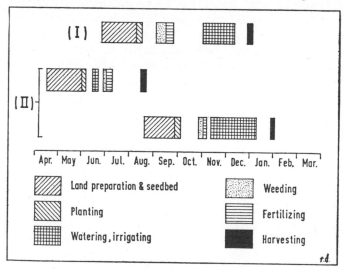

FIGURE 1: Juan—yearly work pattern on rice. I: unirrigated land; II: irrigated land. (After Diaz and Von Oppenfeld.)

TABLE I. Population and Yields of Rice and Maize in Certain Asian Countries, 1961–62

Country	RICE (JAN. 1961–JULY 1962)			MAIZE (JAN. 1961–JULY 1962)			POPULATION	
	Area Harvested (Thousand Hectares)	Paddy Production (Thousand Metric Tons)	Yield (100 kg./ hectare)	Area Harvested (Thousand Hectares)	Production (Thousand Metric Tons)	Yield (100 kg./ hectare)	Total Mid-1961 (Thousand)	Average Rate of Increase 1958–61 (Per Cent)
Japan	3,301	15,523	47.0	43	116	27.0	94,050	0.9
South Korea	1,128	3,706	32.8	–	–	–	25,375	2.9
Taiwan	782	2,508	32.1	–	–	–	10,971	3.7
Mainland China*	31,500	85,000	27.0	n.d.	n.d.	n.d.	646,530	2.4
Federation of Malaya	389	926	23.8	–	–	–	7,137	3.2
North Vietnam*	2,316	4,660	20.1	–	–	–	16,690	2.1
South Vietnam	2,354	4,609	19.6	–	–	–	14,494	3.9
Ceylon	484	897	18.5	–	–	–	10,167	2.7
Indonesia	6,816	12,528	18.4	2,518	2,298	9.1	95,655	2.3
Burma	4,068	6,851	16.8	–	–	–	21,527	2.1
Pakistan†	9,698	16,118	16.6	482	495	10.3	94,547	2.1
India†	33,859	51,223	15.1	4,468	4,064	9.1	441,627	2.2
Thailand	5,654	7,845	13.9	316	592	18.8	27,181	3.0
Philippines	3,179	3,910	12.3	2,014	1,194	5.9	28,727	3.3
Cambodia	1,191	1,250	10.5	101	147	14.5	4,740‡	n.d.
Laos	620	540	8.7	–	–	–	1,850	2.7

n.d. No data.

–Production insignificant on regional scale.

* Production estimates unofficial and tentative. Mainland China: production 1960–1 and tentative. Mainland China: production 1960–1; population December 1957; rate of increase 1957–60.

† Population totals exclude Kashmir and Jammu (3.56 millions in 1961).

‡ 1958 figure.

SOURCE: F.A.O., *Production Yearbook 1962*, Rome, 1963, Tables 16 and 18, and U.N. *Demographic Yearbook 1962*, New York, 1962, Table I.

irrigation water. Like Miguel, Juan also cultivates a small vegetable plot on some rougher land nearby; and with three separate crops of rice a year, plus his vegetable patch, he puts in almost twice as many working hours on the farm as Miguel.

Juan's rice year begins in April (not July as in the case of Miguel) on the seedbed of his irrigated plot (Fig. 1). The first crop from this plot is harvested in late August or early September. Preparations for a second irrigated crop follow immediately: the rice is planted at the beginning of October and harvested at the beginning of February. On the unirrigated plots Juan's operations are essentially the same as Miguel's, except that he can if necessary spare some water from his irrigated plot if rain does not come when he wants it: his seedbed is prepared in July and the crop is ready in late December. It may be mentioned here that Juan was found to differ from Miguel not only in his use of irrigation but also in that he gave more care to the crops and even applied some fertilizer to them. The result was a total of 6472 kg. of rice from his 2.78 hectares, a yield more than twice as heavy as that of Miguel (2328 kg. per hectare as against 918). In addition, like Miguel, Juan occasionally assisted other farmers, and for his work he received 673 kg. of rice during the year.

The Progress of Irrigation

Juan is fortunate in having part of his land served by pump irrigation because only 12 per cent of the cultivated area of the Philippines is irrigated, and further because local pump irrigation from streams is itself a new feature there, large-scale programmes dating only from 1952.

Under Spanish rule relatively little attention was paid to irrigation apart from some small diversion-distribution systems constructed by the friars in the provinces of Rizal, Laguna and Cavite, that is, immediately around Manila. These covered about 24,000 hectares, but all gradually fell into disuse through silting. Under United States rule, which began in 1898, an Irrigation Division was created (1908) and started a national programme of gravity irrigation using diversion systems of the low weir type. With the independence of the Philippines (1946), the irrigation programme was greatly intensified with the primary objective of attaining self-sufficiency in rice, and since 1950 it has been heavily assisted by United States funds. Prior to independence, the total area served by irrigation works completed under the national programme stood at 86,000 hectares. This area was expanded to 317,400 hectares by March 1964. A further 53,000 hectares were served by local pump irrigation. As yet the major gravity irrigation systems are heavily concentrated on the rice-producing Central Plain of Luzon (Fig. 2). The most important schemes completed there since 1946 are

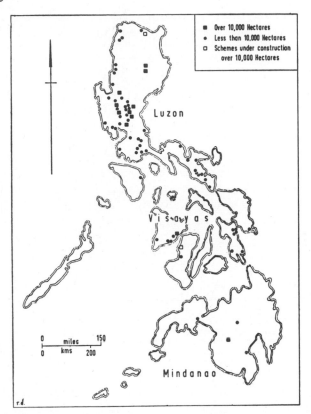

FIGURE 2: Distribution of gravity irrigation schemes, 1964.

the Pampanga river and Pampanga-Bongabon schemes in Nueva Ecija province (18,000 and 12,000 hectares respectively) and those on the Agno river, Pangasinan province, which irrigates 25,000 hectares, and on the Tarlac and the Camiling rivers, Tarlac province (each 10,000 hectares). The largest irrigation scheme in the Philippines remains that on the Angat river in Bulacan province, which serves 27,000 hectares and was completed as long ago as 1927. Apart from the Jalaur river scheme in Iloilo province, Panay, which irrigates 11,400 hectares, the Libungan river scheme in Cotobato province, Mindanao (11,500 hectares), and a project under construction on the Bago river in Negros Occidental (20,000 hectares), little has yet been accomplished in the Visayas and Mindanao. Further, a major weakness common to all the gravity irrigation schemes is that they make little provision for dry-season irrigation since they lack storage facilities. The policy of the Irrigation Division so far has been to guarantee only wet-season crops, and the national irrigation programme has only very recently begun to embrace multi-purpose river development projects with the construction of the Marikina River scheme, near Manila, which when completed will provide for hydro-electric power and flood control as well as for irrigation of 5800 hectares of land.

Miguel and Juan Revisited

From what has been presented so far it may appear that a large part of the solution to the problem of producing more food in the Philippines at least from the rice-growing areas of the Central Plain, lies in techno-logical improvement, especially the construction of water conservancy schemes. Unfortunately the solution is by no means so simple, as some further details from the case of Miguel and Juan will show. It will be recalled that at the end of the crop year discussed above Miguel had raised 2112 kg. of rice and had earned 880 kg. more: a total of 2992 kg. Juan, with part of his land irrigated, had produced 6472 kg. and had earned an additionl 673 kg: a total of 7145 kg. The Diaz-Von Oppen-feld survey showed, however, that as regards personal benefit from their crops Miguel and Juan finished the year roughly equal.

After the harvest, when Miguel's landlord, the planters and the harvesters had received their shares, when some rice had been set aside for seeds and when Miguel had paid off the debts he had accumulated over the year (mostly to his landlord), there were only 220 kg. of the rice he had grown left for his family (Table II). Of the 880 kg. he had

TABLE II. Miguel: Disposal of Rice Crop and Off-farm Rice Earnings

	Kilograms	Percentage
Rice Crop		
Landlord's share	660	31
Planters' share*	396	19
Harvesters' and threshers' share	308	15
For seed	88	4
Miguel's share:		
To creditors	638	30
For home use	22	1
TOTAL YIELD	2112	100
Off-farm Rice Earnings		
Sold	704	80
For home use	176	20
TOTAL	880	100

* Advanced initially by landlord.
SOURCE: Based on R. C. Diaz and H. and J. Von Oppenfeld, *Case Studies of Farm Families in Laguna Province, Philippines,* College of Agriculture, University of the Philippines, Laguna, 1960.

TABLE III. Juan: Disposal of Rice Crop and Off-farm Rice Earnings

	Kilograms	Percentage
Rice Crop		
Landlord's share	2046	31.5
Share for planters, fertilizer, gasoline and oil*	1232	19
Harvesters' and threshers' share	972	15
For seed	176	3
Juan's share (all to landlord as creditor)	2046	31.5
TOTAL YIELD	6472	100
Off-farm Rice Earnings		
To creditor	440	65
Sold	13	2
Home use	220	33
TOTAL	673	100

* Advanced initially by landlord.
SOURCE: Based on Diaz and Von Oppenfeld, *op. cit.*, p. 50.

earned, he had to sell 704 kg. to raise some cash for day-to-day living expenses. Thus in all only 198 kg. of rice remained for home consumption, an amount quite inadequate for his family for the year. Another year of debt was in prospect.

It is significant that although he produced more rice than Miguel, Juan fared even worse if anything (Table III). He returned home from all three harvests without a single grain of rice. After shares had been set aside to pay for the planters, harvesters, fertilizers, for seed and for fuel for the irrigation pump (requiring 37 per cent of his crops), the landlord took all the remainder: 31.5 per cent of the crops as his share and 31.5 per cent in payment of debts. Further, of the 673 kg. of rice Juan earned from other farmers, 440 kg. had to go to the village shop to settle his accumulated account. A little had to be sold for ready cash, leaving only 220 kg. for home use. Like Miguel, then, Juan faced yet another year of poverty and debt. He could well question the benefit of irrigation and improved methods of cultivation.

The Basic Problem

What the above case study demonstrates quite clearly is that unless the desired technical improvements in agriculture in the underdeveloped nations of the world can quickly be made to yield tangible benefits to the peasants, they will be very slow in being adopted. In a recent survey of 3800 farmers in the Central Plain of Luzon reported by Von

Oppenfeld 53 per cent were shown to have no marketable rice surplus: they produce rice largely to pay off their accumulated debts, which often carry extremely high rates of interest, and to provide the necessary shares for their landlords and for hiring labour. The basic problem is thus the breaking of a particularly strongly established cycle of rural poverty; and technological improvement is only one facet of the answer. It will not affect the continuance of several important factors contributing to the perpetuation of the cycle. One of the strongest of these factors is established social custom. The best example is the strength of the kinship groups in the *barrios*. It is well known that in the Luzon villages ". . . a member of a kinship group rarely makes a decision on his own", that is, without consulting relatives, and the net effect is delay and often the stifling of the ambition of the most active. On the economic side, perhaps the most immediate problem is the shortage of available capital for small-scale, local improvements by individual farmers, for this leads to under-equipment on the farms and, worse, to easy descent into heavy indebtedness, usually into the power of the landlord. This raises the question of tenancy, which has an important geographical aspect and in many senses is the most fundamental of the factors involved in the cycle of poverty.

The Tenancy Problem

Although the proportion of the total farm areas of the Philippines that was operated by full owners in 1948 (the latest year for which statistics are available) was as high as 61.6 per cent, this figure fell very low in certain areas, notably the rice-growing parts of the Central Plain of Luzon. In Pampanga province, for example, only 5.9 per cent of the total farm area was operated by full owners, while the figures for Nueva Ecija, Bulacan, Tarlac, Manila and Cavite, all primarily Central Plain provinces, were 20.2, 20.5, 22.5, 24.0 and 25.0 per cent respectively (Fig. 3). In recent years problems connected with tenancy have steadily increased in scope and seriousness in this region, and much of the support given by the Luzon peasantry to the Communist-dominated *Hukbalahup* movement immediately after the Second World War stemmed directly from them.

The most frequent form of tenancy arrangement is share-cropping, a frequent, though now illegal, division of the crop between landlord and tenant being 50 : 50. The official Philipine government reply to a 1952 United Nations questionnaire on land reform stated that: "Some 95 per cent of all tenant farmers are share tenants. As a minimum they pay 30 per cent of the gross output (after harvest costs) as a rental, but the majority pay 50 per cent or more". Often, as has been indicated by the foregoing case study, most of the tenant's share is

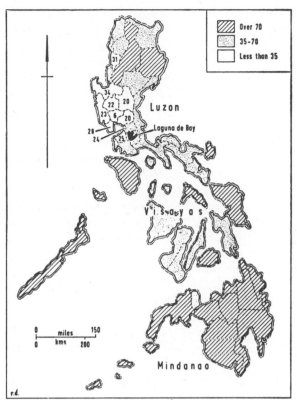

FIGURE 3: Percentage of farm area worked by full owners, 1948.

already mortgaged to the landlord against debts incurred between harvests. The landlord is thus in a position of particular power over the tenant, and it is the frequent misuse of this power that has given rise to postwar outbreaks of what can only be described as class warfare on the Central Plain.

The Philippine government attempted to introduce a measure of reform into this situation in 1954 with a new Agricultural Tenancy Act. This law provided that where the normal rice yield was more than 1760 kg. per hectare the landlord's share should be 30 per cent if the tenant supplied all the labour, farm animals, implements and hired labour for transplanting and harvesting. In areas where average yields were below 1760 kg., the landlord's share was to be 25 per cent.

The Agricultural Tenancy Act was followed by a Land Reform Act in 1955. The objective in this case was twofold: to accelerate the opening-up of new agricultural land, which had been proceeding so slowly in Mindanao and the outlying islands as itself to constitute a serious problem; and, of more immediate importance, to facilitate the division and redistribution of private land in areas where agrarian conflict exists. Unfortunately the Philippine Congress inserted into the Act, as submitted by the administration, provisos that land expropriation proceedings could only be initiated in respect of areas of not less than 300 hectares of contiguous area if owned by an individual and of 600 hectares if owned by a corporation, and that acquisition proceedings could be started only by petition of the majority of tenants of an estate. The former proviso especially greatly reduced the scope of the Act. In Pampanga province, for example, even before the 1955 land reform started, there were only 8 *haciendas* with contiguous areas greater than 300 hectares: thus there were only 13,800 hectares available for redistribution, out of a total farm area of 67,400 hectares, only 5.9 percent of which was worked by full owners in 1948. Some landowners deliberately broke up their estates by comparatively minor sales of land. Even where the law could be applied, land reform proceeded very slowly, while the provisions of the law regulating the sharing of crops were widely disregarded. In a word, little that was effective was done to improve the serious situation that exists. The peasant continued to receive little incentive to adopt improved practices.

The Agricultural Tenancy Act and the Land Reform Act were superseded by a new consolidated law, the Agricultural Land Reform Code, in August, 1963. Again, the bill was finally approved by Congress only after a series of amendments. Agricultural share tenancy has been declared contrary to public interest and is to be abolished. The intention is that all land held in share tenancy, except fishponds, saltbeds and land principally planted to permanent trees, such as coconuts, citrus and durian, is to be transferred to leasehold tenancy, the lease to be calculated at 25 per cent of the normal harvest for the three years preceding the transfer, less the cost of seeds, harvesting, threshing and processing. After the leasehold system has been created in an area, expropriation proceedings will be taken against any estate of over 75 hectares if demanded by more than one-third of the leaseholders on the estate. The expropriated areas are to be reorganized into owner-occupier "family-sized" farms, the actual extent of which will vary according to the quality of the land and the prevailing cropping pattern. Special agencies are to be established to extend technical assistance, credit and legal help to the peasants during the changeover, which from current indications seems destined to be very gradual. Only a pilot scheme has been set up so far, in Tarlac province. As a piece of legislation, this is clearly the most ambitious land project yet undertaken in the Philippines. It remains to be seen whether it can be successfully implemented.

From what has been outlined above it will be apparent that in the

Philippines, as indeed all over the world, the problem of raising the level of food production is an extremely complex one. The geographer can readily point out areas in which it appears that the full potential of the environment for food production has not yet been exploited. But commonly the reasons lie in the realms of economics, sociology, medicine or even politics as well as in the need for technological improvements such as the provision of irrigation facilities. In this paper one major point has been made. It is that tangible benefits to the peasants of the underdeveloped nations must be guaranteed in schemes of agricultural improvement through the introduction of effective legislation to provide for social justice at the lowest levels of society and the vigorous enforcement of such legislation. If the only result of improvement schemes appears to be the further enrichment of the larger land owners then, by aggravating an already dangerous social situation, they can be worse than useless. With further population growth this basic, underlying problem becomes more and more pressing. The resulting situation in the Philippines is now such that, as Golay has hinted, the time available for the development of the economy in an evolutionary (as opposed to revolutionary) manner may well prove too short if the problem of rural poverty, in all its aspects, is not speedily tackled.

7. Arid Zone Development: A Reappraisal Under Modern Technological Conditions

David H. K. Amiran

*The arid regions of the world—regions of deficient moisture—
have been areas in which the development of a productive
agriculture has been limited. Traditional patterns of life have
been either nomadic herding or sedentary agriculture in
oases where sufficient water is available to support permanent
settlement. Lack of water, the chief impediment to
increased agricultural development, has been alleviated in
some arid areas by modern irrigation and cropping practices.
Traditional agricultural practices have been altered and*

*yields and output have been improved considerably. As a
result, prospects for substantial production increases
in other parts of the arid zone have greatly improved.*

In classifying an area as *arid* one is applying to it a negative value
judgment—of deficiency in moisture. Throughout the ages the utilization
of moisture-deficit regions has followed one of the two following patterns: an extremely sparse and widespread pattern of occupancy
coupled with the most extensive type of land use—generally pastoral
(the nomads of many arid areas were the representatives of this type);
interspersed in this extensive pattern there existed the most intensive
type of land use, sometimes linked to extremely high population densities, as in the oasis settlements.

These traditional patterns of occupancy in arid lands were adapted
to certain stages of economic and social development. They were often
actively conditioned more by factors outside the Arid Zone than by
those inherent in it. The modern technological revolution and its concomitant social factors have caused profound changes in these patterns,
making reappraisal essential.

The Traditional Way of Life of the Nomad

In an amazing example of adaptation to a meager and unreliable environment, nomadic people have managed to live in arid lands of many
continents, apparently since time immemorial. The majority were pastoral nomads, some, like the aborigines of Australia, hunters and col-
lectors who domesticated no animal other than the dog. Most of them,
benefiting from a somewhat more favorable environment, lived essentially in semiarid lands; others, such as the Tuareg of the Central
Sahara, roamed the forbidding core areas of the arid realm. In contrast
to pastoralists in non-arid areas, nomads all have these conditions to
contend with: the very low carrying capacity of their pasture grounds;
the constant threat of overgrazing; and the erratic character of the
climate, or more particularly, of its moisture element, which makes
what little pasture might normally be expected, as well as the water
supply, highly undependable.

Nomadism is the optimum adaptation of non-industrial populations
to the occupance of fully arid areas outside of oases. It might, therefore,
be a final form of adaptation, and small groups may adhere to nomadism as long as they continue to exist. They represent a social anachron-
ism in our day.

Source: *Economic Geography*, XLI (July, 1965), 189–210. Reprinted by permission
of the author and the editor. The author is professor of geography, Hebrew University, Jerusalem.

Among the various adaptations to environmental conditions, nomadic life is distinguished by its high mobility. Generally speaking, the more arid the environment, the more frequently the nomad will be on the move, and the greater the distances he will cover. In less arid areas movements might be rather restricted and amount to a regular seasonal exchange of grazing grounds. One might say that the basis of the nomadic economy is comparable in its unreliability to the fluctuations of desert rainfall, thus modifying Gottmann's *bon mot* that the Beduin's "standard of living is as low as the average rainfall" of his environment.[1]

The raising of livestock for their own sustenance and for sale was by no means the only economic base of life for most of the nomadic peoples. The interposition of the Arid Zone between the humid tropics and the humid low-latitude lands created a varying demand for trans-desert transportation. For this the nomad provided beasts of burden, and related services, such as that of guides. These desert caravans assumed a rather similar and quite distinct character in various desert areas. In providing caravan services the nomad held a monopolistic position which he utilized in a ruthless way. Prices were set as high as possible. In addition, the nomad often extracted *protection fees* from the traveller, which had to be paid to the tribe (or tribal head) of each consecutive area traversed. The traveller who refused to pay, or to pay sufficiently, was waylaid and robbed by the same nomads who otherwise would have been his caravan men and guides. This system was possibly brought to the extreme by nomadic people in Inner Asia for whom the raiding of caravans became a national sport and a legitimate element of the social fabric.[2] The immorality of the practice took on an absurd cast when Beduin of the Moslem faith regularly raided the pilgrim caravans proceeding to the holy cities of Mecca and Medina.

The Oasis Husbandman

Very different was the character of traditional oasis occupany. Here we have to distinguish between natural and artificial oases. The former normally had a water-supply which provided the essentials for agricultural occupancy: not only water, but, also, consequent on its occurence and the biological processes it activates, arable soil (it is the lack of soil which makes the arid desert sterile).

As both water and soil were decisive factors in oasis cultivation, they were sometimes used to their full capacity. To mention but one ex-

[1] *Geographical Review*, Vol. 39, 1949, p. 687.
[2] Even in Palestine raiding by Beduin was officially recognized as a social institution as late as 1931. Instructions to census officers specified as one of the criteria for determining age: "A youth who has taken part in a tribal raid." Cf. E. Mills: Census of Palestine 1931, Part I. Report. Alexandria, 1933, p. 331.

ample, in the oasis of Pica at the foot of the Andes in the Atacama Desert of northern Chile, a number of men often share in the ownership of a single fruit tree, such as a fig. Each is entitled to a specified share of the fruit and has to contribute a commensurate share of his water allotment and work. In order not to waste a drop of water, cultivation here is *clean* in the extreme, every blade of grass or other undergrowth being carefully weeded out as a useless water consumer.

In meeting the challenge of a forbidding arid environment deficient in the one indispensable element, man has evidenced remarkable ingenuity in providing and assuring a water supply. The underground *qanats*, so highly developed in Iran, spate water farming practiced in many Near Eastern lands in the past, and many other methods testify to the skill and adaptability of Arid Zone man.

But it is not only, and not always, the amount of water and soil available which determines the extent of cultivation and the size of population of an oasis. Its location might also be a determining influence. The considerable fluctuations in importance of oasis towns with the rise and fall in importance of the trade routes along which they are located and which they serve as staging posts is evidence of this. In extreme cases such towns have flourished in certain periods only to be totally abandoned in others. Here, the basic principle of demand and supply finds a comprehensive expression in the survival or cessation of settlements.

The history of many towns along the *silk route* through Central Asia is a fitting example, that of the ancient towns of the Negev of Israel another. In the latter case, a group of over a half dozen towns existed in a halfway position in a relatively elevated area on a major regional route of ancient times, serving the trading empire of the Nabateans. In line with their purpose as caravan servicing towns they produced a limited supply of fresh fruit and certain other crops by a most ingenious mastering of nature's limited water supply in an area where annual rainfall is as sparse as two to four inches (50–100 mm) and commensurably unreliable. At the height of its development this area must have had a population of little less than 50,000. After the tenth century A.D. it was almost totally abandoned and only a few Beduin lived here until the first recent settlements were founded in the nineteen-fifties. Similar fluctuations between prosperity and total abandonment are characteristic of the *silk route*, Trans-Saharan routes, and routes in the Andean region.

One feature illustrates the unique single-purposed nature of oasis settlements. They are always oasis *towns*. Villages are a decided minority of the settlement fabric. The normal size-pyramid of settlement is here inverted.

Obviously, not all oases are developed to their full capacity. Under-use of the agricultural potential of oases is by no means uncommon.

Furthermore, considerable fluctuations in cultivation may occur even in the same oasis region. It is by no means exceptional for the physical potential of production of an oasis to be larger than the economic one. The lack of a market or its location at a distance which makes marketing there unprofitable might render the physical resources of an oasis economically unusable. Careless and incomplete use is sometimes made of the available water in an oasis: the waste is in many cases in striking contrast to its scarcity in the surrounding arid region as a whole.

In certain other cases, cultivation initiated in response to specific demands is perpetuated long after cessation of the original demand by sheer inertia, lack of adaptability, and lack of demand for an alternative. A striking case is the continued cultivation of alfalfa in some valleys of the northern desert of Chile. This originated at a time when fodder had to be provided both for the mule trains servicing the mines in the adjacent districts of the Andes and to a more limited extent for the cavalry. For some decades now the mines have been served by trucks and the army is motorized as well, but the farmers in the Lluta and other valleys still grow alfalfa, which no longer really has a paying market, for sheer want of an alternative demand.

The Husbandman of Semiarid Lands

The oasis farmer operates under considerable handicaps. Isolation, great and therefore expensive distances to markets, a strictly limited development potential, and sometimes the permanent threat of raids by the nomad population of the surrounding desert, or oppressive "taxation" by them, are his major disadvantages.[3]

Very different are the geographic factors conditioning life for the farmer in semiarid regions. He lives in a climatic region which permits of a suitable agriculture anywhere, not only in an oasis. He does not inhabit an area isolated by great stretches of barren desert but a region continuous with those of denser settlement and of "normal" agroclimatic conditions. In contrast to the oasis farmer of the desert proper, who has a limited though rather stable water supply and who does not expect rain (if it comes, it is more often a curse than a blessing), the farmer of semiarid lands has to cope with instability of rainfall as his major natural hazard (Figs. 1 and 2), both the amount and time of occurrence being erratic and critical. It is the farmer of semiarid lands who lives in frequent fear of drought, not his counterpart in the arid oasis.

[3] To simplify matters no reference has been made here to the population of the long drawn-out river oases. They are spared many of the disadvantages of oasis people and share others. In some cases extreme congestion and population pressure distinguish river oases to an even higher degree than a groundwater oasis. The Nile Valley is the classic instance.

There are other risks with which man has to cope in semiarid lands. This being a natural frontier region, nature is at a rather delicate balance easily upset by ignorance or carelessness in unbalancing the natural processes in operation, such as removal of natural factors protective against the forces of erosion and the resultant widespread affection of certain semiarid lands with soil erosion of various degrees of severity. As the fluctuations of the moisture factor frequently occur

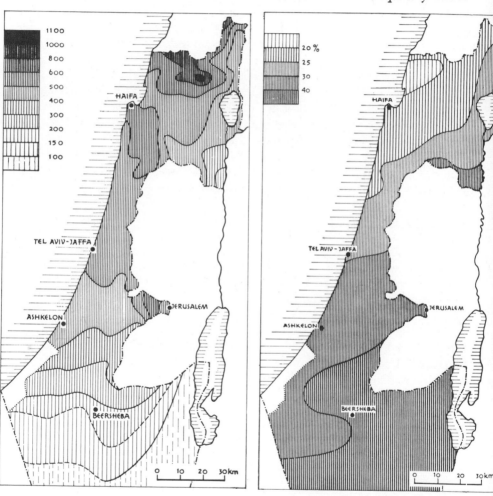

FIGURE 1: Israel, average rainfall (mm), 1921/50. (According to Atlas of Israel, Sheet IV/2a.)

FIGURE 2: Israel, variability of rainfall 1947–1962, in per cent (relative standard deviation $(\delta/\bar{p})$).

These two maps express in various forms the factor of climatic risk in the south of the area shown. Map 1 illustrates the steep gradient of decreasing rainfall southward; map 2 stresses the great extent of area where variability exceeds 30 and 40 percent.

in series of moister and drier years, it often has occurred that a moist spell lured new settlers not sufficiently accustomed to the climate into extending cultivation unduly into the arid fringe, only to face harsh disappointment in the next dry spell. The North-American Pioneer Fringe tells this story.

Finally, enjoying a favorable climate as compared with the arid desert, and allowing for a continuous area of cultivation, the semiarid zone holds great attraction for the nomad, whenever weather is unfavorable and the pasture gives out in his tribal area. At these times, which are often also times of crop failure for the semiarid farmer, the latter is exposed to raids by nomadic hordes from the desert, compounding the climatic problem.

As many semiarid areas have a prolonged dry season, it is by no means accidental that deep-rooting plants form part of their agricultural heritage. The fruit tree has been a characteristic element of such lands for centuries, even millennia. Magnificent orchards of olives, figs, and other fruit trees as well as vineyards of many generations' standing grace the countries around the Mediterranean and lands of similar climate. They provide the maximum stability to traditional agriculture available under these climatic conditions. Furthermore, a certain amount of irrigation near villages, especially for vegetables, has been practiced for many generations.

Again, in contrast to the arid area proper, semiarid regions have a normal pattern of settlement with a multitude of villages topped by a normal pyramid of towns.

The Change: Standard of Living

Conditions as outlined in the preceding chapters may be said to be essentially those of a past which no longer exists other than in the most out-of-the-way areas (note, however, the stipulation made below).

The advent of the modern way of life, our present-day wage economy, the prospects offered by industry in need of ever greater numbers of labor, and the common aspiration to achieve higher standards of living—have basically unbalanced the traditional order. Those areas which have to be classified as marginal as a result of both the limited economic standard attainable in traditional agriculture and their erratic climate have joined full-scale the trend toward rural depopulation. Obviously, mountains and lands on the border of aridity have been most severely affected.

In order to keep their places in the world economy, semiarid and arid lands now have to compete for manpower with other areas. Today an agriculturist who suffers repeated crop failure due to drought, locust, or others of the Arid Zone's storehouse of calamities, will quit farming and join the world's growing and generally man-hungry labor force in industry and services. Only by far-reaching progressive development can arid lands share in the world's material advancement and maintain their populations. Located in sensitive natural border areas, they must either progress or else suffer regression; no longer is choice of conservative stability governed by an antiquated rural economy feasible.

The major elements creating this situation and an outline for future development form the major subject of this paper. The one important proviso which should be made, however, is the following: that this outline appears to be applicable only to lands and populations in the technically and economically advanced countries of the world. Those populations—especially in some countries in Asia—which still lack sufficient capital to be used in the national economy and which are coping with a population pressure out of all proportion to the possibilities of gainful employment are outside the scope of the development sketched here. As for those countries where the creation of employment at subsistence wages for much of the population has yet to be achieved and where the immediate aim is a larger, rather than smaller, input of labor per unit of land cultivated,[4] their respective arid areas can hardly be expected to follow the type of development with which we are concerned here.

There is another qualification which must be made: it is the warm part of the Arid Zone with which we are concerned here; for most of its cooler areas the following is not applicable.

Stability by Irrigation in Semiarid Lands

As far as agricultural settlement is concerned, the obvious need is to free the semiarid farmer from the risk of drought. Even in years of *normal* rainfall he labors under conditions of potential evapotranspiration in a number of times in excess of total rainfall. From the point of view of the agriculturist, the excessive water loss by evapotranspiration is a greater calamity than the low average rainfall. As evapotranspiration is conditioned to a high degree by temperature and duration of sunshine, both very stable factors in semiarid climate, it maintains permanently high rates in striking contrast to the considerable variability of rainfall.

To counteract this disadvantage and to provide the semiarid farmer

[4] Cf. V. K. R. V. Rao: Population Growth in its Relation to Employment in India, in S. N. Agarwala, edit., India's Population: Some Problems in Perspective Planning (Bombay, 1960). This case has been forcibly stated by G. Kuriyan: India's Population Problem, *Focus*, Vol. 5, No. 2, October, 1954, p. 4, as follows. "Many people think that mechanization of agriculture would be a panacea for the ills of India. Nothing could be further from the truth. Mechanization results in producing a higher yield per man employed, not a higher yield per acre cultivated.

with a stable basis for his agriculture, exposed as little as possible to fluctuations, modern farming in these regions tends to be based increasingly on irrigation. In progressive areas it turns almost exclusively to irrigation farming.

By these technical means the farmer of the warm, semiarid zone now turns into an advantage the same climatic factor whose negative implications made this development necessary: namely, the persistence and reliability of high temperatures. He but rarely suffers from frost and does not face the hazards of overly moist or cool seasons at harvesting time with which farmers in other climates must contend. The different phasing of climates permits him to produce his products in advance of the marketing season of adjoining areas and reap the higher prices of out-of-season products in addition to his near-monopoly in producing *subtropical* crops, especially fruit, of which citrus is a striking and remunerative example. To an ever-increasing degree, therefore, the semiarid farmer is introducing out-of-season and specialty crops as cash crops in addition to the staples raised for his own needs and the national economy. These relatively high priced crops find a steadily expanding market in an economy of rising standards of living. However, only a prosperous economy can afford to consume sizable quantities of agricultural products which have to bear relatively high transportation charges; there is thus a mutual interdependence between the conditions for these developments.

Areal Concentration in Semiarid Development

It is not only the distance the products have to be shipped from producer to market which makes semiarid crops relatively expensive. To provide the semiarid-land farmer with the essential means for reliable and sustained production an adequate irrigation network is essential. The installation and maintenance of this network with all its multiple feeder lines [5] (often including permanent charges for lifting the water) is a considerable factor in total production costs. More often than not the provision of the water itself, from drilled wells or by damming,[6]

[5] Costs remain considerable even under modern conditions, where water is supplied by pipeline, and if, as is increasingly common of late, plastic piping is used for last-stage feeders.
[6] With all the advantages of dammed reservoirs built to utilize river or runoff water naturally available instead of artificially drilling for underground water, one must not forget the disadvantages of storage reservoirs in arid areas. First there is the problem of high evaporation losses implicit in the arid climate. None of the many processes for minimizing evaporation by monomolecular films or other means which have passed the laboratory stage has performed satisfactorily as yet under field conditions. As a result, water stored in open-air reservoirs in arid areas has to be used early, when the need for it is least urgent, to avoid the loss of most of it by evaporation. The time factor is thus highly unfavorable, as the need for water becomes

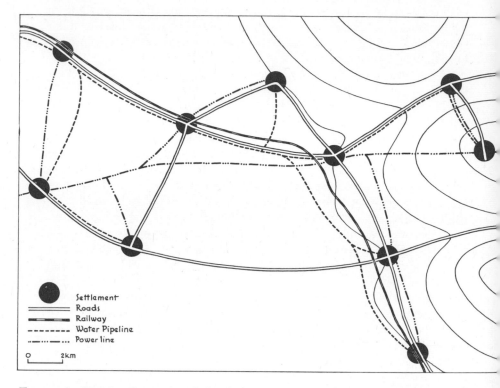

Figure 3: Dispersed pattern of development for a rural development area with dispersal of villages, located at advantageous points for either topography or road connections.

involves a sizable capital outlay which has to be met both initially and by gradual amortization.

If, then, all new agricultural settlement has to be equipped with full-scale irrigation networks, the price of irrigation installations must be a

---

greater with the passing of time after the last rainy season during which the reservoir was filled. During the latter part of the dry season, when the need for irrigation water is greatest, the amount left in the reservoir is scant—perhaps even nil.

A second disadvantage is the highly erratic nature of the supply: during a spell of dry years a reservoir might store up only small amounts of water for several years running; in extreme cases reservoirs are known to have been filled to capacity only once in about 20 years. The other disadvantages are those which reservoirs in arid lands share with those in other regions—some of which can be met by appropriate management methods. These include high sediment fill, and the risk of sudden overload with intensive rains and consequent danger of a catastrophic burst of the dam.

It is too early to determine how far methods of underground storage of flood water in artificially charged groundwater levels will be a practical solution. Some countries are experimenting with this at present. In any event, the system obviously has to be fitted to specific local geohydrological conditions.

major consideration in planning new settlements. Assuming that a project aims at establishing ten villages of 100 units each, one possibility would be to establish ten villages in a given pattern of dispersal at selected, advantageous locations. This would involve the provision of a major pipeline network throughout the whole area, including that part not, or not yet, cultivated by the ten villages (Fig. 3). The alternative would be to let pipeline economy rule the project. The same ten villages would then be concentrated into as small an area as feasible, requiring a minimum of main pipeline and a dense network of feeders. The total length of pipeline will be much shorter than in the first case. All or a high percentage of the land served by the system will be cultivated. Obviously—the water supply installations being expensive—the second, concentrated pattern is much cheaper than the first. Or, to put it differently, the same amount of investment capital can produce more villages within the modern, concentrated pattern, than was permitted by the old, dispersed one.

In short, in the development and operation of an irrigation agriculture, the unit length of pipeline or other water conduit is the yardstick of efficiency. This same yardstick applies to all other *linear services*. The more concentrated the area inhabited and cultivated, the shorter will be the total length of roads, railways, power lines, and any other linear installation required to service it adequately and efficiently.

The same principle applies in quite a different way. Every rural population requires a certain number of professional and technical personnel. These are both general service personnel, as teachers, doctors, municipal and government administrators, etc., and agricultural specialists: tractorists and maintenance personnel, agricultural extension officers, experts in specific fields such as pest control, veterinarians, etc. If the majority or a considerable number of the people manning a certain development project have insufficient experience in agriculture, the ratio of agricultural instructor personnel will be relatively high.

Again, a doctor or a horticultural expert can serve the population of quite a number of villages, provided they are located close enough to one another so that traveling to his clients, or their traveling to him, does not consume too much time. Otherwise, with a dispersed settlement pattern, the doctor or extension officer will, with the same amount of time and work, be able to attend to fewer clients in a much smaller number of villages. Most of his time will be spent not in professional work, but in driving. If it is the teacher, he will probably have to limit his teaching to the children of one or two villages, with classes only partially filled, whereas he could with the same amount of effort teach many more children from a greater number of villages located close together.

In planning agricultural settlement for semiarid lands requiring irrigation and, therefore, concentration of cultivated areas, a method must be developed which will meet the problem of limited funds and professional and technical specialists and at the same time make life for the new settlers more convenient. Such a pattern has been devised and applied in the *operational regions of settlement*. It was applied first in the Lachish Region in Israel in 1955–1956 and later in additional projects in that country, in the Namsang Region in Burma, and elsewhere. The principle is to build a settlement pattern of some six to ten agricultural villages, located close to one another. In a central position between them a *service village* is located, where all the professional and service personnel reside (Fig. 4). As the distance between any one agricultural village and the service village will not exceed 20 minutes' driving time, the service personnel can adequately attend to all agricultural villages. Once this whole group is settled to full capacity, the entire operation is repeated, preferably in an immediately adjoining

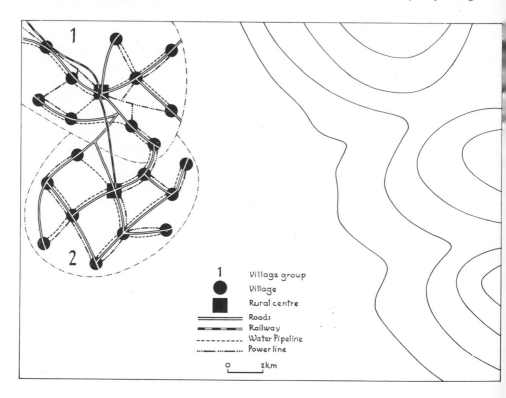

1 Village group
● Village
■ Rural centre
═ Roads
━ Railway
-------- Water Pipeline
...■...... Power line

0   2km

FIGURE 4: Pattern of rural development by operational regions. The map shows two adjacent groups of villages (Numbers 1 and 2) each consisting of ten agricultural villages and one centrally located rural center. By comparison with the pattern illustrated in Figure 3, the concentrated pattern makes for an over 50 per cent economy in roads and requires less than one-third the length of water pipelines and power lines of the dispersed pattern of Figure 3.

area, for rational utilization of linear installations of minimum length. A whole operational region consisting of a number of groups of villages, each with its service village, will have one town where regional services and administration as well as industrial establishments can be located.

It should be noted that in semiarid lands very often the expansion of cultivation into an adjoining region is possible. As agriculture here is water-intensive, while the amount of water available tends to be limited, arid areas have more land available than there is water for its cultivation. This results in a common experience of many Arid Zone areas: an intensification in the use of their agricultural land brings about a restriction of the cultivated area to those lands which are most advantageous.[7]

This modern concept is in direct contrast to the theory of expanding *pioneer settlement* in semiarid lands. It is also different from the old philosophy according to which the scant and unreliable rainfall in semiarid countries require large units of land per farmer and, therefore, can sustain sparse settlement only. With modern technology and competition for manpower based on higher standards of living attainable elsewhere, the opposite is true. The old-time sparse settlement pattern of semiarid lands induces rural depopulation. However, it is concentrated settlement on rather small units of nearly fully irrigated land which has proven economically successful, competitive, and leading to a stable population.

Here again we find additional proof for a general rule in the geography of settlement: that more advanced development does not lead to a more even distribution of cultivation and population density, but, rather, to greater diversification and contrast. The end-effect should approximate a continuous area of dense agricultural settlement, abutting on a most sparsely occupied area. The areal relation between the two and the location of the border at any given time will be critically determined by the availability of water as a major factor.

Sometimes water—surface or underground—is available locally, but it

---

[7] A special case, unfortunately affecting populations of considerable size, is critical salinization of soils in arid lands under irrigation. Sometimes this equals in area the land newly reclaimed for cultivation. Cf. Salinity Problems in the Arid Zones (UNESCO, Arid Zone Research, Vol. 14, 1961); L. Bernstein: Salt-affected Soils and Plants, in The Problems of the Arid Zone (UNESCO, Arid Zone Research, Vol. 18, 1962), pp. 139–174; K. S. Ahmad: Land Use in the Semiarid Zone of West Pakistan, in Land Use in Areas with Semiarid Mediterranean Climates (UNESCO, Arid Zone Research, Vol. 26, forthcoming). With certain exceptions where salinization results from contamination of water with saline or similarly mineralized rocks, salinization is characteristic of the large alluvial valleys. The clayey and other fine-grained alluvial deposits, which are fairly impervious and, therefore, do not permit of efficient and quick drainage of the soil, retain the mineralized precipitates of the water after losses in volume of liquid sustained through evaporation. Whereas salinization is thus a severe problem in the alluvial valleys of permanently flowing rivers which enter the arid area from outside, it is of little significance in most arid and semiarid areas with their episodic regime of flow where the local soils are fairly permeable and allow of good drainage.

is unusable due to excessive salinity. In exceptional cases this salinity affects only certain valleys, whereas others are not affected by it. The outstanding example known to the author is a series of valleys crossing the northern desert of Chile in the following order, from north to south: the valley of Tacna (in Peru)—no salinity; Lluta valley—salinity problems of soil and water; Azapa—no salinity; Camarones—salinity problems of soil and water (1500–1800 mg/1). This obviously indicates that the salinity is caused by contamination with rock of excessive mineralization (in this case, partly volcanic derivatives). Such a situation, therefore, is amenable to treatment by removing the water from its natural conduit before it enters the contaminating strata and leading it downstream in an artificial conduit.

Another special case should be noted: settlement in arid and even semiarid lands is often of the highland type, of which the mountain oases of South America are a most prominent example. As their distribution is basically conditioned by orography, obviously an extensive continuous pattern can develop here only as far as the extension of land of high altitude permits. Many altitude oases will remain isolated and far apart.

Non-Agricultural Uses of Arid Lands

Apart from the agricultural and pastoral use of lands to the extent possible and practical, and from its role in regional transportation (mainly trans-desert routes), mining was the only other important activity in the economy of arid lands. Irrespective of the great difficulties and expense involved in a large-scale mining operation under arid conditions, large mining enterprises were maintained in the arid parts of all continents, especially since some mineral resources are conditionally related to the aridity of climate in their genesis or conservation (e.g., the nitrates of the Atacama Desert in Chile). This type of activity certainly will continue and even intensify as the world's need for minerals grows.

Two developments have introduced new non-agricultural uses for arid lands, opening important vistas for some of them. Both are linked to modern advances in transportation technology, which makes their implementation practicable. The first is related to the fact that modern industrial development requires for certain industries an ever-increasing amount of space for plant development. Furthermore, technological advance makes the reconditioning or even renewal of plants and machinery mandatory.

Urban congestion and high real estate prices can seriously deter the expansion of the area of a plant located in the center of a town or even in its established industrial quarter. For a corporation faced with the need to increase its plant space the possibility of moving to an arid area might offer sufficient advantages to counteract the disadvantages inherent in any removal to a new site. First, there is the frequently unlimited availability of land in arid areas (for both plant and housing of personnel) and its commensurately low cost, as compared with the scarce and generally expensive land available in any city. Furthermore, the dry and warm climate in an arid area may make it possible to perform certain operations in the open, or else in no more than a roofed-over shed. The same economy may be achieved in the storage of material awaiting processing and of the finished product. All this will minimize the standard building area required and thereby considerably lower the cost of plant construction in arid, as compared with humid, climates. This, together with the low cost of real estate and its general availability, constitutes a powerful inducement for industry to move to arid areas. The more "pleasant" climate, contrasting with that of the old industrial areas, is an additional advantage for the plant's labor force. Considerations such as these have played an important role in the movement of industry westward to southern California and elsewhere.

Such development was impracticable as long as technology was still at the stage where long-distance transportation was cumbersome, time consuming, and, therefore, costly. But nowadays—when many large firms move managerial and technical personnel between their various plants by aircraft owned and operated by the firm, and when long distance shipping of goods by rail or truck or in combination, piggyback fashion, is common—distance ceases to be a deterrent.

While the availability of low-priced land has for some time been an attraction to industry, wide, *empty* spaces have recently begun to attract military establishments and testing grounds. The increasing range and destructive power of modern weapons require for their development and testing such large areas as are only rarely available in settled zones. The same applies in part to military maneuver areas. Both kinds of operations, therefore, are making increasing use of the large empty spaces found in arid regions. The addition of service population and general activity connected with these operations is often significant.

A second development locally "peopling" arid lands benefits equally from modern advances in transportation and comparably low real estate prices in arid areas. The gradual and steady rise in living standards increases the number of people who can afford regular vacations away from home. To them the possibility of vacationing, at costs within their reach, in a place with fine, sunny weather naturally holds great attraction. This is increased for those who can time their vacations to coincide with the climatically most unpleasant season at their place of residence, generally the winter. Whereas a few generations ago "winter resorts in the desert" were few, catering only to the few who could afford the time and cost of going there, in the present age of speedy air transportation, recreation bonuses, and a generally increased standard of living, the number of clients at these resorts grows steadily. The scenic beauty of many arid areas, especially in hilly and mountainous localities, serves as an additional attraction, as do the remains of ancient cultures sometimes found there.

Arid lands also hold a more permanent attraction than that generated by tourism and vacationing. In a considerable number of nations today, the combined result of a rising standard of living and an increasing longevity increases the number of men and women who reach retirement age in financial conditions permitting them to escape the often unpleasant climate of the towns where they spent their working lives with smog and hard winters, by taking up residence in a sun-bathed arid area. Particularly for elderly persons, the warmth of arid climate throughout most of the year, even at midday in winter, holds great attraction. *Retirement towns* thus have become part of the social fabric of wealthy nations such as the United States. It might be expected that they will become more numerous and gradually form part of the settlement fabric of other countries as well.

The increasing use of arid lands for tourist and retirement purposes, as well as for the establishment of industrial plants, is the result both of rising standards of living and decisive advances in transportation technology and the concomitant lowering of prices.

The Changing Transportation Factor

In the past, apart from serving the small demand for interior transportation, the main significance of arid areas in larger regional transportation patterns was in the operation of trans-desert routes connecting the non-arid areas which they separated. Transport on these desert routes was difficult, trying, often hazardous and expensive. The main difficulty was the dearth or complete absence of facilities for supplies along the route —service stations offering food, pasture and water. Often, therefore, the road had to be lengthened considerably by proceeding from one oasis to the next, where water and food were available for men and animals. Wherever possible, routes followed the fringe of the desert along the outermost margin of settled land. Often, too, use of the road was restricted to the climatically less severe season, while for part of the year it was virtually closed to normal traffic. The sparse population of these areas did not create any demand for trade along the road worth mentioning. All this, plus the extortion practiced by the desert nomads who serviced the caravans and sometimes plundered them, made this type of transportation strenuous, expensive, dangerous, and unreliable. Small wonder that whenever possible interregional transportation circumvented deserts rather than passing through them, often without actually losing time by doing so and with a gain in economy. Whenever this happened, it meant severe regression to the arid area thus bypassed. (Witness the outflanking of Trans-Saharan routes by maritime transportation, and the case of the *silk route* of Central Asia outflanked by maritime transportation along the south coast of that continent.)

Many of these considerations remain valid today, even with mechanized transportation. Most significant of all, probably, is the fact that the low population density and the low economic level of arid areas make it impossible for them to create or maintain a reasonable roadnet out of their own resources. Worse still, a long desert route has to traverse great distances which do not create any demand for transportation and offer no revenue for maintenance of the road. Yet every kilometer or mile of the many hundreds or sometimes thousands along the route requires maintenance. The cost becomes particularly excessive when assessed per tons of freight or number of travellers or vehicles using the road. Maintenance of desert roads is especially costly for two reasons: arid climate and its geomorphological influence places great strain on desert routes. Unmetalled roads produce, under the impact of traffic, the well-known *washboard pattern*, the *calamina* of the North Chilean desert, which, if travelled at velocities below 75 kilometers per hour (45 mph), badly shakes both vehicle and passengers. At all velocities it plays havoc with vehicles, creating the need for a complete tightening of the body after less than 1000 km, and it reduces their useful lifetime. Metalled roads, on the other hand, need expensive maintenance because of the cracking of the road cover and the outwash and gullying from occasional floods.

This latter factor makes desert railways expensive installations. If flood damage is to be avoided, valleys must be crossed by bridges of an extraordinarily wide span, irrespective of the fact that water might be flowing under them only half a dozen times a year for a few hours every time, or even only at intervals of several years. But these floods are often violent and voluminous and create a whole group of *wadi*-beds which might easily have a total width of one or more kilometers. The engineer building a railway hardly has a choice but to bridge them safely. His colleague, constructing a desert road, has the tantalizing choice between building wide and expensive bridges, or dispensing with them, and then carrying out emergency repairs of washed-out stretches after every major flood.

Considering all these factors inherent in the physical nature of the desert—its emptiness, and the long, economically sterile distances of desert routes—the disadvantages under which surface transportation has to operate here are obvious. Under the conditions created by modern transportation technology, the use of aircraft is much more desirable for desert transportation than surface craft, traditional or mechanized. Aircraft can span long distances without having to pay for the maintenance of every mile. The same type of airport is required in arid and in humid areas. Again, sufficient land for an airport will be more readily available than is generally the case in densely settled, humid areas. Apart from the rare sand- and dust-storms, the limitations on flying weather are at a minimum in arid areas, with their minimal cloud cover and their generally good visibility above ground. It is only around midday that the uplift generated by the great heat and the reduced density of the air notably limit the payload of an aircraft.

The aircraft is no less advantageous in servicing the widely spaced desert settlements. The relatively modest freight and seating capacity of aircraft, especially of medium and smaller types, always allows the achievement of a satisfactory load factor. The gain in traveling time is so decisive that the introduction of air transportation generally brings about a marked decline in the amount of surface transportation within a short time. Furthermore, all mechanized transportation, air transportation in particular, makes caravan traffic old style, obsolete. This, of course, severely unsettles the economy of the nomadic peoples of the desert who serviced the caravans and often that of the oases towns as well.

The Future of Nomadic Populations

In trying to assess the future development of arid lands, a number of considerations should be kept in mind. The advancement of arid areas depends upon the possibility of creating standards of living comparable with those in other areas; otherwise, increasing severe depopulation seems to be the prospect.

The pastoral nomad will be less and less characteristic of these lands: already now he is turning for part, or even all, of his living to conventional modern employment. The Beduin of Saudi Arabia who works for the oil companies or is indirectly linked to the oil economy, or his opposite number in Israel who works as a wage laborer in construction or agriculture, are but two examples. This process by no means results from directed guidance "from above," but is the natural adaptation of the nomad population to the decreasing returns offered by the traditional way of life and to a steep increase of possibilities in conventional employment. It is significant that the nomad rather readily relinquishes his nomadic habits, if he has a chance to do so. In most formerly nomad-inhabited lands there is today a pronounced simultaneous transition to one of two patterns: seminomadism and sedentarization while maintaining rural occupation in full or in part; or removal to towns and amalgamation into the urban working population.

The Beduin, in taking to a sedentary way of life, tends to preserve those habits of organizing his settlement to which his nomadic tradition has accustomed him, especially a wide dispersal of houses. Whereas this was reasonable procedure in a tent encampment on land that is marginal for lack of water or other reasons, it becomes excessively wasteful in villages situated on good agricultural land or land the Beduin occupied previously, which has been made productive through irrigation. In a certain area in Israel some 5000 sedentarized Beduin occupy an area of more than 10,000 hectares, whereas an equal normal sedentary population would occupy no more than 200. Such a dispersal not only is wasteful of land and prevents rational planning of land use but is also detrimental to the development of adequate services in *villages* built with such dispersal. Roads, electricity, water supply, and sewage disposal become excessively expensive when they have to serve a village so widely dispersed and to be paid for by so small a population. In actual fact, these services will not be available to such dispersed settlement, or else they will become available only at a late date.

The attempt to maintain the traditional, pre-modern way of life of the nomad, wasteful of land and making adequate services unfeasible, is irreconcilable with a modern economy. The nomad can either maintain his traditional practices and economic level (but in doing so will have to remain outside the sphere of modern Arid Zone development), or he can partake of modern developments and amenities, but will have to adopt the techniques, including those of settlement, without which modern Arid Zone development is impossible. The first alternative would require geographic separation between modern Arid Zone occupants and nomads, thus perpetuating the contrast between nomad and sedentary settler; with certain exceptions, the possibility of such a development appears less than likely.

Urban and Industrial Development

In contrast to the role of the nomad, whose importance in many arid areas is decreasing toward insignificance, the importance of urban and industrial development is increasing. Since in the Arid Zone, in contrast to humid lands, the area between the cities generally does not generate economic values,[8] it is correct procedure to restrict development to a minimum area, avoiding unproductive investment. The resulting occupance pattern will be intensive urban development in a minimum of cities, with large empty areas in between. Only in this way is it possible to attain the modern standard of services—in education, health, administration, etc.—essential for a progressive, industrial society.

This modern Arid Zone development, gaining considerable mo-

[8] Kuei-sheng Chang (in Geographical Bases for Industrial Development in Northwestern China, *Econ. Geog.*, Vol. 39, 1963, pp. 341–350, reference, p. 348) commented on this, remarking that, for industries established in arid areas, inertia of location "will be even greater than is the case with those in well-populated humid lands."

mentum in certain regions, permits industry to benefit from the variety of advantages noted above. These include the availability of cheap and extensive tracts of land for plant location and a pleasant, healthy climate. In addition to the processing of local mineral resources (the only important industry of arid lands in the past), footloose industries having a low location factor are becoming ever more important now. As the resources of arid regions are quite limited, this often raises the problems of priority in resource allotment. This involves, first and foremost, decisions concerning the use of water. A modern town in the arid area proper has a high per capita consumption of water. In addition to the usual domestic requirements, water has to be provided for air-conditioning installations and for the gardening necessary to provide a reasonable amount of greenery. Tucson, Arizona, to take one example, consumed, in 1961, 680 liters (180 gallons) per capita per day. Amounts such as these,[9] which equal quantities of water which could be put to good use in Arid Zone agriculture, imply a need for careful planning in the allocation of water resources.

In developing industry in arid and semiarid areas, the topography of the site must be carefully taken into account. The great ranges in daily temperature characteristic of arid climate, especially when wind is feeble, tend to create near-ground inversions. If this occurs in a topographical basin, partly or fully enclosed, all impurities in the air are constrained below this inversion. The result is industrial smog. Los Angeles is the extreme, but by no means the only example. Santiago de Chile shows the same trend of development, as do other industrialized cities in arid and semiarid areas, though in more rudimentary stages.

The lack of a regional hinterland providing a broad and balanced economic basis is an intrinsic weakness in the development of arid [10] areas in general,[11] and of the towns located there in particular. The town more often than not tends to be a single- or few-purpose town, based on only one economic factor, such as mineral exploitation, service to regional roads, or other specialized services. Any major negative change affecting this particular basis can be fatal to the town, a single-purpose town being no less vulnerable to natural or economic crises than an agricultural settlement practicing monoculture. In humid regions, a town will gradually adjust to major economic changes by shift-

[9] Restated, 146,200 cu.m. per day (38.7 million gallons per day), totalling 53.36 million cu.m. per years, or 14,125.5 million gallons per year for the 215,000 inhabitants of Tucson.
[10] This does not necessarily apply to semiarid areas.
[11] E. Otremba *in* Die Flexibilität des Wirtschaftsraumes, *Erdkunde*, Vol. 15, 1961, pp. 45–63, especially, p. 48, stresses the limited flexibility of the economy in arid regions. Large areas with a low population density deny those of their inhabitants who are poor in capital resources the possibility to develop a conservation economy. Only too often they induce destructive exploitation of a scant—and delicate—environment.

ing its economic activity to the utilization of other elements provided by its environment. A town in an arid area lacks this possibility. But for a town to be *permanently* viable, it *must* have a sufficiently broad base; it also must have a sufficiently large population. Without either of those, its economy will readily falter in a crisis, bringing about gradual or sudden deterioration, and often abandonment, of the town. This explains the phenomenon of *ghost towns* in deserts, abandoned through the shifting of a trade route, exhausted of a mineral resource, or change in mineral economy or technology. In humid areas, ghost towns are quite rare,[12] as here a sufficiently diversified environment allows for adjustment to change by shifting emphasis to a different type of economic activity.

Problems of Development in Arid and Semiarid Areas

Arid Areas

The geographer planning the development of arid areas is faced with standards basically different from those applicable to humid lands. This applies first to climate. Whereas planning in humid areas can be based on *average* values of rainfall, such averages have no validity in arid areas proper. Complementing this, however, is the fact that within the limits of a few generations, climatic fluctuations are only a minor factor among those affecting land occupancy in arid areas, *minor,* that is, in respect to the general limitations imposed by the environment.

The arid area proper is essentially a non-agricultural environment. Furthermore, the few oasis areas are definitely fixed by edaphic factors (water and soil) over the location of which man has no control. The same holds true for settlements based on mineral exploitation. The arid region, therefore, admits of local, spotty development only. Even within this framework, the actual development of local potentials—or at least the degree of such development—depends on the integration of the arid area in a wider regional, and sometimes interregional, geographic frame. This applies equally to modern use of arid areas for recreational and retirement purposes. The disappearance for any reason of these economic and other background conditions will cause a severe decline and often eventual abandonment of the settlement which thereby loses its *raison d'être.* When changes in regional conditions make a given arid area development obsolete, it is essential to evaluate calmly and without emotional bias the objective prospects of the area in question. Taking due account of all economic and political factors, it might be preferable to withdraw the population from the obsolete arid area and resettle them in a less arid environment, under more favorable conditions. Such

[12] Certain ghost towns in humid areas are the result of a comparative single-purpose economy, as those left in the Amazon basin after the collapse of the rubber boom.

resettlement, including the initial assistance to the resettled population, would generally be cheaper than expensive improvement or maintenance projects for an essentially unproductive, marginal population. Certainly, it would prevent much human misery; and many such places are gradually abandoned anyhow.

At the present stage, little can be done by way of appraising the possible revolution in Arid Zone development once desalinization of brackish underground water or even of seawater becomes practical—economically practical, that is. Whereas a variety of processes have been developed (distillation, separation of salts by freezing or by means of membranes, and others), many of which have achieved technically satisfactory operation, none of them has reached as yet an economically acceptable level of performance, except when water prices are of no economic concern. It is reasonable to assume that further development will in the first stage affect semiarid areas by making demineralization of underground waters of medium salinity economically practical. But whenever these processes become economically practical, the whole question of the utilization of arid lands will have to be appraised anew.

Semiarid Areas

As stated repeatedly, semiarid lands permit of continuous development, as opposed to the spotty development characteristic of arid areas proper. The reason for this is the more advantageous climate of the former, but this same factor makes semiarid lands much more dependent on climatic conditions and sensitive to fluctuations. Relatively minor changes in climate may have significant effects on the precarious balance of any semiarid environment.

As a dependable water supply is the *sine qua non* of development under modern conditions, all agricultural planning in semiarid areas must be based on a reliable safety level of water availability. And as any natural water supply depends on rainfall and its fluctuations, planning must be based on recharge at *average minimum* values of precipitation to prevent withdrawal beyond replacement level and permanent damage to water resources whenever there is a series of years deficient in rainfall. Such a series of subnormal rainfall years, characteristic of semiarid climates, is the more dangerous, as climatic drought is generally followed by a time during which the availability of groundwater is reduced, thus prolonging the time during which the amount of water available is restricted. Only planning based on average minimum rates of recharge provides the safety margins essential for development in a semiarid climate, with its frequent and sizable fluctuations of rainfall.[13] This is in significant contrast to humid areas,

---

[13] During a series of subnormal rainfall years an underground water resource can be depleted critically by excessive withdrawal of water. Near the sea, such excessive lowering of the groundwater level might lead to a reversion of hydraulic gradients

where fluctuations in rainfall are so limited as to make planning based on average rainfall safe.

The necessity for a managed water supply makes advanced development in semiarid lands and in arid lands outside of oases dependent on stable political conditions. Moreover, as technical incompetence can have grave effects, a proper standard of education is another prerequisite for such development. Any breakdown in proper management or in political stability will first and foremost affect the marginal areas near the border of aridity. In the course of history, it is they who have most often experienced abandonment and re-occupation: it is here that the border of settlement shows its most conspicuous retreats and advances.[14]

Semiarid areas have important advantages for development over arid areas: they permit of spatially continuous occupation; they can be linked to, and benefit from, services in the adjoining humid areas, such as transportation networks and, sometimes, water supplies; and they have relatively easy access to humid area markets.

Both arid and semiarid areas have climatic advantages such as dry air, a considerable number of hours of sunshine,[15] and others, constituting basically favorable health conditions. But these advantages can be used for spatially continuous development only in semiarid areas, as they alone have a continuous soil cover. For agricultural development, five factors must be considered essential: climate, soil, water, population, and markets. Within the limits of a few generations, climate and soil may be considered non-variables; neither, therefore, can be positively developed, though both may be negatively affected by mismanagement. This is most evident with soil, which in many semiarid regions has been subjected to destructive cultivation methods resulting in soil erosion of varying severity. In a few instances climate, as well, has been adversely affected, notably in the case of industrially-induced smog. Water and population are the major factors which permit of introduction and planned development within a semiarid environment.

---

and a consequent infiltration of seawater causing a gradual salinization of the groundwater near the coast. Neither type of damage can be expected to be redressed automatically by an ensuing series of wet years.

Mountain oases in semiarid areas benefit from a lesser degree of climatic instability, as the fixed influence of the orographic factor brings about greater reliability in rainfall.

[14] The phenomenon may be observed, among other places, along the southern border of settlement in Israel, where over the centuries the fringe of permanent settlement has oscillated over more than one hundred kilometers. (Cf. D. H. K. Amiran: The Pattern of Settlement in Palestine, *Israel Exploration Journ.*, Vol. 3, 1953, reference pp. 250–257.)

[15] Cf. H. E. Landsberg's map, "Total Hours of Sunshine (Annual)," 1:15 mill., in H. E. Landsberg et al.: World Maps of Climatology (Berlin, Göttingen, Heidelberg, 1963). According to this map, most semiarid areas have more than 2600 hours of sunshine per year—the arid core areas over 3000 and the Central Sahara over 4000.

Both have a considerable degree of mobility and, therefore, of instability. Water is especially susceptive to destructive exploitation through use in excess of replacement rates. Improper use and application of water without complementary drainage may lead to salinization of both water resources and soil. Finally, the importance of the availability or development of markets as a prerequisite for the development of semiarid areas has been stressed above.

Considerations of economic and of physical geography, then, lead to some basic conclusions about the development of semiarid lands. First, under modern economic and social conditions requiring irrigation and, consequently, areal concentration, it is impossible to attempt merely partial development of a semiarid area without courting certain failure and causing human misery; the history of the Near and Middle East, to cite but one regional example, provides ample evidence for this. For most projects, it is impracticable even to spread development over a considerable number of stages. To be viable, a development area has to be provided with a large number of essential installations some time near to the start of its operation. It is this necessity to make a large part of the total investment at once, instead of financing the project out of the accumulating gains of the early stages, which makes Arid Zone development initially so expensive.

Moreover, conditions in semiarid lands no longer permit of *pioneer settlement* by hardy individuals seeking out virgin land on which to set up their homesteads. Nor do they permit of *virgin and idle land development* according to a planned pattern, but without any, or without full, irrigation. Having become an essential factor in the agricultural development of semiarid lands with their fluctuating rainfall, irrigation has led to the replacement of the pioneer settler by the highly organized development project, generally managed by the government or some public agency.

Secondly, as semiarid agriculture operates in an area where nature is in a delicate state of balance (the closer to the border of aridity, the more delicate the balance), nothing is easier than to create an imbalance here. The semiarid area, therefore, requires conservation management at a high level of competence. In arid areas a development project can fail with less dire consequences: in semiarid areas failure generally involves the irreparable destruction of natural resources— through soil erosion; man-induced salinization of soil, or of groundwater, or of both; destruction of vegetation and elements of the natural fauna, including that of the microfauna essential for regeneration of the soil; pollution of the air by industrial smog; and other examples of man's misuse of land The majority of these destructive effects imply irreversible changes in the environmental inventory.

A further consideration requires due attention. Any well-executed development project in a semiarid or even arid area brings about improvements and creates new amenities, thereby unbalancing the existing natural equilibrium. If at a later date the area experiences regression, and these new amenities are no longer maintained in working condition, only the imbalance remains. A new balance will be struck eventually, at a lower level than the original one. Among the striking examples that can be cited are: the extension of agricultural cultivation into semiarid areas without permanent maintenance of such cultivation with conservation farming will lead to soil erosion; installations of water conduits (canals, qanats, pipelines), with subsequent cessation of their maintenance as well as a failure to maintain drainage of the land to which the irrigation was applied, will lead to swamp-formation or soil-salination, or both; establishment of settlements along a trade route, followed by abandonment of the route, will leave the population destitute, the settlements falling in ruins, and bring about the physical deterioration of the settlements, as well as of the road, which sometimes becomes virtually impassable. Two deleterious factors, therefore, combine here: actual deterioration resulting from cessation of maintenance of a man-induced change; and the lack of adaptability to changes of environmental factors characteristic of arid areas.

To sum up, the border conditions and ensuing instability of nature makes semiarid areas a very difficult object of development. The delicate balance of nature here can easily cause damage instead of advancement unless development is very carefully planned and competently executed.

Education—Key to Arid Zone Development

The Arid Zone offers certain possibilities for development: they are quite restricted as to place and type of use for the arid area proper, but today seem rather attractive when advanced methods of technology for semiarid areas are considered. For a population successfully to develop a semiarid or arid area today requires high technical and managerial competence and skill. Without these, it is impossible to develop the potential of such areas with full conservation of resources, giving proper attention to the delicate balance of nature near the border of aridity. The full development and utilization of special marketing potentials (e.g., the introduction of out-of-season food products and their well-timed marketing, or the development of a resort industry) require equally high skills. Clearly, in order to permit modern development in the Arid Zone—that is, to endeavor to maintain a population in a semiarid area with the general present-day competition for manpower created by high standards of living offered elsewhere—an educationally advanced population is a prerequisite.

But the Arid Zone, on the whole being a marginal area of the world's *oikumene*, has but a scant population [16] which, due to its low numbers and density, tends in many instances to be undereducated.

As there cannot be the slightest doubt that under modern technological conditions Arid Zone development can be achieved only by educated people of considerable skill and competence, education seems to command the highest priority for Arid Zone development at present. If Arid Zone development in general raises problems of two types—technical and educational—priority no doubt must go to the solution of the educational problems.[17]

Obviously, every technical installation requires proper competence for its operation. As modern Arid Zone development is possible only with full use of technological equipment, it requires technological competence in a wide stratum of population. Even such traditional skills as might be found in a local population—and they may be highly developed skills, as those of the *karezkan* of Afghanistan or the *moghanis* of Iran constructing and maintaining qanats—will apply within the framework of their specific tradition and experience only, but will often be of little help in maintaining complex modern technical installations, not to mention the problem of their initial design and construction.

The need for technical competence starts right at the roots of modern Arid Zone development, as affecting both its arid and its semiarid sectors. Water as the basic factor requires particularly high qualifications for proper management. To mention but a few points involved: withdrawal of water for irrigation has to be scaled according to natural recharge rates to avoid deterioration of the resource in quantity or both in quantity and quality, by turning increasingly saline. Furthermore, water for irrigation has to be applied in optimum amounts and at optimal times. No useful purpose is served by irrigating with too much water—i.e., more than the amount the plant requires and more than the soil can absorb. Apart from being wasteful of water, this might actually decrease yields and lead to waterlogging and even to salinization of soils. But it is a common experience that a high percentage of irrigators

---

[16] According to a compilation for 1960, assuming a world population of 3 billions, the Arid Zone comprised 36 per cent of the world's land surface but only 13 per cent of its population or 384 millions, having an overall density of a little less than 8 per square kilometer. The figures for the semiarid area only are, of course, slightly more advantageous—viz., 16 per cent of land area, 9 per cent of world's population, density 13 per square kilometer. The world's population density for 1960 has been computed as 22 per square kilometer. Cf. D. H. K. Amiran: Man in Arid Lands, in E. S. Hills, edit.: The Arid Zone (UNESCO, forthcoming); H. L. Shantz, in Gilbert F. White, edit.: The Future of Arid Lands, Washington, 1956, reference, p. 5; Peveril Meigs: Distribution of Arid Homo-climates (UN, Maps 392/3, 1952).
[17] It must be considered most auspicious therefore, that at UNESCO's Paris symposium (1960) evaluating *The Problems of the Arid Zone* (published as Vol. 18 of its Arid Zone Research series, 1962), section IV, four papers (pp. 429–475) were devoted to a discussion of: public awareness and the educational problem.

overirrigate,[18] especially those who have started irrigating relatively recently. They do so in the naïve and erroneous assumption that if irrigation is useful, the more so the better. Irrigation at optimal time—i.e., when evapotranspiration losses are at their lowest, usually at night— will also be practiced only by farmers who recognize the advantage of the economy in water which can thus be achieved and practice the necessary public-spirited discipline in the face of the obvious inconvenience involved.

Under present conditions development in many countries of the Arid Zone is offered *technical assistance*. But although financial and technical assistance can initiate development and supply equipment, the continued operation and correct functioning of such projects depends on the availability of sufficient local manpower competent to handle them. Technical assistance can install equipment and design projects and plants, but will prove useless unless matched by educated, competent, local operators. Where these are lacking, the best plant will deteriorate through improper maintenance and operation. No good is done to any population by supplying it with equipment it is incompetent to handle, or by initiating projects it is incompetent to manage. Widespread basic education and a sufficient amount of advanced education are the prerequisites for any modern development. This applies in an especially high degree to development in the Arid Zone which, with its inherent marginality, requires particularly careful handling and is particularly beset with difficulties.

A proper standard of education is essential at all levels. Without it scientific and technological advances cannot be transferred from the research laboratory to the farm or the workshop.

One obviously can only very moderately accelerate the time needed to provide a population with good educational standards at all levels required. Basically, it is therefore the standard of education achieved which will set the pace for Arid Zone development in any given area.

It is the human factor which will decide the use made of any area in the Arid Zone. Any action affecting the natural environment here has to succeed in making harmonic use of nature's elements and must be competently managed. Failure in this respect will result in failure of the project. As most development projects will concern semiarid lands, failures will inevitably initiate a process of active regression, of deterioration of the environment. The marginal character and delicate balance of this area decrees that an imbalance of environment, man-induced in this case, must be followed by either development or regression. It is here that man must assume great responsibility in Arid Zone development. It is there that the geographer of a planning team will find one of the greatest possible challenges.

[18] Cf. Amiran, *op. cit.*, n. 8, p. 707.

8. Wisconsin Cheese and Farm Type: A Locational Hypothesis

Gordon R. Lewthwaite

Economic geographers, always concerned with the factors underlying the peculiar locational pattern of special types of economic activity, have advanced several theories to explain or predict the establishment of these locations and locational patterns. In this selection, Lewthwaite offers a further explanation of a pattern of agricultural activity. The Cheese Belt is a recognizable subregion of the well-known Dairy Region that extends east from Minnesota across Wisconsin and Michigan into New York and New England. Lewthwaite examines the Cheese Belt, noting that cheese production, a highly specialized processing activity, has locational characteristics quite different from those of fresh-milk dairying or butter production. Economic geographers frequently start with a theory of hypothesis concerning locational patterns and then investigate in the field to test it; in this selection, however, the hypothesis is derived from the empirical data collected in the field and from statistical data.

Both in the world in general and in Wisconsin in particular, the localization of the cheese industry has long posed something of a problem to the economic geographer. For it is characteristically concentrated in highly specialized regions which form sharply defined "islands" that are surrounded by broad zones where other branches of dairy manufacturing (particularly the "twin industry" of butter-making) tend to predominate. This striking locational feature also appears quite conspicuously in the overseas dairylands of Western Europe and New Zealand, but it is forcefully exemplified in Wisconsin, which leads America in cheese production.

Nor is this precise regionalization a momentary feature: it is rela-

SOURCE: *Economic Geography*, XL (April, 1964), 95–112. Reprinted by permission of the author and the editor. The author is professor of geography, San Fernando Valley State College, California.

tively permanent. Admittedly, as Loyal Durand has affirmed, the present pattern has resulted from a long migration that progressively shifted the locus of cheese manufacture form its original centers in New England and New York into the Midwest: as the eastern portions of the Dairy Belt were drawn into the orbit of the urban milksheds, areas farther westwards seized the opportunity to expand their dairy manufactures. Nor has such territorial displacement yet ceased, for urbanization, the increasing swiftness and efficiency with which milk, butter, and cheese are transported, and the development of a wider range of sophisticated dairy products have led to a continuing encroachment on existing cheese-manufacturing regions, while the formerly clear-cut territorial subdivision which prevailed when every dairy factory produced its proper product has been blurred by the development of "flexible" and "multiple-product" plants which vary their operations with relative demand. But this has been the case only during the last two decades. During most of the history of the state, the different dairy

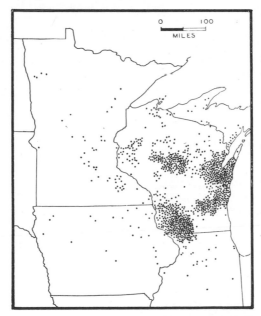

FIGURE 1: Cheese factories, c. 1950: the regional setting. (Sources: Illinois, 1944: Loyal Durand, Jr., "Cheese Region of Northwestern Illinois," *Econ. Geog.*, Vol. 22, 1946, p. 25; Iowa: The Iowa Dairy and Food Division, *Annual Report*, 1950, pp. 67–68; Minnesota: Minnesota Department of Agriculture, *Bulletin of Information*, 1950, pp. 49–50; Wisconsin: Wisconsin Crop and Livestock Reporting Service, Special Bulletin No. 3, 1950, p. 50; Michigan: Loyal Durand, Jr., "The Lower Peninsula of Michigan and the Western Michigan Dairy Region: A Segment of the American Dairy Region," *Econ. Geog.*, Vol. 27, 1951, pp. 163–183.)

products were manufactured in specialized and separate plants which clustered within rather strict territorial boundaries, and it is this inherited regional pattern which still prevails.

Strong hints of this pattern became apparent in the very earliest days of the Wisconsin dairy industry. Sharp localization had appeared before 1870, and, as the successive maps reveal (Fig. 3–6), continued to intensify until areal specialization assumed its relatively stable form after the turn of the century. In the southeastern counties, it is true, the early cheese industry gave way to butter manufacturing which was in turn displaced by condensery and market milk competition, but in the southwest—from the Illinois line northward through much of the driftless hill country and west to the Mississippi—"Swiss" and "American" or Cheddar cheese production maintained their initial advantage. Another early American cheese region was initiated in Sheboygan County, and spread along the Lakeshore, merging southeastward into the foreign and "brick cheese" region of Dodge County and simultaneously extending westwards to establish a somewhat tenuous connection with the central American type cheese region, which began to emerge as the Lakeshore region was finding its limits. Still farther west, other concentrations of cheese factories became established in the northern and more especially the northwestern counties adjacent to Minnesota, but it was butter manufacturing which became paramount on both sides of the Mississippi: the "tri-state butter region" includes much of western Wisconsin as well as Minnesota and Iowa.

FIGURE 2: Location of Wisconsin cheese regions.

Economic Inertia and Ethnic Factors

Thus a definite and enduring pattern was formulated, a pattern which has evoked a variety of explanatory hypotheses. Some authorities have stressed the impetus given by initial choice and the confirming effect of economic inertia. This interpretation is strengthened by the fact that several districts, notably the foreign and American cheese-manufacturing regions in the southwest and the brick cheese and Lakeshore districts in the southeast, were initiated in the 1860's and 1870's. It was then that factory methods were applied to cheese (but not to butter) making, and during that period slow and unrefrigerated transportation imposed less of a handicap upon cheese than upon butter, and relative prices favored cheese. The formation of the Central and Northwestern cheese districts likewise coincided with the technological and financial revival of the industry about the turn of the century.

Other interpretations of the pattern contradicted or rather complemented this factor by stressing the ethnic element. Cheesemaking was an art confined to the chosen few and most apparent among immigrant groups from Switzerland, the Netherlands, Germany, and Italy, as well as from New England, New York, and Ohio, and such skill required tradition sustained by training. In Wiest's opinion, areal concentration of technical ability had much to do with localization, while Loyal Durand, rejecting the assumption that cheese regions owed their location to natural influences, "particularly local summer environment," attributed "much more importance [to] such factors as national origins of the population, the advantage of an early start, traditions in the industry, and name and advertising value," together with economic inertia.

But even at first glance this thesis (however valid within certain limits) fails to account for some conspicuous trends in the historical geography of the industry. Many a time the cheese industry, fairly enough launched, proved abortive—as in Illinois, Iowa, and Minnesota —while one major cheese region which was solidly established in northeastern Illinois and southeastern Wisconsin was transformed into the "Elgin butter region" before 1900, historical impetus notwithstanding. And the ethnic factor has also been given undue credit. Colonies of Swiss or Dutch people began cheesemaking in a number of districts only to give it up for other occupations, and even the Green County Swiss filled their wheat sacks rather than their cheese vats in pioneer days. "National" cheeses, furthermore, changed hands in a bewildering fashion, with Swiss adopting the Dutch-Belgian Limburger, and Germans choosing to make English Cheddar, and in one instance an originally Swiss-established industry was found to be operating under the management of a Scot whose "inherited skills" were in coal mining! Moreover, the distribution of national groups forms a bewildering and changing territorial mosaic which bears little resemblance to the cheese regions. Besides, people of very different ethnic origins chose much the same occupations when they came to live in the same region. Such considerations do not, of course, eliminate the fact that due weight must be attributed to early start, tradition, and national origins of the population, with some Swiss, in particular, displaying a marked "cheese bias." Traditional skills were undeniably a critical factor during the crucial period when economic viability had to be demonstrated, and reputation counts for something even in established industries. But it is contended that these influences remained continuously effective only where sustained by supporting factors.

Location Relative to Market

Such supporting factors undoubtedly included both the economics of relative location and the influences of the physical environment. The comparative perishability of various dairy products and their differential abilities to bear freight rates are reflected in the zonal pattern of milk utilization. In principle, those dairy industries which yield perishable and bulky products and return a high value from a limited area (such as whole milk) have first choice of the costlier land nearest the market, while those which compress the milk-yield of an extensive area into compact and relatively durable form (particularly butter) are relegated, by the selective force of competition, into areas which are economically and geographically marginal.

This economic law undoubtedly helps explain some features of the geographical pattern. Apart from a fluctuating surplus which may be processed into more durable products, market milk has long displaced all dairy manufacturing from the overlapping urban milksheds near Chicago and Milwaukee, while condenseries and evaporated milk plants which make products ranking next to whole milk in use-value and bulk, find their somewhat diffuse zone in southeastern and (more recently) central Wisconsin. Since cheese retains some 10 per cent of the bulk of the milk and butter uses only 5 per cent, the cheese regions are appropriately wedged between the southeastern condensery belt and the great butter region which extends across western Wisconsin, Minnesota, and Iowa. In brief, the principle gives meaning to the pattern, a theme constantly reiterated, with variations, by analysts of the dairy industry. In Cassels' words, the distribution of butter and cheese production seems "consistent with . . . theoretical analysis. . . . The actual arrangements lack the precision and symmetry of our geographic illustrations, but they do show the influence of the underlying economic forces."

But again the theory does not match the facts of distribution so closely as one might expect. Admittedly the broad pattern, and especially the expansion of the city milksheds and condenseries into the southeastern counties, does not reflect this locational force—but neither the historical nor the geographical detail suggests that it is effective in any immediate sense. During the formative period, dairymen were always conscious of the influence of freights on choice of product, and were also somewhat aware that the costs of butter transport were proportionately less than those of cheese. But in most discussions that appear in the records they consistently bracketed these products together as favored by freight rates, and rates were pronounced only a very minor factor in the total complex of cost and choice of product. Nor was the effect of relative location sufficient to prevent the development of the butter industry in southeastern Wisconsin *between* the market-milk and cheese regions—a pattern which was theoretically anomalous. Furthermore, what freight zones have ever matched the highly irregular boundaries of the Midwestern butter and cheese regions? There have indeed been zonal freight distinctions especially along the Mississippi and along a line from Green Bay through Madison to Monroe in the southwest of the state, but these have never even approximately corresponded with the geography of butter and cheese production. If, therefore, the factors of relative location and freight zones have governed the distribution of cheese production. it has been as a broad and permissive framework rather than as a locally effective determinant.

The Physical Environment

Does the physical environment, therefore, offer the key to the pattern? Many have thought so. It has undoubtedly been accepted as a crucial territorial control by generations of Wisconsin cheesemakers and farmers. It also finds solid support from more critical sources. It was contended by dairy experts and economists and geographers that cheese-making—as differentiated from butter-making—required both the freshest and purest of milk and a favorable "temperate" pastoral environment during the delicate and vulnerable curing process. Coarse or weedy pastures, stagnant water, and, most particularly, hot, dry, and dusty summers were predicated as excluding the industry.[1] On the other hand, the production of cheese was deemed to be favored by a well-distributed and adequate rainfall, atmospheric conditions which were cool, equable and humid, terrain which was rolling or hilly and mantled with soils (preferably limestone) of modest fertility, along with pastures which were both clean and luxuriant Such optimum condi-

[1] S. M. Babcock and H. L. Russell, "The Cheese Industry, Its Development and Possibilities in Wisconsin," University of Wisconsin Agricultural Experiment Station Bulletin 60, May, 1897, pp. 9–14.

tions were approximated in few areas and Wisconsin was conspicuous among the restricted territories which stood to gain.

This theme was developed both as explanatory of the broad national and international pattern and in localized detail. The concentration of

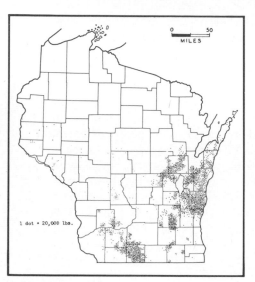
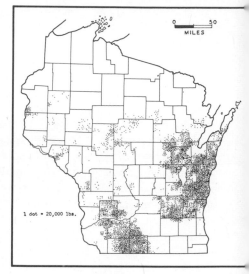
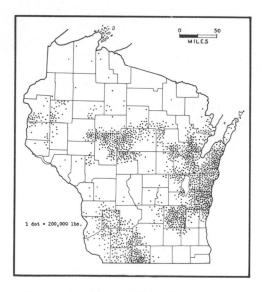
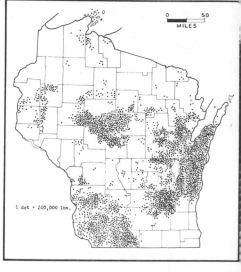

FIGURE 3: (upper left) Cheese production, 1895. (Source: Wisconsin State Census, 1895.)   FIGURE 4: (upper right) Cheese production, 1905. (Source: Wisconsin State Census, 1905.)   FIGURE 5: (lower left) Cheese production 1927. Note that the dots have ten times the value of those in Figs. 3 and 4. (Source: Wisconsin Crop and Livestock Reporting Service.)   FIGURE 6: (lower right) Cheese production, 1949. Dots have ten times the value of those in Figs. 3 and 4. (Source: Same as for Fig. 5.)

European cheese production in the cooler northwest of the continent and the Alps and uplands of Switzerland and Italy was emphasized as significant of climatic controls which were also discerned in the localization of North American cheese regions. From New England and New York, the industry had spread into Canada and Ohio, and then moved into Wisconsin. As early as 1863, a United States Commissioner of Agriculture had concluded that on environmental grounds "the southern half of the United States and the prairie states west make no cheese, never made much, and never will," [2] and it was not unnatural for Wisconsin dairymen to proclaim that cheese manufacture must inevitably concentrate within their state, for "the great cheese belt of America is climatically determined." [3] Western and southern neighbors did not share the "favored cool zone" which margined the shores of the Great Lakes, and urban milksheds were bound to engulf the cheese districts of the northeastern states.

This comfortable doctrine—only occasionally disturbed by jaundiced glances in the direction of Washington and Oregon—was extended to explain the detailed pattern of localization within Wisconsin itself, and it was elaborated to include a number of factors which were only indirectly climatic. It was noted by agricultural specialists such as Hibbard that the cheese industry successfully occupied the hill country of southwestern Wisconsin but consistently failed in competition with butter on the undulating lowlands to the east,[4] while others, including Whitbeck,[5] Whitson and Baker,[6] developed the thesis in some detail. As will later be seen, the links postulated between climate and the choice between butter or cheese were intricate and partially indirect, but the general conclusion may be simply stated. It was affirmed that areas with long, warm summers, warm nights, and long growing seasons specialized in butter production, while cooler areas turned to cheese. Rather precise boundaries—a mean summer isotherm of 69° F, a factory season isotherm of 65° F, and a growing season of 150 days (Fig. 11) were postulated, and the prediction made that future expansion would conform to the same potential limitations.

Without denying elements of truth to this analysis, it must be affirmed that it did not correspond with the factual detail. As Trewartha demonstrated in a more refined investigation, the climatic data did not warrant so close a fit, either in Wisconsin or the dairy belt in general, and

[2] United States Commissioner of Agriculture, *Annual Report*, 1863, p. 383.
[3] Babcock and Russell, *op. cit.*, p. 19
[4] Benjamin H. Hibbard, "The History of Agriculture in Dane County," *Bulletin of the University of Wisconsin*, Economics and Social Science Series, Vol. 1, No. 2, Madison, 1905, p. 178.
[5] Ray Hughes Whitbeck, "The Industries of Wisconsin and Their Geographic Basis," *Annals Assn. of Amer. Geogrs.*, Vol. 2, 1912, pp. 55–64.
[6] A. R. Whitson and O. E. Baker, "The Climate of Wisconsin and Its Relation to Agriculture," University of Wisconsin Agricultural Experiment Station Bulletin 223, July, 1912, p. 54.

and it is a patent fact that expansion subsequent to the early analysis did not follow the predicated pattern. . . . The butter and cheese industries continued to subdivide further areas of the state with notable disregard for summer temperatures and growing seasons, and no conceivable selection of isotherms can be found to match.

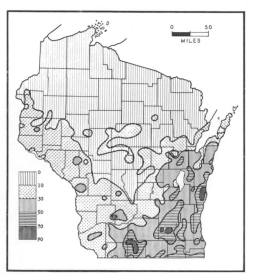
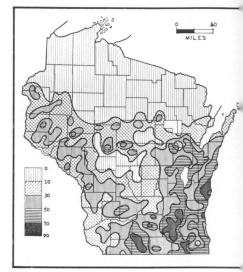
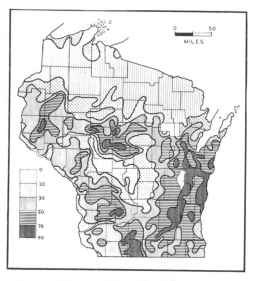
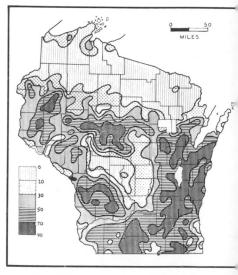

FIGURE 7: (upper left) Milk cows per square mile, 1895. (Source: Wisconsin State Census, 1895.)   FIGURE 8: (upper right) Milk cows per square mile, 1905. (Source: Wisconsin State Census, 1905.)   FIGURE 9: (lower left) Milk cows per square mile, 1928. (Source: Wisconsin Crop and Livestock Reporting Service.)   FIGURE 10: (lower right) Milk cows per square mile, 1949. (Source: Same as for Fig. 9.)

A closer correspondence was sometimes postulated, however, with the distribution of other physical features such as relief. Thus Jones and Darkenwald state that "cheese manufacture tends to become specialized in rugged, marshy or remote areas," and in Wisconsin there has, of course, been a partial association of cheese with the southwestern uplands and of butter with the southeastern lowlands. But the degree of correspondence which was manifest in Dane County on the eastern boundaries of the southwestern cheese region did not extend to the western and northern margins, nor did it reappear elsewhere—with the possible exception of areas southward from Lake Winnebago and the western edge of the Lakeshore region. But no consistent association can be deduced: indeed, it has alternatively been maintained that it is butter rather than cheese manufacture which characterizes rugged regions, a contention not without point if the butter-producing counties along the Mississippi are contrasted with cheese districts such as the Lakeshore and Central regions.

The attempt to associate the cheeese industry with soil types appears more defensible. Cheesemakers have often affirmed that limestone soils are particularly favorable, and dairy experts have agreed that success "has been in general confined to the limestone belt" and that Wisconsin's soil variations were related to a real specialization in different types of cheese. Again, the detailed correspondence of cheese and limestone seems lacking even in southwestern Wisconsin, nor does scientific experiment confirm folk-conviction regarding "lime-enriched milk." But there is, in point of fact, a remarkable coincidence between the configuration of the Lakeshore and Central Wisconsin cheese regions and soil types; the western extension of the Lakeshore industry has closely coincided with the Kewaunee-Poygan and Onaway-Kewaunee soils— reddish brown clay, or loams overlying red clay—while as Durand insists, in the Central region "the distribution of cheese factories corresponds almost exactly with . . . thc Colby silt loam." These loams were surrounded by tracts of poorer, lighter soils which have normally been characterized by the predominance of creameries—a notable reversal of the situation in southern Wisconsin where creameries occupied the better or at least more productive areas, while cheese factories were relegated to the less productive hillier tracts.

Agricultural Maturity and Choice of Product

Before considering the significance of this relation between soil and product, some further hypotheses need explication. It has often been urged that the distribution of butter and cheese industries is related to the different phases of agricultural evolution, that they are appropriate to different stages in the sequent occupance of dairy regions. This was constantly urged by the influential William Dempster Hoard who maintained that as pioneering dairying with milk-production in summer alone was replaced by compact settlement with year-round production, the economic advantage shifted from cheese to butter and Sammis later advocated the same transition. In the initial phase, the traditionally small cheese factory was considered the appropriate plant: it could operate with half the number of cows required for a creamery, be more independent of refrigerated transport, and yield whey as a by-product valuable in hog-raising. But once dairy farming was fairly launched, it required skim milk (the by-product of butter-making) for calf-raising, and grew to the point where the creamery could be sustained. "In general," said Sammis, "the choice between delivering milk at a creamery or cheese factory depends mainly upon whether the farmer wants to raise calves or hogs.

But others, while stressing the factors of sequent development and the relative significance of livestock raising, have read the progression differently. The cheese factory must have fresh milk, which (at least until recently) meant milk from the immediate vicinity. The creamery and particularly the "centralizers" could accept staler milk and particularly cream from a wide radius. Their hinterland was much more extensive. It was thus the butter industry which would most appropriately fit the circumstances of scattered pioneering, while the cheese industry could inherit the region when dairy farming matured.

Corn, Hogs, and Seasonal Dairying

Nor has the antithetical association of cheese with hog-feeding and butter with calf-raising been conceded. Many insist that hogs also thrive better on skim milk than on whey, and, where hogs abound, the creamery with its by-products of skim milk and buttermilk gains favor with the farmers. Thus, it is argued, butter-making fits better with hog-raising, and hog-raising is related to corn growing. And corn growing has been urged as antithetical to cheese production in a variety of ways. McCarty, for instance, urges that it is the fact that corn-fed cows give milk which is rich in butterfat which makes corn-rich regions appropriate for the creamery, whereas Wisconsin herds, lacking corn, give milk with a low butterfat content: dairy development was thus deflected from butter to cheese. "In this way," he concludes, "the Wisconsin cheese industry represents a nice adaptation to the geographic environment." But this is a dubious assertion: the fat-content of milk would seem connected more with the breed of cattle than with the corn ration, nor does there seem to be any evidence that the amount of corn in the bovine diet defines the cheese/butter boundaries. Much more common is the assertion that corn-growing forms the basis for livestock feeding, particularly hog-raising, and that this in turn imposes the choice of the creamery. In Wiest's opinion,

Differentiation between the production of butter and cheese seems to be due primarily to the adaptability of the soil to raise sufficient quantities of corn necessary in the feeding of hogs. When the yield of corn is reasonably large, the hog may be made an adjunct of the butter industry by the utilization of skim milk. Where the yield of corn is very low, hogs must be eliminated, and it then becomes more profitable to make cheese than butter.

It is this thesis which was repeatedly advocated by such authorities as Whitbeck, Baker and Whitson, Lee and Taylor, and Blanchard. To compress and fuse their somewhat varied arguments, it was contended that the direct effect of summer warmth on the distribution of the butter and cheese industries was reinforced by the influence of temperature and growing season on the distribution of the corn crop (Fig. 12). Corn took precedence over pasture in warmer districts, providing both silage and grain. The silage supported production of milk in winter when butter was a more profitable product than cheese, while the grain corn (supplemented by skim milk and buttermilk) formed an excellent hog-ration. Furthermore, the more profitable and important the corn crop, the less time there was for attention to the dairy herd in summer: it was winter dairying and creamery supply which better fitted the cycle of seasonal labor. On the other hand, cheese was favored where the climatic factor reduced grain corn, silage, winter dairying, and hogs together. There a pasture-based milk-cow ration was characteristic, time and labor could be devoted to the dairy herd rather than to crops, and summer milk production was accentuated during the season when the price of cheese was more favorable than that of butter.

Again the explanation does not seem wholly invalid, but is it adequate? Insofar as it ties the cheese industry to climatic distributions, it is subject to the same objections of territorial inexactitude as the contention that summer temperatures imposed definite territorial controls. With reference to the agricultural aspects, it scarcely seems possible to conclude (at least at first glance) that the distribution of silage corn, grain corn, winter dairying, and hogs have much to do with the complicated distributions of dairy industries, in some areas at least. It is obvious that the cheese industry in the southwest corner of the state ousted creameries from a neighboring fringe of corn-rich and hog-breeding territory, but failed to advance into areas to the north where corn was less abundant. And it is clear that the Lakeshore and Central cheese-specialty regions have greater corn production than creamery-oriented areas which surround them.

An Integrating Thesis

There are, then, a number of different and indeed disparate theories to account for the pattern. "The luck of the game," the impetus of an early start, local reputation, ethnic factors, location relative to market and freight zones, climate, relief, soil, phase of development, the number of milk cows available, the relative significance of calves and hogs, the fat-content of the milk, the importance of corn—all are invoked, and not without contradiction. But it is here suggested that there are recurrent features which may be integrated with other elements into a broader hypothesis, that there is in fact a pattern rather than a random distribution. It is postulated that the localization of the cheese industry is primarily controlled by the localization of intensive, specialized dairy farming.

Absolute Intensity of Dairying

This unifying principle involves both areal intensity of milk production and a commitment to dairy specialization permitting only a moderate degree of interlocking with other farm enterprises. Absolute or areal intensity of dairying has, at least in the past, been a prerequisite to the success of the cheese industry, at least on a substantial scale—a factor decidedly more significant than other and more publicized controls. Though the small cheese factories typically required less than creameries, they were more exacting in other respects. Cleanliness and freshness of milk were vital, a fact which sharply restricted the radius of milk procurement when means of transport were limited to horse and buggy, and when efficient means of refrigeration were lacking. True enough, as some have emphasized, that (given the irreducible minimum of milk) a scattering of cheese factories could move into pioneering districts and thus capitalize on their limited milk requirements and the durability of their product, but the intensification and expansion of dairy farming was essential if factories were to multiply and a compact cheese region to emerge. Within such areas, the economic law of comparative advantage gave the territorially-restricted cheese industry first choice over the almost ubiquitous butter industry. Only in limited areas did there exist the prerequisite supplies of fresh whole milk, while the cheese factory, with its more complete utilization of milk-proteins as well as butterfat, could outbid the competition of the creamery which manufactured a product of a lower use-value. The higher prices paid by the cheese factories—especially conspicuous during the summer—were particularly significant where milk production was the main business of the farm, and even during times when cheese prices were temporarily depressed the close social and economic cohesion which characterized the neighborhood factory stood it in good stead.

The intensity of milk production resulted from more than the mere numbers of milk cows: specialist dairy farmers, usually holding modest acreages of land, were likely to secure more milk per cow—a fact which was particularly pertinent on the notably smaller farms of the southwestern Swiss-cheese and Lakeshore regions. The selection of dairy breeds was also involved. Naturally, the Holstein (and the ethnically-favored Brown Swiss) tended to predominate in the cheese regions

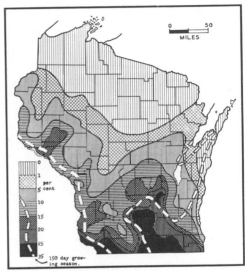

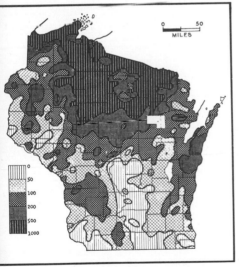

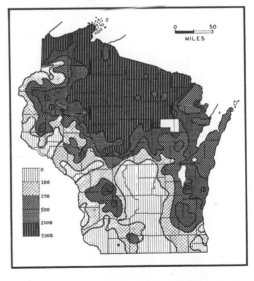

FIGURE 11: (upper left) Cheese factories and climate, 1910. (After A. E. Whitson and O. E. Baker, Wisconsin Agricultural Experiment Station Bulletin 223, July, 1912.) FIGURE 12: (upper right) Proportion of improved land in corn, 1905. (Source: Same as for Fig. 11.) FIGURE 13: (lower left) Milk cows per 100 acres of corn, 1928. (Source: Wisconsin Crop and Livestock Reporting Service.) FIGURE 14: (lower right) Milk cows per 100 acres of grain corn, 1945. (Source: Same as for Fig. 13.)

where butterfat was less relevant and abundance of low-fat milk was required, while the Guernsey and to some extent the Jersey became significant where the quantity of milk mattered less than the butterfat content (Fig. 17). Though perhaps initially more a consequence than a cause, this differential selection of breeds nevertheless served to confirm a choice based primarily on the economics of intensive dairy farming.

Degree of Dairy Specialization

But the cheese industry was typically associated with dairy farming which was not only intensive but *specialized*. And here analyses which concentrated on the significance of corn growing and livestock feeding are congruous with at least many of the facts of distribution and of farm economics. A cropping program and the associated feeding of hogs or beef cattle tended at one and the same time to dilute the relative specialization as well as the absolute intensity of dairying. For competitive elements deflected time and attention away from the chores of the dairy herd, diminished at least the relative significance of the milk-check to the farmer, and at the same time increased the feeding value of the by-products of butter rather than cheese manufacture, that is of the protein-rich skim milk and buttermilk which formed such excellent complements to corn-fodder. Furthermore, crop production tended to foster production of milk in winter as well as summer—a seasonal extension made possible by the growth of the essential fodder on the farm and furthered by the annual cycle of farm chores; pasture-based dairying was naturally biased toward concentration in the summer season. The extension of cropping and winter milk production was therefore a feature accompanying the maturation of dairy farming, especially in areas with level relief, better soils, or warmer climate as in southeastern Wisconsin (Figs. 11 and 18). And, as was often contended, this seasonal pattern did in fact produce a profitable deflection of milk from the cheese to the butter plants and later to the condensery and urban milk markets.

There was thus an economic and geographical nexus between the choice of dairy product and the type of farming, the latter serving as a major localizer of the cheese industry. Where dairying was *both* intensive and specialized, the cheese industry usually became predominant; where dairy farming lacked either areal intensity or became diluted by intermixture with other crop-and-livestock enterprises, the cheese factory yielded to alternative enterprises. But this localization of production has operated within constantly changing social, commercial, and technological conditions. The principles of regionalization need, therefore, to be comprehended within their setting of historical circumstance.

The Establishment of the Cheese Industry

When the Wisconsin cheese industry was first launched in the 1860's, haphazard agriculture and wheat cultivation were characteristic. Farm butter was an almost ubiquitous product, but cheese soon won favor as an article of commerce. The application of the factory system to cheese-making—which preceded its application to butter-making—both eased the production and standardized the quality of cheese while butter lagged in the domestic phase, and the simultaneous expansion of the British cheese market stimulated production at a time when transportation facilities were sufficient for cheese but scarcely for the more perishable product butter. The cheese industry thus became entrenched in some areas of southern and eastern Wisconsin as agricultural evolution was terminating in the development of dairying.

Localization within particular districts, however, was more a result of social circumstance than of locally selective environmental or agricultural controls. Thus it was Swiss settlers who established the foreign cheese industry in the southwestern hills and to some extent in Dodge County to the east, and New Yorkers and other easterners who launched American cheese production in scattered areas from Richland County in the southwestern hills to Sheboygan on the Lakefront. In the extreme southeast, local initiative was reinforced by territorial expansion from previously established centers in Illinois. Thus an industry dependent on specialist skill and community support began to spread from initially separate nuclei.

Expansion of the Butter Industry

But the territorial pattern was to change before the turn of the century. Despite continuing growth around the regional cores in the southwestern, Dodge County, and Lakeshore districts, cheese factories were dislodged from the southeastern counties while butter gained almost exclusive control in the previously uncommitted areas of central and western Wisconsin. This development was related both to contemporary progress in the butter industry and to backsliding in the cheese industry. Stimulated by the example of the cheese factory, butter-makers developed the creamery and capitalized on a variety of socio-economic factors and especially technological refinements which culminated in the Babcock butterfat test and the separator. The farm separator and the cream-gathering system—reinforced by the the cooperative movement—won the support of thousands of Midwestern farmers who had little interest in the exacting chores of cheese-dairying but much concern with wheat and corn, cattle and hogs. The success of cropping and meat production at once precluded the development of intensive and specialized dairying, intensified the demand for skim milk and buttermilk, and expunged the infant and uncertain cheese industry in Iowa and most of Minnesota.

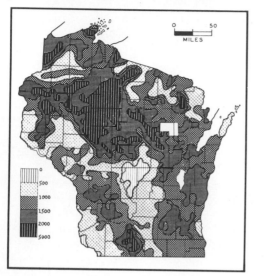
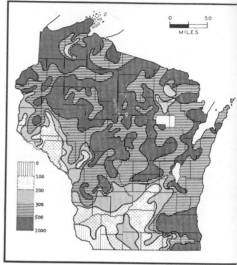
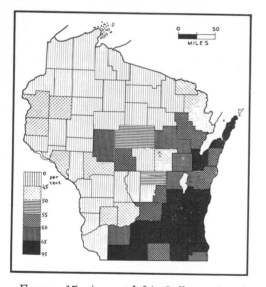
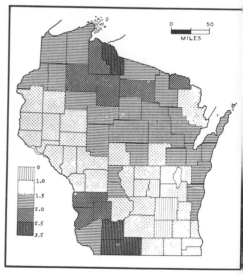

FIGURE 15: (upper left) Gallons of milk per acre of cropland, 1928. (After original map supplied by Wisconsin Crop and Livestock Reporting Service.)   FIGURE 16: (upper right) Ratio of milk cows to swine, 1928. (Source: Wisconsin Crop and Livestock Reporting Service.)   FIGURE 17: (lower left) Holsteins as a percentage of all cattle, 1930. (Source: Wisconsin Crop and Livestock Reporting Service.)   FIGURE 18: (lower right) Ratio of summer (June-August) to winter (December-January) milk production. (Source: Wisconsin Crop and Livestock Reporting Service.)

Cheese to Butter in the Southeast

These factors also applied, though with somewhat reduced force, in areas of western Wisconsin where dairy farming was either diluted with competitive farm enterprises—as near the Mississippi—or reduced in intensity by the intractable environments of northern cutover or central sand plain. But the retreat of cheese factories from southeastern Wisconsin reflected more complicated forces. In part, this zone, with its somewhat longer growing season, warmer summers, and level productive surface, witnessed the merging of the Corn Belt and the Dairy Belt. Compared with the specialized dairy regions in the southwestern hills and the Lakeshore, this southeastern area was characterized by a complex of climatic conditions, soil, and surface configuration which encouraged greater attention to corn, hogs, calf raising, and winter dairying—all factors which furthered the trend from cheese factories to creameries. But this tendency was accelerated by the temporarily profitable development of combined butter-and-cheese manufacture: when the butterfat was sent to the churn the skim milk was made into either "skim" or "filled" cheese, the latter a cheese "enriched" with introduced fats. Both practices, in the long run, proved damaging to the cheese industry, particularly in the 'eighties and 'nineties. And since skimming and filling were largely confined to areas with winter dairying and spread concentrically from northeastern Illinois, it was southeastern Wisconsin which joined the rest of the "Elgin district" in becoming "a region deservedly noted . . . for its excellent butter and poor cheese." When the manufacture of such cheese was prohibited by legislation the transition to butter was completed.

Recovery and Expansion of the Cheese Industry

Elsewhere the cheese industry was reinvigorated by general factors including an improving market, technological progress, and a vigorous educational campaign, and by a variety of local factors which varied from place to place. In the southwest, the foreign cheese industry was fostered by economic success, continuing immigration, and a strong community commitment which spread by social osmosis from the Swiss to other nationalities. The American cheese factories immediately to the north were characterized by a spirited response to educational efforts, and the region lay beyond the margin of the southeastern zone of winter dairying and "filling." Further to the east, the Dodge County factories continued to flourish since concentration upon Limburger and more especially the locally developed brick cheese was both remunerative and adaptable to the evolution of winter dairying, while the adjacent Lakeshore region, farther from the Illinois line and characterized by summer dairying, was excluded from the expanding zone of skimming and filling, and its technological backwardness was partially offset by a particularly favorable climate. Success was also attributed to local leadership and financial support, cheap freights consequent on a strategic waterfront location, and adoption of a "Yankee" activity by a largely German community whose small farms and notable thrift contributed both to the intensification of milk production and to the tenacity of the cheese industry.

Other local factors also became evident as new cheese regions emerged in the center and northwest of the state—regions barely discernible in 1905 but which were fully defined by the 'twenties (Fig. 5). Wisconsin dairy leaders deliberately promoted the cheese industry in central and northern Wisconsin, urging that while many an area could produce butter, few had the climatic qualifications to manufacture high-grade cheese. Growth was furthered as the Central region began to function as a "receiver" for colonists from the older and crowding cheese regions, an influx fostered by economic opportunity and ethnic similarity—Germans in the center, and Swiss and other nationalities (including French-Canadian) in the northwest.

The Fundamental Correlations

Nevertheless, local factors were not in themselves sufficient: they proved permanently effective only where dairy farming became both intensive and specialized. The pertinence of this factor may be verified by cartographic analysis of the distributional association of the cheese industry and *intensive* dairy farming, an association which always existed but which is particularly clear after 1895 when detailed and comparable data on cheese production and milk cows became available (Figs. 3–10). The degree of correlation of cheese factories and dairying in the southeastern counties was, of course, progressively obscured as condensed, evaporated and market milk production successively invaded this locationally vulnerable region, but elsewhere the areal correlations stand clear. In 1895 the solidly established nuclei of the cheese regions of the southwestern, Dodge County, and Lakeshore districts were duplicated by dairy intensities, a relationship more fully manifested in following decades as the Lakeshore industry merged with the brick cheese region to the southeast, and extended westwards until it reached the limits of supporting soil types: by the 1920's the Lakeshore region was partially linked across the Shawano upland to the very precisely defined Central cheese region, an area which consolidated to the south of the rough terminal moraine and found its physical limits in the Colby silt loams and related soils, an area which developed an intensive dairy economy. With the addition of the somewhat indefinite cheese districts which emerged in and around Barron County near the Minnesota state line, the Wisconsin cheese regions had been formulated and a distinctive "Cheese Belt" extended westward from the shores of Lake Michigan—a pattern which has been confirmed or at least repeated in each succeeding decade.

But the degree of *specialization* in dairy farming was also relevant to the distribution of cheese factories—a fact also subject to a measure of cartographic analysis. In the 1920's, when the cheese regions had then become maturely formulated and comparable, certain correlations were evident. The map revealing the ratio between milk production and the total acreage of cropland (Fig. 15) is particularly significant, especially if the sparsely settled northern tiers of counties be eliminated from consideration, while cartographic presentation of the ratio of cows to corn (Fig. 13) also confirms the contention that in the cheese regions the competition of corn was reduced, both in the Cheese Belt proper and to a lesser extent in the southwestern districts. But the differentiation of grain corn (Fig. 14) from silage corn indicates a further distinction: the former, being more a feature of the Corn Belt, tends to dilute dairy farm intensities and conflict with the cheese industry, while the latter reinforces the congenial emphasis on milk rather than meat production.[7]

The distribution of milk cows in relationship to other and alternative livestock also provides further general—though perhaps less clear-cut—repetitions of the basic pattern. Hogs (Fig. 16), the characteristic animals of the Corn Belt, have been in general less associated with cheese than with butter regions—condenseries and urban milksheds apart. Beef cattle are infrequent in cheese regions as compared with the Corn Belt, while among dairy breeds the Holstein, with its high yield of low-butterfat milk, manifests a characteristic association with the cheese factory: Guernseys are "butter breeds" (Fig. 17). Furthermore, the map indicating the degree of concentration upon milk production in the summer season (Fig. 18) confirms the fact which was so strongly affirmed by earlier analysts: summer dairying and the cheese industry have gone hand in hand.

It is this association with a particular agricultural complex which explains the otherwise puzzling correlations of the cheese industry with physical features such as soil type, surface configuration, and climatic conditions, for these largely controlled the distribution of intensive and specialized dairying. There is, of course, the pertinent question as to which came first, the chicken or the egg, for the initial establishment of the cheese industry was itself a factor favoring the local development of specialized dairy farming—but it was not the most general or compelling influence. The regional distribution of such dairy farming reflects rather the operation of the economic law of comparative advan-

[7] Unfortunately the relevance of the first available *township* data on grain and silage corn ratios (1945) to earlier situations is reduced by the development of hybrid corn in the intervening period, but *county* figures for 1930 show substantially the same patterns as for 1945.

tage in a context of varying locational and physical conditions. In southern Wisconsin specialized summer dairying was largely restricted by corn-and-hog competition to the somewhat less productive southwestern hills, while in cooler central and northern Wisconsin intensive dairying failed to materialize on the poorer sand plains and cutover but consolidated on the clays and loams of what became the Lakeshore and Central cheese regions. It was thus through the medium of the agricultural complex that climate, soil, and relief exerted their influence on the localization of the cheese industry.

The Changing Pattern

It is not, of course, contended that this link with the farm type imposed an absolute and rigid control: it was rather a broad framework within which other factors might prove locally effective. Nor is it likely to remain determinative. In fact, this long-standing connection has become attenuated in the last few decades. Quite apart from the continuing encroachment of urban milksheds in the southeast and elsewhere, the manufacturing branches of the dairy industry have been profoundly modified by the general adoption of whole-milk collection and by the development of "multiple product" or "flexible" plants. Like the cheese factory, these receive whole milk, but unlike both the traditional cheese factory and creamery they make a wide range of products which may include cheese as well as butter, and almost invariably include dry skim milk. For diversification of the market and technological change are altering the terms of competition between different dairy products, and the Wisconsin cheese regions have been hemmed in and penetrated by large and highly competitive plants which pay high prices for fresh whole milk. Simultaneously, the farmers are ceasing to know or even to care what is done with the milk they sell to the manufacturer, for farm feeding now depends less upon the retention of skim milk and whey, and more upon the purchase of such products in processed form. Even the farm and factory statistics which have enabled precise cartographic definition of cheese regions in the past are now vanishing—but that is another story.

Conclusion

Suffice to conclude that though the causal connections have weakened, the cheese industry still preserves much of its time-honored correlation with specialized and intensive dairy farming. It was the type of agriculture which both expressed the influence of various natural factors such as terrain, soil, and climate and in turn created an economic bias for or against specialization in cheese production. Viewed broadly, the

Cheese Belt localized in the wedge-shaped zone of intensive and specialized dairying which formed between the Corn Belt to the south and the Shield and cutover regions to the north. It was not that any single agricultural element formed an exclusive determinant, but several factors blended to form a guiding framework and shape the Cheese Belt. To the south, the success of cropping and meat production forced dairy farming into a subordinate role. Small grains such as oats, barley, and wheat were contributors, but it was the massive production of grain corn which largely undergirded the farm system and ultimately determined the predominance of the butter rather than the cheese industry. Silage corn—normally associated with cooler summers and shorter growing seasons—was here much less significant, meat rather than milk production was emphasized, and hogs and beef cattle competed with and reduced the dairying sector of the farm economy. Thus Corn Belt agriculture synthesized a number of factors which were inherently inhospitable to the cheese industry, and even where fairly intensive dairying was intermingled with ingredients of Corn Belt farming—as in much of southern and parts of western Wisconsin—the cheese factory was placed at a disadvantage; it was the butter industry which prevailed in most of Illinois, Iowa, and Minnesota.

But northward of this zone the "Corn-Belt complex" was weakened and dairying prevailed. In some areas—as in the sand plains of central Wisconsin and more particularly in the harsher and intractable north—dairy farming maintained a leading role but was scarcely intensive, and not even the predominant butter industry, based on milk or cream procured from scattered farms, could be described as flourishing. But, in the intermediate belt, wherever soils and relief permitted, dairy farming became both specialized and intensive. And this became cheese territory *par excellence*. The major regions lay in the zone which progressively extended westwards from the shores of Lake Michigan through central Wisconsin toward and to some extent across the Minnesota state line. The Swiss and American cheese regions in the southwestern counties were more transitional in their location, being closer to the margins of the Dairy Belt both economically and geographically. But in this area of driftless hill country the pressures of Corn Belt farming and winter dairying were sufficiently weakened to give social factors and historical impetus a critical role. In these southwestern regions, the partial congealing of the northern and western boundaries through several decades seems to have been a response to a more-or-less balanced market for butter and cheese though in the postwar period the cheese industry, favored by prices, has advanced to the Mississippi, moving into areas with strong Corn Belt characteristics. Nevertheless, in Wisconsin and the Midwest in general, it is the inherited patterns which still prevail.

9. Taming Trees
Erhard Rostlund

Economic use of forest resources in the future may well
follow the principle that, "in the long run, whatever proves to
be biologically incorrect will never be economically sound."
This selection condemns many current practices in forest
exploitation and conservation and suggests that a more
naturalistic, rather than an "orchard," approach to reforesta-
tion is, "in the long run," biologically and economically
more desirable. As world population increases, and if the use
of natural resources continues to be as profligate as at
present, a better understanding of ecology and of the world
as an ecological system (or "ecosystem") is required
among scientists, businessmen, and political leaders.

The next stage of the relationship between man and the forest will perhaps be known to our descendants as the time in history when forest
trees were domesticated. We are already on the threshold of that stage;
the process of selective breeding that changes a wild species to its domestic form is well under way with certain timber and pulp trees, and,
if successful, may lead to the end of forests as we know them. There
will no doubt always be something called forests and something called
men on this planet, but the question is what kind of forests and what
kind of men.

The most comprehensive recent statement of what man has done and
intends to do in the forest is contained in the speeches and scientific
reports given at the fifth World Forestry Congress held at Seattle,
Washington, in the fall of 1960. At that meeting, which was attended
by delegates from 65 countries, a keynote was sounded by Binya Ran-
jan Sen of India, Director General of the Food and Agricultural Organization of the United Nations. Speaking of the rapid world population
growth and the rising demand for wood, he said: "Modern forestry can
no longer consist of a simple return to nature or of a slavish submission
to it; the use of fertilizers, irrigation, soil working, vegetable selection
and hybridization are the new weapons at forestry's disposal for ob-

SOURCE: *Bulletin of the Atomic Scientists* (October, 1961), 326–30. Copyright 1961
by the Educational Foundation for Nuclear Science. The late Professor Rostlund
was on the staff, Department of Geography, University of California, Berkeley.

taining yields which exceed the limits set by nature." Egon Glesinger, Director of the Forestry and Forest Products Division of the FAO, spoke with similar confidence of higher yields to come, and suggested that the most important development was the trend toward establishing plantations of quick-growing species, a method so promising that it has led some people to advocate the sweeping removal of tropical hardwood forests and their replacement by new plantations. According to Glesinger, 20 or 30 years from now the world will probably need twice as much industrial wood as is used today. In the United States; the Forest Service estimates that by the end of the century the sawtimber growth in this country must be at least doubled to meet the need, and similar reports from other nations suggest the existence of a widespread and insistent belief that somehow the forest can and must be made to produce more wood than in the past. There is evidence that the productivity of the forest can indeed be raised, but how large an increase we can count on, and how permanent it might turn out to be, are questions that have as yet no definitive answers.

It is by no means certain that the quick-growing plantations acclaimed by Glesinger will give the best result in the long run. The plantation method is a form of monoculture at fast pace. Plantings are usually of a single species, for example maritime pine in the Landes region of southwestern France, or Monterey pine, which has been used since the twenties on about a million acres in Australia, New Zealand, South Africa, and Chile. Superficially these monotonous stands with their long rows of uniform trees may resemble fields of corn or other row crops, but the trees are not domesticated, and most of them are not even on the road to domestication. Except for some recently organized gathering of seed from the best-looking trees in the hope of improving the breed, the large plantations have not been laboratories for selective breeding aimed at developing desirable traits, such as straight trunks, superior wood, and resistance to disease. But even so, these plantings are of great interest. In the first place, they represent one of the major impacts of man on the forests of the world—many woodlands have been drastically altered, and forests have been made where none existed before; and second, and perhaps even more important, the experience with the planting of single species in the past offers the most significant lessons in the history of silviculture.

The lesson was condensed into one short sentence by H. Leibundgut of Switzerland in his report at the forestry congress: "In the long run, whatever proves to be biologically incorrect will never be economically sound." He based his argument for the superiority of naturalistic silviculture over orchard silviculture, or of natural forests over artificial plantations, on the well-documented history of forest management during the last two centuries in central Europe, particularly in Germany, Switzerland, Austria, and Czechoslovakia.

Beginning in the latter part of the eighteenth century and continuing in the nineteenth, concurrent with the industrial revolution and probably caused by it, the forests of central Europe underwent a great change. In order to gear timber production to the demands of industry, the practice of clearcutting, planting, and harvesting on quick rotations was widely adopted, and mainly spruce or pine were planted, for they were most in demand and paid best. The result was that oak, beech, maple, ash, and other hardwoods almost disappeared from many forests, leaving virtually pure stands of pine or spruce in their place. The practice became a system of monoculture that gave high yields and good profit in the short run; but after a few generations of trees had been harvested it became obvious that all was not well in the woods. The trees became sickly, their growth was stunted, and yields dropped; the forest became increasingly susceptible to damage from storm, frost, insects, and fungi, and, beneath it all, the soil deteriorated. The system produced an impoverished plant community that was both physiologically and sociologically unhealthy; it was "biologically incorrect" and therefore economically unsound.

Richard Plochmann, in *American Forests*, speaks of the wretched state of affairs today in some of the Bavarian forests, because of the monoculture system, and says that for the sake of conservation and soil care it will be necessary to re-establish mixed strands of conifers and hardwoods on more than one third of the forest acreage of southern Germany. He calls this reconversion, which may require 40 to 50 years, central Europe's most urgent problem in silviculture. The same problem exists in the planted pine forests of southwestern France. Other reports at Seattle stressing the value of creating mixed stands in order to improve the forest came from the Ministry of Agriculture in Czechoslovakia, and from the Academy of Sciences in Ukraine. It is too soon to judge the chance of success of the young pine plantations in the southern hemisphere, but some of the signs are not encouraging. In New Zealand, as reported by A. D. McKinnon, regeneration of Monterey pine is good but the pathological record is not; rather severe attacks of fungi and insects have taken place, and "epidemic occurrence" of the sawfly has caused great damage to the trees. One cannot help but wonder whether old mistakes are being repeated. It is almost a rule of entomology that the risk of insect outbreaks is naturally greater in pure stands than in mixed forests.

In short, it can scarcely be said that the permanent value of monoculture on forest plantations has been demonstrated. Nevertheless, the trend mentioned by Glesinger not only exists but seems to have great pressure behind it, and I suppose that man, who has a remarkable capacity for forgetting or ignoring mistakes, will keep on making plantations, perhaps even to the extent of the "sweeping removal" of tropical

forests and their replacement by Monterey pine or some other species
approved by industry.

The Taming Process

But mere planting of trees is not domestication. Man's ability to domesticate is not exercized in the management of trees or plantations but in
the management of genes and chromosomes which carry the hereditary
traits of the plant. Man discovered, or rather gradually became aware
of, this ability a long time ago. More precisely, what he found was that
individual plants of the same species are not always exactly alike but
often vary considerably, that the variable characteristic is sometimes
inherited by the next generation. By selecting and breeding individuals
with such an inheritance, man might succeed in developing a plant
very different from its ancestors, and much more useful. It was this discovery several thousand years ago that enabled man with some of his
food plants to cross the threshold of the first great domestication, a step
that led to agriculture, profoundly altering much of the plant world
and changing man's way of life.

The ancient plant breeders did not have our concepts of genes and
chromosomes, but they could see that some plants had good visible
traits (phenotype). Fine appearance, however, is not always a sign of
good hereditary factors concealed in the genes (genotype), for fine
looks can be caused by some fortuitous favor of the environment, such
as an unusually good supply of food, water, or sunlight. There must
have been many fruitless experiments with attractive but deceptive
phenotypes in the past. But once in a while man hit upon valuable genotypes that responded to selective breeding, and new varieties of plants
were developed. Today, on the threshold of what may become the second great plant domestication, that of forest trees, the problem is essentially the same as it always has been, namely finding promising
genotypes to propagate. The difference lies in the vastly superior equipment, greater amount of accumulated knowledge, and more highly
organized research of our time.

The basic problem might be stated simply, but the techniques employed by the tree breeder are numerous, and the genetic material provided by nature is exceedingly complex. It has been found by experiments that changes in the genes and chromosomes (mutations) and increase in the number of chromosomes (polyploidy), both of which
sometimes occur naturally, can be induced artificially by exposing seeds,
buds, or shoots of trees to various types of radiation—gamma rays,
x-rays, neutrons from atomic piles—or by heat treatment, or by application of certain drugs and chemicals. The purpose is to try to develop
faster growth, larger size, or some other desirable and hereditary trait

in the tree. Work of this type is still largely experimental but may well produce results of great practical importance in the future. At the present time the two most promising techniques in applied forest genetics are hybridization and the plus-tree and seed-orchard method.

The promise of hybridization lies in the possibility of obtaining from the inbreeding of two related individuals or the crossbreeding of races or species an offspring that is superior in one or more respects to the parents (hybrid vigor or heterosis). Occasionally hybridization may even bring out or release qualities that were latent in the parents, so that a new characteristic appears. Experiments are in progress in many countries and interesting hybrids have been achieved, as a few examples will show. Several new oaks produced at the Kharkov Agricultural Institute in Russia were described at Seattle by S. S. Piatnisky. One of them, which has been given the name of *Quercus Vyssotskyi*, was obtained by crossing the common oak of Western Europe *(Q. robur)* with an oak from the Caucasus Mountains *(Q. macranthera)*. Another new oak, named *Q. Timirjasevii*, is the offspring of the same Caucasus oak and the bur oak of the American prairies *(Q. macrocarpa)*. These new hybrids are larger and grow faster than the native oak and are particularly suitable for the arid steppes because of their great ability to endure drought.

The work of J. W. Duffield, F. I. Righter, N. T. Mirov and their associates at the Institute of Forest Genetics near Placerville, California, has led to a better understanding of the nature of pines and to the development of many new varieties. At the Forestry Congress, Righter discussed some of them, including a cross between pitch pine and loblolly pine *(Pinus rigida x taeda)*, which originated at Placerville in 1943, and is now reproduced in large numbers in Korea for reforestation projects in that country. This hybrid is as frost-hardy as the native Korean red pine, is more resistant to insect attacks, grows faster and straighter, and makes better lumber. The example is of unusual interest not only because of the new pine itself but because it shows, first, the possibility of economically successful mass production of a hybrid and, second, the adaptability of a tree that was developed in California and transplanted to a very different habitat in Korea. The first is an achievement by man, the second mainly a matter of chance, for adaptability to a foreign ecological situation is something that cannot be bred into a plant in its homeland. According to Righter, the problems of mass production and adaptability are still obstacles that make the widespread establishment of hybrids difficult or uncertain.

Mass Producing Trees

The plus-tree and seed-orchard method has the advantage of being a form of mass production, and adaptability is hardly a problem, for the technique is used mostly for the improvement of trees in their native habitat. As employed in its latest form, in the forests of the south in the United States or in the Scandinavian countries, the method involves several steps: (1) selecting superior trees in the forest, known as elite or plus trees; (2) grafting cuttings from the plus trees on rootstock already established in orchards; (3) obtaining seeds from the orchards planted in nurseries; and (4) transplanting seedlings from the nurseries to the forest when they are a few years old. An important advance over the older method of merely collecting seeds from the best trees is the application of the grafting technique and the establishment of orchards on a large scale; the grafting multiplies each plus tree, making mass production of seeds feasible, and the orchards and nurseries make it possible to protect the seedlings during their first few years. By selecting and propagating plus trees possessing certain traits known to be hereditary and others that might prove to be, it is hoped to breed a race of fast-growing, tall, straight trees, with trunks of large diameter and little taper (the less the taper the greater the volume), few and small branches (the fewer the branches the less knotty the wood), good self-pruning ability, and strong resistance to pests and diseases.

As expressed at Seattle by Helge Johnsson, director of the Swedish Tree Breeding Association, the aim is mass production of the type of tree that will "convert the largest possible part of the total production into usable timber." The emphasis is on both quality and quantity. The notion that quality of wood will be less important in the future because most of it will be ground up to obtain its cellulose fibers for the pulp and chemical wood industries was most emphatically denied by Johnsson on the ground that quantity, which always will be desired, is contingent upon quality: it is the best trees that will always give the highest yield. The final outcome of the great experiment with plus trees and seed orchards cannot yet be seen, for the progeny of the plus trees must still be tested for a long time in order to find out whether the improvement, if any, is stable, or whether coming generations will tend to revert to mediocrity.

Larger trees and faster growth will mean heavier demands on the soil. As might be expected on the threshold of agricultural forestry, while some people are trying to domesticate the trees and make crops of them, others are working on the problem of the preservation and improvement of the forest soil. Like modern farmers, they seek the solution in the use of chemical fertilizers. The problems of the agricultural forester are partly technical, partly economic: the identification of deficiencies in forest soils; the determination of how different species of trees in different situations and regions respond, if at all, to different amounts and different types of fertilizers; the application of the fertilizers, whether by hand, from airplane, in the form of solutions, or as pellets; and whether, after all, it pays to go to all the trouble. The prob-

lems of soil fertilization are probably at least as complex as those of
applied forest genetics, and experiments in both have shown promising
but not yet conclusive results.

Beyond the Threshold

The technical problems of tree breeding and fertilization of forest soils
will no doubt be solved, but other problems may be more difficult, and
there is even the question of whether all of us wish to cross the thresh-
hold into the new world of agricultural forestry. Perhaps we have no
choice, but we might at least give some thought to what full domestication of forest trees will mean, and ask whether any alternative exists.

The forest is not just a collection of trees producing wood and cellulose for man. The forest is a complex community of many living things,
most of which have no monetary value, which is not to say that they
have no value; and the relationship between man and this community is
also very complex. This complexity was reflected to some extent at the
forestry congress in its choice of multiple use as a central theme, and in
the number and variety of subjects discussed, among which (besides
silviculture, soil, logging, and other topics of the forest industries
proper) were water and watershed protection, grass and grazing, wildlife, parks, campsites, and other forms of recreation. All these activities will be affected for better or worse by the domestication of the forest.

And a domesticated *forest*, not just domesticated trees, is what we
must expect, for there is no reason to think that this domestication will
stop with plants, any more than did the earlier one that led to agriculture. When we look at cattle in the pasture or corn on the former prairie
we are seeing not just domesticated animals and plants but a domesticated landscape, in which nearly everything is the work of men or more
or less under his control: pasture grasses, weeds, pests, vermin, and
birds, nutrients and microorganisms in the soil, drainage pattern and
water supply, and sometimes even the very slope and lay of the land.
When the era of agricultural forestry comes we can expect man to assume the same complete control over everything in the forest community, and the crops of trees will not resemble our forests any more
than a field of hybrid corn resembles the original prairie vegetation it
has replaced.

Just when that era will come is hard to say but surely not in this century nor in the next. Forestry is necessarily concerned with the long
run and so is domestication. The change in a wild species resulting
from selective breeding which is called domestication may require an
uninterrupted experiment running through many generations of the
plant, and since a tree generation is from 20 to 30 up to 100 years, our
descendants 400 or 500 years from now may possibly have truly domes-

ticated forests. The significance of the time perspective in forestry is that after several centuries, when the science of genetics and the technique of tree breeding will have advanced greatly and will perhaps have developed the perfect tree, the population of the world and the demand for wood and cellulose will also have increased greatly. The economic pressure for the sweeping removal of forests as we know them and their replacement by stands of perfected trees will then be irresistible.

It is not possible, of course, to see clearly what the forest of our descendants will look like, but by projecting the dominant trends of the present time we can try to imagine the goal toward which we seem to be striving. In the ideal forest of the future, then, the trees will be tall and straight with cylindrical trunks and small branches and foliage. Like prize cattle, they will be highly efficient organisms converting the flow of energy and nutrients into a maximum of cellulose and a minimum of material not useful to man. The undergrowth of today's forest, the colorful plants that lend variety and beauty to it, will not be tolerated in the cellulose belt, any more than that sort of thing is allowed in the feed lots of the Corn Belt, for it would be poor agronomy to permit so many weed plants to waste the nutrients and the water of the soil. For the same reason wildlife will not clutter up the aisles between the supertrees. Since the trees will resist attacks by insects, and since there will be no other plants to serve as alternate hosts to them, there will be no insects, and no birds, to disturb the bovine tranquility of the cellulose groves. Will there be people camping in this silent and lonely "forest"? I think so, but I cannot quite make out what kind of people.

An alternative does exist. In our dealings with nature we might, as Marston Bates suggests in *The Forest and the Sea*, "make every effort to maintain diversity." The same ecological wisdom guides the foresters who believe in "naturalistic silviculture." They are not opposed to but welcome the improvements contributed by forest genetics, they are in favor of and seek to practice the most modern methods of management, but one of their cardinal principles is that the forest must be conserved as a *forest*, with its natural beauty and wildlife preserved as nearly intact as possible. They also claim that only such a forest can be economically sound in the long run. This kind of silviculture might not take us across the threshold into true agricultural forestry, but it might save a true forest for our descendants.

10. New Methods of Appraising the Role of Fisheries in World Nutrition

Georg Borgstrom

The food resources of the sea are being drawn on increasingly and are likely to be utilized much more as the food producing capability of the land becomes less adequate to feed the rapidly growing world population. This selection outlines a new and practical method of evaluating the role of fisheries and fishing in feeding individual nations, and establishes measures of a desirable balance between agriculture and fishing. This type of economic analysis differs greatly from the locational studies considered earlier. It may prove, however, to be of great importance and influence in determining national economic policies and have a direct effect on national living standards as well.

I began this study because of encountering in geographical, agricultural and nutritional text-books and papers, innumerable statements belittling the role of fisheries. These were frequently accompanied by unsubstantiated statements about the limitless potential of the sea in providing fish for human feeding.

These statements showed the lack of simple, readily conceivable ways of gauging the real significance of fisheries; particularly they revealed the substantial difficulties encountered in comparing fisheries with agriculture.

Figures of consumption of fish per head do not provide any suitable yardstick for assessing the value of fish either in the economy or the actual feeding of a country, because they have no relationship to other foods, either those provided by agriculture or imported.

Basically two methods are employed to achieve comparison between fish and other foods. These relate to: (1) calorific value, and (2) the protein content. The bearing of these two distinct standards is set out in Table I and the implications of the comparison will repay careful study.

SOURCE: *Fishing News International*, I (October, 1961), 33–38. Reprinted by permission. Tables and illustrations have been updated. The author is professor of geography and food science, Michigan State University.

The first three columns cover consumption per head, the calorific value of the particular nation's average diet and the percentage of calories provided by fish. For three reasons this method is highly irrelevant. The range of variation is small: the highest value is 3.1 per cent, the lowest 0.3 per cent, with one single value of 6.2 per cent. As these values relate to the national diet they mean nothing in the case of "fish-eating" countries, because the percentage depends on whether the total calorific intake is high or low. The second reason for deriding the calorie measure is the fact that fish justifies its place in diet not as a source of calories but as an essential carrier of high quality protein. (Geiger and Borgstrom, 1961.) The third reason for discount is the evident effect on the final calorie figures of fatty or lean fish.

Yet, relying on this calorie assessment, some writers advance the notion that fish is insignificant nationally and globally and that it could easily be replaced by agricultural commodities. Could it? Look at Japan. Fish provide her with only 3 per cent of her calorie intake. But fish is quite indispensable to her national food supply. Palpably the yardstick is faulty.

No, the only sound appraisal of the place of fish in diet is to recognize it as a source of animal protein and compare it with nutritionally equivalent items such as milk, meat, poultry and eggs.

Fish as Animal Protein

The simplest way to measure fish against other animal proteins is to compare, on a global basis, the total amount of various animal proteins (see Graph I). Here fish immediately emerges as a major factor—12.2 per cent of the whole. And, most significantly, one must notice that fish is a primary source of animal protein to nutritionally low standard nations, that is, it feeds—or, at least, fills the gap between starvation and subsistence—far more millions than does either milk or meat. More than two-thirds of the world's meat and milk is consumed by fewer than 600 million people. But the number of humans to whom fish constitutes more than half of their average daily animal protein exceeds 1,500 million!

Columns 4 and 5 of Table I show in detail the amount of animal protein consumed per head per day in most countries in the world and the percentage of that fish protein to the total animal protein consumed. These columns reveal that in the generally well fed Scandinavian countries such as Norway and Sweden approximately 16 per cent to 17 per cent (almost one-fifth of the total animal protein consumed) is ascribed to fish. In countries like Spain and India one-fourth of the animal protein intake is from fish, one half in the case of Ceylon and Indonesia. But in Portugal and Japan close to three-fifths of all animal protein is of fish origin, while in Thailand it is nearly three-quarters!

Importance of Protein

One cannot, however, be satisfied with figures of this general nature; they disregard the appreciable differences prevailing as to nutritional standards between countries as measured by the total amount of animal protein being consumed annually. The United States in column 4 is shown to consume 66 grams *per capita* per day, which is equal to 51 pounds of animal protein in a year. At the other end of the scale there is Indonesia where the daily intake is only one-tenth of the U.S. figure!

Plainly, more adequate methods for appraising nutritional needs are required, particularly when geographical and economic factors are brought to interplay with nutritional data.

I passed, therefore, to considering how many people did fish feed in each nation? On the current protein standard of each country just how many people could possibly fill their entire animal protein requirements from fish? To make this estimate the protein in fish used as food was computed. To it, in cases where it applied, was added the protein content of fish meal and solubles used in producing other food commodities such as poultry, pigs, etc. A conversion factor of five was used here to divide this latter sum and provide a figure for adding to the protein directly consumed in fish. (The small amount of fish used as fertilizer was ignored because of insufficient statistical data.)

From that data a combined total was arrived at as to the people fed directly and indirectly by fish. That figure is given in column 2 of Table II. Column 1 gives the total population of the country concerned and column 2 the percentage of that population supported directly and indirectly by fish.

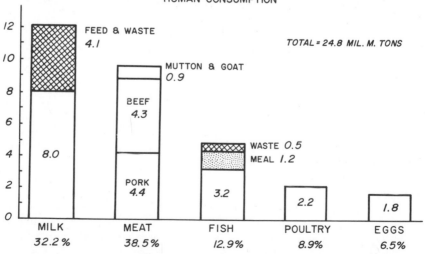

ANIMAL PROTEIN
(1963–1965)
HUMAN CONSUMPTION

From the combined estimate it can be inferred that the world's total fish supported population exceeds 670 million, of whom 535 million are in Asia, approximately 50 million in Europe (excluding U.S.S.R.) and 46 million in Africa. More than 21 million refer to the U.S.S.R. This table, together with the first table, clearly bears out the far greater relative importance of fisheries to Asia. Portugal is the only European country which follows this Far Eastern pattern.

Many observations and interesting conclusions can be drawn from this material but it is still desirable to relate fisheries into the natural resources of a country or region. By formulating fisheries in agricultural terms it should be feasible to relate fisheries to the productional capabilities of each individual country.

Basic Question Asked

To do this, therefore, I posed the following question: How many acres of tilled land would be required if an amount of animal protein equal to that from fish were to be provided vicariously through milk?

Answering this question involved a whole series of complex calculations. To simplify them, the assumption was made that skim milk was used for feeding domestic animals as a substitute for fish meal. This introduced a minor error as naturally the butter fat produced simultaneously could be used for partially feeding a certain number of human individuals. For the moment, that point was ignored, but where this factor was analysed it turned out that the oil of the fish used in meal production provided a corresponding amount and in several cases a larger quantity of fat than would be the case with milk.

The result of these calculations is embodied in columns 3, 4 and 5 of Table II. Read them carefully.

In my view, this way of reasoning gives a clearer conception of the importance of fish to each individual country and the magnitude of the feeding burden which the fish industry is actually carrying. It also offers the geographer a chance to conceive fisheries in concrete figures such as acreage and enables the agricultural economist to have at his disposal commensurate figures allowing a direct comparison between fisheries and agriculture.

The acreage calculations are based on F.A.O. figures and other sources as to the milk producing capacity (milk yield per head) related to acres. The figures are, in effect, minimum figures: they are based on the most efficient and, from the acreage point of view, the least costly way of producing animal protein. Secondly, on the assumption of an effective ley-farming with added feed they mean the soil is adequately and intensively utilized. This justifies a direct comparison with arable acreage disregarding pastures and other untilled soil. So in terms of acres all these figures in reality would be much higher.

TABLE I. Assessing the Importance of Fish in Nutrition (1963–65)

	Fish meat eaten per head p.a. kilograms	Calories in nation's diet per head	Calories in fish eaten and % of diet		ANIMAL PROTEIN PER CAPITA PER DAY IN GRAMS		Percentage of fish protein in total animal protein
					Total	Fish	
Belgium & Luxemburg	5.5	3080	19	0.6	49.7	2.7	4.3
France	7.7	2970	37	1.3	59.5	5.2	8.8
Greece	10.2	2960	38	1.3	35.9	5.7	14.6
Italy	5.8	2770	24	0.9	32.6	3.4	10.4
Netherlands	5.5	2970	20	0.7	51.1	2.1	4.1
Portugal	22.6	2640	75	2.8	29.4	14.1	48.0
Spain	13.8	2850	45	1.6	28.0	6.5	23.0
U. K.	9.5	3260	28	0.9	53.1	4.2	7.9
W. Germany	6.6	2920	24	0.8	50.9	3.4	6.7
E. Germany	10.7	3040	14	0.5	35.2	5.4	15.2
Poland	3.7	3350	16	0.5	37.6	2.0	5.0
Hungary	0.73	3050	5	0.2	37.9	0.6	1.6
Denmark	19.0	3330	69	2.1	59.8	9.6	16.0
Finland	9.6	2950	41	1.4	56.8	5.2	9.2
Norway	20.4	2960	69	2.3	50.5	9.8	19.4
Sweden	20.8	2970	73	2.4	54.1	7.6	14.0
U.S.S.R.	14.7	3200	52	1.6	42.0	7.2	17.2
Canada	6.9	3090	26	0.8	62.4	3.8	6.1
U.S.A.	5.1	3140	21	0.7	65.6	2.6	4.0
Mexico	2.6	2640	7	0.3	23.8	1.2	5.0

Country							
Costa Rica	1.5	2460	5	0.2	20.3	0.7	3.5
Cuba	10.2	2750	32	1.2	29.6	5.0	16.8
Jamaica	11.0	2240	57	2.5	22.7	8.5	37.2
Argentina	2.9	3100	10	0.3	47.9	1.4	2.9
Brazil	2.2	2950	11	0.4	18.7	1.6	8.6
Chile	8.4	2560	40	1.6	28.9	4.6	15.9
Peru	7.3	2150	32	1.5	18.3	4.1	22.4
Venezuela	13.4	2240	43	1.9	25.4	6.2	24.4
Burma	13.0	2050	25	1.2	19.0	6.4	49.2
Ceylon	6.2	2080	35	1.7	7.9	4.6	58.5
China	11.0	1900	40	2.1	7.0	5.5	77.9
India	1.1	2110	4	0.2	5.7	0.6	10.5
Indonesia	4.7	1980	16	0.8	4.5	2.2	48.8
Japan	27.8	2340	80	3.4	23.6	13.1	55.4
Pakistan	1.5	2260	5	0.2	9.5	0.8	8.5
Philippines	15.7	2020	55	2.7	15.7	7.8	49.5
Taiwan	13.2	2380	64	2.7	17.1	10.2	59.7
Thailand	14.0	2185	35	1.6	15.2	6.9	45.3
Egypt	5.1	2930	19	0.6	12.6	2.6	20.6
Israel	6.6	2820	17	0.6	39.7	3.0	7.6
Turkey	2.2	3110	7	0.2	15.9	0.9	5.7
S. & SW. Africa	8.7	2820	55	2.0	31.5	5.9	18.7
Australia	5.5	3160	20	0.6	60.0	2.8	4.7
New Zealand	6.6	3460	21	0.6	75.3	3.3	4.4

TABLE II. Without Fish Many People Would Starve, UNLESS (1) Each country replaced that fish protein which now supports the equivalent of its total population stated in column 2. (2) This would necessitate increasing the arable farm land by the respective percentages given in column 3. (3) The extra milk needed to replace the fish protein is shown in column 4. (4) If meat were chosen to replace the fish protein, the extra needed is in column 5.

	Total population (millions) (1963–65)	This % pop. obtains animal protein from fish (theoretical figure)	% additional arable land needed to replace fish protein	Extra milk needed over present production %	Extra meat needed over present production %
Belgium & Lux.	9.6	14.4	75	42	74
France	46.6	11.3	13.5	20.5	38
Greece	8.4	19.9	17	159	100
Italy	50.0	13.7	19.5	43	96
Netherlands	11.7	16.2	165	63	130
Portugal	8.3	49	60	392	184
Spain	30.5	31.4	34	195	162
Switzerland	5.6	11.4	133.5	33	86
U.K.	53.0	18.0	65	97	130
W. Germany	56.6	17.6	73	58	94
E. Germany	17.0	17.8	22	47	59
Poland	31.2	7.5	8.5	12.5	21
Hungary	10.1	6.7	8.9	35	34
Yugoslavia	19.2	6.6	6.3	34	28
Denmark	4.6	28.3	24	11	37
Finland	4.5	14.3	23.5	17	84
Norway	3.6	29.4	84.5	63	174
Sweden	7.6	21.8	23.5	23	98.5

U.S.S.R.	230	15.7	13.5	28.5	57.5
Canada	18.4	7.9	4	18	25
U.S.A.	181.0	7.7	6	36	30
Mexico	36.1	8.0	12.5	60	50.5
Costa Rica	1.23	5.7	8.5	30	17.5
Cuba	7.6	18.8	51.0	50	54
Jamaica	1.8	44.8	120	558	283
Argentina	21.3	3.5	3	11	4.5
Brazil	79.9	8.8	7.5	25	16
Chile	7.8	23.6	23.5	119	96
Peru	10.3	31.4	72	241	157
Venezuela	8.7	24.7	86	106	82
Burma	24.2	23.8	17	680	1,200
Cambodia	6.2	32.1	31	538	301
Ceylon	10.7	60.2	42	412	668
China	765	28.5	19	823	42
India	462	10.8	4	36	146
Indonesia	104	50.7	19	7,620	144
Japan	97.5	74.4	214	798	986
S. Korea	27.6	43.0	59	450	106
Malaya	7.8	70.6	12	1,550	110
Pakistan	110.8	9.3	6.5	38	63
Philippines	28.3	50.0	72	6,640	287
Taiwan	11.7	88.5	113	11,080	126
Thailand	29.7	46.8	24.5	652	140

TABLE II. Without Fish Many People Would Starve (cont.)

Algeria	11.3	8.6	4	41	39
Egypt	28.4	20.7	18	224	74
Israel	2.3	17.4	74	103	235
Morocco	12.9	20.3	22	95	48.5
Sudan	12.8	1.3	2	4.5	2.5
Tunisia	4.5	9.2	3.5	36	23
Turkey	29.8	5.7	2.0	13	33
Ghana	7.0	26.6	30	956	196
Kenya	9.1	5.0	6	30	46
Nigeria	56.8	3.2	3.5	229	43
Senegal	3.4	28.0	13.5	199	495
S. & S.W. Africa	18.1	22.6	31	71	610
S. Rhodesia	4.1	18.5	29	239	59
Uganda	7.4	21.0	14	55	31.5
Australia	10.5	4.9	2	7	6
New Zealand	2.4	3.9	5	1.5	2

But the purpose of this study was merely to find ways of measuring in readily conceivable terms the significance of fisheries; for that purpose, and for safety, minimum figures were preferred. So this is entirely a theoretical computation to establish a point. For huge countries like the United States and U.S.S.R., which cover a wide range of climate, soil and varying agricultural efficiency, this computation has little meaning, but for most other countries the figures are definitely of importance in establishing a due appreciation of comparative values.

Falls Short

For instance, glib talk about agriculture in several European countries as "feeding" their population is frequently exaggerated. On this estimate, Norway would have to increase its arable acreage by 64 per cent and the United Kingdom by 38 per cent to produce a comparable amount of animal protein to that now provided by fish. Thus, fisheries are indispensable to their present standard of living. To a few countries fisheries constitute their only means of survival. To this group belong Japan, Taiwan, Thailand and, surprisingly enough, Israel, Egypt and Puerto Rico.

It should be underlined that these assertions are based exclusively on

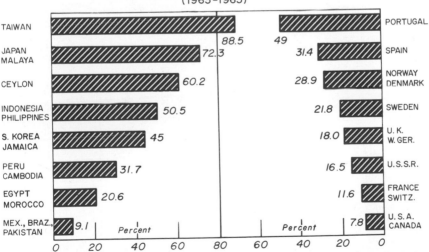

FISH POPULATION
(1963–1965)

This graph shows the percentage of the population of various countries which could be supported by the protein in the fish normally consumed. Note the high percentage of population supported by fish in the Asiatic and some South American countries compared with the lower population in European countries (with the exception of Portugal), North America, and Antipodean areas. Fish is fundamental in supporting at least 1,500 million people in the areas indicated whereas in what can be loosely described as the Western world it is of importance to only some 680 million people.

what is actually consumed by the respective populations. What is landed by their fishing fleet or exported enters into the statistics of the receiving and actually consuming countries. The figures show, too, that in countries like Peru and Chile fish have already acquired a very dominant position. To a degree these figures reflect population pressures and are useful for analysis in that field. A new population density concept emerges, which is now being analysed in a special book by the writer.

In some Central American countries and others which are compelled to import bacalao, salted and frozen fish to cover part of their needs, the situation is most precarious. Several of these countries—Israel,

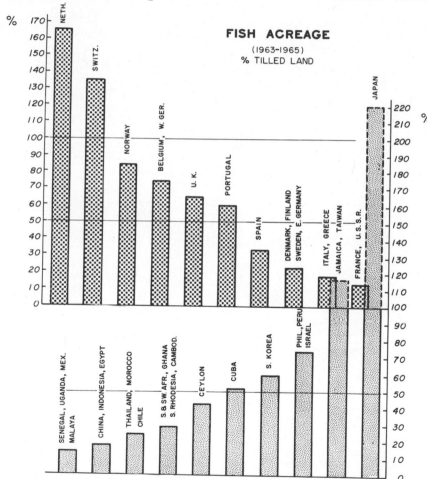

If the fish supply of the world suddenly disappeared and the populations had to rely upon agriculture for sustenance, the arable soil farmed in the various countries would need to be increased by the percentage as shown in order to replace that protein now derived from fish. In most countries the task is simply physically impossible because the land is just not there.

Jamaica, Haiti, Trinidad—undoubtedly would never be in a position to expand their agriculture to the extent needed to replace the animal protein given by fish.

Solid Comparisons Possible

It thus becomes possible to measure the degree of dependence of fisheries, not in diffuse percentage figures, but in concrete agricultural terms. Nutritional improvements accomplished through agriculture may

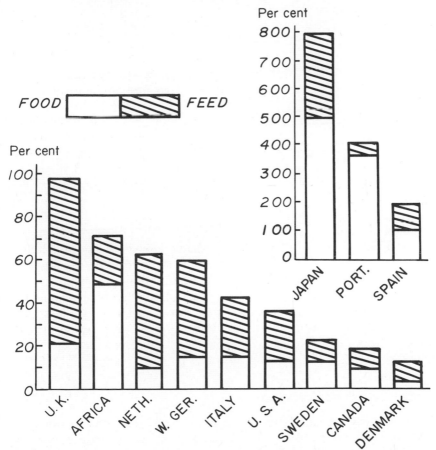

FISH BALANCE IN MILK

(INCREASE IN MILK CONSUMPTION REQUIRED TO COMPENSATE FOR FISH)

This graph shows the percentage increase in milk production that would be necessary to replace the protein hitherto provided by fish. The hatched portion of the columns represents that protein derived from fish meal fed to stock; the solid portion indicates the fish consumed directly as food.

be analysed and compared to what can be achieved through fisheries. It also appears possible to establish geographical areas which may be obliged to extend their reliance on fish resources.

Care should be taken to use these acreage figures in a correct way. Naturally, if the yield of each acre and each cow were appreciably raised above the present protein yields, these figures would be influenced. As they stand they merely reflect the current situation. But it is imperative to reiterate that the figures as they stand are minimum ones. Furthermore, in many countries an expanded livestock production would have to move into less optimal conditions and thus require more acreage than the present well-established dairy farming demands.

The extent to which the present dairy production in each country would have to be increased to compensate for the loss of fish is impressive. Naturally it can be maintained that these calculations reflect the poor development of particular dairy industries. Undoubtedly, they can be improved and will be improved by better techniques, but in very few cases can it be maintained that dairying ever could displace fish. Even in the United States, with its low fish consumption, profound changes would ensue if fish were cut out and a 21.6 per cent increase in the dairy production required. The repercussions on the surplus situation would be alarming.

It is not infrequently recommended that Japan should expand substantially her dairying industry and rely less on fish. This suggestion is beyond comprehension. It would imply depriving at least 30 million people of their daily food intake. The key to Japan feeding her expanding human population, at present 96 million, is to rely heavily on the sea for supplementary animal protein and leave the soil primarily for fat and carbohydrate production and secondly, to provide insufficient amounts of basic plant protein.

In addition to the column which shows how dairying production would have to be increased, another column shows the expansion necessary in meat, if protein were to be produced this way, in quantities equal to what now is obtained through fish. Even here a great number of new relationships reveal themselves. For instance, they show why U.S.S.R. attaches such great importance to the expansion of her fisheries—they undoubtedly will provide better results than her continued drive for cattle and hog raising!

Useful Yardstick Provided

The prime purpose of this study has been to discover and propound an effective and practical common-sense yardstick for evaluating fisheries in relation to agriculture. Close study of the tables will show that that has been done. In practical terms it is revealed that through their sea fisheries, each country now has the use of a considerable land-acreage.

For instance, Belgium is in effect "farming" 69 per cent extra "land" at sea; the United Kingdom 38 per cent, Germany 28 per cent, and Japan as much as 186 per cent. Without their fish supplies the protein thus provided would have to be secured from their land area (and where would they get that land?) or by imports.

Two points remain to be made. The first relates to the validity of my calculations. It is obvious that they cannot be accepted at face value; but, basically, they serve the purpose of indicating general magnitudes, and permit meaningful comparisons between countries.

The data has been collected from F.A.O. food balance sheets in all cases where available. In some instances figures for protein intake have been calculated on the basis of the consumptional studies (Food Balance in Foreign Countries) published by U.S.D.A. Foreign Agricultural Service. In a few rare cases the protein consumption has been computed by using catch figures to which have been added imported quantities or subtracted exported quantities. In a few cases catch figures as well as export and import figures are fragmentary. Some of these data, therefore, are reasonable estimates rather than accurate commercial statements. Frequently, figures are missing for several years or are only given occasionally, so it is envisaged that some of these figures may in future have to be adjusted in detail. Presumably, such adjustment will not greatly influence the overall picture.

Throughout this study the term fish has been used to include fresh-

U.S.
POULTRY PROTEIN BALANCE

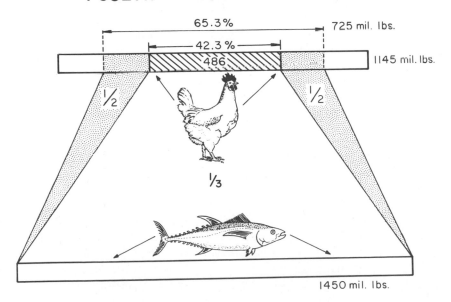

water supplies and some non-fish organisms commercially used; but in general the protein discussed is overwhelmingly true fish protein.

The second point covers the perspective opened up by my calculations in relation to the problem of feeding the world's expanding population. In latter years the annual net growth of the human population amounts approximately to 55 million people. To provide merely this yearly additional human load with animal protein from the seas on the United States standard, the present world catch would have to be almost doubled each second year. On the more modest Japanese standard, the total world catch would have to be doubled each tenth year, yet with nothing done to alleviate the grave shortages already prevailing in several crucial areas. Even more dramatic comparisons could be made and multiplied indefinitely, but they properly belong to another article. In this, my purpose has been to produce a simple method for assessing and evaluating the rôle of fisheries in world production.

The tables reveal that, big as the resources of the sea are, they are definitely minor when measured against the needs of the oversized human race. Our only recourse would appear to be an organized farming of the seas but this necessitates a tremendously expanded programme for oceanographic and fisheries research. Man's conquest in this field seems to the writer to be infinitely more urgent than probing into the universe. The billions of money now squandered in that space race would provide a much more solid and dependable basis for cultivating the oceans and settling some problems on earth.

Finally, I hope this paper reveals in a new way the tremendous degree to which mankind already is seabound in effect, to a far greater degree than generally is realized, even among fisheries experts not to speak of the lay public.

11. Changing Patterns of Pit Location on the New South Wales Coalfields

M. G. A. Wilson

In primary extractive industries, location and access are of paramount importance in reaching the decision to exploit a mineral deposit; frequently, more accessible but lower-grade deposits are exploited long before richer deposits in remote locations are utilized. Principles of location, as well as the background and economic significance of this kind of decision, are analyzed in this selection about an important Australian coal-mining region. There are few important proved coal deposits in the Southern Hemisphere; Australia, however, appears to have sufficient supplies not only for domestic needs, but for substantial exports as well. The locational factors considered in this Australian example are applicable to most coal deposits wherever they may be found.

The major studies of the location of economic activities have little to say about the extractive industries (other than agriculture) for, as Hoover noted, these constitute the simplest example of the location problem;

We need not enquire whether production will take place at the source of the material, or at the market or somewhere else, as we must for manufacturing. That question is settled for us. Extractive industries are by definition located at the source of their material; their location involves merely a choice among various possible sources . . . the lowest combination of cost-plus-freight determines from which source any consumption point will be served.

This point of view has been adopted, substantially unaltered, by other students of the location problem. Lösch, for example, commented that

the location of any particular coal mine, for instance, cannot be fully explained by the presence of coal. Only the whole relationship between production and demand that results in profits will make clear why coal is mined at just this spot and at no others. Which of the possible mines will actually be worked depends among other things on its technical productivity and the local prices of the factors of production on the one hand (cost curve) and transport relations to the market (demand curve) on the other.

and McCarty and Lindberg have succinctly summarized these views thus:

producers must select from among the known locations of mineral deposits those most suitable for selling their products in existing or anticipated markets.

These analyses of the location problem relating to the mining industries have obvious relevance at the broadest level, e.g., the coalfield. But although their conclusions are frequently couched in terms

SOURCE: *Annals* of the Association of American Geographers, LVIII (March, 1968), 78–90. Reprinted by permission. The author is professor of geography, Monash University, Australia.

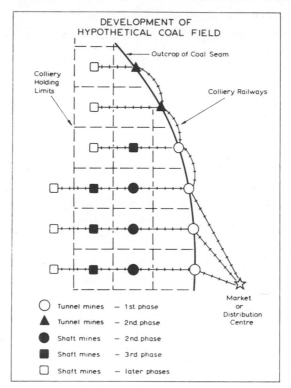

FIGURE 1: Development of hypothetical coalfield, showing the progressive movement away from the outcrop and the periodic substitution of working for transport costs.

of a single mine there has not, to the writer's knowledge, been any development of the principle as it applies to the location of individual pits in a coalfield. Yet it would seem that pit location, and more particularly the changing distribution of mines associated with the progressive development of a field over a period of time, might be considered from the same point of view, for production costs on any coalfield will tend to vary according, *inter alia*, to depth, distance from the outcrop, and seam characteristics, whereas freight charges will, to some extent at least, be affected by the length of on-field haulage; for example, from pit head or tunnel mouth to shipping point. It is not unreasonable, therefore, to expect that individual entrepreneurs might attempt to locate mine holdings on a field so as to minimize these combined charges, though the range of possible locations may be expected to vary from time to time under the impact of such factors as changing technology or the exhaustion of working areas.

On the basis of this expectation a simple multi-phasic model of coal-field development may be constructed (Fig. 1).

An Evolutionary Model

In an hypothetical coalfield containing one thick, continuous seam dipping gently from the outcrop, production costs will tend to increase with distance from the outcrop as tunnel mining gives way to shaft workings and short shafts are followed by deep ones. Initially, therefore, development on this coalfield should be by tunnels into the outcrop. Furthermore, assuming increasing transportation charges with increasing distance from some central shipping point, then these first mines should locate on those sections of the outcrop closest to or most accessible from this point.

In the course of time, increasing demand, the exhaustion of the early worked coal, and growing underground haulage distances would necessitate the opening of additional collieries. Initially at least, depending upon the extent of the coalfield, the amount of outcrop available for development, and the size of individual colliery holdings these, too, might open on the outcrop, though at ever increasing distances from the shipping point. Eventually, however, the rising costs of surface haulage (and in many instances the expense of installing these haulage facilities) would reach a level at which total costs might be reduced by working coal at greater depths but in closer proximity to the shipping facilities. Thus a second phase of development, shaft mining, would commence.[1] In the event of all outcrop areas having been taken up, this second tier of pits, working first those areas closest to the export point (or market) would again be taking up a least-cost location within the framework of resources remaining for exploitation.

Later stages in the development of the field would follow along similar lines, with additional tiers of pits operating at still greater depths and attempting to compensate, wholly or in part, for this depth by working first those sections of the field remaining for exploitation in closest proximity to the shipping point and probably also by operating at a large scale.

As it stands, this scheme has rather limited application. The physical preconditions, though common, are by no means universal; nor is a single shipping point or market usual. Modifications to either assumption would result in some change to the expected pattern of pit distribution. For example, several outcropping seams of similar quality would increase the opportunity for later collieries to operate on more distant outcrop areas, thereby reducing the need for shafts to deeper portions of the first-worked seam. Given a quality difference, however (and it is common for the lower seams of a series to have a higher quality), then it would seem probable that the pattern of exploitation might remain

---

[1] Under present technology inclined rather than vertical shafts would probably be employed, even to depths in excess of 1,500 feet.

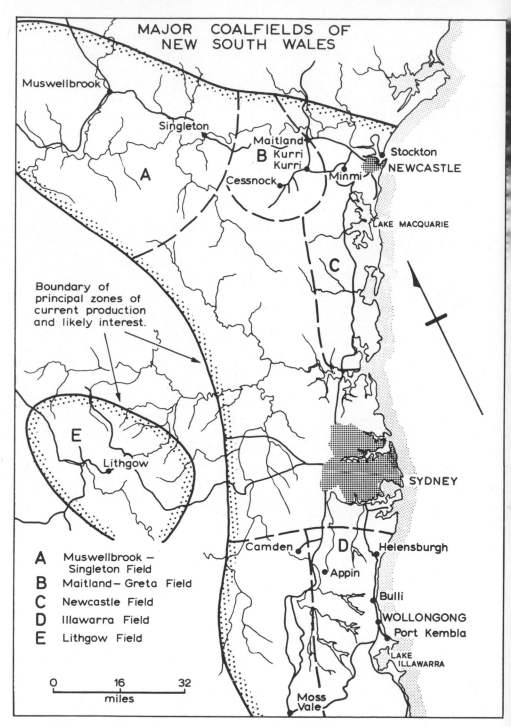

FIGURE 2: Location of the main working coalfields in New South Wales, Australia.

basically as suggested in the original model. The multiplication of market or distribution points or the introduction of new transport systems, by changing the costs of surface haulage might also modify the pattern of development. Nevertheless, the principle should continue to operate. Early mining, whether restricted by the prevailing technology or not, should tend to locate on outcrops at minimum distance (cost) from the consuming or distributing points; later pits would take up increasingly less favorable locations, *i.e.*, further away and/or at greater depths.

The operation of this principle can now be illustrated in three of the main coalfields of the State of New South Wales (Fig. 2).

The Newcastle Example

In terms of its physical make-up and market location the Newcastle coalfield does not depart greatly from the original model. The coal measures are disposed in a basin within which the lowest seam outcrops between Newcastle City and Minmi (some eight miles to the west) and the remaining seams, varying in number from about ten to four-

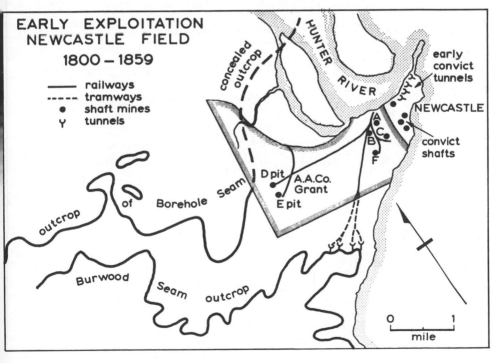

FIGURE 3: Early exploitation on the Newcastle Coalfield, 1800–1859. Mining commenced in the convict pits, then moved to the Agricultural Company grant. After the breakdown of the company's monopoly, areas still further afield were exploited.

teen according to locality, appear at the surface progressively further to the south and west (Figs. 3 and 4). Moreover, since the inception of mining a large part of the total production has been consumed in, or exported through, Newcastle. The opening up of the coalfield and its subsequent development have taken place in a number of more or less clearly defined stages.

Phase One: Early Exploitation

First workings on the Newcastle field were concentrated on outcrops in the headland and hills on the southern shore of the Hunter River estuary. Several tunnels were driven and linked to the simple loading jetty by a slab road to facilitate the manhandling of baskets and barrows. Between 1801 and 1817 additional entrances were driven in the outcrop in the same general area and even the first ventures into shaft mining (forced by drainage and ventilation problems in the tunnels) were similarly restricted to the slopes immediately above the outcrops (Fig. 3). In the absence of mechanization affecting either

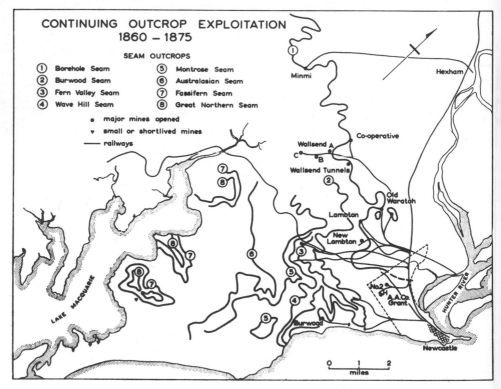

FIGURE 4: Continuing outcrop exploitation, 1860–1875. During this period most mines were opened on or close to the outcrop of the Borehole Seam (the lowest in the series). Some few other tunnels were opened on the outcrops of higher seams.

mining or transportation these pits could be said to have taken up something approaching a least-cost location, at least in terms of the then current knowledge of resources.

The grant in fee simple of 2,000 acres of the coalfield and a monopoly on the coal trade to the Australian Agricultural Company in 1829 restricted mining in the ensuing twenty years to the general area of the present inner suburbs of the City of Newcastle. Lacking any knowledge of the existence of other coal seams and unable to open up the original pits extensively or systematically after several years of haphazard convict working, the Company was forced to sink new shafts (Fig. 3). Each was situated at an increasing distance from the shipping staiths, and linked to them by inclined planes and horse tramways. But none was more than a mile from the staiths, and all operated under substantially similar physical conditions.

With the breakdown of the monopoly in 1848, grant holders in other parts of the Newcastle field were permitted to work coal. Because of the extent of the Company grant, however, new least-cost locations were invariably at much greater distances from the port, though still outcrop orientated. Thus while the Company continued to expand its workings by sinking larger pits still further afield within the confines of its holding, other areas on the fringe of the Company holding and in the Minmi area were also opened, the former gaining access to the port of Newcastle *via* a private mineral railway and a series of tramways, the other by a private railway to the Hunter River at Hexham.

Phase Two: Continuing Outcrop Exploitation, 1860–75

After 1860 the steady rise in domestic coal requirements and the growth of the overseas export trade resulted in the establishment of a number of large, highly capitalized pits [2] and the acquisition of mineral rights or freehold title to most of the remaining coalfield. But the actual spread of mining took place in a series of stages approximating the predicted pattern. In the first stage of this boom period mines continued to open up the outcrop of the Borehole seam between the western

[2] The rise of such pits has been explained substantially by Gollan in his discussion of the monopolistic combination of colliery proprietors in the Newcastle field; "The tendency to combine was further accentuated by the fact that the optimum units for the production of coal are large. On virgin fields where coal outcrops at the surface, men with little capital could begin operations, but once the coal had to be won from any depth, the sinking of shafts and the provision of surface and underground equipment involved heavy capital outlays. This places a limit on the number of companies likely to operate," R. Gollan, *The Coal Miners of New South Wales* (Melbourne: Melbourne University Press, 1963), p. 13. But this explanation overlooks the fact that many of the larger mines were essentially outcrop workings, and were, to all intents, opening a virgin field. Consequently it seems necessary to give greater emphasis to the cost of providing surface haulage facilities than to the shafts and other equipment.

margin of the Agricultural Company's grant and Minmi. The Waratah mine opened as a series of tunnels into an outlier of the seam in 1860; the Wallsend pit commenced production in 1861; the Co-operative mine at Plattsburgh, the first Lambton tunnel opened in 1862, and Brown's New Lambton tunnel began in 1867 (Fig. 4).

For the inner mines, such locations were clearly the most advantageous available. Those at the extremity of the field, however, had to balance the advantages of an outcrop location against the disadvantages of constructing as much as ten miles of private railway and, in the Wallsend case, of becoming common haulers, operating passenger and goods services and hauling coal from its own as well as from neighboring mines.

Phase Three: Shaft Mining

With hardly an exception these outcrop mines worked holdings ranging in size from 1,000 to 10,000 acres, extending back from the outcrop

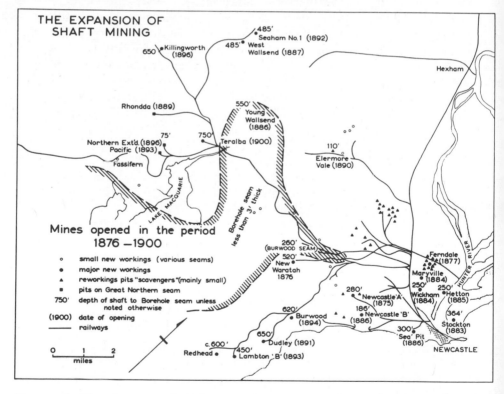

FIGURE 5: The expansion of shaft mining, 1920–1939. After the development of the outcrop areas on the Borehole Seam the main collieries opened were shafts to deeper areas of the same seam. Other, smaller mines were also established on the outcrops of the upper seams and in abandoned early workings.

for as much as two to three miles. Later development, therefore, was forced down dip by at least this distance to where the Borehole seam was several hundred feet beneath the surface and, over a considerable area, had thinned and deteriorated to unworkable levels (Fig. 5). After 1875, therefore, would-be entrepreneurs were faced with two major alternatives, to follow the seam to still greater depths by shaft mining in those areas where it remained workable, thereby establishing a second tier of mines, or to commence operations on one of the upper and generally inferior seams outcropping still further to the south. Initially, at least, the former seemed to be the more attractive, for the Newcastle "A" pit and the new Waratah mine were sunk in holdings on the eastern extremity of the field and therefore closest to the port [3] (Fig. 5).

In the following decade, however, further development of this type was eschewed, partly for reasons relating to the deterioration of the Borehole in those holdings immediately to the west, but partly, too, it would seem, because of the need to raise considerable amounts of capital to finance the purchase of extensive holdings, to undertake deep workings, and to construct even greater lengths of private railway. Instead, peripheral expansion was replaced by a return to the core area to work a hitherto concealed and inaccessible section of the Borehole seam under the Hunter River estuary and the ocean (Fig. 5). But although this move runs contrary to the hypothesized scheme of development it remains consistent with the underlying least-cost principle. To some extent working costs were increased by the need to operate under water and considerable thicknesses of waterlogged alluvium, in coal that was more than usually disturbed by the intrusion of doleritic dikes and by local seam undulations, and in leases that were necessarily attenuated (by the need to locate pit heads on dry land) and therefore relatively inefficient in terms of underground haulage. Cost advantages were gained, however, from the greater thickness of the seam (up to thirty feet) and from the virtual absence of surface haulage. The Stockton pit, for example, shipped its entire output from staiths adjoining the pit head, and none was more than half a mile from coal loading points.

With the development of this restricted outlier completed, a second period of peripheral expansion commenced (Fig. 5), at first on the Borehole seam, but later, and less significantly, on the steaming-quality Great Northern seam. Between 1884 and 1900 the second tier of shaft mines to the lower coking seams was completed with the sinking of the West Wallsend-Seaham-Killingworth-Teralba mines (operating at depths between 400 and 750 feet and at distances of from twelve

[3] It is significant that the Waratah pit, working at greater depths and incurring higher haulage costs than the Newcastle mine, was forced to cease operations for a period during the 1880's on the grounds that it was too expensive.

to seventeen miles from the port) and the southward development along the coast to Burwood, Dudley, and Redhead, under a similar cover, more conveniently located, but still dependent upon private railways for coal haulage. After 1889, however, the more accessible outcrop of the Great Northern seam was also worked in the Teralba-Fassifern district in the immediate vicinity of the main northern railway line. Thus, bearing in mind the effects of local seam deterioration, the pattern of development throughout this period does not seem to have departed greatly from that hypothesized. There seems to have been a more or less ordered expansion of mining first into properties closest to hand, later into those more distant or containing deeper coal.

Phase Four: Deep Shafts and Dispersed Tunnels

Since the turn of the century few major pits have opened on the Newcastle field though there have been innumerable small pits whose distribution pattern will be considered in a later section. After the virtual completion of the second line three possible locations remained:

1. at still greater depths on the important lower seams,
2. on outcrop areas of the upper seams, or
3. down dip on these same seams.

Steel industry requirements have, of necessity, been met by the further development of the coking coal seams at depths of more than 800 feet, *e.g.*, the John Darling colliery at Belmont (Fig. 6). Others, looking unsuccessfully for the Borehole seam west of Lake Macquarie or satisfied with household and general markets, were content to open up further areas of the Great Northern seam in the Fassifern district, but since the beginning of the 1950's the most important developments have occurred in association with the construction of base-load generating plants around the southern margins of Lake Macquarie. There surface haulage costs are negligible, for the mines adjoin the plants and scale, mechanization, substitution of inclined for vertical shafts, and a captive market are some compensation for deep working.

The spread of first-working mines on the Newcastle field seems, then, to have been more than a random affair. In stages one and two, the outcrops of the most accessible seams were acquired and opened almost in entirety. In the third phase deeper or more difficult sections of the main seam were opened by shaft mines operating initially at steadily increasing distance from the shipping point, but throughout at increasing depths. In the final phase the locational choice for developmental pits was limited to the most distant extremity of the main outcrop (not opened until the 1920's), areas containing this seam in workable form at even greater depths, or still further afield in holdings

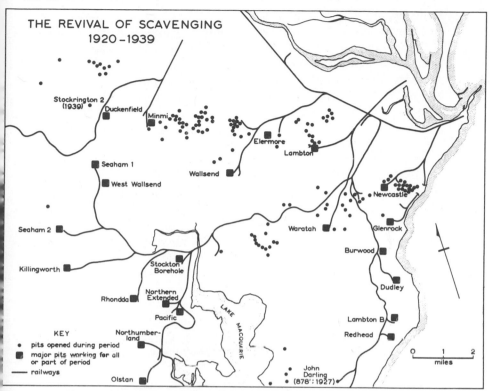

FIGURE 6: The revival of scavenging, 1920–1939. During this period of industrial and economic depression many scavenging pits were opened to mine coal left in abandoned workings, especially in the old Newcastle, Wallsend, and Co-operative mines.

containing either crop or dip sections of the upper seams. For a variety of reasons all have been utilized, but in each instance the basic principle seems to have had some relevance.

Scavenging: A Major Locational Departure

Hitherto, attention has been directed solely to the first working collieries. Analysis of the register of mine openings and closures [4] indicates, however, that these constitute only a small proportion of the actual openings on the field. Plotting and dating the other pits reveal a situation that has no place in a model so simply conceived and so little elaborated upon as that proposed earlier. Briefly stated, there is a clearly apparent order of succession among coal mines, each large pit spawning in its wake a host of smaller mines working, for the most part, in unextracted pillar coal, in remnants or corners of an old mine, and

[4] Maintained in an incomplete form by the New South Wales Department of Mines, and added to from a close scrutiny of all Annual Reports from that Department since 1876.

producing from a few hundred to a few thousand tons annually. Furthermore, there is a periodicity to their development that is related not only to the mortality of the parent pits, but also to the prevailing economic or industrial conditions.

The first important phase of reworking began in the Ferndale, Lambton, and Waratah areas during the 1880's, and continued on into the first decade of the twentieth century, reaching maximum development at times when a significant amount of un- or under-employment in the large pits encouraged miners to go into business on their own account, selling their few tons each week from a hand or horse-drawn cart to householders or small scale industrialists. When the larger pits resumed full-time work, however, these scavengers usually declined as rapidly as they arose.

The second period characterized by scavenging coincided with the extremely depressed years 1920–39, during which several hundred small mines, most of them reworkings, were opened in all parts of the field (Fig. 6). Most rose rapidly to peak production and just as rapidly closed, frequently within the year. The general relationship between reworking and periods of industrial stress explains the occurrence of this phenomenon but the widespread distribution at this time may be attributed to the contemporaneous closure of a number of the larger pits, particularly those with extensive holdings, e.g., the Wallsend, Cooperative and Newcastle collieries.

It seems clear that the location of reworking pits is little influenced by the relative costs of production and surface haulage. On the whole, these mines will be confined to the shallowest sections of the field, but with no particular market to supply and often no expenses to meet, almost any locality on or near the outcrop suffices.

The South Maitland Example

The South Maitland coalfield resembles the model situation even more closely than the previous example. Like the model it has, to all intents, only one seam; further, since most coal leaves the field along the one private railway line, East Greta Junction (where this line joins the State system) may be considered as a common distribution point.[5]

The outcrop of the Greta seam was first discovered near East Greta during the 1870's where it was worked in a desultory fashion for some time; but not until the completion of detailed exploratory work in the 1880's was the full significance of the field known (Fig. 7). Early developments were concentrated on the easternmost sections of the outcrop, but met with little early success owing to the thickness and steep dip of the seams (40–50°). After the success of the East Greta

[5] After East Greta Junction transport charges on coal proceeding to Newcastle from most of the South Maitland mines would be identical.

Company's mine and the return of prosperity to the coal industry around the turn of the century, however, development became more general. By 1906 all coal bearing land along the outcrop and at distances of several miles from it had been taken up. Actual colliery development, however, was less rapid but again it seems to have occurred in a series of discrete stages (Fig. 7).

The first workings were, as it has been pointed out, tunnels into the northeastern extremity of the outcrop. From 1900 to 1905, however, additional mines opened the crop as far as Abermain. Between 1905 and 1910 several shallow shaft mines and another tunnel were opened to form a second tier in the eastern and central parts of the field. Between 1912 and 1918 additional tunnels were opened, taking the crop workings practically to their western limit, but in the same period one more pit was added to the second tier and a third tier of deep mines was begun in the eastern area. After 1921 the field was further developed by the addition of the final outcrop mines, the last shallow and medium shafts and two more deep mines.

Throughout this comparatively brief period of development locational choice seems to have been strongly influenced by the changing relationship between "technical productivity and the local prices of the factors

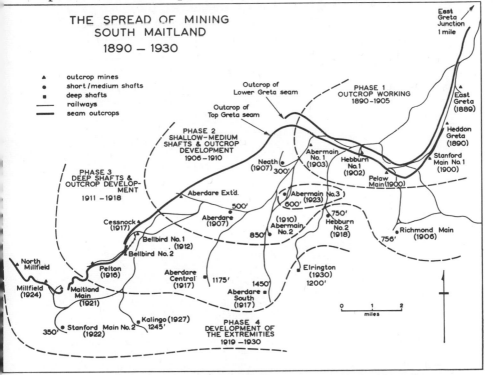

FIGURE 7: The spread of mining on the South Maitland Coalfield, 1890–1930.

of production on the one hand, and transport relations to the market on the other."

Although the early tunnels worked rather more steeply dipping seams than those further to the south, there is little reason to suppose that production costs were vastly dissimilar. And in the period 1907–1915, at least, because all were less than eight miles from East Greta Junction, rail freight rates were identical.[6] The landed cost of coal from each pit at the Junction, therefore, should not have differed greatly. Because the costs of mining tend to increase with depth and shaft mining tends to be more expensive than tunnel workings, production costs in, say, the Aberdare Extended mine should have been rather less than in the shaft mines established contemporaneously.[7] But each of the shafts was considerably closer to the Junction, and on the basis of rates obtaining in the previous decade haulage from the shafts would have been as much as four pence per ton lower (or approximately four percent of the current f.o.w. Newcastle selling price). To some extent, therefore, the more favorable winning costs of the tunnel mine should have been offset by the greater haulage charges, and once again (particularly if some allowance can be made for improving efficiency with the passage of time), it might be suggested that the change from tunnels to shafts in preference to continued outcrop development represented a least-cost solution to the location problem. In the remaining periods the same argument may be advanced to explain the simultaneous extension of the outcrop and the progressive development of two tiers of shafts, though there is little concrete evidence upon which to base such a thesis. What little there is, however, confirms the contention that the deepest pits were the most difficult and costly to work and provides a rough estimate of the freight savings possible by locating away from the outcrop.

The Illawarra Example

The Illawarra coalfield is far removed from the model in terms of developable surface extent. Its several seams outcrop in sequence in

---

[6] A statement of rates applying to coal hauled by the South Maitland Railway occurs in *Report of the Royal Commission on the Coal Industry* (Sydney: Government Printer, 1930), p. 275.

[7] Justification for this generalization is contained in a letter written to the author by the Superintendent of Collieries, J. & A. Brown, Abermain-Seaham Collieries Ltd., Hexham, May 21, 1964, from which the following passages have been extracted: "I have no doubt that the cost of coal at the pit head did in fact increase with distance from the outcrop . . . Unquestionably the best mining conditions occur in the outcrop mines . . . greater difficulties being encountered in control in the deep shafts due to the effects of crush and creep. It must also be borne in mind that the shaft mines were better able to take advantage of technological advances, and had less underground haulage, but the necessity for shaft winding was, in itself, a heavy cost imposition on the deeper mines."

the clifflike face of the Bulli escarpment and are therefore exposed only along a narrow strip. Beyond the scarp extensive areas are reserved for water catchment and in large part are inviolate for mining purposes. Under these circumstances there can be no second or third tier of mines, at least not in this part of the coalfield. In earlier times, too, the great depth of the coal beyond the scarp acted as a deterrent to shaft mining even in those areas not used for catchment purposes. Least-cost locations, therefore, would seem to be influenced more by distance from market or shipping points than by physical characteristics affecting production costs.

Early collieries on the Illawarra field operated spasmodically in the 1850's and 1860's supplying small quantities of coal to the restricted Wollongong market by bullock team and later the Sydney market by team-hauling down primitive bush tracks to the shore, loading into small boats, then transshipping to schooners. These difficulties were too great for profitable working, however, and the industry failed to flourish.

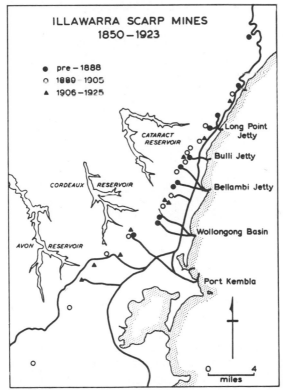

FIGURE 8: The development of mining on the Illawarra Coalfield, 1850–1923. The early collieries seem to have clustered directly inland from the few available shipping points. After the completion of the railway the gaps were infilled.

The first of several boom periods on the Illawarra field took place between 1877 and 1905. During this time all available sites on the outcrop of the uppermost seam and some holdings containing only the lower, high-ash seams were taken up and opened out. But once again this development seems to have taken place in stages that can be clearly associated with changing transportation conditions (Fig. 8).

Pre-Railway Collieries

Between 1877 and the completion of the Sydney-Wollongong line in 1888, eight mines opened on the scarp and another at Helensburgh, on the plateau to the north. Each outcrop mine was dependent upon an inclined way to the base of the escarpment and was linked by private rail or tramway to a shipping point, either the State-owned loading chutes at Wollongong Basin or one of the private jetties along the coast. The need to minimize initial costs as well as haulage charges seems to have had considerable influence upon the location of these pits, for in this period there was a pronounced clustering of collieries in areas directly inland from the few suitable shipping places, i.e., the jetties constructed in the lee of each projecting headland or submerged reef sufficiently large to offer some protection from the southwest swells and with sufficient depth of water to accommodate small colliers (Fig. 8). At Coalcliff the first tunnel opened almost directly onto the jetty; the North Illawarra Company's tunnels were situated immediately north and south of the line to Long Point jetty; and the South Bulli, Bellambi and Broker's Nose mines (operated by the one company) were almost directly inland from the Company's jetty at Bellambi Point. Even the earlier pits seem to have been similarly located, Bulli hauling to Bulli Point, and Osborne-Wallsend and Mt. Pleasant hauling to the Basin.

Post-Railway Location

The opening of the Illawarra line released the scarp mines from complete dependence upon water haulage. In the next few years other mines opened between the jetty-oriented clusters and by 1905 most of the more important collieries had been established, relying in the main, on direct rail haulage to Port Kembla for shipment. Since that time, too, haulage charges from all parts of the field have been virtually identical.

The post-World War II expansion of the Port Kembla iron and steel industry has been responsible for the most recent and probably the most significant modification to the pattern of pit location in the Illawarra field, the development of the Bulli seam in the Appin district (some twenty-five miles northwest of Pork Kembla) at a depth of from 1,500 to 1,800 feet. Lacking even direct access by rail, it can only be assumed that such a distant location with coal so deeply buried represents the least-cost location (consistent with the required quality) remaining after a century of exploitation in a fairly restricted coalfield.

Conclusion

The aim of this study has been to show that the spread of mining on the main coalfields of New South Wales has followed an orderly pattern consistent with the continuing search for a least-cost location. On the three coalfields examined it is clear that the changing pattern of first workings has in fact involved, on those fields with suitable physical conditions, the periodic substitution of production costs for transportation charges or *vice versa*, and in the other, development away from those areas offering maximum accessibility. The link between these effects and the postulated cause, *i.e.*, a deliberate attempt to minimize total delivered costs, is less clearly demonstrated, however, although there is some supporting evidence relating to both production and transport components on the South Maitland field. Nevertheless, it seems reasonable to claim that the strong similarity between the predicted and the observed patterns of first workings location on these fields may be explained in large part by the least-cost hypothesis. The location of second or later workings does not lend itself to such an explanation, however; rather, they have a rationale of their own relating to the life cycle of the primary pits.

12. The North Sea Gas Bonanza
Trevor M. Thomas

Western Europe has long been dependent on large oil imports from the Middle East and elsewhere and has had only limited supplies of natural gas. Recently, chiefly as a result of improved exploration and drilling techniques, the North Sea region has shown substantial proved oil and natural gas deposits. These new resources will have great economic importance for the densely populated and highly productive area of Northwestern Europe—one of the most concentrated industrial regions of the world. The details concerning exploration rights, continental and national limits, and the number of major corporations involved demonstrate the complexities of resource exploitation and utilization beneath international waters.

SOURCE: *Tijdschrift voor Economische en Sociale Geografie* (March–April, 1968), 57–70. The author is a research officer, Cardiff, Wales.

With an annual increase of nearly 10 percent in its rate of usage, natural gas is today the fastest-growing source of energy. It accounts for something like 18 percent of the world's energy supplies. Nuclear power is undoubtedly becoming more competitive, but for the next five years, at least, the bulk of the world's additional energy requirements is likely to be forthcoming from oil and natural gas. The wider usage of natural gas has been greatly facilitated by the adoption of practical methods for its transportation by sea, both in refrigerated form by ship and in its normal state through seabed pipelines. In the earlier days of hydrocarbon exploitation there was much wanton and shortsighted wastage of associated natural gas, as in the Turner valley oilfield, Alberta, and in some of the Midwest fields in the United States. The discovery within the last decade of large reservoirs of non-associated gas in Europe and North and West Africa has directed attention on the value of these as a source of energy or fuel, even through the initial explorations were directed at the finding of liquid hydrocarbons. An estimate made in 1964 placed the world's reserves of natural gas at about 22.30 billion cum. (22.30×10^{12}) within which total the United States had 7.82 billion cum., Canada 1.05 billion cum. and Western Europe 1.47 billion cum. Upward revision of these figures, particularly in respect of Western Europe, is now necessary.

It has been calculated that not less than 25 percent of the world's recoverable oil and natural gas is located in off-shore fields. Other than Antarctica, off-shore drilling is in progress in the continental shelf areas of every continent. More than 70 countries are actively engaged in some degree of off-shore exploration or development and already about 200 million tons of oil per year, or 16 percent of the non-Communist world's annual production, is being derived from off-shore sources. To a water depth of 300 m. the continental shelf areas of the world embrace 27,984,000 sq.km. Careful estimates suggest that 16,042,000 sq.km. (57.3 percent of the total) could possibly contain petroliferous reservoirs.[1] Much of these off-shore resources are likely to be found in the younger sediments of Tertiary of Mesozoic age which normally show a higher yield than the Palaeozoic sedimentary rocks.

The North Sea can now be bracketed with the Louisiana off-shore and the Persian Gulf as being the most active continental shelf exploration areas in the world. It was the discovery in 1959 of the Groningen gas field in the northeast Netherlands, the second largest in the world, which focused attention on the 500,000 sq.km. of the North Sea as a possible major petroliferous province. Interest was again stimulated by the fact that within the adjacent regions of England, northwest Germany and the Netherlands lesser resources of oil or gas were being

[1] L. G. Weekes, "World Offshore Petroleum Resources," *Bulletin of the American Association of Petroleum Geologists*, Vol. 56, No. 10 (1965), pp. 1680–1693.

exploited within beds of Millstone Grit, Coal Measure, Triassic, Middle Jurassic and Lower Cretaceous age, as well as within subdivisions of the Permian above the Rotliegendes sands, the host rocks of the Groningen gas. Western Europe also had the fastest-growing fuel market in the world; much of its indigenous coal industry was uneconomic; the production of cheap nuclear energy was still a good way off and increasing dependence on imported Middle East oil was accentuating growing balance-of-payments deficits.

Natural Gas Discoveries in the Netherlands

Since the initial discovery in 1959, when the first substantial quantities of gas were struck at a depth of about 2,750 m. in the Rotliegendes sands below the village of Slochteren in the Province of Groningen, an intensive exploratory programme has established the fact that this gas field covers at least 600 sq.km. The latest official estimates of the reserves within this field place them at about 1.64 billion cu.m (1.64×10^{12}). During 1965 no less than 17 gas discoveries, some of a substantial order, were made in other parts of the Netherlands. New gas reservoirs were found in the Rotliegendes sands, Lower Cretaceous sandstones and dolomites of Zechstein (Permian) age. The most significant find in rela-

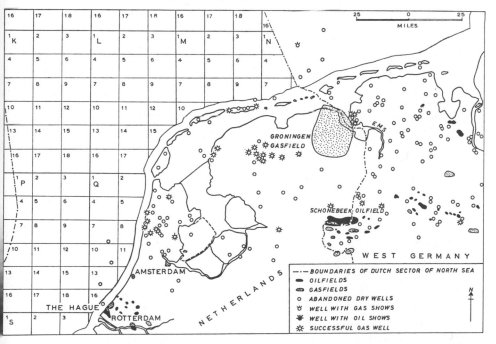

FIGURE 1: Natural gas discoveries in the Netherlands and adjoining areas to December, 1967.

tion to the North Sea operations was the striking of gas in the Rotliegendes sands below the eastern end of the Frisian island of Ameland
(Fig. 1). Changes in the regulations governing the issuance of drilling
permits after December 14, 1965, greatly restricted the scale of exploratory effort in 1966 and 1967. In 1967 a total of 30 wells were drilled
in the Groningen gasfield; twenty-nine of these were completed as gas
producers. In October 1967 the Netherlands government announced
that it was granting exploration permits, covering 6,200 sq.km. in the
southern section of the country and embracing portions of Zeeland,
North Brabant and Limburg Provinces, to three oil companies or groups.
The national production of natural gas was expected to reach 35.68
million cu.m. per day in 1968, and increase of 86 percent over the
1967 figure.

Recent Exploration for Oil and Gas in Britain

American, Canadian and British oil companies currently hold exploration licences covering part of the Central Valley of Scotland and much
of England other than the Lake District, East Anglia, Devon and Corn-
wall. Most companies have undertaken some preliminary geological
or seismic work within their zones of interest, but with few exceptions
the scale of drilling operations has been extremely limited and by
no means comparable with that completed on the main petroliferous
basins within the North American continent. Indeed, with the increasing
tempo of assessment or step-out drilling in the North Sea discovery
areas, quite a few companies are losing interest in their British land
holdings and so are thinking in terms of giving these up or farming
them out to other concerns. British Petroleum has in recent years
concentrated much of its exploratory effort in the immediate vicinity
of the established oilfields of the East Midlands. Several new productive
wells have thus been topped off, particularly within the Gainsborough
field. In the Tatsfield-Bletchingley area of Surrey, Esso Petroleum discovered commercial quantities of gas in the Jurassic in 1965. This small
gas field is considered to be capable of producing 0.28 million cum.
per day for 6 or 7 years.

In northeast Yorkshire relatively small quantities of gas have been
produced from the Upper and Lower Magnesian Limestone of Permian
age in the Esk Dale district. Since 1963 this area has been the scene
of intensive exploratory activity, directed mainly at finding large gas
reservoirs within Permian. Boreholes previously completed showed
that reading downward the Permian succession comprised the Upper
Evaporite Group, the Upper Magnesian Limestone, the Lower or Main
Evaporite Group (equivalent to the Middle Marl and Middle Magnesian limestone), the Lower Magnesian Limestone and the Basal

Sands. Isopach maps indicate that the Upper Evaporite Group increases in thickness from less than 38 m. in the west to nearly 150 m. near Esk Dale and south of Scarborough. When followed in an easterly direction the increase in thickness of the Main Evaporite Group is even more spectacular. With massive rock salt and some seams of magnesite this is in places more than 300 m. thick in the coastal belt from Esk Dale to North of Flamborough as compared with 45 m., or less, from the Vale of York westward. Showing fractured reef dolomites of variable porosity the Upper Magnesian Limestone ranges for the most part between 45 and 75 m. in thickness, but the Lower Magnesian Limestone thickens to more than 135 m. locally beneath the coastal strip between Whitby and Scarborough. The Basal Sands, the equivalent of the Rotliegendes sands of Groningen and in which the bulk of the North Sea gas has been found, are less than 8 m. thick over much of east Yorkshire. Precise borehole information is lacking, but they could well be more than 30 m. thick below Holderness and much of northeast Lincolnshire. East of a line from Esk Dale to Hull the top of the Upper Magnesian Limestone lies at depths exceeding 120 m.

About a year before the first gas strike was made in the North Sea the Canadian Company, Home Oil, obtained a 50 percent interest in a farm-out from British Petroleum of some 373,464 ha. of this highly prospective northeast Yorkshire area lying south of Teeside, north of York and west of Scarborough. In the summer of 1966, after four disappointments, the fifth in a series of seven exploratory holes, selected for the area, encountered five productive gas zones with a net pay thickness of 64 m. within a depth range of 1,667 to 1,780 m. in the Middle Magnesian Limestone at Lockton. This well was reported to have an absolute open flow potential of 14.44 million cu.m. of gas per day which made it the most promising in the whole North Sea province. However, the first three step-out wells, all located within three miles of the discovery well, failed to find commercial quantities of gas in the Middle Magnesian Limestone which comprised tight unyielding dolomites. Work is now proceeding on a separate structure near Ralph's Cross (Fig. 2): this complete change around in the sequence of events indicates all too clearly that within the Permian basin in the southern half of the North Sea exploitable resources cannot be adequately assessed, even where structural conditions appear favourable, until a fair coverage of exploration wells has been completed. Elsewhere in Britain it does appear that the practically virgin area, insofar as deep drilling probes are concerned, covering Holderness and much of Lincolnshire could well repay intensive programmes of exploration. A borehole near Leominster in Herefordshire has been 'spudded-in' in the Old Red Sandstone and is being directed at a pronounced seismic structure in the underlying Lower Palaeozoic; to say the least this is highly

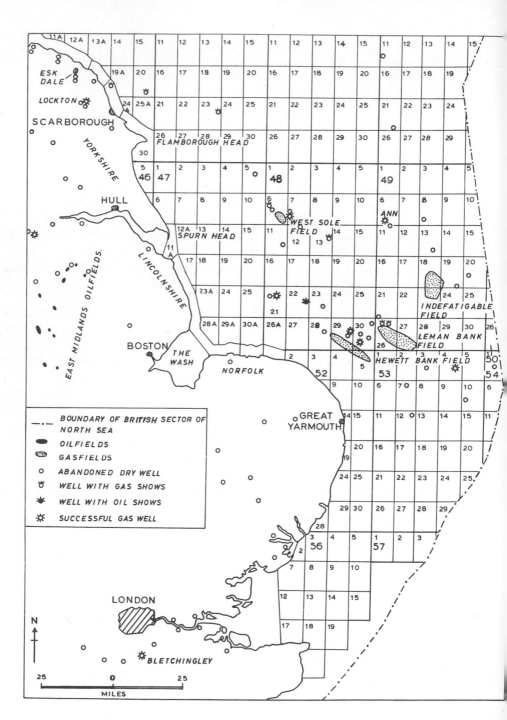

Figure 2: Gasfields and other discovery wells in the southern half of the British sector of the North Sea to December, 1967.

speculative since no commercial quantities of oil or natural gas have been previously recorded in Britain in rocks older than the upper part of the Carboniferous Limestone.

General Geological Features of the North Sea

The North Sea shows a complexity of structural form and abrupt lithological changes within the component rock groups as well as many sharp faulted contacts. Consequently geological mapping based on seismic and aeromagnetic surveys is by no means simple and is prone to considerable error because of wide variations in interpretation. Many inferences have been made by projecting the trends of coastal exposures, but an accurate map of the seabed will only be provided after an intensive boring programme has been completed. The solid rocks are for the greater part masked by a veneer of superficial deposits of varying degrees of coarseness and ranging up to several hundred metres in vertical thickness.

It would appear that the North Sea is not a simple downwarp, but comprises three main zones of thicker sedimentation, namely the North West German Zechstein basin, the English basin and the Norwegian basin, with intervening zones of uplift. The English, or British, basin contains Tertiary, Cretaceous, Jurassic, Triassic, Permian and Carboniferous sediments. Permian and Triassic beds are particularly well developed in a series totalling 1,500 to 2,400 m. in thickness.[2] There has been considerable flowage of Permian salt beds so that salt domes, rolls and pillows are evident to within 30 km. of the coastline of east Yorkshire. One borehole actually penetrated no less than 1,950 m. of salt. The Trias shows no salt domes but contains wedges of salt, up to 60 m. thick, at two main levels. The Rotliegendes sands, or Basal Sands of the Permian, are up to 210 m. thick in the eastern sections of the English basin, but thin to 30 m., or so, towards the Lincolnshire coast. They are liable to be interleaved with shales; one borehole recorded 180 m. of shale. Refraction studies reveal that the Chalk and Upper Magnesian Limestone (Permian) occur widely throughout the English basin, but efforts to map the extent and likely thickness of possible reservoir rocks, both in the Permian and the Trias, are rendered highly speculative on account of the diapiric salt intrusions which have brought about abrupt lateral changes in the thickness of the encompassing sediments. The seismic and aeromagnetic maps released suggest that a broad zone on the southwestern margins of the English basin and lying east of the English coastline between Flamborough Head and Norfolk contains several anticlinical structures with closures of 75 to

[2] P. E. Kent, "North Sea Exploration—a Case History," *Geographical Journal*, Vol. 133, Part 3 (1967), pp. 289–301.

300 m. Some of these have lateral extents of more than 269 sq.km.; others, although apparently showing steep flanks, cover no more than a few square miles and might well be bounded in part by faults trending generally parallel with the long axes of the upfolds. It is likely that many of these domed or periclinal structures were induced, or at least accentuated by salt movement within the main evaporite horizons of the Permian. In these upfolds there is always the danger that there is a lack of closure in depth or if this is present it may be displaced laterally and so does not lie directly below the apex of the upper convexity evident in the overlying sediments.

Even prior to 1965, there was fair knowledge of the structure of the seabed off the German and south Danish coasts within the Zechstein basin. Seismic information had been more readily interpretated and the outlying islands formed intermediate points of great value for interpolating the seaward extension of the known structures from the major embayment of the coastline.[3] A Permian evaporite salt dome province is known to extend westward for 320 km. Many of these salt domes or swells are of piercement type with average widths of 6 to 8 km. and a general north to south trend in the vicinity of the East Frisian Islands. Further north they are of less frequent occurrence, swing round in axial trend to southwest to northeast and sometimes reach 8 to 16 km. in width. In the vicinity of Helgoland salt movement was intensive; here salt swells and associated diapiric structures are separated by broad deep sedimentary troughs with thick Tertiary and Mesozoic sediments. Between the Zechstein, or northwest German basin, and the English basin there is a broad zone of gentle folding or flat-lying beds with a vertical thickness of at least 3,600 m.

Although much seismic work has been undertaken little information has been released concerning the Norwegian basin and the relatively deep waters lying east of the Aberdeenshire coast of Scotland. Thick Tertiary and Jurassic sediments with some trough faulting are thought to feature a large part of this area.

Legal Aspects and the Granting of Drilling Licences

The Convention on the Continental Shelf adopted at the United Nations Conference on the Law of the Sea at Geneva in 1958 was ratified on June 10, 1964, after agreement on its findings by the required 22 countries. It gives coastal nations the right to exploit minerals under their continental shelves which are defined as the seabed and subsoil of the superjacent waters to a depth of 200 m., or beyond that limit to where the depth of the superjacent waters permits the exploitation of

[3] T. M. Thomas, "The North Sea and Its Environs: Future Reservoirs of Fuel?" *Geographical Review*, Vol. 56, Part 1 (1966), pp. 12–39.

the natural resources. International boundaries are determined by agreement, or failing this, by the drawing of median lines and connecting limits projected seaward from the extremities of the coastlines of the countries concerned.[4]

The regulations formulated for the award of production licences in the British sector of the North Sea appeared so attractive that applications were made from representatives of practically all the major oil companies in the non-Communist world. Thus rather more than 78,000 sq. km. of concessions, divided or gridded for the greater part into blocks of 12 minutes of longitude and 10 minutes of latitude, were granted in September 1964. After agreement on the central median line of the North Sea had been reached with Norway and the Netherlands, licences covering a further 127 blocks were awarded on November 24, 1965. With this award of new licences a total of 106,600 sq.km. (including 1,300 sq.km. in the Irish Sea) of the British off-shore area is now under close investigation as a possible source of hydrocarbons. The minimum work obligations incorporated in the licences involved the expenditure of about £110,000,000 in seismic surveys and drilling during the first 6-year period of their validity. On a strict interpretation of the Continental Shelf Convention the relatively narrow trough of deep water embracing the Norway Deep, immediately off-shore from southern Norway, posed problems. However, agreement was reached with Britain whereby the existence of this trough was ignored. Oil companies were invited to submit applications for off-shore production licences during the period May 1-June 15, 1965, for the entire Norwegian shelf to 62° N with the exception of a strip abutting on the still unsettled median line with Denmark. Concessions covering nearly 40,000 sq.km. were granted in this first main issue on terms rather better than those in the British sector because it was felt that the prospects for major hydrocarbon discoveries were less promising and the physical difficulties for any eventual exploitation were certainly greater over much of the area.

In Denmark a 50-year concession covering the whole land area, territorial waters and the extra-territorial waters of the continental shelf was granted to one concern. The latter was later linked with two foreign companies to form a consortium.

In west German waters about 85 percent of the shelf area was until recently held by the International North Sea Consortium, in the first place an all-German group but later expanded to include British, Dutch, American and French companies. The remaining 3,640 sq.km. is under licence for exploitation by no less than 15 companies combined into groups holding various percentage interests.

After successive governments had failed to draw up licence-awarding

[4] H. W. Shawcross, baron, "The Law of the Continental Shelf," *World Land Use Survey Occasional Papers*, No. 5, Bude, England, 1965, pp. 35–42.

regulations tenable to the oil companies, new legislation introduced in August 1967 has brought in applications from 56 companies or consortia for concessions covering 100 of the 180 blocks or lots into which the Dutch section of the continental shelf has been divided. As in the British sector this subdivision has a longitudinal and latitudinal basis, but the individual blocks are considerably larger since there are 18 to the full degree quadrilateral as compared with 30. Many of these applications overlap for the obvious reason that the seemingly most favored zone with a good chance of eventual successful exploration extends west and northwest from the Provinces of Noord-Holland and Zuid-Holland towards the newly-discovered gasfields in the British sector. The results of these applications will be forthcoming in the first quarter of 1968 and drilling could be underway in the latter half of the year. The Dutch North Sea regulations differ in a number of ways from those imposed by the British Government. In the first place the preliminary applications are for exploration licences only. If a commercially promising oil or gas strike is made, the company concerned must re-apply for a production licence. In the event of this being for the production of oil the Government will require a 50 percent State participation and in the case of possible gas production up to a 40 percent stake. Oil companies have not been greatly enthused over these production licencing terms, but to counteract any dissatisfaction Dutch licences will be granted for rather longer periods and on slightly easier rental and royalty conditions than their British counterparts.

The small Belgian and French sectors of the North Sea straddle the so-called East Anglian-Brabant Uplift which is unlikely to contain hydrocarbon-bearing rocks. As far as is known no future drilling is envisaged.

Gas Finds in the British Sector of the North Sea

The first well in the British sector of the North Sea was 'spudded-in' on the Dogger Bank on December 26, 1964. Eight wells were completed in 1965 and by the end of September 1967 a total of 74, including 12 discovery, 14 appraisal and 5 production wells, had been drilled. The figure for completions was expected to pass the century mark early in 1968. The drilling programme is running 6 to 12 months behind schedule because of the world-wide shortage of sea-going rigs, the failure of British shipyards to complete their constructional programmes for new rigs by the promised delivery dates and an unusually heavy crop of accidents or mishaps. Despite the considerable experience gained in off-shore drilling in such areas as the Gulf of Mexico, with their seasonal hurricanes, the oil companies and other interests concerned were not fully prepared for the full severity of the adverse conditions in the North Sea with its fogs, gales, sudden squalls, vicious wave formations and strong bottom currents. The moving of the monster drilling rigs into the drilling locations was thus on occasion a hazardous operation. The tragic loss of British Petroleum's jack-up rig Sea Gem pin-pointed the grave risks involved. A study of the 23 major accidents associated with mobile rigs in the world's off-shore drilling areas reveals that in 14 cases, jack-up rigs were employed whilst more than 50 percent of the mishaps took place when the rigs were moving or preparing to move.

Although the drilling programme has been delayed the results achieved have been outstandingly spectacular and far above the expectations of most people. To date 4 substantial commercial gasfields and possibly 4 others of a lesser order have been proved. Under North Sea conditions it is generally considered that a commercial gasfield is one capable of yielding at least 1.40 million cu.m. of gas per day from no more than 4 or 5 production wells at a point within 160 km. of the coastline and for a period of 15 years. Assuming, at the extreme likely case, a net pay zone of 150 to 210 m. the minimum lateral extent of such a field would only be a square mile, or thereabouts. A yield of 1.40 million cu.m. per day represents about 4 percent of the current British gas consumption and is less than half the average daily quantity of gas imported in liquified form from Algeria to Canvey Island in Essex.

These new underseas gasfields all lie within a 110-km. zone trending southeastward across the quadrilateral bounded by the meridians 1°E and 2°48′E and the parallels 53°50′N and 52°50′N. The landward or western side of the gas-bearing zone, as it now appears, lies 65 km. east of the Holderness coast of east Yorkshire and 25 km. northeast of the Norfolk coast. North of Holderness, both in the sea areas within reasonable proximity to the coastline and in the remoter areas farther east in the vicinity of Dogger Bank, no commercial quantities of gas have yet been found. The drill tests so far undertaken suggest that no gasfields with the lateral extent of Groningen are likely to be present. The majority of the fields discovered are associated with rather steep-sided structures in which the reservoir rocks, whilst displaying a notable thickness, have a somewhat restricted areal spread. The Basal Sands of the Permian (equivalent to the Rotliegendes sands of the Netherlands), as expected, form the main host rocks for the gas reservoirs, but the potentialities of the area have been increased by the finding of large quantities of gas in the Magnesian Limestone groups of the Permian and in the Bunter sandstone of the Trias during the course of drilling operations in 1966.

The first commercial strike was made by British Petroleum in September 1965 at a point some 65 km. east-north-east of the mouth of the Humber (Block 48/6) (Fig. 2). Nearly 150 km. of net pay was encountered at depths of between 2,700 and 3,000 m. in the Basal Sands and lying below the flanks of a salt pillow 600–1,800 m. thick. Initial flow rate was 2.95 million cu.m. per day and the gas showed a 94.7

percent methane content. The company were so confident of a commercial find, even on the results of only one successful well, that surveys were quickly put in hand for the construction of a pipeline to the coastline north of the Humber. This 40-cm. pipeline, encased in concrete and placed at depths up to 3 m. below the seabed in a coarse boulder clay containing large erratic blocks, was completed in the first quarter of 1967. The restricted preliminary flow of gas to the shore terminal at Easington thereafter established a new world record for the time taken to bring a new off-shore field into production. The subsequent development work has not, however, been carried out without attendant physical difficulties. The Basal Sands were largely found to comprise rather tight silty sandstones much of which were in need of extensive fracturing before they would release the gas. Thus of the 9 wells drilled in the field to the beginning of August 1967, one was lost in the Sea Gem disaster, 2 have been abandoned and the flow from the others ranged from 0.1 to 1.2 million cu.m. per day. Five other groups of companies have drilled 6 wells in neighbouring blocks, but only the Amoseas Group found an extension of the field eastward into the adjoining 48/7 Block. Current development plans have been stepped up to include at least 13 production wells so that the pipeline, with a capacity of rather more than 5.7 million cu.m. per day, will be utilised to its practical limit. Total expenditure may therefore exceed £40,000,000. The available reserves should be in excess of 0.15 billion cu.m. The flow of gas ashore will average about 2.85 million cu.m. per day during the winter of 1967–68.

In the spring of 1966 Shell/Esso announced a major gas find 65 km. east-north-east of Cromer on the Leman Bank (Block 49/26). A net pay zone of 210 m. was struck in the Basal Sands of the Permian from a rig operating in 35 m. of water. Later appraisal drilling has shown that the structure covers more than 80 sq.km. and could give a yield as high as 56.6 million cu.m. per day from a possible reserve of more than 0.43 billion cu.m. The dip of the beds is, however, rather steep in places whilst the structure is cut off to the north by a northwest to southeast fault. There is some evidence for a limited degree of interleaving with shales, but for the most part the sands appear to be clean and well sorted with good porosity. Beginning in August 1967 the group has planned 10 development wells; perhaps as many as 20 will eventually be required. This gas-bearing structure has been proved to extend eastward into the adjoining block (49/27) where the Amoco/Gas Council group has proved gas in commercial quantities, with its share of the total reserve likely to exceed 0.15 billion cu.m. The laying of a 75-cm. pipeline, having a carrying capacity of 28.5 million cu.m. per day, was completed in a few months in the middle of 1967 along a seabed course of 54 km. to the 80-ha site of the new gas terminal under construction at Bacton on the North Norfolk coast. Eventually this plant is expected

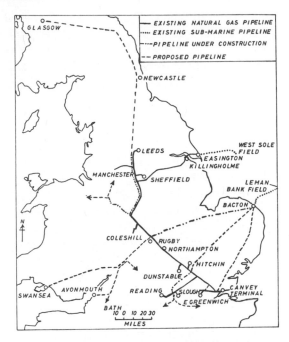

FIGURE 3. Generalized map of the Gas Council's Natural Gas Transmission System.

to handle up to 70.8 million cu.m. of gas per day. No 'unitisation' agreement has yet been reached between the Shell/Esso and Amoco/Gas Council groups on the apportionment of the reserves within this field. The treated gas will eventually be carried westward from Bacton along three 90-cm. Gas Council pipelines to join the main Canvey Island to Leeds pipeline (Fig. 3). Gas from this field should be available before the middle of 1968.

Following on quickly from this major Shell/Esso discovery the Phillips group released details of a successful completion on what might prove to be a commercial field of lesser significance. This is located 64 km. practically due east of the British Petroleum field; at this remoter position it is 130 km. from the Holderness coast of east Yorkshire and 100 km. from the nearest point on the North Norfolk coast (Block 49/6). On test the well flowed at a rate of 0.5 million cu.m. per day through two 0.95 cm. chokes. The pay zone extends through a 90 m. interval below a depth of 3,300 m. This small gasfield (now known as Ann) could possibly yield up to 2.8 million cu.m. per day. A step-out well a few miles to the southeast was, however, dry.

Again in the spring of 1966, a third major gasfield—the Indefatigable field—was located some 40 km. to the southeast of the Ann field by the Amoco/Gas Council group. The initial well, located in 33 m. of water, recorded 88 m. of gas-saturated porous Basal Sands, a flow rate of 0.7 million cu.m. of gas per day and reached a final depth of 2,567 m. A step-out well 8 km. to the south flowed at the rate of 0.68 million cu.m. per day and it would seem therefore that this field is capable of producing at least 14 million cu.m. per day and perhaps as much as 34 million cu.m.

After a succession of dry holes recorded by various companies, the successful quest of the Arpet group resulting in the finding of a fourth major commercial gasfield—the Hewett field—some 32 km. west of the Leman Bank (Fig. 2) has to date proved to be one of the most interesting events in the North Sea search for new sources of hydrocarbons. This gasfield is of real significance on three separate counts. First, it is situated within 27 km. of the nearest point on the Norfolk coast. Secondly, the gas-bearing levels lie at depths of less than 1,500 m. Thirdly, the gas occurs in three separate formations, the middle and more productive pay zone being in lower Bunter sandstone. On test the gas yields on restricted choke from the reservoir rocks at depths of 900, 1,260 and 1,440 m. were 0.14 million cu.m., 0.65 million cu.m. and 0.05 million cu.m. per day, respectively. The first step-out well 2 km. to the southeast recorded flows of 0.78 million cu.m. per day from the upper Bunter around 900 m. and 0.51 million cu.m. a day from the lower Bunter at about 1,260 m. In January 1967 this field was proved to extend more than 16 km. to the southeast in an anticlinal structure showing an average width of about 3 km. In the adjoining 52/5 block the Phillips group, in proving this extension, tested 1.60 million cu.m. per day from the upper Bunter at about 840 m., 0.60 million cu.m. from the lower Bunter at 1,260 m., 0.02 million cu.m. from the Upper Magnesian Limestone at 1,320 m. and 0.27 million cu.m. from the Lower Magnesian Limestone at 1,470 m. Preliminary estimates suggest that this field will be capable of supplying up to 14.16 million cu.m. of gas per day.

An announcement was made in July 1967 by the American-owned Signal Oil and Gas group that it had possibly found a further commercial gas field about 38 km. southeast of the Leman field in Block 53/4. On test the gas flowed at the highly impressive rate of 1.57 million cu.m. per day from two pay zones at relatively shallow depth, possibly in the Middle Magnesian Limestone. The first step-out well 4 km. to the east-south-east was, however, dry.

Another discovery was made in August 1967 by the Placid Oil Company in Block 48/21 at a point about 40 km. north-north-west of Cromer. A pay zone of 21 m. was encountered at a depth of 2,250 m. in the Basal Sands. This flowed on a production test at the rate of 0.59 million cu.m. per day through a 1.9 cm. choke. A special feature of this well was its tested yield of 50,000 tons per year of condensate, the first recorded from the Basal Sands. Nevertheless, an appraisal well sunk only 3 km. to the west was dry.

In September 1967 the Arpet group recorded a successful sinking less than 8 km. northeast of the Hewett Bank field. On initial testing this flowed at a rate of 1.46 million cu.m. per day on a 2.5 cm. choke.

Dry holes obviously provide valuable geological information for planning later drilling and so few details are released concerning their findings. Perhaps the most significant of these dry holes was the well drilled by the Continental/Conoco group in the block immediately west (49/17) of the Indefatigable gasfield and the test undertaken by the Burmah group in Block 42–23 some 45 km. east-north-east of Flamborough Head. The Continental well struck a 19-m. pay zone which yielded 0.10 million cu.m. of gas per day; tests at lower levels failed to indicate commercial quantities of gas and the site was abandoned as an uneconomic proposition. This failure to establish an exploitable field after initial promise gives an insight into the disappointments to be expected in North Sea exploration where porosity and lithology of the reservoir rocks are equally as crucial as suitable structure. After much expectation the Burmah test which penetrated a major structure to a depth of over 3,900 m. and well into the Carboniferous was a complete failure. This structure was one of the largest picked out by aeromagnetic surveys in the whole of the British sector of the North Sea. It is rumored that no Basal Sands of the Permian were found and this might suggest that these are entirely absent or are, at best, very thin in northern waters. Operating in 63 m. of water the new semi-submersible drilling rig utilised, despised its great bulk, was blown off location during one of the worst storms experienced in the North Sea. Instead of the normal 90 to 100 days the drilling operation took more than 200 days to complete and is thought to have cost something in the order of £2,-500,000. A long sequence of mishaps, the root cause of this excessive expenditure, perhaps to some degree gives a foretaste of the difficulties likely to be encountered if and when wholesale drilling activities are eventually undertaken in the deeper and more exposed waters lying east of the Scottish coast.

Indications of Oil Resources in the British Sector of the North Sea

The Arab-Israeli war in June 1967 and the subsequent closure of the Suez Canal have re-emphasized the desirability of discovering commercial quantities of oil in the North Sea. Hopes of this is still running high, but the findings to date have been somewhat disappointing. In October 1966 the Burmah group of companies announced that its well in Block 48/22, just over 32 km. north of Cromer, on test yielded flows of 0.20 million cu.m. of gas per day and 4,000 barrels of crude oil in 4 days of intermittent testing from fractured dolomite in the Middle Magnesian Limestone at depths around 2,025 m. Later reports from the well, however, indicated that it had passed through 60 to 90 m. of rather tight dolomites below the pay zone whilst the underlying Basal Sands contained no gas. The eastward extension of this same structure was drilled from the adjoining block a few months later; the dolomites of the Permian were found to be of low permeability and unyielding.

The Burmah group was the first to drill in the northern waters east of the Scottish coast. In July 1967 it revealed that its well in Block 29/23, about 290 km. east of Edinburgh, had encountered only minor traces of oil in a total depth of 3,600 m. It had no immediate intention of testing other blocks in this general vicinity. Shortly afterwards a dry well was completed in Moray Firth and a similar abandonment, in this case at a depth of 1,800 m., was recorded in September 1967 at a point 95 km. east-south-east of Aberdeen.

Drilling Results in Extra-British Waters

In May 1967 the German North Sea Consortium announced that after completing 11 wells without commercial success in more than 2 years of drilling, mainly in the southern half of the German sector of the North Sea lying north and northwest of the East Frisian Islands, future operations would be suspended. Most of these wells had been continued below the base of the Rotliegendes Sands into the underlying Carboniferous to depths ranging up to 4,724 m. Gas [5], with a nitrogen content of more than 50 percent was tested in these sands at three of the wells. The rocks sections recorded confirmed the speculation that the Zechstein evaporate basin covered an extensive section of the southeastern quadrant of the North Sea lying south of the Ringkobing-Fyn uplift which traverses southern Denmark. Nevertheless the conclusion was reached that methane-bearing reservoirs like those off the British coast and Dutch islands were absent.

In the Norwegian sector, the first drill test in 90 m. of water, at a location 160 km. southwest of Stavanger and 350 km. east-north-east of Aberdeen, is reputed to have struck basement rocks at about 540 km. However, reports on a second test within Norwegian waters at a point 180 km. west of Stavanger indicated in June 1967 that although the well was abandoned and the rig transferred to a site further south traces of oil had been found. By the end of 1967, five wells had been completed in Norwegian waters. The negative results achieved and the nature of the rock succession encountered suggested that previous seismic interpretations had only limited degrees of reliability. A programme of shallow stratigraphic testing might therefore be attempted before any further substantial sequence of deep drilling is undertaken.

[5] R. E. King, "Petroleum Exploration and Production in Europe in 1966." *Bulletin of the American Association of Petroleum Geologists,* Vol. 51, No. 8, pp. 1512–1563.

At the time of writing only one well had been sunk in Danish extra-territorial waters. Tests in Tertiary and Upper Cretaceous sediments at a westerly location near the unsettled boundary line with Dutch waters provided indications of oil and traces of gas.

In 1961–1962, four wells were drilled off the coast of Zuid-Holland. Abandoned at depths ranging up to 2,460 km., these were directed mainly at finding oil in Cretaceous rocks which, east of the Hague, contain several small productive fields. Because of the delays in formulating satisfactory legislation, as previously described, no further exploration has taken place to date.

Marketing Problems and Competition with Other Forms of Energy in Britain

There seems little doubt that sufficient natural gas has already been discovered to sustain a production potential of about 85 million cu.m. per day (roughly three times as much gas as the Gas Council is now supplying to its customers) for 20 to 30 years. This gas offers a vast new cheap supply of indigenous energy with important implications for increased productivity, easement of the pressing balance-of-payments problem and, more directly for the domestic purchaser, a possible reduction of the weekly fuel bill. An accelerated usage of large quantities of cheap natural gas does on the other hand raise the possibility of conflict with other interests; it might be considered as likely to bring about disruptive threats to the continued usage of traditional fuels, principally coal, which supplies nearly 60 percent of the present-day energy requirements. Town gas, produced from coal or imported oil and amounting in total to some 28 million cu.m. per day, currently accounts for about 6.5 percent of these needs. It has been confidently predicted that North Sea natural gas will be supplying as much as 20 percent of Britain's energy consumption within 15 years. Forward estimates made only a few years ago suggested that in 1970 about 10 percent of Britain's oil imports and some 6 percent of its coal production would be required for gas making. The practically certain eventual elimination of these needs will save some £60,000,000 per annum in the import bill with respect to crude oil requirements. On the vital question of exports one might well ask the question how big an element is the price of energy in manufacturing costs? In some industries this might be as high as 30 percent; in the iron and steel industry it certainly ranges up to 15 percent. Studies undertaken in the European Economic Community suggest that exporting industries have a higher fuel cost element than those catering mainly for the home market. A cheap energy policy with reductions of 10 to 20 percent in fuel costs could conceivably greatly increase the competitiveness and marketing prospects for a fair range of British manufactured goods.

The only contract yet finalised for the supply of North Sea gas is that between British Petroleum, as supplier, and the Gas Council for up to 2.8 million cu.m. per day at 5d. a therm over a period of 3 years. The Minister of Power acted as arbitrator in this deal, but it was stressed that this high price was intended to act as a stimulus to further exploration and was not to be taken as a precedent for future negotiations. Subsequent price consultations between the oil companies and the Gas Council have been protracted and up until December 1967 no definite agreement had been announced. Quick calculations suggest that in cases of major strikes like the Shell/Esso Leman field, which with a northwest to southeast length of at least 20 km., is a major gasfield on world standards, a marketing price of 1½d. to 2d. per therm would give an adequate return on capital invested. From the oil companies viewpoint gas at 1½d. per therm would seriously imperil part of their fuel oil market because this other main product is currently being sold to buyers such as the Central Electricity Generating Board at prices equivalent to 4½d. a therm. The oil companies are also not in favor of cost-plus or sliding-scale contracts since these would tend to result in a concentration of exploratory effort only in the most promising areas. A fixed price would allow the big fields to carry the costs of exploiting the smaller ones. A middle-of-the-road price in the order of 3d. to 3½d. a therm would ensure a continuation of the present rate of exploratory activity or indeed stimulate an acceleration of this. Smaller firms would also be encouraged to retain their interests. The Government has given some indication that it regards 2.8d. per therm as the top realistic 'beach-head' price for North Sea gas. The disruption of Arab oil supplies, consequent upon the Arab-Israeli war, might help to raise this ceiling price marginally, although the counter argument against this possibility might stress the greater incentive now given to the oil companies to search for oil in the Norwegian basin east of the Scottish coast. Devaluation is another factor which has complicated the all-important price issue. Apart from the West Sole gasfield American companies have varying stakes in all the North Sea discoveries. Having expended outlays exceeding $200 million they now argue, quite forcibly, that the eventual agreed price of the gas should be raised on a pro-rata basis so as to give them the same return on their capital investment, in terms of dollars, as they would have received if devaluation had not occurred. If a satisfactory financial gain is not forthcoming the threat to cut down on North Sea activities is not an idle one since there is a world-wide shortage of drilling rigs and promising underseas areas are being investigated elsewhere.

Until the full flood of North Sea gas starts flowing around 1969–1970, the Gas Council must obviously consider the possibility of spasms of excessive demand arising during periods of extreme cold. Nevertheless, the expenditure of large capital sums on such items as new oil gasification plants by the North Western Gas Board and the building of further surface storage tanks for liquified methane at Canvey Island must be open to questioning. The signing of a 15-year contract for the annual importation of 700,000 tons of liquified methane from the Hassi R'Mel field in Algeria to the terminal on Canvey Island took no account whatsoever of the potential of the North Sea as a major gas producer. Fortunately the stage was not reached whereby definite agreements had been concluded with other gas producers, such as the Netherlands and Nigeria, for additional imports.

The Gas Council stated in June 1967 that massive capital expenditure totalling about £1,450 million over the next 5 years would be needed to bring the North Sea gas to the consumer: £810 million would be required for bulk transmission and storage systems. During this period annual increases in the usage of gas were expected to range between 9 and 16 percent whilst big industrial users were thought likely to more than double their 1966 consumption rates by 1971. A metallurgical works at Rainham, Essex, producing high-grade alloys of tungsten, molybdenum, vanadium, titanium and niobium, in July 1967 became the first large industrial user of North Sea natural gas. Bulk supplies of natural gas delivered under conditions of a high load factor could eventually effect greater all-round efficiency in the chemical, ceramics, glass and cement industries. Cut-rate purchasing of large quantities of gas on the basis of a high load factor by heavy industry direct from the oil companies without the intervention of the Gas Council, desirable as it would obviously be, is not likely to be forthcoming. It has been estimated that if natural gas became available to the steel industry of the Sheffield area at 1d. a therm cheaper than the most economic alternative source of power, then the price of steel could come down by about 2 percent.

For much of the country, detailed plans for new natural gas pipelines have been held up pending more information on the likely size and potential yield of the North Sea fields. The 530-km. pipeline system installed between the Canvey Island terminal and Leeds for the transportation of imported Algerian gas has now been adapted as a key trunk line. A 60-cm. feeder link into this has been completed from the Easington shore terminal to a point immediately southwest of Sheffield. Figure 3 provides a generalized picture of the likely national network. It seems unlikely that the construction of the pipeline system and the necessary modifications to existing consumers installations will proceed as quickly as the natural gas becomes available. Although by August 1967 limited quantities of gas from British Petroleum's West Sole field were being supplied to 8 of the 12 Area Gas Boards in the country, some degree of doubt must be expressed on whether the extension of the pipeline network to the territories of the Wales, Scottish and South-West England Gas Boards will be fully accomplished before 1970 especially when regard is taken of enforced post-devaluation deflationary cuts in spending by the nationalised industries.

There is little doubt that this new indigenous source of energy, when fully on tap, will hasten the rundown of the coal-mining industry, particularly within the uneconomic coalfields of South Wales, Lancashire, Durham, Northumberland and Scotland which show recurring losses and where any major degree of increased mechanisation is difficult to achieve. Assuming a 3 percent annual growth rate in the economy, the Ministry of Power has forecast that by 1975 natural gas will be supplying 50 million tons of coal equivalent (approximately 113 million cu.m. per day) out of a total inland fuel consumption of 350 million tons of coal equivalent.[6] Some measure of reprieve is being given to the coal industry to 1970 in the hope that the closure of uneconomic pits and more general all-round efficiency will raise productivity levels. Nevertheless the Government is sticking to its plans to build 8,000 MW of nuclear-power, electricity-generating, capacity between 1970 and 1975 and it remains convinced, despite doubts expressed elsewhere, that nuclear-power costs will fall dramatically within the next few years to a level which will make it the cheapest source of electricity by the mid 1970's. Between 1975 and 1980 the output of nuclear power might therefore increase from 35 to 90 million tons of coal equivalent and this would then play a greater role than natural gas in effecting a possible decrease in the use of coal from 120 million tons in 1975 to 80 million tons in 1980. Estimates of energy sources in 1980 were not quoted in the Ministry of Power's report on Fuel Policy because of the obvious uncertainties involved in forecasting this far ahead. Subsequent to devaluation the report was withdrawn from circulation for possible review.

It has been frequently stated that the utilization of natural gas for the making of electricity is a wasteful process, the thermal efficiency being reduced to 40 percent, as compared with 60 to 80 percent if burnt directly. Taking note of the rate at which schemes for the conversion from the usage of 'town gas' to natural gas are taking place it appears unlikely that the Gas Board will be able to dispose of more than 42.88 million cu.m. of the latter per day by 1970 when perhaps something in the order of 105 to 113 million cu.m. per day will be available for sale. One obvious usage for this surplus is in power stations, possibly in place of fuel oil if political conditions and prices warrant this. A 1,000 MW power station would take about 7 million cu.m. of gas per day after simple conversion. In this context it is of interest to note that in the United States natural gas accounts for over a fifth of the electricity

[6] Fuel Policy, Ministry of Power, London, Her Majesty's Stationary Office, 1967, p. 36 (Subsequent to devaluation this report has been withdrawn).

produced. Cost analyses suggest that for each kilowatt produced there is a 7 percent reduction in the capital costs of a power station built specifically to burn natural gas. A preliminary study of possible seasonal use of gas at power stations has been carried out by the Gas Council and Central Electricity Generating Board.

Special steels for high duty pipe are not available in Britain, but at present must be purchased from the United States or European countries. To cope with this increased demand for steel pipes arising from the North Sea gas discoveries a new £3 million plant is being constructed on Tees-side. Some oil companies claim that insufficient regard is taken of the high costs and technical difficulties of pipe-laying, particularly in deeper water, and these factors should give added weight to their case for a reasonable agreement on the loaded price of gas. Apart from the risk of extreme adverse weather conditions during laying operations, a major physical hazard in many areas, is the rapidly changing morphological pattern of loose superficial sandy or gravelly material on the seabed. A shallow-water pipeline to carry up to 14 million cu.m. of gas a day might be laid for £71,250 a km., but in waters 75 m. deep this could well increase to beyond £137,500 a km. With the discovery of further gasfields there seems every likelihood that the separate oil companies will fully investigate the possibilities of joint pipelines to cut down on these extremely high costs.

Prospects

Although precise estimates of reserves and the exact delineation of the boundaries of the several commercial gasfields discovered to date will not be forthcoming until further drilling has been completed it does appear that more than 0.85 billion cu.m. of gas (0.85×10^{12}) has already been found in the southern half of the British sector of the North Sea. Some estimates based on available geological evidence are at a cautious level, but there are strong grounds for assuming that total reserves within the broad range of 2 to 3.5 billion cu.m. will eventually be proved. It has been clearly demonstrated by the excellent results achieved that the North Sea is a major hydrocarbon province. Even within the component British or English basin where drilling has been concentrated the density of these probes is very thin when comparisons are made with older established petroliferous provinces. Several companies have yet to drill their first well whilst more than 80 percent of the concession blocks remain untested. It may well be that the reserves of gas within the broad belt extending west and northwest from the Groningen gasfield across the Netherlands sector of the North Sea through the southern half of the British sector to northeast Yorkshire are as high as 7 billion cu.m. (7×10^{12}), and practically equal to the total reserves of the United States. In the present hotbed of drilling activity lying east of the English coast between Flamborough Head and northern Norfolk there are still several promising structures which have not yet been drilled. Again where the structural indications, as revealed by seismic surveys, appear less promising there are likely to be significant lithological or porosity variations, particularly within the Permian and the Bunter, providing facilities for gas or even oil entrapment. Faults with substantial throws are known to be present and these could provide additional trap elements. Stratigraphic traps or high porosity wedges are not readily determined by geophysical means and other than by chance or fortuitous discovery the pinpointing of these must await a later phase of drilling after all the available evidence from previous tests has been fully assessed and correlated.

Speculation has been rife concerning the possibility of oil discoveries, as distinct from natural gas, in segments of the northern basin lying east of the Aberdeenshire coast. Extensive concessions are held here, particularly by Shell/Esso.

No doubt much of this interest has been stimulated by the limited occurrence of Lower Carboniferous oil shales in the central portion of the Lothians basin in southeast Scotland. Similar sequences of folded Carboniferous rocks are likely to be present for some distance to the east, but great thicknesses of overlying Tertiary and Jurassic sediments are probably devoid of hydrocarbons.

From the British standpoint it is perhaps fortunate that failure by successive Dutch governments to draw up satisfactory legislation has held up the issue of exploratory and production licences for the Netherlands continental shelf. Postulations on extensions of known structural trends suggest that the central section of this will most certainly contain gasfields of the same order of magnitude as those in the southern half of the British sector and perhaps with a greater degree of concentration.

Great disappointment is felt in West Germany that the extensive prospecting with several deep wells completed has yielded nothing of economic significance in German waters. On present indications one also cannot hold any great degree of optimism for the prospects of discovery of commercial quantities of hydrocarbons in the Danish and Norwegian sectors of the North Sea.

Conclusion

The coastal fringe of Texas and Louisiana west of the Mississippi delta now contains the greatest complex of petrochemical plants in the world. The huge gasfields of this area supply both the energy and much of the raw material for this concentration of industry. With major new sources of natural gas now available from the adjacent seabed one might be expected to speculate whether a similar build-up of industry is about to transform the coastal fringes of Lincolnshire and Norfolk, in particular. Perhaps this Gulf of Mexico littoral is an exceptional case and does not offer a realistic comparison since the more recent discovery elsewhere of large quantities of natural gas has brought about nothing like so drastic a transformation. It seems more likely that gas terminals on the east coast of England will form the foci for long distance distribution rather than the nuclei of concentrated industrial development and any related major influx of new labour consequent upon the establishment of employment opportunities in the field of petrochemicals will be into the peripheries of existing townships rather than into more remote locations in the sparsely populated coastal strips.

The continued delay in arriving at a satisfactory agreement on the 'beach-head' price of the gas between the oil companies concerned and the Gas Council, the monopoly buyer, has caused some degree of frustration. With more than a 60 percent participation by foreign companies, mainly American, fears have been raised that much of the eventual profits will be taken out of the country and the benefits of a new indigenous cheap source of energy will accordingly be reduced. This and the future wholesale redundances now almost certain to be forthcoming in the coal-mining industry have created some public support for the eventual nationalisation of natural gas operations. Consternation amongst the oil companies is obviously apparent; they forcibly point out that the full credit for the value discoveries must rest on their own shoulders since no other system could have resulted in so many wildcat wells being drilled and so many finds being made as quickly. To accomplish this they were given every inducement by the Ministry of Power in 1964 who speedily produced such farsighted laws and operating regulations for the British sector of the North Sea; any amendments to these, the oil companies stress, would be a retrograde step and an impediment to progress.

A Labour Party study group's report released in August 1967 advocates a midway course to total nationalisation in the setting up of a National Hydrocarbons Corporation. Stressing the profound effect North Sea gas may have on Britain's balance of payments it suggests that the Corporation would:

(i) Purchase all the gas available at appropriate supply prices.

(ii) Select consumers on the basis of the effect that significantly lower energy costs would have on the balance of payments either through improved substitution (e.g., aluminium, petrochemicals, including fertilizers) or enhance export opportunities (e.g., iron and steel, cement, ceramics and glass).

(iii) Avoid its use in industries where it would immediately and indirectly replace even low-cost coal (e.g., thermal generating plants in the East Midlands).

(iv) Ensure its use in industries and other outlets where fuel oils and other petroleum products have been substituted for coal.

(v) Use it as the basis for new industrial/urban growth points within the framework of the Government's regional development policy.

III. SECONDARY ECONOMIC ACTIVITY

The manufacture of an infinite variety of products to meet man's various needs dominates economic activity in many parts of the world. The intensity of the spatial impact of these secondary economic activities, however, varies from place to place over the earth's surface. Such differences result from many factors: the availability of natural resources, the power supply, transportation facilities, the labor supply, the market, the capital available for investment, and the varying skill and ingenuity of different peoples and their cultures. The development of a higher degree of manufacturing ability and productivity is the goal of all emerging countries. Most nations, including those that are highly industrialized, are still highly dependent, however, upon trade to provide raw materials as well as manufactured products that they do not produce themselves. Thus, the character of secondary economic activity varies greatly over the earth.

Some nations—Japan, for example—have developed an advanced stage of economic development based primarily upon the skill of the people and the ability to trade for needed materials and to compete in international markets with their products. In all countries, there is a varying emphasis in the degree of economic activity in different parts of the political unit. Thus, the study of economic geography should contribute to understanding the significance of and reason for spatial variations of manufacturing at different levels—local, national, and international.

This section begins with articles illustrating the major bases of secondary activity. Power is an absolute necessity for the development of manufacturing. The Industrial Revolution accentuated the need for and the search for sources of power to operate the machinery of production. Industry relies primarily upon coal, petroleum, and hydroelectric power with nuclear energy a potential for the future. Commonly available wind, tidal, and solar power may also play a more important future role and certain countries, such as Iceland and New Zealand, have vast amounts of untapped geothermal energy and heat. Eyre illustrates well the significance of electric power in Japan.

Raw materials utilized in manufacturing must normally be transported by some means to the processing site, just as the finished product must be transported to the consumer. The role of transportation varies greatly as is aptly summarized by Berry. The availability, skill, and cost of a labor supply has an impact upon the type, location, and success of secondary activity. Although Prociuk considers the manpower problems in a portion of a communist state, labor is, of course, a key factor in the western and largely subsistence worlds as well.

The two articles which follow by Pred and Ullman consider a variety of factors important to the development of economic activity. Pred introduces concepts that help to understand the flow of manufactured material, and Ullman throws light on the reason for regional growth as he develops his case for the importance of the amenity factor.

Thompson's article then considers the role of theory in analyzing the evolving manufacturing activity in diverse areas of the world. The search for valid and useful generalizations, concepts and theories is occupying the attention of more and more researchers in economic geography. Hurley's treatise on automobile production illustrates certain principles and that of Lindberg on the Swedish paper industry still others. Quantification, model building, and more sophisticated techniques in general are providing more powerful tools of analysis as illustrated in the Lindberg research.

13. Japan's Electric-Power Supply
John D. Eyre

Japan has recently emerged as the third leading industrial nation in the world behind the United States and the U.S.S.R. The energy source for this remarkable postwar growth has been electric power. In this selection, Eyre indicates how the electric power industry is areally coordinated and organized by private enterprise and the government to the benefit of manufacturing growth in all parts of Japan. The example of Japan illustrates the significance of electric power to economic development in most industrial nations. The fact that thermal power is primary and hydro power is secondary is also generally true worldwide, with such notable exceptions as Norway. And, like other countries, Japan also has to import coal and petroleum to supply the

> *thermal power. Thus, many of the power problems faced by Japan are not unique, and similar regional organizations of the industry are found in other industrial countries.*

A prime ingredient in the remarkable economic growth and stability of Japan during the past decade has been the dramatic increase in the supply of electric power for residential, industrial, and commercial use.[1] Between 1952 and 1963 energy sales by electric utilities had an average annual increase of more than 12 percent. Both installed capacity and output of electric energy roughly tripled, the former to 29,142,-000 kw and the latter to 136,758 million kwh. Japan has moved to fifth rank in the world in installed capacity, behind the United States, the Soviet Union, the United Kingdom, and West Germany. In electric-energy output, however, it has passed West Germany and is challenging Great Britain. Behind this advance are striking changes and improvements in Japanese electric-power technology, territorial organization, and coordination of power production.

Increases in Electric-Power Consumption

In 1951, when Japanese electric utilities underwent a major reorganization, the power situation was deplorable. During the years of the Allied Occupation there had been only partial rehabilitation of war-damaged plants and virtually no new construction. Power was rationed, with punitive prices for overuse; and the frequent power failures were a hardship the Japanese people had learned to take in their stride. The fact that manufacturers could obtain only a fraction of their power needs retarded industrial revival. After 1951 the revitalized electric utilities pushed ahead with ambitious rebuilding and expansion programs. But in spite of their best efforts the demand for power remained well ahead of the supply as the Japanese economy moved into high gear. It was not until 1959 that the gap between demand and supply narrowed appreciably, and it was not until 1962 that a balance was achieved. Present expansion plans call for the supply to keep at least a short step ahead of the demand, and thus to encourage and facilitate further economic growth.

Consumption of electric power has increased in all sectors of the

Source: *The Geographical Review*, LV (October, 1965), 546–62. Reprinted with permission of the author and the publisher. The author is professor of geography at the University of North Carolina.
[1] Statistics used in this article are derived from the annual English-language report of the Overseas Electrical Industry Survey Institute, Inc., *Electric Power in Japan*, 1963 edition (Tokyo, 1963). The 1961 and 1962 editions were also helpful. The Japanese fiscal year extends from April 1 to March 31; hence the 1963 conditions discussed here are more specifically those of March 31, 1963.

economy. Leading the way is industry, whose production has risen at an average annual rate of at least 15 percent since 1951. With its large appetite for electric power, industry consumes 83 percent of the national output. The growing industrial demand stems in part from the greater number and larger size of factories and in part from a steady national shift from light to heavy manufacturing. Leading consumers of electric power are the iron and steel industry, pulp and paper, machinery, chemicals, nonferrous metals, and textiles. The Japanese National Railways has switched from coal-burning to electric and diesel locomotives, and the mileage of electrified tracks grows yearly.

A steady residential demand for electric power has been created by the postwar construction of new and better-wired houses and apartments to replace wartime losses and to house the additional population. Even more important is the widespread adoption of electrical appliances by the Japanese as their incomes, living standards, and electric supply have improved. The full range of electrical equipment familiar to Americans is now an accepted part of the average Japanese middle-class home. Prices for most items are low enough that even low-income groups can aspire to ownership. Electric fans, radios, irons, and kitchen gadgets are commonplace. A mid-1963 survey of degree of market saturation showed that TV sets have reached 65 percent of their potential sales, refrigerators 30 percent, washing machines 50 percent, rice cookers 50 percent, vacuum cleaners 20 percent, and foot and bed warmers 40 percent. All this indicates both the mass popularity of the appliances and the large market for them that still remains. Air conditioning is being installed in large hotels, office and government buildings, department stores, and automobiles. A bright future is predicted for home air-conditioning units and space heaters. Commercial establishments have better lighting than before, and many of them have invested in neon-sign advertising.

Hydroelectric versus Thermoelectric Power

Electric power in prewar Japan was derived from a large number of relatively small run-of-river hydroelectric plants. The few thermoelectric plants were small and inefficient and were designed to provide supplementary power during low-water periods. In 1952 the hydrothermal ratio was 63:37, but as more thermal capacity was added the relative importance of hydro began to slip. Of the record-breaking three million kw of new generating capacity added in 1962, four-fifths was thermal, and thermal capacity pushed ahead of hydro for the first time. Thermal capacity continues to expand about three times as fast as hydro, so that the 1952 hydro-thermal ratio will probably be reversed in the near future. In 1963 there were 15,005,000 kw of thermal and 14,137,000 kw of hydro generating capacity.

Present Japanese electric-power policy, as enunciated by the national government and put into practice by the private electric utilities, is "thermal primary and hydro secondary." This means that thermal power is now relied on for the base load and hydro power has been demoted to a peak-load role. A number of reasons underlie this historic shift. Perhaps the most obvious is the fact that after so many decades of river harnessing few good sites remain in the accessible lower and middle reaches of the major Japanese rivers. Remaining quality sites are chiefly in the more remote upper reaches, where there are few transportation facilities and an abundance of construction problems created by the rough topography. Large dams in the more interior sites call for special engineering design and long construction periods, and costs are high. In contrast, thermal plants can be built near the power market in a relatively short time, so that the power supply can match the swiftly rising demand. Equally attractive are the fairly low construction costs of the modern thermal plant and its high operating efficiency. Properly designed, it can be expanded with new units as demand warrants.

The average size of new Japanese thermal plants is growing larger; new plants commonly consist of two or more generators, which often have a capacity of more than 200,000 kw, grouped together in a single plant complex. In 1952 the average capacity of steam plants was 50,000 kw; in 1963 it was more than 200,000 kw. In 1960 the largest thermal plants were a 624,000-kw facility in Osaka, a 600,000-kw facility in Chiba, east of Tokyo, and a 596,000-kw facility in Nagoya. Large for their day, they have now been upstaged. The Nagoya plant, 816,000 kw in 1963, reached 1,256,000 kw when two additional units were completed in 1964. The new Yokosuka plant at the entrance of Tokyo Bay, with a 1963 capacity of 530,000 kw, will be expanded to 1,930,000 kw by late 1966. In March, 1963, ten thermal plants of more than 400,000 kw were in operation and eight were under construction. Of the remaining thermal plants, which numbered 613 in 1963, many are owned and operated by private companies to supply power strictly for their own needs.

The new thermal plants have ultramodern equipment and an operating efficiency double that of ten years ago. Improvement in engineering design has made possible larger boilers capable of handling severe steam pressure. Until several pears ago Japan had to import large boilers and other special plant furnishings from the United States because of the technological lag during and after the war. However, technical hookups with American electrical firms and domestic improvements in design and manufacturing now enable the Japanese to place a growing share of their contracts for heavy generating equipment at home.

Fuel accounts for almost two-thirds of the cost of Japanese thermal power. Until 1955 plants were fired with domestic coal, but thereafter fuel oil grew in importance as the electric utilities strove to reduce costs and increase efficiency. Fuel oil is cheaper than coal except in the areas near coalfields (northern Kyushu, western Hokkaido, and the Joban area northeast of the Kanto Plain). Between 1956 and 1960 the consumption of fuel oil by electric utilities increased sixteen times (to 4,960,000 kiloliters). The switch to fuel oil added to the mounting economic woes of the Japanese coal-mining industry, and political pressures were brought to bear on the government to compel the electric utilities to use coal as their main fuel. However, countering pleas by the utilities for rationalization of their plant operations prevailed, and in 1960 the government empowered them to build strictly oil-fired plants. The main thermal plants are on the coast, where they serve the principal markets and easily receive fuel (Fig. 1).[2] Fuel usually comes from one of the refineries that also dot the coast and is stored in tanks near the plant.

Fuel oil has not pushed coal entirely out of the picture. Coal is still used in all but the largest and newest thermal plants, and the use of coal of low caloric value is under experimentation. Specially designed plants are in operation at Nakoso (295,000 kw) in the Joban coalfield, at Ube (275,000 kw) in western Honshu, and at Wakamatsu (150,000 kw) in northern Kyushu. A new plant at Niigata, on the Sea of Japan, is the first to be fired in part with natural gas, obtained locally. This plant will be increased to a 750,000-kw capacity. The first atomic-power plant, which is financed jointly by the Japanese government and private utilities, is under construction at Tokai Village in Ibaraki Prefecture. It has a planned capacity of 166,000 kw and a 1965 completion date. The site for a second reactor has been selected in Tsuruga Peninsula of Fukui Prefecture, on the Sea of Japan coast. The Japanese government has set a goal of 1,000,000 kw of atomic-generated power by 1970.

In 1963 there were 1,578 hydro plants in operation. As in prewar years, the average plant is small, less than 10,000 kw, but five plants, all of postwar vintage, have a capacity of more than 200,000 kw: Tagokura (380,000 kw) and Oku-tadami (360,000 kw) in Fukushima Prefecture; Sakuma (350,000 kw) and Miboro (215,000 kw) in Gifu Prefecture; and Kurobegawa #4 (258,000 kw) in Toyama Prefecture (Fig. 1). Five equally large dams are under construction; when finished in 1968, they will include Azumi (642,000 kw), Japan's largest hydro facility, on the upper Shinano River in Nagano Prefecture.

---

[2] This map is compiled from data and maps received from the nine main Japanese private utilities and the Overseas Electrical Industry Survey Institute, Inc. Consult "Nihon denryoku-zu [Map of Japanese Electric Power]," 1:800,000, 3 sheets, Chiri Chosa-jo [Geographical Survey Institute], Tokyo, 1949, for locations of generating plants and transmission lines in the early postwar period.

Postwar hydro facilities have several features in common. Most are storage plants, in contrast with the earlier run-of-river plants. The power output from a dam-impounded reservoir is freer from seasonal fluctuations than that from a plant which relies on stream flow. Some large dams also stabilize river flow enough to benefit downstream hydro plants. Most of the plants are in the mountainous interior of central Honshu and were built at great expense. To reduce costs and speed construction, a variety of dams have been used: an arch for Kurobegawa #4, the fourth highest of its kind in the world; rock-fill for Miboro; straight gravity for Sakuma, Tagokura, and Oku-tadami; and hollow gravity for some smaller dams. An innovation used in several projects is pumped storage, in which off-peak power is used to run giant pumps that lift discharged water to the storage lake. The augmented supply is then used to produce power at peak periods. The largest of this type is Hatanagi #1 (137,000 kw) in Aichi Prefecture, but six dams now under construction will exceed it in capacity, led by the Azumi project mentioned above.

Transmission Improvements

The prewar voltage of trunk transmission lines was 110 kv and 154 kv. Since 1951, however, higher voltages have been needed to transmit the output of new large generating plants long distances, to facilitate inter-regional power exchanges, and to cope with the growing power demand in the manufacturing belt that extents from Tokyo Bay westward through the Inland Sea borderlands to northern Kyushu. Lines of 220 kv and 275 kv now make up about one-fourth of the total transmission lines. They encircle the Tokyo, Nagoya, and Osaka metropolitan areas and link the facilities of electric utilities in western and central Japan into a single power grid. Research is under way to make 400-kv lines feasible in the near future. Heavier lines have called for improved steel towers able to withstand typhoons and severe climatic extremes.

Except for high-voltage lines used to deliver power in wholesale lots on contract to factories and other large installations, the standard supply voltage is in two classes. The standard high voltage is 3,000-volt, though a fifteen-year program was begun in 1959 to increase this to 6,000-volt in order to reduce power losses and increase the carrying capacity of the lines. More than 40 percent of the program's goals have been completed already. With the standard low voltage, 100-volt or 200-volt, the emphasis is on maintaining a stable rate and improving service to the consumer.

As the result of historical development, Japan is divided into two frequency areas: western Japan, 60 cycles; and eastern Japan, 50 cycles (Fig. 1). The division presents an obstacle to the smooth interregional exchange of power, which has been overcome only in part by the installation of duofrequency power plants in the hydro installations of central Honshu near the dividing line. Power can be dispatched either westward or eastward, but with serious losses.

Among the most significant recent developments is the policy of "wide area coordination," first put into effect in 1958. This relates to the building of transmission lines that will stimulate power exchanges between electric utilities instead of leaving each to rely solely on its

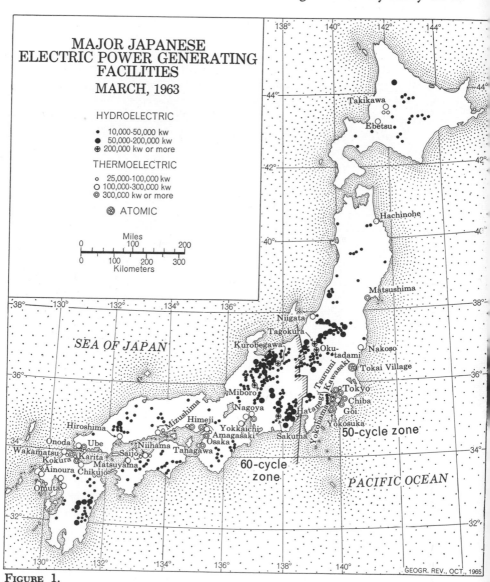

MAJOR JAPANESE
ELECTRIC POWER GENERATING
FACILITIES
MARCH, 1963

HYDROELECTRIC

• 10,000-50,000 kw
● 50,000-200,000 kw
⊕ 200,000 kw or more

THERMOELECTRIC

○ 25,000-100,000 kw
○ 100,000-300,000 kw
◎ 300,000 kw or more

⊛ ATOMIC

GEOGR. REV., OCT., 1965

FIGURE 1.

own power resources. It is creating, in a sense, a coordinated power grid for most of Japan. Shikoku and Kyushu have been joined to the western Honshu grid, and Hokkaido is left as the only major island not able to draw on electric power from outside sources. The benefits of the linkage were obvious in the bad drought years of 1960 and 1962. The 1962 drought was the worst since 1947, yet the supply of electric power remained relatively constant through the interregional power-

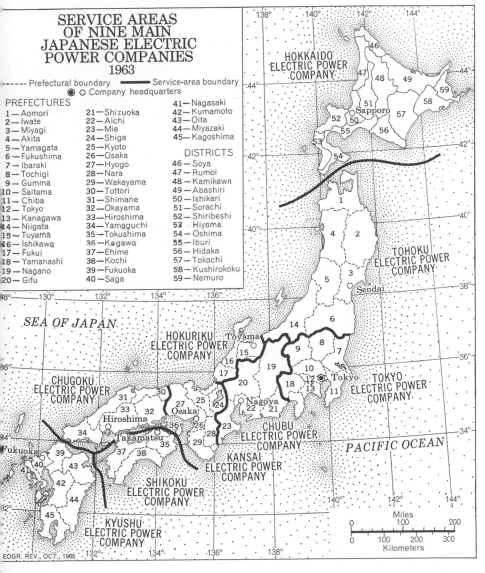

SERVICE AREAS
OF NINE MAIN
JAPANESE ELECTRIC
POWER COMPANIES
1963

----- Prefectural boundary ▬▬ Service-area boundary
◉ ○ Company headquarters

PREFECTURES

1—Aomori	21—Shizuoka	41—Nagasaki
2—Iwate	22—Aichi	42—Kumamoto
3—Miyagi	23—Mie	43—Oita
4—Akita	24—Shiga	44—Miyazaki
5—Yamagata	25—Kyoto	45—Kagoshima
6—Fukushima	26—Osaka	
7—Ibaraki	27—Hyogo	DISTRICTS
8—Tochigi	28—Nara	46—Soya
9—Gumma	29—Wakayama	47—Rumoi
10—Saitama	30—Tottori	48—Kamikawa
11—Chiba	31—Shimane	49—Abashiri
12—Tokyo	32—Okayama	50—Ishikari
13—Kanagawa	33—Hiroshima	51—Sorachi
14—Niigata	34—Yamaguchi	52—Shiribeshi
15—Toyama	35—Tokushima	53—Hiyama
16—Ishikawa	36—Kagawa	54—Oshima
17—Fukui	37—Ehime	55—Iburi
18—Yamanashi	38—Kochi	56—Hidaka
19—Nagano	39—Fukuoka	57—Tokachi
20—Gifu	40—Saga	58—Kushirokoku
		59—Nemuro

HOKKAIDO ELECTRIC POWER COMPANY

Sapporo

TOHOKU ELECTRIC POWER COMPANY

Sendai

SEA OF JAPAN

HOKURIKU ELECTRIC POWER COMPANY
Toyama

CHUGOKU ELECTRIC POWER COMPANY

Hiroshima

Osaka

Nagoya

Tokyo

TOKYO ELECTRIC POWER COMPANY

CHUBU ELECTRIC POWER COMPANY

PACIFIC OCEAN

KANSAI ELECTRIC POWER COMPANY

Takamatsu

Fukuoka

SHIKOKU ELECTRIC POWER COMPANY

KYUSHU ELECTRIC POWER COMPANY

Miles
0   100   200
0 100 200 300
Kilometers

GEOGR. REV., OCT., 1965

FIGURE 2.

sharing plan and the availability of large amounts of thermoelectric power that were unaffected by adverse weather and could be fed into the interregional grid.

Territorial Organization[3]

After the pioneer company began commercial operations in Tokyo in 1887, a large number of other electric companies were organized. Through their efforts, electric technology and equipment were imported from abroad, and a native electrical-equipment industry was established. Rivers were harnessed, power lines spread across the countryside into most villages, towns, and cities, and Japan became one of the most highly electrified countries in the world. In the 1930's government control over the electric utilities tightened in keeping with the military effort on the Asian mainland. In 1939 all privately owned generating and transmission facilities were taken over by the government, and in 1942 their distribution systems were also organized under state control.

In 1951 the electric-power industry was decentralized and returned to stockholder control, after lengthy deliberation by the Allied Occupation officials and industry leaders. Nine main private companies were created, each with its own exclusive service area: Hokkaido, Tohoku, Tokyo, Chubu, Hokuriku, Kansai, Chugoku, Shikoku, and Kyushu (Fig. 2). In general, company generating and transmission facilities are within the service area. However, some companies with great power needs, such as Kansai and Tokyo, reach beyond their own areas into neighboring company areas for power.

The nine companies had 73.2 percent, or 21,338,000 kw, of Japan's electric-power capacity in 1963 (Table I). They have built all the large postwar thermal plants, have accumulated the huge sums needed for expansion, and remain the only primary suppliers of electricity to consumers. At the same time, they are closely regulated by the national government in such matters as rates, new construction, and financing and accounting. The industry is under the immediate supervision of the Public Utilities Bureau of the Ministry of International Trade and Industry, and river control and the use of agricultural and forested lands bring the industry into working relations with at least several other ministries.

Of the remaining electric-power capacity, 6.5 percent is held by about forty small wholesale utilities, some of which handle power from dams and power stations financed by the prefectures, and 12.5 percent by

[3] This section is based almost entirely on materials received by correspondence with the nine main private utilities. These include the 1963 annual reports and system maps of the companies and miscellaneous pamphlets on historical and technical phases of company operations.

TABLE 1. Electric-Power Production in Japan, 1963

Electric Utility	Service Area Customers (sq km)	(1000)	CAPACITY (Mw) Hydro	Thermal	Total	Annual Sales (1,000,000 kwh)
Main electric-power companies	368,937	23,392	9,827	11,511	21,338	106,145
Hokkaido	78,486	966	393	546	939	4,268
Tohoku	79,466	2,744	1,519	682	2,201	12,002
Tokyo	39,225	6,541	1,840	3,602	5,442	28,749
Chubu	39,131	2,982	1,404	1,612	3,016	15,114
Hokuriku	12,276	730	1,036	None	1,036	6,010
Kansai	27,873	3,949	1,868	2,387	4,255	21,122
Chugoku	32,056	1,753	630	858	1,488	6,220
Shikoku	18,380	999	337	248	585	3,235
Kyushu	42,044	2,728	800	1,576	2,376	9,425
Electric Power Development Company			2,136	150	2,286	
Other private electric utilities			1,221	659	1,880	
Industry-owned			953	2,685	3,638	
GRAND TOTAL			14,137	15,005	29,142	

SOURCE: *Electric Power in Japan, 1963* [see text footnote 1 above], 8–9.

private industries for their own use, usually on a small scale. The remaining 7.8 percent is operated by the Electric Power Development Company (E.P.D.C.), which was created in 1952 with most of its stock owned by the Japanese government. Its chief task is the development of power resources beyond the financial powers of the nine private utlities. It is concerned mainly with the construction of large dams and power plants and has its own high-voltage transmission lines to carry power to major markets and to link company areas in the power grid. The E.P.D.C. sells all its power directly to the nine electric utilities for eventual distribution to customers.

Power generation by the nine electric utilities is highly uneven in amount, kind, and geographical distribution. This fact is made abundantly clear in the following brief evaluation of each company and its facilities.

HOKKAIDO ELECTRIC POWER COMPANY (Headquarters: Sapporo) / The main Hokkaido markets for electricity lie in a north–south belt around Asahigawa-Sapporo-Muroran. In the northern part of this belt is the Ishikari coalfield, the largest in Japan, and to the east are the central mountains, from which the principal river systems of the island radiate.

It is no surprise, therefore, that Hokkaido E.P.C. stress both thermal (58 percent) and hydro (42 percent) generation.

Most of the company's hydro facilities, including the largest, 51,000 kw, are along the Ishikari River system, on the western and northern flanks of the central mountains. Small plants are scattered around the fringes of the island wherever water resources and markets occur together. In recent years the company has tackled the relatively undeveloped water resources of the western Hidaka Mountains, where three large dam projects are under way. East of the mountains the E.P.D.C. is active in dam and power-plant construction along the upper reaches of the Tokachi River system. The largest of its plants, 140,000 kw, is also the largest in Hokkaido. Power generated moves eastward to Kushiro and westward to Sapporo-Muroran by E.P.D.C. transmission lines.

Virtually all thermal capacity dates from 1952 and, except for a small plant in the northern tip of the island, is concentrated in three localities. The largest plant, 225,000 kw, is at Takikawa, north of Sunagawa. In Sunagawa there are two plants, 54,000 kw and 70,000 kw, and Ebetsu, outside Sapporo, has a 195,000-kw plant. All burn locally mined coal. A 250,000-kw expansion now under way at Ebetsu will make this the key plant in the system.

TOHOKU ELECTRIC POWER COMPANY (Headquarters: Sendai) / Until 1958 Tohoku E.P.C. relied almost entirely on hydroelectric power, and in spite of recent rapid growth thermal output still lags in a 69:31 ratio. Southern Tohoku has some of Japan's best undeveloped water resources, which make it a key area in the operations both of private utilities and of the E.P.D.C. Before the war Tokyo electric-power interests invested large sums in power plants in Fukushima and Niigata Prefectures. These facilities now lie within the Tohoku E.P.C. service area but are still owned by Tokyo E.P.C. and continue to pour power southward to the Tokyo metropolitan area. Also, the largest postwar dam projects along the Tadami River system of Fukushima and Niigata Prefectures were built by the E.P.D.C., and power from them is consigned to the Tokyo area. The net result is that large blocks of power generated within the service area of Tohoku E.P.C. neither are controlled by the company nor can be used to stimulate local industrialization.

The hydro facilities of Tohoku E.P.C. are in two groups, one in northeastern Akita Prefecture (the largest 31,000 kw), the other in the south along the Tadami River and its downstream continuation, the Agano (the largest 78,000 kw). The company's main transmission lines lead east-west through the Tadami River area, supplying the industrial cities of Niigata Prefecture, and northward to Sendai, the main regional market, and the iron-steel centers of Kamaishi and Hachinohe.

The largest facilities along the Tadami River system, Tagokura and

Okutadami, are operated by the E.P.D.C. Tokyo E.P.C.'s hydro plants (the largest 53,500 kw) lie along the several short rivers that flow into or out of Lake Inawashiro. There are two other important noncompany operations. The Japanese National Railways has three power facilities along the Shinano River in southern Niigata Prefecture and transmits power along its own lines to its operations in the Tokyo area. Farther north, in Iwate and Miyagi Prefectures, the E.P.D.C. and Iwate Prefecture have erected dams and power plants along the Kitakami River system as part of a TVA-like regional development plan.

The thermal power situation is much simpler and is focused on the large modern plant (525,000 kw) at Matsushima, east of Sendai. Hachinohe has a plant (150,000 kw) for local needs, with a large expansion under way. The Niigata plant, fired in part with natural gas, has a capacity of 150,000 kw but will be expanded gradually to five times its present size. The Nakoso plant, which uses low-grade Joban coal, is under the management of a small private electric utility.

TOKYO ELECTRIC POWER COMPANY (Headquarters: Tokyo) / Tokyo E.P.C. is the largest of the companies and claims to be the largest privately owned power company in the world.[4] In 1963 its power sales were 27 percent of all the electricity consumed in Japan and filled the power needs of about twenty-six million people, including those in the Tokyo metropolitan area.

To meet the extraordinary demands of its service area, the company has relied primarily on large thermal plants, and thermal capacity outstrips hydro in a 66:34 ratio. The ten plants grouped around Tokyo Bay are the largest concentration of thermal capacity in Japan. They comprise plants in Tokyo, two of them (482,000 kw and 375,000 kw) on reclaimed land along the waterfront and a third on the Sumida River (77,500 kw); in Kawasaki (525,000 kw) in Tsurumi (130,000 kw and 517,500 kw); in Yokohama (350,000 kw); in Yokosuka (530,000 kw); and in Chiba (600,000 kw); and also the Goi plant now under construction. Most of these plants have been built since 1960, and some are already being expanded. The Yokosuka plant is getting 1,400,000 kw more, Yokohama 525,000 kw, and Kawasaki 175,000 kw, and the Goi plant will have an installed capacity of 1,060,000 kw. Thus the present 3,587,000 kw of thermal capacity around the bay will be increased

[4] In 1964 it "became the world's largest generator of electric power with a total official capacity of 7,170,000 kw. The Pacific Gas and Electric Company of the United States formerly held the world's top capacity at 6,860,000 kw. The new leading position by Tokyo Electric was achieved on July 29 when the Fourth Plant, with a maximum capacity of 350,000 kw, of its Yokosuka thermal power station on Tokyo Bay began operating, raising its capacity to 1.230,000 kw. The total thermal power generating capacity of the company is now 5,190,000 kw, in addition to its existing hydroelectric capacity of 1,980,000 kw" (Japan Information Service, Consulate General of Japan, New York, *Japan Report*, Vol. 10, No. 14, July 31, 1964, p. 10).

by 3,160,000 kw by 1969, to a total of 6,747,000 kw. The Chiba and Goi plants are of special geographical interest because they will provide large amounts of power to spark industrialization along the little-developed east shore of Tokyo Bay.

Tokyo E.P.C. is dependent on hydroelectric sources that lie beyond its service area. As has been indicated, it infringes on the southern Tohoku E.P.C. service area with its Lake Inawashiro complex, and it also draws power from the E.P.D.C.'s large Tagokura and Oku-tadami facilities. Its several plants along the Shinano River of southern Niigata Prefecture include its largest (165,000 kw). From Chubu E.P.C.'s service area to the west comes power from plants along the Shinano River in Nagano Prefecture and the E.P.D.C. operations at Sakuma. Within its own service area, most smaller rivers have been tapped, and there has been some large-scale development along the Tone River of Gumma Prefecture. New dams and power plants are being built along several rivers in Ibaraki Prefecture and along the Shinano River in Nagano Prefecture is the massive Azumi project. The fact that the company has undertaken the Azumi project, normally the investment province of the E.P.D.C., indicates the financial resources it commands. The Tokai Village atomic-energy project of the national government is also within Tokyo E.P.C.'s service area and will eventually supply power to its grid.

CHUBU ELECTRIC POWER COMPANY (Headquarters: Nagoya) / Chubu E.P.C.'s service area includes one of the richest and best-developed water resources in Japan and has as its main market the Nagoya, or Chukyo, area. Once noted as a textile-ceramics-lumber and light-manufacturing center, Chukyo is undergoing an economic transformation, spearheaded by new heavy-chemical plants, iron and steel works, and the booming auto assembly lines of Toyota Motors. Emphasis on heavy industry is growing, and there is a related boost in electric-power demand. In 1956 the light-heavy industry ratio in the company's service area was 65:35; in 1960, 52:48; the target for 1970 is 33:67.

Hydroelectric power forms 46 percent of the company's power output. Facilities are clustered along the Kiso, Tenryu, and Oi Rivers, all of which flow into the Pacific Ocean, and the Shinano River, which empties into the Sea of Japan. The largest and newest plants are along the Oi River and include the Hatanagi #1 pumped-storage dam. On the neighboring Tenryu River are the Sakuma and the two Akiba dams (34,900 kw and 45,300 kw) of the E.P.D.C.; other E.P.D.C. operations are at Miboro. Both of Chubu E.P.C.'s neighbors, Tokyo E.P.C. and Kansai E.P.C., have installations in the company's service area and siphon off large blocks of power for their own use.

Thermal capacity exceeded hydro in 1960; it is now growing five times as fast and makes up 54 percent of the company's output. The base load is centered on power from a Nagoya plant that had a 816,000-kw capacity and was expanded to 1,256,000 kw by late 1964, when it became temporarily the largest thermal plant in Japan. Two older Nagoya plants (285,000 kw and 140,000 kw), a plant at Yokkaichi (341,000 kw), and a small one at Shimizu provide supporting power. A new 660,000-kw plant at Yokkaichi was in operation by late 1963, fired with fuel oil pumped in from an adjacent petroleum refinery. Late 1964 brought new power from a plant at Owase (750,000 kw) in southern Mie Prefecture.

HOKURIKU ELECTRIC POWER COMPANY (Headquarters: Toyama) / This company has the smallest service area and was the only company that did not have any thermal capacity in 1963, mainly because it has some of Japan's finest water resources. However, the monopolization of three of its best rivers by Kansai E.P.C., the increasing costs of dam construction, and the growing demand for power compelled the company to invest in a thermal plant, which was completed in Toyama in 1964, with a capacity of 156,000 kw; a planned addition will double its capacity in 1966.

Of the company's 123 hydro plants, 94 are less than 10,000 kw and date from before the war, when Toyama Prefecture was a national pacesetter in electric-power generation. These small units are especially numerous in Fukui and Ishikawa Prefectures; Toyama Prefecture has larger and newer facilities. Generation is largest on the Joganji, the Jinzu, and, to a smaller extent; the Sho and Oyabe Rivers. The largest company installation, Wadagawa #2 (122,000 kw), is on the Joganji.

KANSAI ELECTRIC POWER COMPANY (Headquarters: Osaka) / Kansai E.P.C. ranks second only to Tokyo E.P.C. in generating capacity and has as its main market the Osaka-Kobe-Kyoto area, one of Japan's two largest population and industrial clusters. This area, slow to rebuild in the immediate postwar years, has more recently undergone an economic revitalization. Less importance is placed on textiles and more on diversified manufacturing, including electronics and electrical equipment. Dredges are pumping silt from Osaka Bay to create land for a new heavy industrial complex along the southern fringe of Osaka harbor.

The company obtains more than 90 percent of its hydroelectric supply outside its service area, owing to the scarcity of large rivers within the area and to the far-flung investments of Osaka electric utilities before the war. The principal supply area is Toyama Prefecture, along the Sea of Japan, especially along the Kurobe, Sho, and Jinzu Rivers. Of the string of company dams and power plants along the Kurobe River, Kurobegawa #4 is the company's largest facility. The Kiso River of central Honshu, which lies within the service area of

Chubu E.P.C., is virtually a Kansai E.P.C. monopoly. Within the company's service area, the Yodo River, which flows out of Lake Biwa, and the Kumano River of the Kii Peninsula are the only streams of consequence in power generation.

The Kansai company, faced with a shortage of new hydro sites within its service area, has been a leader in building thermal plants. Thermal leads hydro 56:44 in present operations. The main plants are in Osaka (624,000 kw, 312,000 kw, and 63,000 kw); Tanagawa (462,000 kw), south of Osaka; Himeji (422,000 kw and 75,000 kw); and Amagasaki, where there is an older plant (140,000 kw) and a newer one (996,000 kw) that is the largest in the system. Impressive expansion plans are afoot. A new Himeji plant that added 595,000 kw in 1965 is designed for an ultimate capacity of 1,850,000 kw; and by 1966, a new Sakai plant will add 1,000,000 kw, half its planned eventual size.

CHUGOKU ELECTRIC POWER COMPANY (Headquarters: Hiroshima) / The main markets of this company are cities along the Inland Sea. Thermal power is especially important in Yamaguchi Prefecture, where the coal from nearby northern Kyushu is cheap and the industrial markets are large. Plants are at Onoda (130,000 kw) and Ube (60,000 kw and 306,000 kw). Hiroshima Prefecture has a thermal plant at Hiroshima (158,000 kw), but it also has the service area's best hydro supply. The situation is reversed in Okayama Prefecture, where the hydro potential is small but the thermal supply is large and is increasing. One thermal plant is in the new industrial zone of Mizushima (125,000 kw), and the other is southeast of Okayama (76,500 kw); the former is undergoing a 156,000-kw expansion. A new plant at Kudamatsu (156,000 kw) in Yamaguchi Prefecture will further strengthen the company's power supply and will lengthen the 58:42 lead that thermal power enjoys over hydro power.

Streams within the service area have little flow because of the relatively small rainfall, and they have marked seasonal fluctuation in volume. To improve these conditions, the company has built large stabilization reservoirs along ten main rivers. The Tada River of Hiroshima Prefecture is the most highly developed and has the largest power facility (51,500 kw). The E-gawa drains into the Sea of Japan, but power generated along it moves to the Hiroshima area. The E.P.D.C. is building a dam and power plant on the Nariha River of southwestern Okayama Prefecture that will be the largest (150,000 kw) in the service area when it is completed in 1967.

SHIKOKU ELECTRIC POWER COMPANY (Headquarters: Takamatsu) / Shikoku E.P.C. has the smallest generating capacity of the nine companies and still relies more heavily on hydro power than on thermal in a 58:42 ratio. Its main hydro facilities are along the Yoshino and

Niyodo Rivers of Kochi and Tokushima Prefectures; the Monobe River of Kochi Prefecture has been harnessed by the prefecture (three dams) and the Sumitomo Metals Corporation. Sumitomo transmission lines carry power northward to the main Sumitomo chemical and metals operations at Niihama, on the Inland Sea. The E.P.D.C. has the largest hydro installation (72,100 kw) in Shikoku, along the Nariha River of southeastern Kochi Prefecture; it sends the bulk of its power northward by its own transmission lines to Saijo.

Thermal plants are relatively new and are few in number. They are at Tadotsu (12,000 kw), Saijo (62,000 kw), Imabari (12,000 kw), and Masuyama (141,000 kw). Two large plants are under construction, at Tokushima (125,000 kw) and Saijo (156,000 kw). When they are completed in 1965, thermal capacity will forge ahead of hydro.

Shikoku E.P.C.'s power supply has been stabilized and strengthened by the completion of the Chugoku-Shikoku Tie Line in 1962 by the E.P.D.C. This high-voltage line makes it possible to import power from Hiroshima across the Inland Sea when supplies on Shikoku fall short. A shorter, low-voltage line was strung across Naruto Strait, between Shikoku and Awaji Island, in 1961 by Kansai E.P.C.

KYUSHU ELECTRIC POWER COMPANY (Headquarters: Fukuoka) / In Kyushu E.P.C. operations, thermal capacity leads hydro by a 66:34 ratio, owing in large part to the juxtaposition of coalfields and principal markets in the industrialized northern part of the island. The main thermal plants are at Kokura (312,000 kw), which uses low-caloric coal, Karita (387,000 kw), and Chikujo (145,000 kw), all in northern Fukuoka Prefecture; at Omuta (264,000 kw) in southern Fukuoka Prefecture; and at Ainoura (174,500 kw) and Omura (66,000 kw) in Nagasaki Prefecture. Under construction are 156,000-kw additions to the Omura and Omuta plants and a new plant of the same size in northern Saga Prefecture. Other plants using low-caloric coal are at Wakamatsu, run by the E.P.D.C., and at Karita, run by a small private utility.

Whereas thermal power predominates in northern Kyushu, central and southern Kyushu are the main sources of hydro power. Plants are clustered along the numerous short rivers of Miyazaki Prefecture, which accounts for 56 percent of the company's hydro capacity. Five installations in southern Kyushu have a capacity of more than 50,000 kw each, and the Hitotsuse dam and power plant, completed late in 1963, has a capacity of 180,000 kw. An E.P.D.C. project now under way in northwestern Kagoshima Prefecture will add 125,000 kw. Most of the power from the hydro facilities moves northward to Omuta-Nagasaki, Fukuoka, or Kitakyushu. Kyushu is linked with the power grid of Chugoku E.P.C. by a high-voltage line across Kammon Strait to Shimonoseki. A line being strung parallel to it will further facilitate power exchanges.

Long-Range Plans

In 1960 the Japanese government drew up an eight-year development plan for electric power as one phase of its "Double the National Income Program." If plans can be transformed into reality, Japan will have an installed capacity of 47,226,000 kw by 1967, or roughly 18,000,000 kw more than in 1963. Projected to 1980, the government forecast is for a generating capacity three times the present size. This projection postulates continuing sound and dynamic economic conditions.

To grow as rapidly as planned, the Japanese electric-power industry must follow the guidelines established in the foregoing review. Large-scale thermal plants will have to provide the bulk—perhaps as much as three-fourths—of the added power supply. Selected large-scale hydroelectric projects will continue to be initiated, primarily by the Electric Power Development Company. It is apparent that the largest private electric utilities, such as Tokyo E.P.C., Chubu E.P.C., and Kansai E.P.C., will have the steepest increases in power demand within their service areas and, in response, will have to push forward most vigorously in new expansion efforts. Finally, the fact that most of the new facilities will be oil-fired will promote operating efficiency but at the same time will increase Japan's reliance on imported energy sources at the expense of domestically mined coal.

14. Recent Studies Concerning the Role of Transportation in the Space Economy

Brian J. L. Berry

In this selection, Berry reviews some of the research that has been done on the role of transportation in the development of economic activity in the United States, Germany, the British Isles, and Sweden. He points out that as society continues to specialize, consumers must obtain their various material needs from increasingly diverse sources of supply. Thus internal and external circulation patterns reflect these changing relationships between producers and consumers.

    The article also provides a comparison between the descriptive studies reviewed in Germany and Britain and the theo-

*retical and analytic research covered in the United States
and Sweden. The American and Swedish studies exemplify
the newer approaches to economic geographic study by
utilizing experimental design, theoretical framework or
models, and statistical and mathematical tools.*

What is the role of transportation in the space economy? How are economic patterns influenced by the nature of available transport networks? Of what significance to the economy are improvements in transport facilities? Recent studies indicate no simple answers to such questions, only that real understanding will come from careful analyses of the complex interrelationships of economic activity, circulation, and transportation systems.

Why should this be so? For better or worse we live in a specialized society. We have every reason to believe that specialization in this society is increasing rather than decreasing. There is a persistent tendency for concentration of the means of production in fewer, but larger, concerns. Concomitantly, standards of life are rising, and differences in levels of living from place to place are being eliminated. Society is at one and the same time becoming more highly specialized and differentiated, more wealthy and uniform. The probability that any two areas selected at random will have similar arrays of production facilities is being reduced; the probability that the same two areas will consume similar baskets of goods is increasing. These trends mean that areas, as producers, are becoming tied to ever-expanding markets, and that, as consumers, they must assemble their needs from increasingly diverse sources of supply.

The complexities of economic interdependence that result from these trends manifest themselves in patterns of circulation in the economy, but circulation patterns are reflections of other things as well—types, qualities, capacities, and orientation of available transport networks, Symbiosis of ubiquitous demands and specialized sources of supplies may be achieved only over the routes of available transport systems. Factors of transportation mould circulation patterns and specify limits to potential symbiotic relationships of producers and consumers, thereby influencing economic interchange.

In view of these remarks it should be no surprise that much careful and painstaking analysis is required to unravel the threads by which economic patterns are related to transport systems. Such analysis is all the more difficult because it has to be undertaken in what has long been a poorly charted no-man's land between the realms of economics

SOURCE: *Annals* of the Association of American Geographers, XLIX (September, 1959), 328–42. Reprinted by permission. The author is professor of geography at the University of Chicago.

and geography. It is therefore with pleasure that this article reviews a series of studies that have pushed the frontiers of understanding far into what was very recently *terra incognita*. These studies include the *Raum und Verkehr* series of the Akademie für Raumforschung und Landesplanung in Germany,[1] the highway impact studies conducted by geographers and others at the University of Washington, Seattle,[2] and investigations of the relationships of bus services, towns, and hinterlands undertaken in Sweden and the United Kingdom.[3]

Contributions have been made in these studies by both economic geographers and location economists. In addition, there has been either participation or active sponsorship by planning or policy-making governmental agencies. Thus, one branch of the Akademie für Raumforschung und Landesplanung is an agency of the West German government, and the highway impact studies were sponsored and financed by the U. S. Bureau of Public Roads in cooperation with the Washington State Highway Department. This kind of liaison between policy-maker and the academic should be welcomed, for it fosters academic interest in problems of practical importance and results in planning based on real insight and understanding.

[1] Forschungs- und Sitzungsberichte der Akademie für Raumforschung und Landesplanung (Kurt Brüning ed.), *Raum und Verkehr I* (Bremen Horn: Walter Dorn Verlag, 1956). 210 pp. Maps, tables, graphs. 6¾ x 9½. DM. 20; *Idem, Raum und Verkehr II* (1957). 146 pp. Maps, tables, graphs. 7 x 10. DM. 16; *Idem, Raum und Verkehr III* (1958). 160 pp. Maps, tables, graphs. 7 x 10. DM. 18.
[2] William L. Garrison, "The Benefits of Rural Roads to Rural Property," *Allocation of Road and Street Costs*. Part IV (Seattle: Washington State Council for Highway Research, 1956). viii and 107 pp. Maps, tables, graphs, bibliography. 7 x 9. Available without charge; Bayard O. Wheeler, "The Effect of Freeway Access upon Suburban Real Property Values," *ibid.* Part V (1956). xii and 142 pp. Maps, photographs, tables. 7 x 9. Available without charge; William L. Garrison and Marion E. Marts, *Influence of Highway Improvements on Urban Land: A Graphic Summary* (Seattle: Highway Economic Studies, University of Washington, 1958). vi and 70 pp. Maps, photographs, tables, graphs, bibliography. 7 x 9. Available without charge; *Idem, Geographic Impact of Highway Improvement* (Seattle: Highway Economic Studies, University of Washington, 1958). xii and 139 pp. Maps, photographs, tables, graphs, bibliography. 7 x 9. Available without charge; William L. Garrison, Brian J. L. Berry, Duane F. Marble, John D. Nystuen, and Richard L. Morrill, *Studies of Highway Development and Geographic Change* (Seattle: University of Washington Press, in press); Edgar M. Horwood, Ronald R. Boyce, and others, *Studies of the Central Business District and Urban Freeway Development* (Seattle: University of Washington Press, in press).
[3] Sven Godlund, "Bus Service in Sweden," *Lund Studies in Geography*. Series B. Human Geography, No. 17 (1956). 72 pp. Maps, tables, graphs, bibliography. 6½ x 9¼. Sw.Kr. 10; *Idem*, "The Function and Growth of Bus Traffic in the Sphere of Urban Influence," *ibid.* No. 18 (1956). 80 pp. Maps, graphs, tables, bibliography. 6½ x 9¼. Sw.Kr. 10; Ordnance Survey of Great Britain, *Local Accessibility*. Map in the 1:625,000 Planning Series, with Explanatory Text (Chessington, Surrey: Director General of the Ordnance Survey, 1955). £—/10/9; F. H. W. Green, "Community of Interest Areas. Notes on the Hierarchy of Central Places and Their Hinterlands," *Economic Geography*, Vol. 34 (July, 1958), pp. 210–26.

The *Raum und Verkehr* Series

The three volumes of the *Raum and Verkehr* series are products of the committee "*Verkehr*" of the Akademie für Raumforschung und Landesplanung. The Akademie has two parts. One is an agency of the German government in Bonn, the other a research center located in Hanover. Both branches are devoted to economic research of a spatial character in order to provide basic information for purposes of effective regional planning. All research is performed by committees, each with limited membership drawn from the restricted list of members of the Akademie.[4] The committee "*Verkehr*" is one such research group.

This "traffic" or "circulation" committee was formed in 1951. Its members took an active part in major discussions on transport policy in Germany in 1954. Out of these discussions emerged the various contributions that were published in the years 1956 to 1958 as the series *Raum und Verkehr*. As the introduction to the volumes indicates, they were not published as policy statements, but as "contributions to an understanding of the complex relations of circulation and the organization of the space economy." To Professor Walter Linden of Essen, chairman of the committee, must go much of the credit for publication of the three volumes, and indeed for the formulation of the committee's research program. Most other members of the committee are economists and planners, including Andreas Predöhl and Otto Schlier, both of whom have made basic contributions to location theory in the past.

The committee outlined for itself an ambitious research program:

1. to improve understanding of the present spatial organization of the economy and of the mutual interrelationships between circulation and spatial order.
2. to obtain information concerning the impact of transportation planning and policies, new construction of transport facilities, and alternative freight-rate practices, in the space economy;
3. to study the most promising measures of transport planning and regulation in order to facilitate regional planning in the economy.

Since the first two of these three objectives are of greater interest to the economic geographer, contributions to them will be dealt with in more detail than contributions to the third.

Raum und Verkehr I

The first article in *Raum und Verkehr* is, appropriately enough, an introduction to and justification for the work of the committee

---

[4] One quarter of the members of the Akademie are economists, one quarter geographers, one quarter planners, and one quarter "others."

"Verkehr." W. Linden, the author, argues that it is impossible to separate the mutual interrelationships of three sets of forces: the economy, circulation, and the state. His article, *"Verkehr und Raumordnung,"* is designed to introduce the reader to the breadth, implications, and complexity of these interrelationships, and to make one major point: if the objective of the state is to achieve an optimum economy by regional planning, one of the most effective ways to achieve this objective is by controlling transportation and therefore circulation. It follows that it is in the best interests of state and economy to have a group engaged in research designed to reveal the role of transportation and circulation in the economy and to develop the most effective means of planning transport networks. Needless to say, the circulation committee is the group so engaged. Linden's introductory discussions range widely. He examines the role of railroads in the economic development of Germany and introduces the reader to problems of competition between road and rail, and to discussions concerning an articulated transport system. The role of inland waterways is mentioned, and pipelines and transmission systems are discussed in their turn. The article concludes with a comment on the role of mail and news circulation and wireless communications.

Three other contributions in the volume examine in more detail the question of developing an articulated public transport system. The first of these, by P. Schulz-Kiesow, discusses the economic character and potential complementarity of transport by inland waterway, rail, and road. Potential complementarity is contrasted with the present competitive relations of transport media. Detailed schemes for articulation are presented. A second essay, by P. Helfrich, examines articulation as a means whereby decentralization may be furthered in the economy. In this essay the 1953 resolution of the Akademie on "Transport Rates and Spatial Order" is reiterated: "Only through the articulation of transport carriers in a public transport network can a harmonious transport system be achieved and needed decentralization of industry and settlement be facilitated." Articulation is considered a prerequisite for spatial equalization of transport costs. With cost equalization (or equivalent subsidy), decentralization should be fostered, and the development of peripheral regions aided. Development of peripheral agricultural regions is discussed in greater detail in the third article concerned with articulated transport systems, by C. Pirath, to whom *Raum und Verkehr* I is dedicated. Pirath presents a careful economic and graphic analysis of transport costs and concludes that by appropriate integration of road and rail the accessibility of backward agricultural regions may be increased without recourse to subsidy.

The first empirical contribution in *Raum und Verkehr* is a study of "Locational Relations and Industrial Structure," by G. Isenberg, a comparison of the old industrial area of Nordrhein-Westfalen and the emerging industrial complex of Baden-Württemberg. It is intended to reveal the consequences for the pattern of circulation of differences in economic development and to show the relations of both economic structure and circulation patterns to available transportation facilities. Nordrhein-Westfalen is an "old" industrial area with coal mining and a raw material-oriented industry of iron and steel, chemicals, glass, and ceramics, dependent upon water and rail transport. Baden-Württemberg, on the other hand, is a "new" industrial area with light industries, especially of the processing and finishing types, using more modern methods, relying upon electric power, and making use of truck transport. Mass movements of goods take place in and out of the old industrial area; it is a heavy consumer of transport inputs. Conversely, high value movements, small in bulk and light in weight, move in and out of the newer industrial area; it consumes relatively small amounts of transportation. Isenberg's essay concludes with a brief discussion of the internal organization of the two industrial regions, the Rhenish conurbation with its concentration and mass, and Baden-Württemberg, decentralized except in the Stuttgart and Mannheim areas. The paper is well supported by statistical evidence, although the reader would have been aided by provision of maps.

There is no lack of graphics in the next empirical study, by R. Hoffmann. Hoffmann asks "How does the postwar circulation pattern in Germany differ from the prewar pattern?" His answer is based upon an excellent series of flow maps.[5] Why should this question be considered of importance? Because, Hoffmann argues, exchange is vital in a specialized society. Study of the frequency, extent, and direction of circulation systems can thus provide an accurate and revealing image of livelihood, settlement, places of production, and their relations via the transport system. Examination of changes in the circulation system can provide dramatic insights into societal change by the same token. This argument is illustrated by inquiring into interregional movements of people in Germany before and after the war and by examining changes in intraregional circulation in the same period. Flow maps are presented for express train frequencies, long-distance expresses, and air connections. These provide clear indications of the reorientation in Germany resulting from creation of the "Iron Curtain." A second series of maps shows equally striking intraregional change resulting from emergence of the bus in competition with the train.

A second article by Hoffmann analyzes the role of *Autobahnen* in

[5] Further development of this answer, and more graphic materials, can be found in an article which Hoffmann published simultaneously with *Raum und Verkehr*: "Der Verkehr als Mittel zur Abgrenzung von Stadt und Umland," *Raumforschung und Raumordnung*, Vol. 14 (1956), pp. 101–106.

This entire issue of *Raumforschung und Raumordnung* is devoted to the analysis of problems of towns and hinterlands and should prove of considerable value to those interested in problems of central places and the central-place hierarchy.

the organization of the German space economy. He makes it quite
clear that *Autobahnen* are in no way "unique." Their impact is a special
case of the effects of the motor vehicle and new roads since the First
World War. Thus, decentralization of settlement and industry, elimination of the need for close ties to water or rail, and increases in the
accessibility of previously backward areas have resulted—whatever the
type of road and whether truck, bus, or private car is the vehicle used.
However, this should not be interpreted as meaning that the *Autobahn*
has no impact. Depending upon location with respect to the *Autobahn*
and length of trip, savings of up to 40 percent of the costs of moving
by ordinary federal highway accrue from its use. It is in this zone that
decentralization is facilitated. Other effects are mentioned as well, although without supporting evidence: centralization of management and
administration because improved access eliminates the need for small
branch offices; decline of small by-passed towns located at distance
from main *Autobahn* intersections; reorientation of traffic-oriented business, such as restaurants, hotels, and service stations. The article concludes with a history of *Autobahn* planning, an analysis of the present
state of the system and its needs, and of priorities in the new construction program.

The remaining empirical study in *Raum und Verkehr I* is an analysis
of the role of branch railway lines in the economic structure of secondary economic regions. I. Esenwein-Rothe, the author, begins by
noting how dangerous it is to generalize about any part of a transport system apart from the larger network to which the part belongs,
but continues with his study arguing that some information is better
than none. He limits his discussion to Niedersachsen on grounds of
availability of data. As a first step, service areas of branch railroads
are delimited for both passenger and goods traffic. Relations of passenger flows to service areas of differing functional character are then
evaluated, and a method for predicting passenger traffic volumes is
developed. Functional information is then used to develop a method
of predicting goods traffic flows. Using estimates of flows, and in light
of several case studies, branch railroads are then classified into three
functional types: service lines for agricultural regions, agglomeration
lines concerned with commuter traffic, and deglomeration lines facilitating movements of both people and goods in decentralized areas.
For each of these three types, tables and graphs are used to compare
population densities in service areas and to study the relations of
differential population densities to school, business, and commuter
traffic. Contrasts in goods carried, seasonal variations in goods flows,
and differences in the direction of bulk movements on each type of
line are revealed.

Raum und Verkehr I concludes with "twelve wishes" concerning traffic statistics presented by Otto Schlier. His wishes are those of every other worker in economic geography and location economics. As *Raum und Verkehr II* shows, however, Schlier has far less reason to complain than his American counterpart, particularly in so far as goods movements by rail, inland waterway, and sea are concerned. In *Raum und Verkehr III*, also, a contribution by Schlier reveals data for truck transport superior to available American equivalents.

Raum und Verkehr II

The four essays of *Raum und Verkehr II* contribute to a single theme: the movement of goods in the German economy. W. Linden again provides an introduction, in this case a discussion of the factors responsible for changes in goods traffic flows. Three detailed studies follow, by R. Arntzen on the structure and development of ore traffic with special reference to the Ruhrgebiete, O. Hördemann on the means of transport of Ruhr coal, and O. Schlier on the circulation of goods in Germany before and after the war.

Linden asks what factors have been responsible for changing patterns of goods traffic flows. He begins with a brief historical survey of trade and trade routes in Northern Europe, from which he suggests the importance of (1) simple facts of demand and supply, considered relative to both areal differentiation and level of technology, (2) the nature of routes and transport media, and the costs of movement, and (3) the political organization of space. These factors are then elaborated in a series of short case studies designed to show how each operates and how they can provide an explanatory scheme for studies of changes in goods circulation. The reader will note the similarity of Linden's factors and those of E. L. Ullman. Ullman describes the "bases for transportation and interaction" as (1) complementarity, which is defined as areal differentiation with the necessary condition of demands in one area and supplies in another, (2) intervening opportunity, which defines the substitution framework of areas, and (3) distance or transferability, an approximation to time-cost relative to length of haul, type of commodity, route, and transport medium. Political factors are considered only incidentally. Both schemes provide useful ways of looking at a circulation pattern, whether static or changing. However, the insights and penetration are less than those forthcoming from techniques of linear programming and associated methods of spatial price equilibrium.

Arntzen and Hördemann both provide simple, straightforward accounts of mass movements of raw materials with respect to the Ruhr. The former considers movements of ore to the Ruhr from diverse German and foreign sources; the latter is concerned with the means by which coal is shipped out of the Ruhr to markets. Both begin with brief historical sketches of their topic; both continue with short accounts of the influences of transport costs upon the pattern of supply, and how this pattern is modified by variations in quality of the raw material being carried. The major part of both articles is devoted to a discussion of data presented in tabular form and in certain cases also mapped. Arntzen tabulates and maps changing sources of ore supply (both domestic and foreign) since the end of the First World War. These data are supplemented by information concerning variations in movements of foreign ores through different ports of entry. Hördemann's tabular materials summarize the movements of Ruhr coal, by truck, rail, and water transport, to foreign and domestic destinations. Maps are again provided. Both authors do a competent job of reporting. If anyone is in need of information on these topics, here are readily accessible sources.

The real wealth of statistics is to be found in Otto Schlier's "Traffic Flows in Germany Before and After the War." Schlier provides detailed information concerning movements of hard coal, coke, briquettes, iron ore, wheat, flour, lumber, vegetables and fruits, gas, and diesel oil. Data are presented in 33×33 matrices that show tonnage flows between 21 German, 8 European, and 4 extra-European origins and destinations for 1938 and 1955 (all movements between German origins and destinations, foreign origins and German destinations, and German origins and foreign destinations appear). The 21 German regions are defined on the basis of the prewar boundaries of Germany. Flows between any origin and destination are broken down by means of transport: sea, inland waterway, and rail. Unfortunately, the regional delineations vary for water and rail traffic. However, maps are provided that show these differences clearly enough. In addition, two tables are included to illustrate the increasing role of truck transport in goods movements, although no information on inter-regional flows by truck is forthcoming.

Schlier's text includes a brief discussion of sources of data and their limitations and of problems of the regional units, and he comments upon each pair of tables. No analysis is attempted. It is hoped that some enterprising student will correct this situation, for the information provided in these tables is far richer than any research worker will find at his disposal in the United States! To bring this point home it will be worthwhile to consider the materials with which Ullman worked.

The best single source of information Ullman had at his disposal was the one percent sample of Carload Weighbill Statistics provided for rail traffic in the United States by the Interstate Commerce Commission. These statistics are reliable only for large flows because of sampling variability and disclosure rules. It is a wonder that Ullman was able to achieve so much by preparing maps of origins and destinations of state-to-state rail traffic (i.e., to point in broad outline the features of American commodity flows). But how much more powerful could have been the analysis, how much more sophisticated the conclusions, if the riches of data presented so modestly by Schlier had been available to Ullman? The American economic geographer has good reason to lament the ill-fated Census of Transportation, strangled in its infancy when Congress withdrew financial support last year.

Raum und Verkehr III

The third volume of *Raum und Verkehr* lacks the single theme of the second, containing five essays concerned with somewhat divergent aspects of economy–circulation–transportation relationships: W. Linden and E. Weber on pipelines and transmission systems, R. Hoffmann on air traffic, K. H. Olsen and O. Schlier on agriculture and circulation, and H. V. Vittorelli on rail and road in Italy.

Linden and Weber introduce the volume with a study of the role of pipelines and transmission systems in goods circulation patterns, and of the impact of these new and improving transport media in the space economy. A brief history of pipeline and transmission technology is provided, with most attention given to electricity grids and to pipelines for petroleum and for producer gas. The authors then attempt to discuss transmission technology systematically, as part of a general theory of circulation, the basic features of which are price–cost relationships, type of commodity, and distance. A major contrast is made between universal transport media such as the truck, and special transport media such as pipelines and transmission systems. This contrast does not apply to the impact of different transport media upon the space economy, however, because whereas rail and water had a centralizing influence upon economic life, it is thought that the truck and the transmission system are effective in promoting decentralization. The authors conclude with a discussion of the increasing significance of transmission systems and pipelines in the German circulation pattern, and with associated policy matters.

In the next essay R. Hoffmann considers the nature and qualities of air transport and evaluates its present and potential role in Germany. A brief analysis of the demand for transportation and the role of each major transport medium introduces the discussion. This is followed by a description of changes in airport traffic between 1939 and 1954, to be integrated with his earlier description of changes in air traffic flows. He notes the centralization of facilities in larger centers, contrasts the service areas of these centers for long and short distance trips, and concludes with policy statements relating to investment in smaller airports.

Relations of agriculture and circulation are the topic in the next two articles. Olsen discusses problems associated with study of these relationships, pointing out the complexity of any sophisticated analysis. Such an analysis, he argues, should take account of the size and specialization of producing areas, differentials in harvest times, possibilities of storage, etc., in so far as outflows from agricultural areas are concerned, of the inflows of requirements such as farm machinery and fertilizer to these areas, and of the movements of persons associated with agricultural production. Each of these types of movement is discussed in general. Schlier follows with data for 1954 concerning receipts and transshipments of foreign agricultural products by product, point of unloading, and type of transport, the distribution of domestic agricultural products by product and means of transport, and the means of transport of agricultural products.

Raum und Verkehr III concludes with a discussion of the history, economics, and politics of the development of and competition between rail and road in Italy. The author, Vittorelli, shows the close relationships of the traffic pattern to regional differences in the Italian economy and illustrates how closely competition between rail and road has been tied to regional economic differentiation. His arguments are well supported by tables, although graphics would have been desirable.

The Highway Impact Studies

It would be of doubtful value to attempt to record all the highway impact studies that have been completed in the United States in the past decade, for the number is certainly several score. It would be equally unrewarding to attempt to review all highway studies at present in progress (by a recent count of the Bureau of Public Roads, more than 40 are in various stages of completion in 26 states). Hence, the following section of this essay will be devoted to a brief and general summary of the character of highway impact studies, and then to a more detailed review of the concepts, methods, and findings of those studies with which the author has the greatest familiarity, the Washington State studies.

As the name suggests, highway "impact" studies are concerned with the effects of highways, particularly new highways, upon settlement, business, industry, and travel. Most of the studies in progress or completed have been initiated and financed by state, federal, or cooperatively by state and federal highway agencies, and conducted either by the agencies themselves or by university or private research groups under contract to a highway agency. Official interest in highway impact stems from at least three sources: (1) the need of highways planners to know about the benefits of highway improvements in order to have guides for the optimal location of future highways; (2) interest in financing of highways, and particularly in equalizing the cost of, or broadening the tax base for, new highway construction by obtaining (as a basis for subsequent action) information concerning the "indirect" or "non-vehicular" benefits of highway improvements; (3) explicit instructions given to the Bureau of Public Roads by Congress in the

Federal-Aid Highway Act of 1956, which authorized construction of the 41,000-mile National System of Interstate and Defense Highways, to report regularly on the economic effects of highway improvements.

Resulting studies have been as diverse in quality and content as the originating agencies and the research groups undertaking them. As the best single summary of highway impact studies now available notes, studies may be subdivided into those emphasizing land values, those emphasizing business, and those emphasizing traffic. They may also be subdivided into those using actual information concerning change, and those which use opinions relating to changes that have taken place. This author also likes to distinguish between "before" and "after" studies, and studies which analyze functional relations of settlement, economic patterns, and relative location via the highway system.

Garrison and Marts review 29 studies that record actual changes subsequent to highway improvements (12 emphasizing land use, 15 emphasizing business, and 2 emphasizing traffic), and 8 "other" studies, most of which rely upon opinion-type data. They bring together diverse studies and provide for each a brief résumé of methods and findings. Their text is brief and to the point, and is supplemented by maps, air photographs, and graphs of changes observed in land values, business, or traffic. Graphics are of high quality.

The majority of the studies reviewed are of the "before" and "after" type. Many attempt to evaluate changes associated with highway improvements by "control area" devices, designed to eliminate regional trends. Each of the studies of land values notes rapid rates of increase in values immediately adjacent to new highways, and a diminution of rates of increase with increasing distance from these new highway facilities. Every study of business summarized is of the "by-pass" type, and tries to evaluate the impact of a new by-pass highway upon the level of business activity in the by-passed town. Results of these business studies are by no means conclusive, although they do suggest that the by-pass, by diverting traffic, has a deleterious impact upon sales volumes of such types of business as cafes and gas stations. The traffic studies give token to the ability of new routes to relieve congestion on old, although they provide no information concerning the traffic-generating ability of new highways.

Without exception, the studies summarized are descriptive and empirical. They start *tabula rasa* and try to measure change and to isolate the influences of new highways. There is no attempt to study functional relations of highways, settlement, and the space economy. The studies lack both an explicit formulation of the highway impact problem and an elegant experimental design.[6] Yet it probably will be studies with

[6] For another discussion of this point see *Economic Impact of Highway Improvement*, Special Report 28, Highway Research Board (National Academy of Sciences–National Research Council, Publication 541, 1957).

such features that best clarify problems of highway impact and highway benefits.

The Highway Cost Allocation Studies

Two volumes of a six-volume series concerned with the allocation of road and street costs are of interest: Garrison's "The Benefits of Rural Roads to Rural Property" and Wheeler's "The Effect of Freeway Access upon Suburban Real Property Values."

The volume by Garrison is a study of "experimental measurements of geographic relationships between rural roads and location utility in three Washington counties with reference to the location of agriculture and rural non-farm residences." It has five chapters, which deal in turn with (1) the conceptual framework of the study, including summaries of the findings of the study and of studies made elsewhere, (2) the design phases of the study; (3) methods of analysis and relationships measured; (4) the relations of benefits resulting from roads and associated tax assessment problems; (5) theoretical models relevant to an evaluation of the study's findings.

The underlying concept is quite simple: property values are an index of the utility of a place, and one of the major factors influencing the utility of any place is its location relative to other places; roads affect property values by determining the location of places relative to each other; variations in the quality of roads are reflected in variations in relative location and hence in variation in property values. Empirical work in the volume is designed to measure covariations of property values and relative location via roads of different quality. On the basis of an evaluation of previous studies, the "before" and "after" technique was rejected as a means of analysis. Instead, the author elected to study functional relations between property values and characteristics of the location and site of the rural residences. Regressions were run measuring location via roads of different quality in simple distance terms, in terms of miles travelled per year; and in terms of the inverse of miles travelled per year. The latter showed the strongest associations with property values. Marked differences were noted between the depreciating effects upon land values of miles travelled per year by rural farm residents over paved and over gravel and dirt roads. As would be expected, location utility diminished more rapidly, and hence property values fell more quickly, the greater the number of miles travelled per year over dirt and gravel roads as compared with paved roads. Location with respect to place of usual convenience-goods shopping and place of usual shopping-goods shopping, determined simultaneously, was the most significant of the location referents for the rural farm residents. For nonfarm residences it was again noted that property values diminished more rapidly as miles travelled over roads of poorer quality increased. In this case the most significant of the locational referents were location with respect to place of work and place of usual shopping.

A second set of measurements related to propensity to travel. Garrison was unable to find any statistical relationship between trip frequencies and either distance travelled or type of road over which the trips were made. Therefore he concluded that a highway improvement would *not* result in an increase in the number of trips made by the rural resident.

In addition, trade areas were mapped for the towns of Snohomish County, although on the basis of preliminary investigation Garrison found no evidence of a central place hierarchy.[7] Several theoretical concepts of value in interpreting the results of the statistical work also are presented, including a theorem concerning the possibility of achieving an optimal solution to the agricultural location problem.[8]

Wheeler's study is, like Garrison's, an attempt to determine the effects of improved access upon suburban real property values. Again, the objective of the investigation was to provide basic information to aid in "allocating tax responsibility for the improvement and operation of roads, streets and highways among property owners, general taxpayers and highway users." Both volumes were prepared at the University of Washington for the Washington State Council for Highway Research, an interim committee of the legislature of the State of Washington.[9] The study focuses upon suburban areas east of the city of Seattle, including Mercer Island and the eastern shore communities of Lake Washington. For many years access to Mercer Island was by ferry. In 1940 the Lake Washington Floating Bridge was constructed from Seattle to Mercer Island. Travel time from downtown Seattle to the island was cut from 45 to 15 minutes.

Wheeler analyzes the effect of this change in access to Seattle on property values on Mercer Island and adjacent east-shore areas. Two types of analysis were used: (1) a "before" and "after" investigation of the values of improved residential property and unimproved land suitable for residential development, using areas north and west of Seattle as "controls" in order to isolate the effects of improved access on Mercer Island; (2) a regression analysis of the covariations of property values, access, and quality of residential land.

[7] Such information was subsequently provided by Garrison and this author in: "The Functional Bases of the Central Place Hierarchy," *Economic Geography*, Vol. 34 (April, 1958), pp. 145–54.
[8] This theorem was later elaborated in an article in these *Annals*. See William L. Garrison and Duane F. Marble, "The Spatial Structure of Agricultural Activities," *Annals*, Association of American Geographers, Vol. 47 (June, 1957), pp. 137–44.
[9] For a general account of the Washington State Council studies see Robert G. Hennes, Bayard O. Wheeler, and William L. Garrison, "Washington Highway Impact Studies," *Developing Concepts of Land Acquisition*, Highway Research Board, Bulletin 169 (Washington: National Academy of Sciences–National Research Council, Publication 529, 1957). This work also includes a discussion of the Dallas Expressway Economic Impact Studies.

From the "before" and "after" analysis it was found that there was a large net increase of property values on Mercer Island over that predicted from study of the control areas. Property values also increased in the east-shore communities more rapidly than in the control areas, although less rapidly than on Mercer Island. Wheeler thus concluded that the effects of the improved access were reflected in rapid upturns in rates of increase of property value, but that with increasing distance from the city center the benefits of improved access tended to diminish. In this section of the study careful use is made of previous work, and the presentation is enhanced by inclusion of "before" and "after" maps of travel time from the center of Seattle, and air photographs of Mercer Island and the east-shore communities. Ample supporting evidence is provided in tables.

However, the regression analysis of property values on access and quality of residential land presents many problems. Although the multiple correlation coefficient is significantly different from zero, the value 0.34 indicates the poor performance of the model. The discussion of reasons for this inadequate performance is unsatisfactory. Wheeler never considers that his theory might be inadequate (which is probably the case) but restricts his comments to technical matters concerning the distribution of errors and the shape of the function fitted.

The Marysville Study

Garrison and Marts's summary of highway impact studies was prepared during the formative stages of a study of the impact of a by-pass highway upon land values, business, and transportation in Marysville, Washington, a small town north of Seattle. Both summary and impact study were undertaken as part of the Highway Economic Studies program at the University of Washington for the Department of Highways of the State of Washington, at the request of the Joint Fact-Finding Committee on Highways, Streets, and Bridges, Washington State Legislature. Both volumes were designed to provide basic information to aid the state government in designing taxation policy in light of highway change.[10]

Investigations in Marysville were intended to complement studies reviewed during the formative stages of the research program. Whereas the previous studies used few indicators of change, the Marysville study provided information in great detail for many indicators. Since the analysis was of a single case, the authors made little attempt to generalize or theorize about highway change, but were content to present entirely empirical results. They showed how traffic which previously passed through Marysville was rerouted as a result of completion of

[10] See the subsequent discussion of benefits and severance damages by Warren R. Seyfried: *Determination of Special Benefits Resulting from Highway Improvement* (Seattle: Highway Economic Studies, University of Washington, 1958).

the by-pass highway. Changes in trade areas in western Snohomish County were revealed by a comparison of data collected in 1954 for the study *Benefits of Rural Roads* and reinterview data for the same sample in 1957. Interviews of merchants and residents within Marysville inquired into such topics as changes in parking and travel habits, and sought opinions concerning inconveniences and noise levels introduced by the new highway. Opinion data for Marysville were compared with similar data collected in Mount Vernon, a town to the north where the highway was improved but continues to run through the center of the town. These inquiries suggested changes taking place or which people thought were occurring: (1) site effects such as inconveniences resulting from increased noise in close proximity to the highway; (2) locational effects such as the worsening of the strategic position of Marysville on the highway system. To provide supplementary information, site and locational effects were then studied in detail in separate analyses of variations in business conditions and land values. The business studies used sales information for 30 business types found in three separate locations in Marysville. Only short-run effects were considered: the "before" period was November 1952–August 1954, and the "after" period was December 1954–August 1956.[11] Many manipulations of these business data are recorded. Similar manipulations were completed for the land value data, using information from warranty deed transfers. However, lacking a satisfactory theoretical basis, the authors were not willing to provide explicit conclusions about the consequences of highway realignment.[12]

The Bureau of Public Roads Studies

Experience built up in earlier highway studies led the University of Washington group into a series of more ambitious investigations sponsored by the U. S. Bureau of Public Roads in cooperation with the Department of Highways of the State of Washington: *Studies of Highway Development and Geographic Change* and *Studies of the Central Business District* and *Urban Freeway Development*. Both volumes are due to be published at the time this review appears.

Studies of Highway Development and Geographic Change has five major sections. The first is introductory, containing a brief general overview of the highway impact problem and an evaluation of contemporary thinking concerning the benefits of highway improvements. Each of the four succeeding sections contains a sample study of some funda-

---

[11] For a long-run investigation see Gerhard Sandner, *Wabern: Die Entwicklung eines nordhessischen Dorfes unter dem Einfluss der Verkehrszentralität*, Marburger Geographische Schriften (Marburg, 1958).
[12] An entirely "plausible" interpretation of the Marysville findings was later presented in Garrison, Berry, *et al.*, *Studies of Highway Development and Geographic Change*.

mental aspect of the geographic organization of economic life, the place of highways within this organization, and the geographic influences of highway change. In each section a preliminary step is to review previous empirical studies and available theory bearing upon the particular problem. Each study then uses this review as a framework within which hypotheses are stated and research is designed.[13]

The first of the sample studies involves relations of highways and business. Four contrasting groups of business types and types of business centers were isolated by means of correlation and linkage analysis: (1) nucleated business centers, arranged in four levels of a hierarchy below the central business district of the regional metropolis; (2) highway oriented "ribbons" arranged with respect to highway traffic; (3) urban arterial types; (4) specialized functional areas, such as automobile row. Data from the Marysville study were then reinterpreted by means of indices of sensitivity to highway change, using the information concerning groups of business types. Two kinds of change were discovered: (1) increase or decrease in sales volumes of highway-oriented business as a result of changes in traffic volumes; (2) centralization of nucleated-type facilities in successively higher-order levels of the hierarchy as accessibility in the system is increased. Thus, with a decline in congestion in Marysville and an increase in the accessibility of the city, growth was experienced in "neighborhood" sectors of the town's economy. But since accessibility to the larger centers of Everett and Seattle also was increased, "community level" facilities in Marysville experienced a period of increasing competition and declining sales volumes.[14]

Relations of urban residential land use and highways are the topic of the second study. First, multiple regression techniques were used to measure the associations of land values with access, described in terms of distance from a variety of locational referents. As in Garrison's study of rural roads, no significant relations were found between distance and value of the residential site. Second, three regression analyses, of lapsed

---

[13] For further discussion of the approaches of these studies see William L. Garrison, "Approaches to Three Highway Impact Problems," paper presented at 38th Annual Meetings of the Highway Research Board, Washington, January 1959, and to be published in the *Proceedings*.

[14] See Brian J. L. Berry, "Ribbon Developments in the Urban Business Pattern," *Annals,* Association of American Geographers, Vol. 49 (June, 1959), for a definition of neighborhood and community level business types. Another study reporting similar effects is provided by Walter C. McKain *et al.,* at Storrs Agricultural Experiment Station, University of Connecticut: *The Economic and Social Effects of the Connecticut Turnpike on Eastern Connecticut* (mimeographed report for administrative use, circulated to Highway Departments, impact study groups, and interested persons, June, 1958). Gerard J. Foster and Howard J. Nelson provide detailed information on traffic and business in their study *Ventura Boulevard: A String-Type Shopping Street* (Real Estate Research Program, Bureau of Business and Economic Research, University of California, Los Angeles, 1958). It is hoped that the "after" complement to this "before" study will be completed to throw further light on the relations of business and highways.

time from home, trip frequencies, and total distance travelled, on 14 social, economic, and locational variables, were used to estimate factors influencing the demand for transportation at urban residential sites. It was found that lapsed time from home and trip frequencies were significantly related only to social and economic variables exogenous to the spatial system. Therefore, like Garrison in the case of rural farm and nonfarm residences, the authors concluded that a change in the spatial system due to highway improvements would *not* have any influence either upon length of time spent from home or upon frequency of trips. Total distance travelled was related to the independent variables only at very low levels of significance. However, since the most significant associations were with factors of location, it was concluded that a change in highway facilities *might* affect total distance travelled, with an unchanging number of trips and total time spent from home.

The third study attempts to relate business structure to the nature of shopping trips made by urban residents. It did not prove possible in this study to establish simple sets of strong relationships, thus reemphasizing the complexity of links between the geographical structure of the economy and highway use. A major difficulty in the analysis was the problem of handling multipurpose trips (which constituted 59 percent of all trips made), especially where more than one business center was visited.

In the final study, consumer movements to a particular class of services, physician care, are analyzed. The study describes trends in the location of physicians as highway facilities change, and discusses patterns of movement for medical care at urban, regional, and national levels. One of the outstanding features of the study is the presentation and use of a spatial price equilibrium model which permits precise accounting of (1) changes in production, consumption, and trade between areas, (2) changes in service areas, and (3) benefits, including both gains and losses, to areas, producers, and consumers. It was found that where the consumption function is elastic, trade will increase and producers will gain as a result of a highway improvement. Where trade and consumption are inelastic, consumers gain through time and cost savings. Because movement to central cities is facilitated by highway improvements, the centralization of medical services is stimulated at the expense of outlying centers and rural areas.

Studies of the Central Business District and Urban Freeway Development also has five sections. The first part is introductory, providing a review of approaches to the study of central business districts and a presentation of the "core-frame" concept as the basis for subsequent analysis. Section two measures change in central business districts since the Second World War. Two aspects of central business activity are considered, retail sales and office space. Declines in retail sales were found, the rate of decline depending upon size of city. Central office space tended to increase, the rate of increase depending upon size of city, with larger cities developing at more rapid rates. In the third section decentralization from the central business district is measured. Insurance offices decentralized 30–40 percent in the period 1946–58. On the other hand electric utility offices tended to remain central, as did banking deposits. Reasons for differences in decentralization trends between various kinds of land uses are examined in detail.

This empirical analysis provided information concerning trends in central business districts and evaluated some of the conditions under which land uses tend to decentralize. Section four deals with the transportation implications of these findings. First, the nature of urban freeway and expressway systems is discussed (no attention is paid to city arterial systems), and the character of particular kinds of routes is clarified (i.e., radials, circumferentials, and inner distribution loops). Particular attention is paid to the resulting cellular structure of urban areas. Second, urban freeway and expressway impact upon city centers is evaluated. Radials are shown to be effective in promoting centralization or decentralization, whereas the inner distributor loop and other circumferentials affect clustering and dispersion of land uses. Land takings for highways and intersections can interfere with business linkages, particularly in the frame (defined in the first part of the study) of the central business district. Most effects are considered to occur in the frame rather than the core, because the core has entirely external transportation connections, whereas routes converge in the frame. In the final section of the volume, tax implications of highway impact research are evaluated in light of current legal thinking regarding taxation of indirect benefits and recognition of severance damages.

Bus Route Studies

Bus route studies are to Europe what highway studies are to the United States; whereas in the United States circulation of people and functioning of the tertiary sector of the economy is by automobile on the highways, the European tends to use the bus.[15] It is therefore to be expected that the focus of the European bus route studies is upon relations of bus traffic, settlements and settlement patterns, and business and trade areas. As is true of the highway impact studies, many of the bus route studies also have a planning orientation. Both English and Swedish studies are designed for use in reorganizing local government. German

---

[15] In Sweden 97–98 percent of all passenger movements by road are on buses, reports Sven Godlund in his "Bus Service in Sweden," *op. cit.* On the other hand, in American cities such as Detroit and Chicago, *where bus service and mass transit are available,* between 76 and 84 percent of all person trips are still made by means of automobile (the former percent is for Chicago, the latter for Detroit); see Roger L. Creighton, "Final Data from all Travel Surveys," *Chicago Area Transportation Study Research News,* Vol. 3 (January, 1959), pp. 18–20.

studies that contribute to the work of the Akademie für Raumforschung und Landesplanung have already been discussed.

British Studies of Local Accessibility

Results of studies of bus routes, bus traffic, and urban hinterlands in the British Isles have been published in the form of a two-part map in the Ordnance Survey's 1:625,000 *Planning Map* series, together with a brief explanatory text. These studies posit a five-level hierarchy of urban centers in the British Isles: metropolis (first-order), provincial center, regional center, local center (fourth-order), and village.[16] Bus traffic data are used to delimit hinterlands of fourth-order (local) centers, because it is argued that "in the course of twenty or more years' experience the bus operators have discovered the most profitable routes by a process of trial and error." Information was gathered from local timetables, and winter bus services on market days were assumed to be most representative of the sphere of influence of a local center. In northwest Scotland steamer services also were included. The map records hinterland boundaries of fourth-order centers, and the populations of the centers and their hinterlands. Centers were defined as places that have regular stage carriage services to places smaller than themselves. Hinterlands were defined as traffic divides. The explanatory text includes a brief comparison of the findings on the map with Smailes' urban hierarchy and with the status of towns at the time of the 1851 census. The remarkable stability of the urban pattern over the last century is noted "reflecting the essential reality of town and country relationships." Practical implications of the findings are discussed, including aids to planning of local administrative boundaries and more effective town and country planning.[17] These studies reemphasize the "fun-

---

[16] For a detailed discussion of each of these levels see F. H. W. Green, "Community of Interest Areas. Notes on the Hierarchy of Central Places and Their Hinterlands," *Economic Geography*, Vol. 34 (July, 1958), pp. 210–26, and the associated work of Ian Carruthers, "A Classification of Service Centres in England and Wales," *Geographical Journal*, Vol. 122 (September, 1957), pp. 371–85. Carruthers has some critical comments concerning the maps of *Local Accessibility*. He also provides evidence that tends to support Lösch's contention of functional differentiation between centers at any one level of the hierarchy. Both Carruthers, and Green in the explanatory text accompanying the planning series maps, compare their results with those of Smailes' urban hierarchy of England and Wales. One wonders about the value of continued *a priori* allocation of towns to classes, details of the hierarchy existing by definition alone, when one sees the typical 20 percent disagreement between classifications.

[17] See similar studies by Hans Carol in Switzerland relating central place studies to local planning: "Industrie und Siedlungsplanung," *Plan* (Nov.–Dec. 1951), pp. 191–206; "Das Agrargeographische Betrachtungssystem," *Geographica Helvetica*, Vol. 1 (March, 1952), pp. 17–67; "Zürichs Aufschwung zur Wirtschaftsmetropole der Schweiz," *Neue Zürcher Zeitung* (7 Aug., 1954); "Sozialräumliche Gliederung und planerische Gestaltung des Grosstadtbereiches," *Raumforschung und Raumordnung*, Vol. 14 (1956), pp. 80–92. Also in the same number of *Raumforschung* are several German studies with similar planning orientation: E. Dittrich, "Das Stadt–Umland–

damental economic and social grouping" which is characteristic of Western society.

Bus Service in Sweden

Studies of bus services in Sweden [18] have been far more profound in scope and implications than their British counterparts. The first of these studies is concerned with "the general course of the innovation process and the growth of the traffic-bearing road system, the size and aim of the passenger flow and the conditions pertaining to ownership." The companion volume examines relationships between bus traffic and urban hinterlands, and associates growth and decline of urban places with strategic location on the bus traffic network.

The study begins with a brief evaluation of the diffusion of innovation waves in Europe, comparing the course of innovation of bus traffic with that for railroads, and associating the sequence of development with European cultures and economies. This section is necessarily brief, since detailed information is lacking. Development of bus traffic is then surveyed in Sweden as a whole. An excellent series of maps is presented showing growth of the bus network from the beginning of the First World War onwards, identifying types of carriers. Associations between degree of urbanization and rapid adoption of innovations are suggested. Four counties are given more penetrating and detailed analysis: Östergötland, Kristianstad, Malmöhus, and Jämtland (E, L, M, and Z counties respectively). Detailed maps show the changing extent of the bus traffic network in each county since the First World War. Isarithmic maps then relate the spread of innovation waves to "saturation" or "equilibrium" levels of bus service over the available highway system, to population densities and distribution, and to distance from major urban centers. The result is a remarkably clear picture of where innovations occur, how they spread, and the conditions under which an equilibrium is reached.

The role of bus traffic in establishing the sphere of urban influence is then examined. Godlund frames his analysis in an excellent critical review of methods of determining urban "centrality," or the degree to which a place is center to a tributary zone. As the review proceeds, Godlund builds up a new index of centrality, ultimately defined as the surplus of urban retail functions over the average for the region in

Verhältnis in seiner planerische Problematik," pp. 65–71; F. Forbat, "Die Bedeutung der umlandbestimmenden Faktoren für die Planung," pp. 71–80; K. H. Brunner, "Der Verkehr als Bindeglied zwischen Stadt und Land," pp. 97–101.
[18] Godlund, "Bus Service in Sweden," *op. cit.,* and "The Function and Growth of Bus Traffic within the Sphere of Urban Influence," *op. cit.* These are the English summaries of a larger study in Swedish: *Bustrafikens framväxt och function i de urbana influensfälten.* For a similar study in Austria see Helmut Schmid, "Das Autobusnetz Osterreichs" *Wiener Geographische Schriften* (Wien: Verlag Ferdinand Berger, 1958).

which the center is located. Extremely strong correlations were found between this index and total arrivals and departures of bus passengers at towns ($r = 0.9$) Therefore, it was concluded that the centrality measure is a good approximation of bus traffic levels. Three indices of centrality were computed for each central place in the four sample counties: for one year before the First World War, for one interwar year, and for one year after the Second World War. Centers were then grouped into five classes.[19] Umlands were mapped for the highest order centers for each of the three time periods. Godlund distinguishes between an *urban field* and an *umland.* The former is continuous, declining with distance from a center; the latter is an area of dominance versus all other places. Umlands obtained from bus traffic data coincide with umlands calculated from indices of centrality.

Upon examination of the maps for any time period it was found that the two levels of central places immediately below the level for which umlands were mapped grouped in the "indifference zones" between the umlands of the higher order centers. Viewing the fortunes of urban places through time, Godlund found that centrality grew most rapidly in centers with the best road connections and bus services, whereas centers which lacked these facilities languished. A tendency for a "metropolitan effect" was also noted, i.e., places close to centers of the highest order have lost centrality as access has been improved and they have been brought within the sphere of the expanding metropolitan community.[20]

The volume concludes with an examination of the planning implications of the findings. Two points are made: that spheres of influence suggest new types of administrative regionalization, and that since the welfare of towns is so intimately related to bus traffic, direction of bus traffic can effectively direct the course of development of towns.

In Conclusion

At least a few concluding remarks should be addressed to the woods rather than to the trees, particularly in so far as the role of transportation in the space economy is concerned. What do these studies contribute? What was already known? What is new?

One should distinguish immediately between the more traditional German and British studies and new departures in American and

[19] No grouping analysis was undertaken, and these classes, therefore, exist by definition alone.
[20] This indicates that transport improvements lead both to relative central place effects and to metropolitan effects, and suggests a possible basis for liaison between central place theory and concepts of metropolitan dominance of McKenzie, Bogue, et al. See D. J. Bogue, *The Structure of the Metropolitan Community. A Study of Dominance and Subdominance* (Ann Arbor: School of Graduate Studies, University of Michigan, 1950).

Swedish investigations. The more traditional works tend to be descriptive and discursive. Using maps and tables, they provide a great deal of information about the movements of goods and people. More important, they reemphasize the mutual interdependence of a specialized economy, circulation and traffic, and the transport system. Circulation results from bringing together areally separated demands and supplies through trade. The amount of traffic is a function of the nature of demands and supplies and of the character of available transport systems. Each means of transport has its own technological characteristics and its spatial layout, or network. The total transport system is a composite of many types of transport acting in unison or competition over a conglomerate of networks. Circulation is limited, directed, and channelled by this composite, conglomerate transport system. It is obvious that relationships are extremely complex, whether they be of the economy-circulation-transport type which gives rise to goods movement or the livelihood-settlement-circulation-transport type, which describes the movement of persons. Change in any one part of the system is likely to be precipitated throughout the whole, and it is hard to think of a satisfactory study of any part which does not take account of the others.

If all that the traditional studies had accomplished had been to point out once again the complexities of these relationships, they would have served a useful function, even though not an original one, as those familiar with location theory will recognize. But *Raum und Verkehr* and the British bus route studies also go a long way towards revealing the nature of some of the relationships, particularly with respect to the economic characteristics and competitive role of different types of transport media and the circulation patterns associated with each.

The American and Swedish studies are highly pointed and analytic. They build up a knowledge of structure and process, placing great emphasis upon construction of an appropriate theoretical framework and a careful experimental design, and on the use of new statistical and mathematical tools. Concern in particular is with highways and highway traffic, by bus or automobile as appropriate, and their relations to occupation, settlement, and movement of persons, and to the nature and status of towns insofar as they function as centers in the tertiary sector of the economy.

Real contributions are made. Let us take the example of highway impact upon central places. The studies found that:

1. The demand for transportation is related to the social and economic characteristics of households, but not to the relative location of the residence. Hence, even if highways change accessibility and, therefore, relative location, they cannot be expected to change the demand for travel and, therefore, trip frequencies. All that can be expected is that at a given level of trip frequency people may be able to travel

farther. New highways do not necessarily generate new traffic, although they can divert traffic from older routes and expedite movement.

2. Centralization takes place in the urban hierarchy because improved access increases the competitive ability of higher-order centers vis-à-vis lower-order centers.

3. New highways facilitate decentralization and suburbanization, and, just as important, result in a "metropolitan effect" whereby expanding metropolitan communities engulf previously independent central places and the metropolis usurps their functions.

These findings are of some theoretical significance. The changes can be and have been quantified in several instances. From the more sweeping German studies there is every indication that similar effects have occurred historically with different types of transport and at different scales than reported in the highway studies. One case is in the centralization of scattered industrial facilities during the nineteenth century, which took place in response to improvements in transportation even in those activities where the rate of technological change was not great.

Technical contributions of the American and Swedish investigations have been just as profound as the empirical and the theoretical. The studies show the rewards which accrue to the research worker from careful problem formulation and experimental design. They illustrate uses of such statistical tools as correlation and multiple regression analysis and such mathematical tools as the spatial price equilibrium model. Yet, as far as techniques are concerned, the studies have barely scratched the surface. As yet we have no geographic examples of the use of multivariate statistics for classificatory work or of mathematical tools such as linear programming. It is to be hoped that we will make full use of the opportunities which they provide.

15. The Manpower Problem in Siberia

Stephan G. Prociuk

The availability of a variety of skilled manpower is important to a nation as well as an individual manufacturing establishment. In all cities, states, regions, and countries, there is internal migration of people who are attracted by employment opportunities or a chance of bettering their occupational status and standard of living. This is also true between

countries, as is well illustrated in the European Common
Market countries by the movement of Italians northward
into West Germany.
   Prociuk's article shows the significance of labor availability.
Among the many problems in the economic development of
Siberia, labor is a major one, the magnitude and complexity
of which Prociuk fully develops.
   Prociuk also indicates the role a strong central government
in a communistic country plays in the allocation of manpower.
Despite this control, however, in the 1960's more people left
Siberia than arrived. This migration of workers causes
severe problems in successfully opening up new territory.

Although many extensive studies have been published in the West on
the economic development of the USSR, a veil of uncertainty, even of
mystery, obscures the picture of development that is taking place in the
Asiatic part of the USSR. Reports on construction projects like the
Bratsk hydro-power station or the aluminium plants at Krasnoyarsk and
Regar [1] often appear in our journals and newspapers, and other projects, such as the exploitation of virgin lands in Kazakhstan, are mentioned from time to time. In general, however, we have at best only a
dim picture of the actual changes introduced throughout vast areas of
Siberia in the last two decades.

There are several reasons for this. One may be some intrinsic and
highly resistant ignorance of many of us about lands known only
through stereotyped images of the 'Asiatic wilderness', associated with
pictures of Gobi-type deserts, inaccessible mountains, camels and tigers,
or of Eskimo-like peoples and their Shaman pagan customs. But our
vision is also obscured by an avalanche of Soviet literature, primarily
fiction and technical publications, that is eagerly sent to the West, although a good basic book on *local* problems of these territories remains
a rarity. Every time one seeks information on specific problems of
Siberian development, a laborious search must be undertaken through
hundreds upon hundreds of Soviet papers (where often the 'Letters to

SOURCE: *Soviet Studies*, XIX (October, 1967), 190–210. Reprinted by permission.
The author, a specialist on the Soviet Union, is on the faculty of St. Andrew's
University, Scotland.
[1] The full capacity of Krasnoyarsk plant is planned to reach 400 thousand tons per
year in the early 1970s. Thus the plant will become the largest of its kind in the
USSR. The Regar plant (in the Tadzhik SSR) was apparently designed on the
drawing board in full details in 1964; it will use the power from both a hydroelectric cascade on the river Vakhsh at Nurek and the natural gas brought by pipeline to Dushanbe from Afghanistan. All the numerous Soviet sources tend· to
emphasize the role of Bratsk power station in the 'peaceful' development of the
adjoining area. They fail to say that one of the primary users of Bratsk power is a
huge uranium-processing plant erected in Ust'–Vichoyeva in the hidden valley of the
river Kosa northwest of Bratsk.

the Editor' provide the most interesting and informative comments),
and one must feel fortunate indeed if a booklet or pamphlet published
in Kransoyarsk, Irkutsk or Komsomol'sk reaches Western shores.

Strangely enough, the institution from which we would expect the
best review of Siberian problems, the Siberian branch of the Academy
of Sciences in Novosibirsk, is not very active in publishing results of its
investigations on the *economic* aspects of opening up new areas in the
region. The Siberian branch, considerably expanded from 1963 to 1965,
has been entrusted with important research in the extra sciences (math-
emathics, cybernetics, physics, chemistry), and it also conducts extensive geological and geophysical studies and field surveys. Unfortunately,
few books have been published in Novosibirsk on the economic and
social implications of new projects launched in Siberia. There is evidence that a computer center of the Siberian branch of the Academy of
Sciences does process some data on economic planning in the Asiatic
part of the USSR, the main task being presumably an optimization
procedure under given conditions. It is possible, however, that the results obtained by the computer do not agree with the official programme of development, and that explains why they remain mostly
unpublished, circulating as semi-classified reports for internal use only.

Although we are highly critical of the 'fairy tales' published in many
Soviet magazines and newspapers about the opening up of Siberia—
especially those which are lavishly illustrated and obviously intended
for foreign readers [2]—we can sincerely admire the courage of Soviet
explorers in Siberia and appreciate the many young people who are
unafraid of physical hardship in the fight for the rehabilitation of
Siberian lands for human habitation and civilization. We do not wonder
that Soviet recruiting authorities found use even for the old English
slogan which says that a feeling of inconvenience is merely inadequate
appreciation of adventure. This slogan, however, does not seem to be of
much help in solving a grave problem which arose almost overnight for
the Soviet government—the problem of *vanishing manpower* in Siberia.

The author recently published a brief study on some aspects of the

---

[2] The inconsistency of these stories is shown by an example. A special issue of
Soviet Union on Siberia (November 1965, p. 30) mentions Yurii Khabardin as the
discoverer of diamond deposits in the Mirnyy area. Khabardin as a young student
of geology apparently received a Lenin prize in 1955 for this discovery. On the
other hand, D. Botting, an English journalist and photographer, reports from Soviet
sources that it was a young woman student, Larisa Popugaeva of Leningrad, who
discovered the Mirnyy kimberlite deposits (see 'Russia, a New Frontier', *International*, vol. 1, no. 3, October 1965, p. 32). Personally we are inclined to give the
full credit for this discovery to those innumerable deportee-prisoners who worked
there and lost their lives in the Siberian taiga while struggling to 'prove their willingness to cooperate with the Soviet regime'. It would be fair to admit that some
Soviet writers of today try to reappraise the exploration work done by political deportees in Yakutia, Kolyma and Chukotka (see the novels on 'treasures' by Dimitrii
Demin, Nikolai Novikov or Valerii Osipov).

industrialization of the sub-Urals. This article, being a continuation of the author's research on industrialization of areas beyond the Urals, reports on problems on colonizing that area and concentrates on the labour situation, which became a nightmare for Soviet planners in the period from 1962 to 1965. There are of course many other problems equally deserving of attention—for example, the vital problem of fresh water supply, not only in Siberia proper but in the wastelands between the Caspian Sea and the Turksib railway, which necessitates the building of huge, expensive atomic-power stations to drive desalination plants, as at Shevchenko on the Caspian Sea. And yet, precisely in this area, rich deposits of metallic ores and minerals were recently discovered, and Soviet scientists do not hesitate to call it 'the second Urals', visualizing this area as one which will become the backbone of the total industrial development of the USSR in the next few decades. Installations similar to that in Shevchenko have also been built in the adjoining areas of Kazakhstan, in particular in the vicinity of Tyuratam (on Syr-Dar'ya near the Aral Sea) and Sary-Shagan (on Lake Balkhash, where Soviet rocket-launching facilities became operational a few years ago). Yet the problem of fresh water still remains as acute as ever. Even in the regions where until recently no one would expect a water shortage (e.g., in areas adjoining the famous Baykal Lake, which alone contains, according to Soviet estimates, one-tenth of the total fresh water resources of our planet), a shortage of drinking water threatens because of the heavy pollution of lake water caused by wastes from the cellulose plants in the Selenga district.[3] The same thing has happened in the once-rich Angara River, where 1800 cubic metres of poisonous wastes are washed into the river *every minute* from Bratsk timber-processing plants.

Excessive Manpower Fluctuation

Whatever the natural difficulties at the present stage of developing Soviet Siberia may be, they seem to be less than those of transplanting skilled and unskilled manpower to those regions for operating and maintaining new installations. We shall not repeat here the readily available figures showing population growth in the Asiatic part of the USSR in the postwar period, since such figures are meaningless without thorough analysis. We also refrain from quoting extensively 1959 census data since they have already become a subject of rather numerous reviews in both Soviet and Western literature. It appears to us superfluous to refer to the much publicized data anew. It is well known, for example, that the index of demographic natural growth in the Kazakh,

[3] The volume of waste to be disposed in Lake Baykal in the late 1960s will amount to 70 million tons per year; see A. Merkulov, 'Trevoga o Baikale', *Pravda*, 28 February 1965.

Uzbek and Kirgiz union republics amounted, in 1961, on the average, to 35.0–40.0 and in the Turkmen SSR even to 40.0–45.0, whereas the overall average for the USSR was 23.8 (and only 21.3 in 1963). The natural population growth in the Siberian regions of the RSFSR is also much higher than in Russia proper. Sonin and Nevel'shtein report that the only regions of the RSFSR showing a natural growth index greater than 30.0 are those belonging to autonomous republics or autonomous oblasts or, as Sonin points out, to regions 'inhabited by nations oppressed by the former tsarist regime'. The natural growth index in Siberia and the Far East also exceeds considerably the average for the RSFSR.

In view of these facts, it becomes increasingly difficult to estimate the true extent of immigration into Siberia in the postwar period and the proportion which this immigration represents in the six million people by which the population beyond the Urals grew from 1945 to 1962.

Considerable data, however, have recently been published by Soviet sources on some regional moves of population which help to draw an overall picture of the current situation. The number of migrants from the European part of the USSR to beyond the Urals in the years from 1926 to 1939 amounted to 3 millions, including those resettled by force or simply banished during the peak period of the regime of terror in the years from 1934 to 1938. From 1939 to 1959, the population of Soviet Asia increased by 35.6 percent (as compared with 9.5 percent for the total area of the USSR). Various specific factors explain this increase: first, the population beyond the Urals was spared the extremely heavy war losses sustained by the western regions of the European USSR in 1941–44: moreover, quite a large number evacuated in 1941–43 from the Ukraine, from Belorussia and from the northwestern districts of the RSFSR, did not return to their former residence and settled down for good beyond the Urals. The impact of the much higher rate of natural growth of autochthonous population in the areas under consideration has already been cited. Also, a new wave of enforced resettlements and deportations came in 1944 and 1945, when hundreds of thousands of North Caucasians and Crimeans became victims, in addition to those Volga Germans who had already been deported in 1941 and 1942. Later, in the final phase of Stalin's regime in 1950–52, there was a marked increase in deportations.

Thus we may see that *voluntary* migration contributed very little to the increase of 35.6 percent in the trans-Ural population in the period from 1939 to 1959. As will be shown, the trend in 1959 to 1964 was reversed, and the number of people that left the Eastern (Asiatic) regions of the USSR for the European sector outweighed the number of settlers and migrants moving from the west to the east. Consequently the statistics show that, as at 1 January 1964, in the three principal Asiatic economic districts (West Siberia, East Siberia and the Soviet

Far East, which together cover 11.3 million square kilometres, 51 percent of the total USSR territory), only 23.5 million people were living
—i.e., only 10.2 percent of the total population.[4]

To get an idea of how many people are actually leaving Siberia and
to what extent the balance of migration there during the last decade
became negative, we will quote a few figures that illustrate the desper-
ate efforts, of the Soviet government to transplant people from the west
to the east and that show the enormous numbers of people being shifted
constantly to and from Siberia.

E. Manevich[5] reports that from 1956 to 1960 apparently more than
1,400,000 people moved into the Siberian area (700,000 were resettled
under the governmental scheme alone. The survey of 1961–62, however, showed that the rate of total growth of population in Siberia was
less than the rate of natural increase. This means that the number of
people who left Siberia in 1956–60 exceeded 1,400,000 and, in fact,
might have amounted to close to 2 million. We possess a detailed picture of resettlement from the Ukraine: in 1946–62, a total of 810,000
skilled and semi-skilled workers left the Ukraine mainly for the east, together with an additional 88,000 peasant families. Assuming that the
average Ukrainian family today numbers 3.8, we arrive at the estimate
of 1,145,000 Ukrainians who were transplanted from home, in most
cases beyond the Urals. Another figure also reveals the magnitude of
the Soviet inter-republican population shifts: 1,230,000 'volunteers',
members of Komsomol, left the European part for Siberia and Kazakhstan in 1955–60. We must also mention large groups of university students of the Ukraine, Belorussia and partly European Russia who are
being assigned, after taking their degrees, to work in new industrial
centres in Siberia. It has been estimated that approximately 17 percent
of all university-level graduates in the Ukraine and 24 percent of the
graduates of the Ukraine *tekhnikumy* were sent, in the period from
1947 to 1959, to other union republics.

Nevertheless, as was pointed out above, the overall balance of population movements became negative in the 1960s—that is, the number
of people leaving Siberia exceeds that of new arrivals. Many Soviet
economists and demographers have published alarming reports on this
phenomenon. Some very early reports were published by Zaionchkov-

[4] Occasionally we find also a figure 10.4 percent in Soviet sources; presumably it
originates in preliminary estimates from the 1962–63 period.
[5] E. Manevich, 'Vseobshchnost' truda i problemy ratsional'nogo ispol'zovaniya
rabochei sily v SSSR', *Voprosy ekonomiki*, 1965, no. 6. Manevich makes a distinction between migrants moved in 'organized' and 'non-organized' ways. This distinction is far from clear. The comment by Zaionchkovskaya and Perevedentsev on
'non-organized' migration is highly interesting and illuminating: . . . the last
[= non-organized migration], of course, takes place under the impact of planned
measures aiming at the development of production forces' (*Geografiya naseleniyā
Vostochnoĭ Sibiri* (M. 1962), p. 87, footnote 2).

skaya and Perevedentsev,[6] who discovered that 145 departures occurred in 1956–58 for each 100 arrivals to the towns of Krasnoyarsk krai from towns of the Ukraine and Moldavia, and 125 departures to each 100 arrivals to the towns of the krai from rural areas of the Ukraine and Moldavia. An equally negative balance occurred in migration movement between Krasnoyarsk krai and the western republics of the USSR *(Zapad SSSR)* and in the case of urban migration between the krai and the Urals, the Kazakh SSR and Central Asia. Large industrial sites in the Krasnoyarsk krai show an even more negative balance—for each 100 new arrivals at the Sorsk molybdenum plant there were as many as 201 departures. A similar situation was observed in the Yakut ASSR: for each 100 arrivals from the Ukraine and North Caucasus (in the original: 'from the south—*yug*—of the European part of the USSR'), there were 220 departures for those areas. Sonin gives us a general picture of the situation in Siberian towns in 1956–59. For every 100 persons arriving from the Ukraine, there were 135 persons returning home. The relevant figures for Transcaucasia were 100: 130, for Central Asiatic republics 100: 142. Even the Kuznetsk Basin area, which belongs to those areas of West Siberia where colonization reached some kind of stability, now shows the same trend: for every 100 new immigrants from the Ukraine and Belorussia there were from 130 to 170 departures (all studies speak of *permanent* departures) back to those republics. Migration from the other areas shows a still higher ratio—the departures for the Baltic republics and the North Caucasus amounted to 300 per 100 arrivals; for Central Asiatic regions the figure ranged from 250 to 270. The influx of migrants and, above all, repatriates to the North Caucasus areas was, in 1959–62, of such magnitude that the share of the above districts in the total increase of population of the whole RSFSR in those three years amounted to 20 percent of that total, although the territory of the North Caucasus area is only 4 percent of the Russian republic.

This situation, especially as regards the North Caucasus, is partly explained by the return of the deportees. As already indicated, all the resettlements to Siberia in 1934–53 were, strictly speaking, typical deportations. Since Khruschev's denunciation of Stalin's deviations, those deportations in many cases were recognized as having been illegal, and 'resettlers' from that period were doubtless permitted to return home. Thus figures on departures from Siberia, exceeding by far the number of new arrivals, reflect nothing more than the return of former deportees. Although there is evidence of various measures taken by the Soviet government to attract these 'victims of Stalinist violence' to the Siberian scene (by granting them several amenities as well as freedom of move-

[6] *Geografiya naseleniya Vostochnoi Sibiri* (see footnote 5), pp. 82–95; this study, greatly enlarged and revised, was also published as a paperback under the title *Sovremennaya migratsiya naseleniya Krasnoyarskogo Kraya* (Novosibirsk, 1964).

ment within the wide borders of Siberia proper), their hardy nostalgia prevailed, and the flow of returning deportees became very strong. We may assume also that the stream of returning settlers was swollen by many other inhabitants of Siberia who decided to take advantage of the opportunity to exchange the cold and unfriendly taiga for the rich sunny steppes of the North Caucasus region.

There is, moreover, ample evidence that even the volunteer settlers of the 1955–64 period—that is, the new immigrants from the European part of the USSR as well as those from some Asiatic republics familiar with the highly unsatisfactory living and working conditions in Siberia —would also leave their assigned locations *en masse* or, as in the case of peasants, the newly created *sovkhozy*. The great majority of workers leave their positions before the expiration of their contracts; in Krasnoyarsk krai, for example, no more than 12 percent of newly recruited workers finished their contracts, the others leaving their jobs prematurely.

Heavy fluctuations occurred not only in Siberia proper but also in the adjoining regions. P. O. Kosyakov reports that in 1955–58 alone there were 265,000 departures registered from the Sverdlovsk oblast as compared with 285,000 arrivals, and 175,000 departures as against 200,000 arrivals in the Chelyabinsk oblast.

High Costs of Resettling

These facts are hardly encouraging for the planning authorities, especially since the transplanting of workers and *kolkhoz* peasants is today a very costly operation. It has been estimated by scientists at the NIIT (*Nauchno-issledovateľ skii institut truda Gosudarstvennogo Komiteta Soveta Ministrov SSSR po voprosam truda i zarabotnoi platy*) that the average cost of resettling one worker from any of the central Russian oblasts to Siberia amounts to 100 rubles, not including various marginal losses.

Thus merely the loss of working time due to transfers amounts on the average to 30 days for one settler. Additional losses are due to the fact that it takes five months for the output of even a skilled worker to return to normal in a new location. We do not know whether this estimate includes the enormous losses that originate in the delay in putting the enterprise into operation because of the unavailability of the required manpower. This explains Manevich's statement in 1965, to the effect that the total cost of bringing one migrant worker to a newly built plant in Siberia amounted to 500 rubles. In view of all the broken contracts and the colossal numbers of settlers returning home soon after arrival, the cost of transplanting them to Siberia represents wasted money and must be written off as a complete loss. Manevich quotes the sum of 2 milliard rubbles as being lost yearly through the fluctuation of manpower beyond the Urals. (*Izvestiya* of 19 June 1963 cites the figure of 3 milliard as representing losses in 1960 from manpower fluctuations in Soviet industry.)

The cost of securing accommodation also adds to the high cost of bringing migrant labour to Siberia. A good account of the extreme difficulties of industrial and civic construction in northern Siberia is given in a recent volume of *Problemy Severa*.[7] This report sheds light on specific problems in securing accommodation and supplies for indigenous populations. The contributors describe difficulties in such towns as Murmansk, Vorkuta, Magadan, Noril'sk and Yakutsk, where the cost of construction of 1 square metre of living space was found to be three times higher than in the southern regions of West Siberia and four times higher than in central Russia. An interesting conclusion was reached by several scientists participating in research on population problems in the Soviet north. They declare that it would be highly wasteful and quite unnecessary to increase further the population of North Siberian towns and industrial settlements, and they advocate the decrease of existing population that would result from a more vigorous introduction of modern technology (great automated processes and plants, particularly in mining and power production, as well as in new chemical complexes). Some authors, significantly, seem to be impressed by examples of advanced development of the Canadian northern mining centres and quote these examples frequently.

Residential construction is difficult and very expensive, not only in Siberian towns but in villages and settlements (*poselki*). In many regions of Siberia numerous ghost towns, or rather ghost villages, exist, like those in former gold-mining areas in the United States and Australia, which at best may be occupied only temporarily by nomadic exploration parties or semi-rural groups of aborigines searching for pastures or for hunting bases. Some of the new *poselki*, hastily built to accommodate fresh parties of settler-explorers, are predestined soon to become ghost villages too, although their construction, however primitive, has been expensive. Soviet authors admit that the primitive way of life in the remote Siberian villages frightens many an initially courageous rural migrant from the European USSR. One must realize that the

[7] 'Stroitel'stvo na krainem severe', *Problemy Severa*, vyp. 10 (M. 1964). V. L. Nevecherya also discusses problems of construction on permafrost soils in his recent papers 'Sezonnoe promerzanie gruntov v taezhnykh raionakh Zapadnoi Sibiri' and 'O metodike rascheta predzimnei vlazhnosti gruntov Yugo-Zapadnoi Sibiri', *Izvestiya Sibirskogo otdeleniya Akademii nauk SSSR*, seriya tekhmeheskikh nauk, 1965, no. 10, pp. 130–9. How important the problem is we gather from a recent report according to which a team of Soviet architects and soil specialists (M. V. Kim, V. Kolyada, A. Zaïdel, M. Bitadze, J. Epshtein and others) was awarded a Lenin prize in 1966 for new methods of construction in permafrost conditions. It is amazing to learn that research centers as distant (in geographical terms as well as in terms of the profile of research) as the Khar'kov Aviation Institute (Ukraine) collaborated with Noril'sk industrial *kombinat* in developing the subpolar towns of the USSR.

attitude of today's migrant is quite different from that of a migrant at
the turn of the century, who could actually become a well-to-do farmer
after colonizing the richest and climatically most favourable districts of
South Siberia.

Dissatisfaction of Migrants

It is of interest to analyse the underlying motivations behind the great
fluctuation of the labour force in Soviet eastern territories. The sincerity
with which these motivations are being discussed in Soviet sources
varies considerably. The more 'official' a given publication is, the more
fragmentary and unreliable is the information given. In his most recent
book, Sonin gives the following picture: 50 percent of all drafted workers leave their jobs in Siberia at their own request; 20 percent leave to
attend schools and colleges, to serve in the armed forces, or because
they have reached the retirement age; 15 percent leave because the
projects to which they were assigned have been terminated or contracts
have expired. Fortunately information is available on the explicit reasons motivating the group of 50 percent reported as leaving 'at their
own request'. It can be broken down as follows: 8.7 percent felt their
wages were too low; 8.8 percent stated they wish to join their families
in other parts of the USSR (especially in those regions which are
climatically more desirable than Siberia); 7.0 percent found themselves
professionally maladjusted: 5.6 percent left because of unsatisfactory
living conditions; and 5.7 percent complained of the low level of cultural activities in Siberia.[8] Sonin, incidentally, is careful not to mention
the remaining 15 percent who leave their jobs illegally; in fact, these
may be added to the first 50 percent of 'voluntary quits', with the difference that permission to leave was not granted or that they were not
patient enough to wait for such leave. Thus we may assume that 65
percent of all migrant workers leave Siberia for a number of reasons
that come as a surprise and a disappointment to planners and managers
of Siberian industry. Referring to rather broad and general causes of
fluctuation, Sonin merely notes that working conditions in the Ukraine
and in the Don and Kuban' areas are much better than in the newly
opened areas in Siberia, not only for the climatic, living and transportation conditions, but the wage level as well. In 1962–63 the wages in
the European north and in the habitable districts of Siberia were only

---

[8] Results of a survey conducted in 1962 in the city of Krasnoyarsk; see V. Perevedentsev. *Voprosy ekonomiki,* 1962, no. 5. The lack of cultural services has been
criticized in the first place by non-Russian migrant-workers. An unusually large
number of 'letters to the editor' has been published in various Soviet papers demanding improvement of supply of books and periodicals in the national language of
migrants, and more frequent visits of non-Russian theatre and opera teams to Siberia.

15 percent higher than in areas of Central Russia,[9] although the cost of living there was frequently twice as high. Manevich reports that the price of milk was 46 percent higher in Siberia, that of sugar 27 percent higher, and that consumer goods, when available, are often three times as expensive as in Moscow or Kiev. According to a newspaper survey conducted in 1965–66, however, the estimates by Manevich prove to be much too conservative, and the cost of living in Siberia was found to be 2.2 times higher than in Russia proper.[10]

An interesting picture of the reasons for manpower fluctuation is given in a collective volume published by Moscow University under the editorship of V. N. Yagodkin. Two contributors, I. A. Akimova and V. G. Vasil'ev, for example, explain that quite a large segment of fluctuating manpower consists of workers dismissed for delinquent behaviour before their migration to Siberia—*inter alia* for breaking 'work discipline' *(narushenie trudovoi distsipliny)* or because of having received court sentences, workers whom the administration of the plants do not trust for some reason, and finally those who were dismissed at the request of the trade unions. Large contingents of such workers are sent to Siberia from Moscow and other large cities; they usually continue their delinquent behaviour in their new locations, creating unrest and disturbing the stability of manpower.

Planning authorities in Siberia make strenuous efforts to replace the migratory labour force returning home or changing from one job to another by recruiting additional manpower in Siberian villages, but so far this has proved unsatisfactory. Moreover, this action has had an adverse impact on agriculture in Siberia where, because of the lack of workers in unusually large *kolkhozy,* the crops per hectare of cultivated land are still low as compared with the west although natural conditions in southern parts of West Siberia are frequently superior to those prevailing, for example, in the Lower Volga areas or the European sub-Urals. Akimova and Vasil'ev also blame poor supplies in Siberia for general disappointment among newcomers. Some had urgent

[9] This would mean that the Ukaz of the Presidium of the USSR Supreme Soviet of 10 February 1960 has been reversed lately. This Ukaz abolished the differentiation of wages in the northern territories of the USSR because '. . . in the new conditions of growth in the above regions any continuance of supplements to the basic wages of workers or of the other concessions previously covered creates in many cases unnecessary expenses (*neobosnovannye izlishenstva*)'. We may add that, according to V. F. Mayer, the wages in the extreme Far North and in the Asiatic part of the USSR in 1963 were still approximately 50 percent higher than the average for the whole of the USSR (in the European north, 20 percent higher; see V. F. Mayer, *Zarabotnaya plata v period perekhoda k kommunizmu* (M. 1963), p. 263).

[10] A. Protozanov, 'Perspektivy neftyanoi Sibiri', *Pravda,* 27 February 1966. Protozanov draws a rather gloomy picture in Siberia today. He mentions a *rapid* decrease of population in northern territories and complains bitterly about frequent and prolonged breakdowns in the supply of milk, meat, vegetables and fruit in many districts of Siberia.

need of such household articles as furniture, kitchen utensils, soaps, cleaners and bed linen, which are extremely scarce in state distribution centres and shops. Even food is scarce because of the lack of *kolkhoz* free markets like those that exist in one form or another in rich agricultural regions in the Ukraine and the Don and Kuban' lands. However, blaming poor living conditions in Siberia for the mass exodus of recruited workers tells only one side of the story. Close scrutiny of local publications and announcements discloses that there is still another major cause of the homeward movement of Siberian settlers. Some hints of this cause are already to be found in Manevich's remarks on sanitary conditions in the east as well as on cultural services, the latter being extremely limited and of low quality.

In fact, a very important factor is hidden behind this stereotyped term of poor cultural services' in Siberia. The best information on this aspect is furnished by a renowned Soviet scholar, V. V. Pokshishevsky, who served as the head of a special commission of the Siberian branch of the Academy of Sciences in Novosibirsk set up to make recommendations for improvement of the manpower recruiting process for new Siberian projects. A study was published in 1962 that reviews the situation in detail and voices various suggestions on how to accelerate the colonization of Siberia. After emphasizing that many of the new settlers come from obviously non-Russian territories of the USSR (Ukraine, Belorussia, Moldavia, Lithuania), Pokshishevsky urgently recommends the founding of schools and cultural institutions (theatres, cinemas, clubs) that would continue to serve the newcomers in their native language and tradition. He says: With the aim of satisfying more fully the cultural needs of the newcomers, bearing in mind their national peculiarities, it is worth considering whether, in the areas of compact settlement of people belonging to particular nationalities, school teaching in their native language can be provided for those wishing it, national houses of culture set up, etc. These measures would facilitate participation of non-Russian population in the migration to Siberia.

Sonin also speaks of the urgent need to pay more attention to specific requirements *(osobennosti)* of migrants, particularly to their traditional habits and customs. Significantly, in his study published in 1959, he is much more emphatic in this respect than in his latest work. It seems that now the acute problem of the national background of migrants being sent to Siberia from the European part of the USSR is being purposely blurred and minimized by Moscow planning authorities, probably with the aim of simultaneous forced Russification of all the migrants beyond the Urals. To feign concern over the well-being of newcomers and to save face, as recently as 1964 a 'climatic approach' was encouraged over cultural and national considerations. Vasil'ev and Akimova, among others, recommended that migrants from the Ukraine should be directed rather to the regions of the Kulunda steepe (Southwest Siberia), whereas the migrants from the areas from around the Caspian Sea may feel happier in settlements in the Soviet Far East.

Agriculture and "Artificial Seas"

Peculiar difficulties developed in the field of agricultural policy. An example is the situation that prevails today in the best-colonized regions, specifically in Southwest Siberia. The population of West Siberia (within the boundaries of the official Soviet administrative divisions) grew from 3.7 million in 1926 to 5.2 million in 1939 and to 6.9 million in 1959. The rural population, however, amounted in 1926 to 3.3 million and in 1959 to 3.6 million only. In other words, the yearly increase of rural population in this 33-year span was only 9,500. A still worse situation can be observed in the eastern regions of Siberia, for example in the Angara area and in Krasnoyarsk krai, where hardly one-third of all the settlements can be viewed as permanent, whereas two-thirds of them are obviously nothing more than temporary living quarters for geological exploration parties, timber workers in the adjoining forests, or hunters settling in the 'village' for only as long as the hunting lasts. The balance of migration in this huge territory was reported in 1959 as follows: new arrivals, 13,805; departures, 13,834; internally only very few settlements show some gain, the others are becoming rather depopulated. In 1939, the Kezhma raion had a population of 12,400, and in 1959 only 10,300. This means that some areas are not only losing all their natural population increase, but even the old-time settlers leave many villages and settlements in considerable numbers.

The same is happening in the area of Srednee Priangar'e (Middle Angara region) around the Bratsk hydro-power station. As early as 1930–40, many villages in this area simply disappeared from the map as their inhabitants switched over to either timber cutting and galipot picking (*dobycha zhivitsy*) or moved to industrial centres in the Kuzbas area. In 1945–60 the process of 'de-agriculturization' of the region went further, when a large percentage of the local population sought employment in new industrial ventures. N. N. Kazansky draws the following typical transition pattern for the Siberian village: *kolkhoz-promkolkhoz-promartel'-rabochii poselok*. We frequently hear about Krasnoyarsk krai, where various industries are scheduled to be created in the near future. The migration situation there, however, tells a different story. In 1948–60 the new arrivals amounted to 1.5 million: at the same time, 1.2 million settlers left the krai, and its yearly population increase was only about 28,000.

Even in such typical agricultural regions as the Khabarovsk and Amur oblasts we notice a rapid decline in rural population. By 1961 the figure was 40,000 less than in 1939. If we take into account that in

1940 the natural growth rate in these oblasts was approximately 33 per 1,000 inhabitants, we realize that the number of peasants who left the villages was enormous. The result was that by 1958 the share of the population of the Soviet Far East employed in agriculture and forestry dropped to a mere 16 percent of the total.[11] What is more puzzling is that the changes that occured in the urban population were not satisfactory either. Skilled manpower in the Far East shows great fluctuations, and there is a trend among migrants, both new and old, to return home to the European part of the USSR. In 1960–61, the Khabarovsk *sovnarkhoz* asked Moscow for a minimum of 2,100 college-trained specialists to be resettled in that area; only 876 were recruited, and of these only 767 actually arrived at assigned places throughout the huge area of the Far East. In 1962–64, 50 percent of that number left their jobs. To cite another example: it is reported that in two years (1959–60), some 50,000 left Sakhalin [12] and, characteristically, the explanation offered is familiar: low local wages, the difficulties of arranging holidays and recreation, poor living conditions and still poorer cultural services are the apparent reasons for the departure of settlers.

Almost all the Soviet analysts of population trends in Siberia who complain about the collapse of agriculture there point to damage effected by huge artificial water reservoirs (lakes) created by the dams of new hydro-electric projects. All the once most prosperous villages, including raion centres on the Angara River, e.g., Motygino, Boguchany, Kezhma (4,300 inhabitants in 1959), will soon disappear under the waters of the artificial lakes created by dams on the Lower Angara and Yenisey. The richest agricultural lands on the Middle Angara and her tributaries are also destined to be converted entirely by waters of the flooded river. According to data published by *Gidroproekt*, the planned Lower Ob reservoir of both the Salekhard and Narukary dams will cover 90,000 square kilometres of the very best agricultural soils available on the Lower and the Middle Ob and Irtysh—the only lands that are of really high agricultural value in this part of Siberia. Still worse damage from flooding will result from the construction of the projected Abalakovo hydro-system on the Yenisey.

The building of the Buktarma hydro-power plant has caused the flooding of an additional 171,000 hectares of land on the Upper Irtysh. Until now, 2.5 million hectares of agricultural land has been covered in the USSR by 'artificial seas', of which 600,000 hectares were the best existing soil in the country. Siberia suffered greatly from these irre-

---

[11] In 1959 this index dropped to 18.5; see A. B. Margolin, *Problemy naradnogo khozyaistva Vostoka* (M. 1963), pp. 196, 200, 202.

[12] *Ibid.* p. 208. In 1957–62 alone a huge total of 1,900,000 people left Siberian villages permanently (G. A. Prudensky and E. S. Lazutkin, 'Ob opyte konkretnykh ekonomiko-sotsiologicheskikh issledovanii v Sibiri', in *Opyt ekonomiko-sotsiologicheskikh issledovanii v Sibiri* (Novosibirsk, 1966), p. 29.

parable losses, and a wave of sharp criticism and anger swept the USSR. Numerous articles have appeared in newspapers, signed by prominent scientists who point out the dangers inherent in this craze for planning super-powerful projects on Siberian rivers. They have particularly emphasized the fact that these projects will not only decimate the rural population in Siberia, and thus seriously aggravate the already difficult food supply problem, but the artificial seas are about to cause unfavorable changes in the local climate, which already presents a grave obstacle to populating Siberia. Unpredictable adverse climatic and vegetational changes resulting from construction of the huge reservoirs became so evident that in June 1965 a special conference was held in Kiev on the matter, at which particular emphasis was given to the fact that hydro-power systems frequently render totally impossible certain vital processes of self-purification of natural waters. Even such an enthusiast of industrial development in Siberia as M. I. Pomus raises serious objections to dam construction on Siberian rivers. He is particularly concerned over the project to harness the Lower Ob. He refers, *inter alia,* to newly discovered rich mineral deposits in the regions of Berezovo, Shaim, Surgut, Bakchar and Kolpashevo, which are endangered by flooding. One of the further consequences of flooding by artificial seas is the swamping of vast adjoining areas. Natural swamps already cover huge expanses of Siberian territory, and the urgent need for drainage is becoming more evident every day.[13] V. V. Pokshishevsky is also strongly opposed to the destruction of old established river settlements in Siberia and on traditional crossroads, ascribing to them the role of natural centres for all further colonization and development in the Asiatic USSR.

The creation of several large artificial seas in the USSR as a result of poorly-planned and badly-built hydro-projects that were the object of Soviet pride in the 1950s had, ultimately, disastrous results for the country. For example, the Lake Sevan system in Armenia, described in propaganda as the 'jewel' of Soviet planning and engineering, caused a major scandal when it was discovered that the lake itself, which feeds all the hydro-power cascade system, might disappear altogether unless certain precautionary measures were taken immediately. The cost of

[13] M. I. Pomus, in *Geograficheskie problemy razvitiya krupnykh ekonomicheskikh raionov* (M. 1964), pp. 347–51. In this connection mention should be made of the mosquito problem in Siberia and of the insecticides used to fight it. The January 1966 issue of the Soviet magazine *Priorda* draws a really terrifying picture of the plague of mosquitos and similar Diptera in Siberia and in numerous regions of Soviet Asia generally. In spite of the intensified use of certain very strong insecticides (which did a lot of harm to local flora too) the Siberian mosquito has developed a remarkable resistance; moreover, it has produced species the control of which is becoming impossible. Soviet scientists are justly alarmed concerning this situation and urge the responsible authorities to launch more research in the field. See also on this subject a collective work, *Krovososushchie dvukrylye Kazakhstana* (Alma-Ata, 1966).

preserving this lake and filling it up again with water would exceed many times the already extravagant cost of the existing system. Lake Baykal in Siberia is also in great danger. The hydroprojects on the Angara, as well as new huge chemical and pulp complexes built around the lake, constitute a serious threat to agriculture and fishing industries. They also bring about a radical change in the icing regime of the lake and its tributaries, with unpredictable effects on the climate and on human living conditions.[14] The magnitude of the damage due to the new construction activities in Siberia is illustrated by the example of the Bratsk hydro-power station; in the final stage of building the dam, 11 million cubic metres of valuable timber were unnecessarily cut and burned because of some 'miscalculation' in planning. All these factors, though seemingly peripheral, nevertheless affect the manpower structure in Siberia to a serious degree.

Women as Labour Factor

One of the most unusual features of the Siberian population pattern is the extraordinary preponderance of women over men. What seems to be a more common pattern in Europe, especially after the war, is unexpected for Siberia: its territory was much less affected by World War II than the European part. Moreover, the extensive transplanting of labour to Siberia—mainly skilled and semi-skilled workers—involved men, particularly young men. In spite of these facts, the number of women, even in East Siberia, amounted to more than 52 percent (in Krasnoyarsk, 52.3 percent) of the total population. The age distribution shows still more striking discrepancies: in the 30–59 age bracket, the number of women rises to 57 percent and in the group aged 60 and over to as much as 65 percent.

The difficulties in attracting new migrants from the west to the east and the availability of a volume of 'unproductive labour', principally housewives, lie behind the current move of Soviet planners to utilize more members of Soviet households. We definitely gain an impression that the pool of 'unproductively employed' has now become some kind of escape ladder for the confused Soviet labour specialists, who suddenly found themselves faced with the impossibility of reverting to the Stalinist methods of deportations that helped to colonize Siberia in 1937–52. As Raymond Hutchings remarks, 'The utility of forced labour to the Far Northeast was that without it the area could not have been developed'.

Many papers were published in 1964–65 on the subject of utilizing

[14] A. Merkulov, *Pravda*, 28 February 1965. The subject of saving Lake Baykal has even reached the pages of *The New York Times* where a letter by the cultural affairs attaché of the Soviet mission to the UN was published in November 1966 on the efforts of the Soviet government to preserve the natural beauty of the lake.

women in the USSR. Projects have also been advanced for the utilization of married women (especially mothers) as part-time industrial workers. Detailed time studies on the Soviet housewife have been made with a view towards determining how much time she might devote to 'productive' work in industry. Only a few authors realize that plans to employ housewives in the factory have little relevance to Siberia, not only because of severe climatic and living conditions, but chiefly because of the type of industry which now prevails in Siberia and which will doubtless prevail for several decades to come. I. I. Chavanidze points out, correctly, that there are practically no prospects of using women more extensively in mining and metallurgical industries, since the mining and refining of nonferrous metals in Siberia is among the most hazardous types of industrial activity.[15] It is true that on the eve of the 1960s discussion had already been opened on building food-processing and textile factories in Siberia; more recent statistical reports indicate, however, that these suggestions were largely ignored and the construction of large metallurgical and chemical complexes was renewed. Enforced utilization of female labour in Siberian industries was already high—the share of women workers in nonferrous metallurgy in Siberia jumped to 24 percent in 1962.[16] There is no doubt that this circumstance also added considerably to the fluctuation of labour (this also applies to the western provinces, where labour safety rules are observed more strictly).

A survey of many recent Soviet studies on the manpower problem leads to several general conclusions. First of all, the period of violent change in the pattern of colonization seems to coincide with the 1959–61 span, and in spite of certain measures taken by the government the changes have persisted in subsequent years. Apparently a distribution of labour has somehow escaped the control of planning authorities. Studies published in 1961 report on results of surveys conducted in central Russian districts (Moscow, Kostroma, Ivanovo, Kaluga, Ryazan', Tula) and reveal that a surprisingly large number of workers remain unemployed. Four years later Manevich reported the identical situation in Moscow and Leningrad, where many young workers born in 1946–48 found 'certain difficulties' in obtaining jobs in their specializa-

[15] I. I. Chavanidze, 'Ekonomiko-geograficheskoe issledovanie trudovykh resursov na primere Vostochno-Kazakhstanskoi oblasti', *Geografiya naseleniya SSSR* . . . pp. 160–7. Chavanidze's frank admission on the extremely hazardous working conditions in the Soviet metallurgical industry stands out as a unique one, the other authors being silent on this point. In what magnitude the hazards really exist is shown in an obscure bibliographical source, *Samtarnaya statistika* (M. 1963); of particular interest are chapters entitled 'Statistika travm i otravlenii', pp. 80–102, 107–16, 219–44.
[16] This is an interpolated figure for *promyshlenno-proizvodstvennyi personal* are: West Siberia 25.6 percent, East Siberia 27.4 percent, Far East 21.4 percent. See A. M. Korneev, 'Usloviva formirovaniya promyshlennykh kompleksov ekonomicheskikh raionov', *Promyshlennost' v khozyaistvennom komplekse ekonomicheskikh raionov SSSR* (M. 1964), pp. 27–30.

tion and remain, in the jargon of official Soviet terminology, 'employed in the household'. Various other densely populated areas of the USSR are also plagued by this problem.

More Problems in the Future

The phenomenon of the mass exodus of resettlers from Siberia to other parts of the USSR, chiefly towards the regions of the Ukraine, the Don and Kuban' lands, North Caucasus, has been constantly reported throughout the 1960s without significant change. Indeed, the deep concern voiced in 1965 (Sonin. Vasil'ev, Petrosyan, Protozanov and others) would indicate that the situation has recently become more aggravated.

Analysis of the available factual material leads to the conclusion that the unusually strong fluctuation of manpower in the USSR, particularly in Siberia, is above all the direct and inevitable result of forcefully transplanting people from their home countries to unfriendly and rugged taigas, tundras and deserts beyond the Urals. Not the slightest consideration is being given to the centuries-old traditions and customs of newcomers from non-Russian union republics, particularly those in the European part of the USSR, that have been precisely the pool for recruiting settlers for Asiatic territories of the USSR for several decades.

Peasants from the warm areas of the Ukraine are being sent to the farthermost northern regions of the USSR; nomadic peoples from the Asiatic republics work as auxiliary, mostly unskilled, manpower at metallurgical plants in the Dnieper area or in the coal mines of Donbas; Lithuanians or Estonians are to be found in the Urals or in the Fast East; Russians from cold northeast Russia are coming by hundreds of thousands to the Crimea, North Caucasus or Trans-Carpathia, renowned for their Mediterranean-type climate. People who have lived for generations in the mountains (e.g., Carpathians) are being recruited for forestry work in the taiga flats of the Komi Autonomous Republic while others from the Ukraine Podol'ye plains are being transplanted to the Altay mountains or the Tannu-Tuva ridges. People accustomed to live in the large cities and the densely populated industrial districts of the European southwest have been resettled in the semi-deserts of Kazakhstan or the isolated tundra lands in Siberia; people from the forsaken villages in the Kostroma and Volgoda oblasts, with a nineteenth-century or even eighteenth-century way of life, are being brought to Riga, Vilnius, L'vov, Chernovtsy: in other words, to cities which, up to 1944, were the outposts of Western European culture in those parts of Eastern Europe, imbued with the heritage of Austrian and German influences and traditions.

The result is chaos and general dissatisfaction among wide strata of the population of the USSR, circumstances which accelerated the depopulation of many important regions beyond the Urals. A. A. Ivanchenko gives a summary report on population losses in Siberia from 1959 to 1963, confronting the anticipated indices of annual population growth with actual ones. His findings are as follows:

	Anticipated Index	*Actual Index*
Soviet Far East	1.9	1.5
West Siberia	1.9	1.5
East Siberia	2.1	1.8
Urals	1.9	1.4

The share of the population of Siberia (including the Far East) in the total population of the USSR *dropped* from 10.3 percent in 1959 to 10.2 percent in 1963; when we include the Urals, the figure drops from 17.6 percent to 17.4 percent. Taking into consideration the fact that the index of natural population growth beyond the Urals was much larger than the one anticipated in the Gosplan studies of the middle 1950s for this area, we must realize that the drop shown corresponds to millions of people who left Siberia.

The collapse of migration policies in Siberia seriously endangered the fulfilment of bold plans that were drawn up by Soviet planners. According to the seven-year plan the eastern part of the USSR should have represented, by 1965, about 29 percent of the whole industrial production of the USSR.[17] Reports published early in 1966 indicate that this goal was not reached; on the contrary, the east's share dropped to the level of 1957. Of particular significance is a considerable percentage drop in the production of iron, steel and chemical fertilizers; coal output and production of electricity rose slightly (by about 1 percent), but the only commodity that was produced in 1964 in a significantly larger volume than in 1960 was natural gas.

Discussing development projects for Siberia in future decades, Pokshishevsky envisaged a total movement of 15 to 19 million migrants, with an additional 5 to 6 million for Kazakhstan by the time that the population of the USSR reaches 300 million. Taking into account the number of migrants needed in the future for the development of Soviet Central Asia, Pokshishevsky envisages a volume of not less than 22 to 29 million people as migrants beyond the Urals in the next three decades or so. Unless drastic measures are taken by the Soviet government, this goal cannot possibly be reached under present circumstances. In fact, strenuous efforts of the planning and propaganda machines, as noted in 1964–65, produced quite unsatisfactory results. Ivanchenko clearly

[17] This figure refers to the whole Soviet east *including Urals.* The Soviet sources are not consistent in this respect, some including the Urals when talking of the eastern part of the USSR, some not.

states that an unwelcome reverse flow of migrants is taking place today, from under-populated areas beyond the Urals and in the north into over-populated areas of the European south.

Different opinions from those of Pokshishevsky, Sonin, Ivanchenko and others have been expressed by a small group of progressive Soviet economists and engineers (e.g., S. Slavin, K. K. Krupitsa, T. V. Rimskaya-Korsakova)[18] who recommend a more vigorous application of mechanization and automation in Siberia instead of amassing people who will await only a moment like the 1959–65 period to return home. against the government, people whose productivity will be low and who will await only a moment like the 1959–65 period to return home. Incidentally, the Utopia drawn by the dean of Soviet fortune-tellers, S. G. Strumilin, envisages, curiously enough, rather the danger of a labour surplus and of greatly increased leisure time (*svobodnoe vremya*) in the USSR in the not-so-distant future, and he urges Soviet scientists to pay more attention to this danger.[19] But for now, Moscow must cope with an acute problem of depopulation in Siberia and of difficulties in the colonization of vast areas by fresh migrants. The large and growing strata of young workers who are virtually unemployed or employed in unproductive processes in some large cities in the USSR (notably in Moscow and Leningrad), but who are definitely unwilling to participate in the opening up of the Siberian wilderness and who, transplanted by force, become a core of unrest and frequently of criminal activity in Siberia, is another equally difficult problem.

The gravity of the problem is now admitted in various quarters. We note, for example, new tones in the speeches of Academicians A.D. Aleksandrov and M. B. Mitin at the plenary session of the all-union Academy of Sciences on 14 December 1965. They were frank in saying that an almost complete lack of sociological studies in the USSR and the neglect of the human factor in economic planning are the primary reasons for the slow progress in many areas of the national economy. Their voices represent an inevitable reaction to many unhealthy beliefs that have tended to aggrandize the Russian achievements in Siberia. Participants in the XX International Geographical Congress in London in 1964 heard papers delivered by V. V. Vorob'ev, V. M. Gokhman and Yu. G. Saushkin[20] which were full of this kind of delusion.

[18] From Leningrad and Krasnoyarsk institutes for experimental construction and architecture, as quoted in *Problemy Severa*, vol. 10 (1964).
[19] S. G. Strumilin, *Nash mir cherez 20 let* (M. 1964), p. 100. How far Strumilin's vision of the future is from present-day reality is shown by the new findings of statistical research (*samofotografiya rabochego dnya*), according to which the actual average working day of a worker in the Siberian mining industry amounts to *10 and more hours* (while theoretically a six-hour working day was introduced several years ago); see Prudensky and Lazutkin, *op. cit.* (see footnote [12]).
[20] V. M. Gokhman, Yu. G. Saushkin, 'Razmeshchenie proizvoditel'nykh sil v SSSR i v SShA', *ibid.* pp. 116–21. Vorob'ev's appraisal of the Russian language as a pro-

The true picture of development in Siberia and of its colonization is a classical example of complex influences of many factors that cannot be eliminated—geopolitical, climatic and strictly political (e.g., the national background of migrants). As has been shown, there is an obvious trend in administrative circles to underestimate or bypass the last two factors. Observation of the history of Siberian development gives scarcely any impression of logic, widom or foresight in planning. One of the worst disadvantages of planning in Siberia has been the overpowering centralization, involving the country in many discouraging and disastrous experiments. As many Western observers agree,[21] the *de facto* backwardness of Russia lies behind this policy of convulsive, rude, frequently megalomaniac and hysterical measures aimed at creating, at any price, a powerful base of resources in the backyard of Russia proper. How much these measures please or displease the Chinese, and to what extent the Chinese attitude influences Moscow's decision-making processes and the attitudes of Siberian settlers as potential defenders of new Soviet frontiers—these are questions which can be answered only by the future.

---

moting factor in the economic development of non-Russian nations living for ages beyond the Urals is as ridiculous as Gokhman's and Saushkin's clumsy comparison of the growth of the American Western states with the development of Soviet Asiatic territories in the 1900–60 period.

[21] Alexander Gerschenkron, *Economic Backwardness in Historical Perspective* (Cambridge, Mass., 1962), pp. 17–18; Alec Nove, 'Was Stalin Really Necessary?' and 'The Problem of Success Indicators' in the collection *Was Stalin Really Necessary?* (London, 1964), pp. 17–39, 83–98; Peter Wiles, 'The Theory of International Comparisons of Economic Volume', *Soviet Planning. Essays in Honour of Naum Jasny* (Oxford, 1964), pp. 77–115. The most recent rather sensational invitation for the Japanese to participate in developing East Siberia becomes not only another proof of the tremendous difficulties in the field of manpower in Siberia but also simultaneously exposes the deficiencies and failures of Soviet planning there.

16. Toward a Typology of Manufacturing Flows

Allan Pred

This attempt to create a "typology of manufacturing flows" emphasizes the major factors that localize industry. Pred's objective is to interpret within a general theoretical framework the factors that influence the volume and length of commodity flows associated with particular places and certain large-scale manufacturing industries. The complexity of the problem is well demonstrated, and the author poses

*valid questions that need to be answered to facilitate
progress in this area of geographic concern. This discussion
of why materials flow from one place to another in an
advanced economy sheds light on the understanding of the
spatial structure of manufacturing activity in such areas.
The resulting typology is arrived at by "using the mechanism
of market potential for distinguishing and grouping relative
locations" of production facilities that have various degrees
of market accessibility—high, intermediate, and low. The
resulting generalizations as well as the method can benefit
the student of economic geography.*

It is clear that large-scale manufacturing plants with identical producing functions but different relative locations within a region or
country will have different flow (volume and length) characteristics.
Likewise, it is clear that large-scale manufacturing plants with dissimilar producing functions but coincident or near-coincident relative
locations will have disparate flow characteristics. However, although
access to markets and other factors have been recognized as influencing
the volume and length of manufacturing commodity flows associated
with particular places and industries, no attempt has been made to
interpret such phenomena within a general theoretical framework.

Related Ideas and Studies

If this problem has not been assaulted directly, it has certainly been
approached obliquely. As early as 1875 the German political economist
Schäffle suggested that large cities have an attractive force as markets
that is directly proportional to the square of their size and inversely proportional to the distance between them and the factories. Similarly,
in 1910, the British geographer Chisholm observed that there was a
relationship between the size of an industry and its ability to compete in
distant markets. But early works such as these failed to be more explicit
in a theoretical sense and made no attempt to compare empirically the
volume and length of commodity flows generated by different industries
and places.

Except for port geography studies, which are basically concerned with
the flow of goods from hinterland to port and from port to port, rather
than with the movement from producer to market, relatively little is
available in the realm of economic flow studies that might contribute to
a generalized typology of large-scale manufacturing flows. This is

Source: *The Geographical Review,* LIV (January, 1964), 65–84. Reprinted with
permission of the author and the publisher. The author is associate professor of
geography at the University of California, Berkeley.

largely attributable to the sparsity of available data. Comparative studies of areal economic interchange have been mainly confined to the analysis of money and Federal Reserve Bank flows.[1] Commodity flow analyses have dealt with the mining, agricultural, and manufacturing sectors of the United States economy [2] but have not interpreted locational variations in length and volume; with all commodities in specific states [3] but have neglected to make comparisons with other states; or with aggregated commodity groups for a large number of states but have failed to contrast the flow characteristics of individual industrial commodities originating in different places.

The input-output methods used to derive "regional commodity balances" prove to be of limited utility for analysis of manufacturing commodity flows because these balances do little more than determine which sectors of the economy provide inputs or absorb outputs for given industries.[4] Input-output procedures, as so far employed, do not illuminate differences in the length and volume of manufacturing flows. Nor does the application of linear programming techniques to product flow studies appear to be any more fruitful, since such analyses usually restrict the problem to "one of minimizing the transportation cost of shipping goods from several production points to several warehouses or consumption points." [5]

[1] For example, Morris A. Copeland: A Study of Moneyflows in the United States (New York, 1952); Norman N. Bowsher, J. Dewey Daane, and Robert Einzig: The Flow of Funds Between Regions of the United States, *Papers and Proc. Regional Science Assn.*, Vol. 3 (3rd Annual Meeting, 1956), Philadelphia, 1957, pp. 139–165; and Otis Dudley Duncan and others: Metropolis and Region (Baltimore, 1960), Chap. 6 (Interregional Flow of Funds). See also Walter Isard's review of the literature in his "Methods of Regional Analysis" ([Cambridge, Mass.], New York and London, 1960), pp. 144–163.

[2] For example, Walter H. Voskuil: Bituminous Coal Movements in the United States, *Geogr. Rev.*, Vol. 32, 1942, pp. 117–127; Stuart Daggett's work on movements of grain, livestock, citrus fruit, and sugar in his "Principles of Inland Transportation" (4th edit.; New York, 1955), pp. 179–266; and Roy J. Sampson: Railroad Shipments and Rates from the Pacific Northwest, *Univ. of Oregon, Bur. of Business Research, Studies No. 6*, Eugene, 1961. For a review of the pre-1947 commodity flow literature see W. H. S. Stevens: Commodity Flow Analysis, *in* Changing Perspectives in Marketing (edited by Hugh G. Wales; Urbana, 1951), pp. 139–157.

[3] Among the more recent investigations using this approach are Sampson, *op. cit.*; Jere W. Clark: The Market Structure of West Virginia Industry . . . 1948–1952, *West Virginia Univ. Business and Economic Studies*, Vol. 4, No. 2. Bur. of Business Research, Morgantown, 1955; and Mary H. Bowdoin: Georgia's Railway Freight Patterns . . . 1949–1955, *Georgia State College of Business Administration, Bur. of Business and Economic Research, Research Paper No. 5*, Atlanta, 1958.

[4] Such methods are discussed in Walter Isard: Regional Commodity Balances and Interregional Commodity Flows, *Amer. Econ. Rev.*, Vol. 43, 1953, pp. 167–180; and Leon N. Moses: The Stability of Interregional Trading Patterns and Input-Output Analysis, *ibid.*, Vol. 45, 1955, pp. 803–826.

[5] A. Robert Koch and Milton M. Snodgrass: Linear Programming Applied to Location and Product Flow Determination in the Tomato Processing Industry, *Papers and Proc. Regional Science Assn.*, Vol. 5 (5th Annual Meeting, 1958), Philadelphia, 1959, pp. 152–162; reference on p. 152.

Economic and location theorists concerned with market and supply areas have contributed some concepts relevant to the problem; for example, Hoover's ideas based on the interdependence of manufacturing locations and Ackley's regarding spatially discontinuous market areas. However, other theoretical constructs have less to contribute to a typology of manufacturing flows based on reality, since they have often assumed either that buyers are evenly spaced over the market, or that complex crosshauling does not exist, and/or that the principal problem is to determine the shape of market boundary lines under equilibrium conditions.[6]

Of more particular interest are the efforts made by Duncan and his associates to "classify" the areas to which the manufacturing outputs of any given metropolist may move. Three market areas are recognized: Area A "is simply the SMA itself"; Area B "corresponds to McKenzie's 'trade area'" (based on newspaper circulation and Federal Reserve Bank or Branch Bank functions); and Area C "is a residual category in the classification, embracing all origins and destinations not fairly clearly localized in 'Areas A or B.'" Although such an approach may be useful in an attempt to comprehend the interrelationships between the metropolis and its "region," it is not well suited to the comparison of similar manufacturing flows from places with different relative locations. The device of three market areas appears to be more concerned with where a city's flows "dominate" than with where they actually go; moreover, such factors as real or economic distance of flows and locations relative to competitors and the national market are not considered. Finally, in each case, Duncan's flow analysis is limited to the most important or "profile" industries of the city.[7]

Perhaps the most helpful concepts for arriving at a typology of manufacturing commodity flows have been produced by so-called gravity and potential model studies.[8] Certain of these studies enable us to gauge a

---

[6] To mention only three: Frank A. Fetter: The Economic Law of Market Areas, *Quart. Journ. of Economics*, Vol. 38, 1924, pp. 520–529; Charles David Hyson and W. P. Hyson: The Economic Law of Market Areas, *ibid.*, Vol. 64, 1950, pp. 319–327; and August Lösch: The Economics of Location (translated from the 2nd rev. edit. by William H. Woglom with the assistance of Wolfgang F. Stolper; New Haven and London, 1954). See also two reviews of the literature: Melvin L. Greenhut: The Size and Shape of the Market Area of a Firm, *Southern Econ. Journ.*, Vol. 19, 1952–1953, pp. 37–50; and Walter Isard: Location and Space-Economy ([Cambridge, Mass.] New York and London, 1956), pp. 143–171.

[7] "Profile" industries are identified by a location quotient similar to that initially put forth by Sargant Florence in "Investment, Location, and Size of Plant" (by P. Sargant Florence, assisted by W. Baldamus; The National Institute of Economic and Social Research, Economic and Social Studies, Vol. 7; Cambridge, England, 1948). For a discussion of the limitations of such location quotients in analyzing regional import-export relations see Isard, Methods of Regional Analysis [see footnote 1 above], pp. 123–126.

[8] The literature is so voluminous that it would be tiresome to refer to any but the most directly relevant works. For reviews of the literature see Gerald A. P. Car-

producer's relative accessibility to the total market of a region or nation vis-à-vis another producer's accessibility to this market. In particular, Harris' market potential, which is measured in terms of economic distance and retail sales, and which may be viewed as a measure of the accessibility of a point to the market in general, provides a framework within which commodity flow statistics from different parts of the United States may be compared [9] (Fig. 1). It is true that the concept has certain limitations (for example, because aggregate retail sales were used in the final construction of maps, it is not possible to discern the distribution of accessibility to the national market for particular manufactured products), but despite its shortcomings Harris' work reaffirms some obvious hunches concerning access to the national market (for example, that Chicago is better located in this respect than Denver) and permits the grouping of cities or manufacturing sites with different absolute locations but similar relative locations (for example, Minneapolis-St. Paul and Birmingham have nearly identical proximity to the national market).

Means of Arriving at a Typology

Using the mechanism of market potential for distinguishing and grouping relative locations, one can generalize with respect to the volume and length of all manufacturing commodity flows associated with production facilities that have, let us say, high market accessibility, intermediate market accessibility, or low market accessibility [10] (Fig. 2). The rather crude distinctions in flow characteristics to be derived from such an initial step can be refined by consideration of three fundamental industry types (defined in terms of cost and location factors) at each of the three kinds of relative locations. The result is a typology of manufacturing flows that has nine basic types, associated with *raw-material-*

---

rothers: An Historical Review of the Gravity and Potential Concepts of Human Interaction, *Journ. Amer. Inst. of Planners,* Vol. 22, 1956, pp. 94–102; F[red E.] Lukermann and P. W. Porter: Gravity and Potential Models in Economic Geography, *Annals Assn. of Amer. Geogrs.,* Vol. 50, 1960, pp. 493–504; and Isard: Methods of Regional Analysis [see footnote 1 above], pp. 493–568.

[9] For an elaboration of the market potential concept see Chauncy D. Harris: The Market as a Factor in the Localization of Industry in the United States, *Annals Assn. of Amer. Geogrs.,* Vol. 44, 1954, pp. 315–348; and Edgar S. Dunn: The Market Potential Concept and the Analysis of Location, *Papers and Proc. Regional Science Assn.,* Vol. 2 (2nd Annual Meeting, 1955), Philadelphia, 1956, pp. 183–194.

[10] The selection of three categories of relative location is purely arbitrary. Any number could have been chosen, but a greater number would have made matters more complicated and possibly have obfuscated the thinking underlying the typology developed here. However, a precedent for three accessibility categories was set by Stewart in his study of the flow of bank checks; the categories used were the Northeast, Deep South, and Far West (John Q. Stewart: Potential of Population and Its Relationship to Marketing, *in* Theory in Marketing [edited by Reavis Cox and Wroe Alderson; Homewood, Ill., 1949], pp. 19–40).

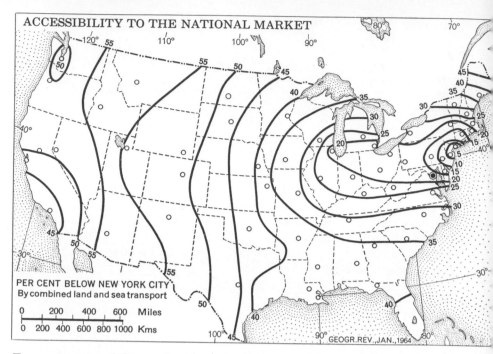

FIGURE 1: Accessibility to the national market. Adapted from map of "Market Potential" by Chauncy D. Harris (see text footnote 9 for reference, p. 324).

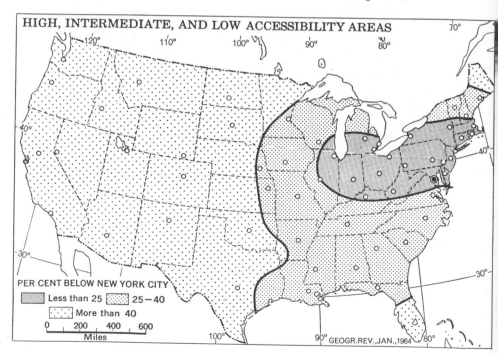

FIGURE 2: Areas of high, intermediate, and low accessibility.

and-fuel-oriented industries at sites with (1) high, (2) intermediate, or (3) low accessibility to the national or regional market; *market-oriented industries* at sites with (4) high, (5) intermediate, or (6) low accessibility; and *labor-and-agglomeration-economy-oriented industries* at sites with (7) high, (8) intermediate, or (9) low accessibility. Finally, and most important, through the use of the Interstate Commerce Commission's *Carload Waybill Statistics* for railroads it is feasible to compare the proposed typology with actual manufacturing commodity flows.

The approach outlined above naturally precludes the consideration of product flows generated by small-scale factories and industries which are ubiquitous and which serve highly restricted market areas. Thus the typology does not include the flows created by plants that greatly increase the bulk or perishability of products and consequently are localized by local markets; for example, "bread bakeries, ice cream factories, ice works, gas works, bottling plants for soft drinks, building construction, newspaper printing." However, recognition of this shortcoming does not enable an immediate consideration of the typology itself. First, two basic corollaries underlying the concept of relative market accessibility must be examined and documented. The first of these is that there is some relationship between market or population proximity and the distribution of manufacturing; the second, that there is some relationship between market accessibility and distance.

Location of Industry in Relation to Market Accessibility

If the amount of manufacturing in an area is a function of that area's accessibility to population and market, then it is clear that there is no need to distinguish industrial flows which serve the household, or "final" consuming market, from those which terminate at other factories, or "nonfinal" markets, where further fabrication takes place. For if this relationship exists, areas with a large consuming market will also have large manufacturing concentrations and therefore large nonfinal markets. Thus the highest (or lowest) density of both types of flow will occur in the same areas.

Intuitively we expect some relationship between population concentration or accessibility and the degree of manufacturing activity. Lösch observed that with "free competition the best location for industrial production is also the most favorable for consumers of industrial goods." This is so because the producer at a point of high accessibility "may be able to gauge the size and composition of the market more accurately. He may be able to establish better contact with customers, effect quicker delivery and servicing, respond to changes in demand more rapidly, and realize intangible administrative advantages from the juxtaposition of production and those sales and service activities which

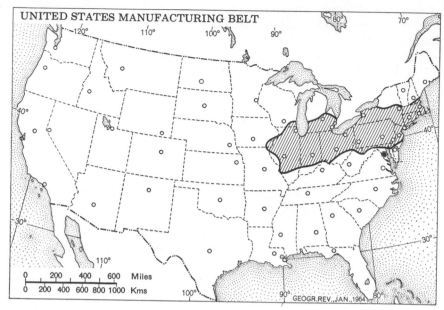

Figure 3.

are market-oriented." Empirical evidence substantiates the intercon-
nection between accessibility and manufacturing. The traditionally defined American Manufacturing Belt (Fig. 3), which contains more than
65 percent of United States manufacturing capacity, coincides with the
belt of highest market accessibility.[11] Based on 1954 data for the
individual states, a correlation coefficient of .936 has been found between manufacturing employment and population. From a sample study
of one hundred nonmetropolitan State Economic Areas, as defined by
the Bureau of the Census, it has been demonstrated that manufacturing
employment varies directly with the population potential (accessibility)
of an area.

Distance and Population Accessibility

Although it is apparent that accessibility to the national market in the
United States is a function of distance from the Manufacturing Belt, or
zone of highest accessibility, it is necessary to substantiate the distance-
accessibility relationship as a more general phenomenon if the proposed
typology is to be more widely applicable. When the United States is
divided into subregions regarded as integral, divorced entities, accessi-

[11] Harris, *op. cit.* [see footnote 9 above], p. 326. The Manufacturing Belt as referred
to here, and in the remainder of this article, is viewed as an amorphous, continuously
evolving area that is more a valid intellectual convenience than an integral region.

bility decreases uninterruptedly with increased distance from the focal area of the subregion. For Europe as a whole the same relationship prevails with respect to population proximity.[12] On a smaller scale distance and accessibility were found to be interdependent in Florida and southeastern Georgia. At a level even lower, that of American metropolises and their "hinterlands," it has been established that areas of above-average population proximity "tend to be located at the lesser distances from a metropolitan center," and areas of below-average proximity "tend to be located at the greater distances from a metropolitan center." In view of this evidence it appears safe to assume that regardless of the scale of analysis—whether nation, state, metropolis and hinterland, or some other unit—zones of high, intermediate, and low accessibility will occur in an orderly sequence over distance, despite patterns of uneven population distribution. If follows that the typology presented here has some degree of applicability to economies functioning in regions of various areal magnitudes.

Manufacturing Flows from Three Different Relative Locations

Disregarding for the moment the factor of market accessibility, we may note some rather obvious and simple observations that pertain to all industrial product flows, irrespective of the relative locations of the points of origin. First, because of the "friction," or cost of overcoming distance, short flows predominate. This is true at the international level (for example, in Europe, where "there appears to be strong tendency to concentrate on 'near' countries"), at the national level (for example, in the United States, where a "large part of the railroad traffic of the country is local . . ."), and at the state level (for example, in West Virginia, where "most of the traffic was [is] shipped relatively short distances"). Second, the longer flows will emanate from the specialized industries of any given area, because by definition such industries have cost advantages over similar producers in some other areas, and because freight rates, by increasing at a rate that is less than proportional to distance, encourage longer hauls. Third, complex crosshauling of similar products will occur because of consumer selectivity and of price discrimination and other types of oligopolistic behavior on the part of the firm.

The export pattern of any large-scale manufacturing plant will naturally be influenced by the relative distance from the consumer concentrations that make up the regional or national market. Thus the producer

[12] It may reasonably be assumed, therefore, that this observation is also valid for proximity to market in Europe. See map in John Q. Stewart: Empirical Mathematical Rules Concerning the Distribution and Equilibrium of Population, *Geogr. Rev.*, Vol. 37, 1947, pp. 461–485.

with a location that has high market accessibility, other things being equal, will have an enormous volume of short flows, as is characteristic of the American Manufacturing Belt. When economies of scale and lower bulk freight rates allow such a producer to compete in areas of low market proximity, the shipments will usually be longer than similar flows coming from points of intermediate accessibility, because accessibility is generally a function of distance, and therefore the intermediate producer will usually be closer to the low-proximity, or peripheral, market. In short, firms with the highest accessibility will have the largest flow volume, and also some of the longest hauls.

By the same logic, large-scale manufacturing facilities localized in areas of intermediate accessibility will have somewhat smaller, but still good-sized, short flows and a large quantity of flows of medium length. The first situation obtains because the nearest markets are by definition of small dimension; the second is a natural consequence of orientation toward the bulk of the national or regional market in the adjacent high-accessibility area. For certain products, then, this type of location means that the bulk of shipments will go longer overall distances than similar shipments originating in high-accessibility areas; for example, "shipments of iron and steel from Birmingham, Alabama, tend on the average to move over greater distances than shipments of iron and steel from other points [in the Manufacturing Belt], because Birmingham is geographically distant from high income, industrialized states." However, because the area of intermediate accessibility is geographically interposed between the areas of high and low access, it follows that its longest flows will not cover as great a distance as the flows moving in either direction between the other two areas. Finally, in a highly competitive situation, the nearest markets, and therefore the shorter flows, of the intermediately located producer will be protected against relatively nearby producers in the high-proximity area by any trend toward rising freight tariffs (as is the case in the United States today), because the percentage fare boosts will necessitate a greater absolute increase in transport outlays for the most distant manufacturer.

A smaller volume of large-scale manufacturing flows will originate in the peripheral, low-accessibility area than in either of the two more propitiously located areas. This fact is an obvious consequence of the smaller amount of industrial activity likely to be found in geographically marginal areas. As in the other two examples, short flows catering to nearby markets will predominate and in some well-populated areas, as in California, will attain considerable proportions. However, because of the attractive force exercised by the large percentage of the national or regional market concentrated in the high-accessibility area, as well as of the prevalence of tapering freight rate structures, a larger percentage of long-distance hauls will characterize low-accessibility areas than those of central and intermediate localities. Certainly this is apparent for a state such as Washington, which "has many more long-distance connections, primarily to the industrial belt . . ."

A Typology Based on Relative Location and Industrial Localization

The foregoing generalizations are greatly limited and altered by the fact that different industries with similiar relative locations may have dissimilar localization factors, or cost structures, which govern their ability to absorb transport costs and thereby influence the pattern of their product outflows. As a consequence of this and other factors, the overall pattern of manufacturing flows associated with any plant or industrial concentration is not as easily compartmentalized as in the preceding paragraphs, but is more likely to occur as a "kaleidoscopic vareity of connections." The picture is further complicated by certain large-scale industrial activities that are economically more prone to occur in certain types of relative locations than in others.

Raw-Material-and-Power-Oriented Industries

The threefold differentiation of flow types described in conjunction with locations of high, intermediate, and low accessibility is most substantially altered by raw-material-and-power oriented industries.[13] The deviation arises largely because the distribution of manufacturing localized by raw materials and power shows little relationship to the distribution of population and market phenomena. This is to be expected in industries localized by physical phenomena, and thus in the United States employment in such industries appears to be largely independent of population proximity. The ramifications of this singularity are apparent: the volume of product flows is no longer a function of relative location. The largest volume of traffic of a given industry is as likely to originate in areas of low accessibility as in areas of high accessibility. Such disorder is not concomitant to manufacturing activities localized by market, labor, or agglomeration economics. But all is not chaos, since some coherent interdependence still remains between the relative location of raw-material-and-power-oriented producers and the distance characteristics of their outflows. Furthermore, the vast majority of raw-material–localized industries sell the largest proportion of their output to other manufacturers, and these other producers, for

[13] Reference to such orientation is in the traditional Weberian sense; i.e., orientation toward a weight-losing raw material (or fuel) whose weight equals or exceeds the combined weight of the product and all other nonubiquitous raw materials used in the manufacturing process. See Alfred Weber: Alfred Weber's Theory of the Location of Industries: English Edition. With Introduction and Notes by Carl Joachim Friedrich (Chicago, 1929); and modifications by William Henry Dean, Jr.: The Theory of the Geographic Location of Economic Activities (Cambridge, Mass., 1938), pp. 18–19.

economic considerations of one kind or another, will be more strongly concentrated in areas of high accessibility than population itself; for example, in 1954 the American Manufacturing Belt contained about 43 percent of the country's population but about 68 percent of its manufacturing. Therefore, the large-scale raw-material–oriented producer will tend to haul a greater share of his production to the area of high accessibility than his counterpart in industries localized by most other factors.

With these observations in mind, the first three types in the typology may be outlined.

1. OUTFLOWS FROM RAW-MATERIAL-AND-POWER–ORIENTED INDUSTRIES IN AREAS OF HIGH MARKET ACCESSIBILITY / Although large-scale producers of this type may or may not have the largest volume of flows, they will have the highest percentage of short flows under almost all imaginable circumstances. This will occur primarily because of proximity to the highly concentrated industrial market. In addition, a raw-material–processing industry in the manufacturing heart of a region or nation generally will not have sufficient cost advantages over competitors in areas of intermediate and low accessibility to enter much of its production into competition in these more distant areas.[14]

2. OUTFLOWS FROM RAW-MATERIAL-AND-POWER–ORIENTED INDUSTRIES IN AREAS OF INTERMEDIATE MARKET ACCESSIBILITY / Producers generating these outflows also may or may not have the largest volume of flows, but they will almost certainly have the highest percentage of medium-length flows. These characteristics are again attributable to the overall distribution of large-scale producers and the concentration of the market in the high-accessibility area, which, in terms of the region or nation, is for the most part at medium-length distances. It is even conceivable that where further fabrication of the product is best done under extremely specialized circumstances, almost none of it will be moved over short distances and the bulk of it will be shipped to the industrial belt. In other words, it will be economically more efficient for the further-fabricated product to be in a sense reshipped from the industrial belt than to be manufactured locally where adequate economies of scale cannot be attained.

3. OUTFLOWS FROM RAW-MATERIAL-AND-POWER–ORIENTED INDUSTRIES IN AREAS OF LOW MARKET ACCESSIBILITY / These producers may or may not have the largest volume of flows, but they will have the highest percentage of long-distance flows. This is consistent with previous state-

[14] This would not be true, however, if concentration of the raw material happened to be particularly great in the high-accessibility areas.

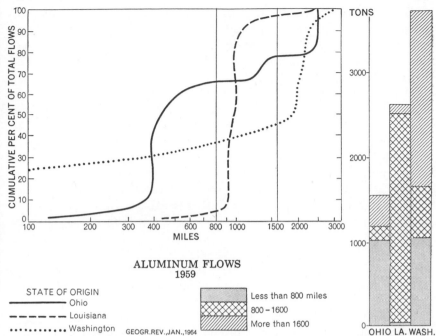

FIGURE 4: Aluminum flows, 1959, based on I.C.C. *Carload Waybill Statistics* (see text footnote 15 for reference).

ments concerning market concentration and freight rates. Short flows are also likely to account for a higher percentage of the total than in the case of intermediately located manufacturers because the local consumers are at a further remove from competing second-stage fabricators in the industrial belt of the region or nation.

Movement of United States industrial commodities on Class I railroads, as reflected by the I.C.C.'s 1 per cent sample of carload waybills,[15] permits a somewhat limited comparison of the typology with reality.[16] Such a comparison is aided by designation of all hauls of 799 miles or less (an approximation of the distance separating New York from Chicago and other points at the western extremities of the Manufacturing Belt), 800–1599 miles, and 1600 miles or more as short, medium, and long flows respectively.

[15] All further references to carload waybill statistics are based on *Carload Waybill Statistics, 1959: State-to-State Distribution, Manufactures and Miscellaneous and Forwarder Traffic* (Interstate Commerce Commission, Bur. of Transport Economics and Statistics, Washington, D. C., 1960). For a discussion of the positive and negative aspects of the sampling technique involved see R. Tynes Smith, III: Technical Aspects of Transportation Flow Data, *Journ. Amer. Statist. Assn.*, Vol. 49, 1954, pp. 227–239; and "Waybill Statistics, Their History and Uses," *Statement No. 543*, Interstate Commerce Commission, Bur. of Transport Economics and Statistics, Washington, D. C., 1954.

[16] Some of the limitations are enumerated at the end of the article.

The cost of power and raw materials overwhelmingly dominates the cost structure, and consequently the locational pattern, of the primary aluminum industry. The distribution of flows associated with this industry essentially reaffirms the principles for the first three types (Fig. 4). The flows from Ohio (producers with high market accessibility) are of the smallest volume, but the percentage of short-distance flows is higher than the percentages for Louisiana (producers with intermediate accessibility) and Washington (producers with low accessibility). Not only did Louisiana have, comparatively, the highest percentage of medium-distance flows in 1959, but 92.2 per cent of its hauls went to points more than eight hundred miles distant in the Manufacturing Belt. Washington had the largest volume of flows—a position it would have difficulty in attaining in industries localized by other factors—and a higher percentage of long-distance flows than either Ohio or Louisiana.

Previous flow studies indicate the same general tendencies for hauls from other raw-material–oriented industries in West Virginia (high market proximity) and in Washington and Oregon.

Market-Oriented Industries

The flow phenomena of market-oriented industries show relative order and cohesion both for their volume and for their length attributes. This is a natural consequence of the previously discussed relationships between manufacturing activity and proximity to population, of the fact that by definition market-oriented industries serve regional or national markets, and of the role played by relative location in determining the spatial part of the market in which any given producer may compete. In addition, the flows of market-oriented industries are somewhat restricted areally because their ability to absorb transportation costs is generally less than that of higher-value-added industries localized by labor or agglomeration economies.

4. OUTFLOWS FROM MARKET-ORIENTED INDUSTRIES IN AREAS OF HIGH MARKET ACCESSIBILITY / Others things being equal, large-scale manufacturers with these orientation and accessibility characteristics will have the largest volume of flows, a high percentage of which will naturally be within the area of high accessibility. However, because of the economies of scale that are often attendant on serving an exceptionally large nearby market, a not inconsiderable amount of freight will also be hauled over medium and longer distances. In other terms, production cost advantages will often allow the centrally located firms to compete in distant markets.

5. OUTFLOWS FROM MARKET-ORIENTED INDUSTRIES IN AREAS OF INTERMEDIATE MARKET ACCESSIBILITY / The volume of short-distance hauls will be considerably less than in the preceding type, because by defini-

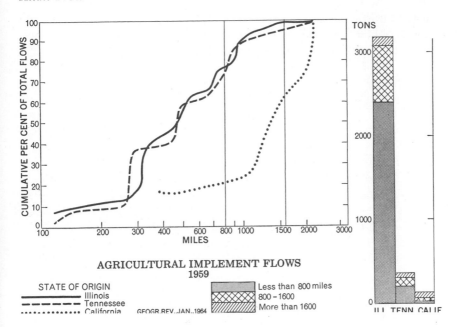

FIGURE 5: Agricultural-implement flows, 1959, based on I.C.C. *Carload Way-bill Statistics* (see footnote 15 for reference).

tion the market within a given radius will be smaller than the market within a radius of equal length in the high-accessibility area. Medium and long-distance hauls will be of small consequence relative to those of more centrally located competitors. The possibility of making inroads into the market of the high-accessibility area will be minute, and in the low-accessibility area there will be competition not only from local manufacturers but also from manufacturers with lower per unit costs located in the more central industrial belt.

6. OUTFLOWS FROM MARKET-ORIENTED INDUSTRIES IN AREAS OF LOW MARKET ACCESSIBILITY / The total volume of these flows will be smallest, in accordance with the size of the local market, though parts of the low-accessibility area, such as the Pacific Coast of the United States, might have movements of reasonably significant dimensions.[17] Movements to points of intermediate and high accessibility would occur only under unusual land taxes or demands or when the conditions of

[17] Note also the comments on the growth of market-oriented industries in such areas of extremely low accessibility as Utah and Colorado in Thomas R. Smith: Locational Analysis of New Manufacturing Plants in the United States, *Tijdschr. voor Econ. en Sociale Geografie*, Vol. 45, 1954, pp. 46–50, reference on p. 48; and John D. Garwood: An Analysis of Postwar Industrial Migration to Utah and Colorado, *Econ. Geogr.*, Vol. 29, 1953, pp. 79–88.

entry necessitated sales beyond the local regional or subregional market (that is, when the local market, or the part thereof unsatisfied by local competitors, only marginally justified the operation of additional large-scale plants).

Sample rail movements of the agricultural-implements industry, an industry largely localized by market considerations, are generally in accord with the statements made above (Fig. 5). Flows from Illinois (producers with high market accessibility) are more than six times the combined flows from Tennessee (producers with intermediate accessibility) and California (producers with low accessibility), and the bulk of the Illinois flows, from points such as Peoria and Chicago, are over short distances. However, the longer-distance flows are not of negligible size. As expected, the tonnage moving from Tennessee plants exceeds that moving from California factories, and is concentrated over short distances. The outflows from California producers are relatively inconsequential, though they exceed those from any other low-accessibility state. The fact that a small absolute amount, but a high percentage, of California's rail shipments of agricultural machinery traveled more than 1600 miles in 1959, to Tennessee (probably cotton-picking implements) and Minnesota (probably dairy machinery), is not of particularly great significance because these long-distance flows did not penetrate the Manufacturing Belt.

Daggett's analysis of the 1950 rail movements of the American iron and steel industry (now considered to be largely market oriented) reproduces essentially the same pattern: 79 per cent of all movements originated in "Official Classification Territory" (roughly conterminous with the Manufacturing Belt plus the remaining, industrially insignificant, part of New England), and 83 per cent of these originations terminated in the same high-accessibility area.

Industries Localized by Labor and Agglomeration Economies

The singular product movements of large-scale industries localized by economies of labor and/or agglomeration are derived from the high-value-added characteristics of most of these industries and their consequent capacity to withstand transportation costs and to move over long distances. In essence, agglomeration economies, whether of the internal, localization, or urbanization types, represent the substitution of transport outlays for production outlays of alternative locations and thereby imply longer finished-product hauls. Similarly, the higher the labor cost per ton of product and the higher the relative percentage of compression (or value added), the greater the distance of shipments that can be tolerated with respect to profit.

7. OUTFLOWS FROM INDUSTRIES LOCALIZED BY LABOR OR AGGLOMERATION

ECONOMIES IN AREAS OF HIGH MARKET ACCESSIBILITY / Other things being equal, large-scale high-value-added industries with central locations will ship the largest tonnage, a considerable part of which will move to areas of intermediate and low accessibility. It is clear that there is some relationship between population proximity and the availability of large labor pools and cheap labor,[18] and it has been argued that agglomeration economies and population accessibility are two sides of the same coin. Consequently, there is an overwhelming tendency for high-value-added industries to choose locations in high-accessibility areas. The long hauls to other areas are nothing more than a reflection of the secondary role of freight costs in the total cost structure of the industries.

8. OUTFLOWS FROM INDUSTRIES LOCALIZED BY LABOR OR AGGLOMERATION ECONOMIES IN AREAS OF INTERMEDIATE ACCESSIBILITY / Flows from these industries will be characterized by short distances and a small volume. Not only will it be difficult to overcome competitive advantages in the areas of high and low accessibility, but flows from the industrial belt of the nation or region will offer stiff competition, and in some instances will even dominate the market in the area of intermediate proximity.

9. OUTFLOWS FROM INDUSTRIES LOCALIZED BY LABOR OR AGGLOMERATION ECONOMIES IN AREAS OF LOW ACCESSIBILITY / By definition, industries of this type are infrequent in areas of low market proximity, though they may be found in subareal high population concentrations or in those rare instances where, as in Colorado, the degree of unionization acts as a locational force. Those industries which do occur in such locations will generate relatively small volumes of traffic which move over generally short distances. Long hauls, as with the previous example, are hampered by the competitive advantages enjoyed by high-accessibility producers, who will also account for a large or dominant part of the low-accessibility area market.

The electric lighting and wiring equipment industry, which produces electric lamps, lighting fixtures, current-carrying devices, and other noncurrent-carrying devices, is a high-value-added industry of the type considered here. The sample rail data once again correspond markedly with the proposed flow types (Fig. 6). Producers of electrical equipment in New York (high market accessibility) transported in 1959 a larger volume of goods than their counterparts in Missouri (intermedi-

---

[18] Cheapness of labor is best determined not by wages per hour but by average labor costs per ton of product (Weber's index of labor costs). See Weber, *op. cit.* [see footnote 13 above], p. 106. For a further discussion of the influence of labor costs on industrial location, see Martin Segal: Wages in the Metropolis: Their Influence on the Location of Industries in the New York Region (Cambridge, Mass., 1960).

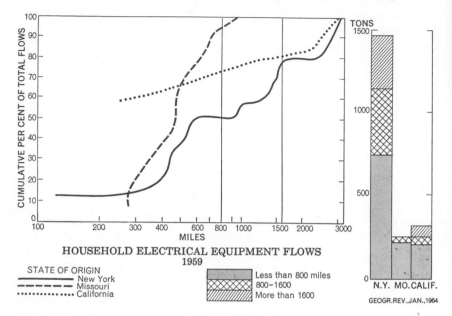

FIGURE 6: Household electrical equipment flows, 1959, based on I.C.C. *Carload Waybill Statistics* (see text footnote 15 for reference).

ate accessibility) and California (low accessibility), or, for that matter, in any other state outside the Manufacturing Belt. Flows from New York were the largest of the three not only within the Manufacturing Belt but also within the areas of intermediate and low accessibility. Flows from Missouri and California were relatively small and short. It is noteworthy that 20.6 per cent of California's flows were to Ohio, New York, and Maryland; but in view of the industry's ability to absorb freight costs, and of the mere 67 tons shipped to these three states, it would be foolhardy to undertake any far-reaching interpretations of this apparent discrepancy.

Flows of high-value-added products from West Virginia (high accessibility) go to most states in the country and thus further substantiate the proposed typology.

Some Remarks on the Typology

The geographic differentiation of commodity flows is an extremely complex problem that requires consideration not only of industrial cost structure and relative location with respect to population and the market but also of areal differences in the distribution of a wide range of other economic, cultural, and physical phenomena. Indeed, the complexity of the problem and the uniqueness of geographic places probably rule out the possibility of any total solution. Therefore the ideas presented in this paper should be viewed as no more than beginning suggestions. In building on concepts that have already appeared in the literature there has been no intention of arriving at inexorable absolute norms from which there can be no deviation (hence the use of the term "typology" rather than "taxonomy," "classification," or some other alternative). Instead, it is hoped, a series of meaningful generalizations have been presented that help to throw some light on the volume and length characteristics of similar large-scale industrial flows originating in dissimilar locales.

To be sure, the generalizations of the typology have numerous limitations. They are economically deterministic to the extent that they are couched solely in terms of cost factors and market accessibility. Sometimes intentionally, sometimes unintentionally, they are vague, imprecise, conjectural, and oversimplified. The review of the literature on which the generalizations are based is far from comprehensive. In an attempt to maintain clarity while building on abstractions, the number of types was arbitrarily limited to nine, a number woefully inadequate to deal with all the permutations of reality; for within each of the types there exists a broad spectrum of possible variations. In the same quest for clarity the more subtle and intricate aspects of crosshauling, freight rates, and demand were bypassed. More important, local short movements by truck and longer shipments on ocean or inland waterways were not considered. This may be viewed as a particularly grievous shortcoming because of the frequently high percentage of traffic that moves by truck or freighter; but, on the other hand, in placing emphasis on short movements trucking was indirectly subsumed, since such transportation usually only "remains relatively economical . . . for distances up to about three hundred miles (generally regarded as the overnight trucking range)."

The typology would perhaps have proved more enlightening if its approach had been inverted; that is, if different industries at identical relative locations had served as the basis of the generalizations. Another alternative would have been to distinguish the industries directly on the basis of value added, rather than indirectly by reference to localization factors.

If the generalizations and the typology itself have their pitfalls, then the empirical considerations presented are also not without fault. Some may contend that the United States is not viewed as a single market by most producers, "yet it provides the opportunity for one market for a significant, critical number of specialized or volume producers," and it should be emphatically reiterated that the typology purports to have reference only to such large-scale producers. The manner in which the I.C.C.'s *Carload Waybill Statistics* were used is also open to question. Even if the statistics are reliable, how is the picture altered by neglect of shipments of less than a carload? How representative a year was 1959? Are the aluminum, agricultural implement, and electrical equipment industries representative of industries localized respectively by raw materials and power, by market, and by labor and agglomeration economies? Are the flows associated with the selected states indicative of overall patterns? Finally, how misleading is the impression created by use of comparisons by states rather than by individual plants?

In view of these and other theoretical and empirical contingencies, it may perhaps be legitimately stated that this paper poses more questions then it answers.

17. Amenities as a Factor in Regional Growth

Edward L. Ullman

Equally important to the flow of commodities, as discussed in the preceding selection, in the development of the economic geography of the United States is the migration of laborers. The United States has had a tremendous input of labor from Europe, Canada, Africa, the Far East, and selected areas of Latin America, such as Mexico, Cuba, and Puerto Rico. This influx of foreign labor and the internal movement of the native-born have made the population of the United States one of the most highly mobile in the world. Ullman analyzes the role of pleasant living conditions in this mobility and evaluates the significance of amenable surroundings as a force in initiating or expanding regional growth. This kind of migration has continued to snowball since Ullman published this article in 1954. California is now the most populous state in the United States and other warm climate areas such as Florida, Arizona, and Texas have experienced phenomenal growth. The new people in an area provide a labor supply, a market, and occasionally a liability such as excessive unemployment. In an expanding economy, the amenity factor assumes major importance in the movement of both skilled and unskilled labor. It is not an all-pervading reason for migration, however, as is shown by the large-scale influx of Negroes from the climatically warm, rural south to the colder, industrial north. The continuing and growing importance of amenities in the overall

economic development of the United States and other world
areas, however, is reason enough for the inclusion of this
selection in this collection. With increased technological
development in such areas as air conditioning, the significance
of the amenities may decrease in the future but this, in turn,
may be offset by increased leisure time and demand for
outdoor recreation.

For the first time in the world's history pleasant living conditions—amenities—instead of more narrowly defined economic advantages are becoming the sparks that generate significant population increase, particularly in the United States. In spite of the handicaps of remote location and economic isolation, the fastest-growing states are California, Arizona, and Florida. The new "frontier" of America is thus a frontier of comfort, in contrast with the traditional frontier of hardship. Treating this pull of amenities puts me, I realize, in the company of promoters and the traditionally uninformed, but if I make myself one with them, it is for new and valid reasons.

Motivation of Migration

Modern writers on migration apparently agree that, except for forced shifts, economic opportunity is its motivating force. In 1934 the distinguished climatologist C. Warren Thornthwaite, commenting on California's phenomenal growth from 1920 to 1930, concluded, "Since the movement is abnormal in most respects, it is inconceivable that it will continue." In 1938, Rupert Vance, distinguished sociologist, said: "On the basis of the exploitation of undeveloped resources of soil, minerals, forestry or water power, there can be expected no revival of the great westward migrations of the past."[1] In 1941, Margaret L. Bright and Dorothy S. Thomas noted that California migration before 1930 far exceeded expectations based on laws of migration such as Stouffer's "intervening opportunity" and concluded: "We are of the opinion that an important part of the migration to California has been of a hedonistic rather than a primarily economic character and has been motivated more by climate and legend than by superior job opportunities."

As everyone knows, the influx into California was greatest between

SOURCE: *The Geographical Review*, XLIV (January, 1954), 119–32. Reprinted with omissions; copyrighted by the American Geographical Society of New York. The author is professor of geography at the University of Washington.
[1] R. B. Vance: Research Memorandum on Population Redistribution within the United States, *Social Sci. Research Council Bull.* 42, 1938, pp. 85–110; reference on p. 92. Vance states further: "The one other chance for continued westward movement is industrialization; and there the Pacific Coast may reasonably expect to supply more of its own needs but not to dismantle the country's prevailing industrial distribution. Nor is it held likely that the California movement will continue at its former rate" (p. 92).

1940 and 1950; even from 1935 to 1940 it was greater than to any other part of the country, averaging more than 175,000 a year, with a net of more than 130,000. *Net* in-migration from April 1, 1940, to June 30, 1941, was more than 300,000; during the war the net rose to an annual average of 422,000, and for the two years after the war the annual average was more than 100,000.[2] Immediately after the war some migrants started east, but within months the flow reversed, and under peacetime conditions the in-migration resumed on a large scale. A relatively high rate of unemployment resulted until Korean war orders took up the slack.

Figures for later years are not available, but reports from movers indicate that 1952 was their boom year for intercity moves, exceeding the previous largest year, 1951, by 20 percent, with heaviest moves toward the west and south. California, Texas, and Florida led, with New Mexico and Arizona also as fairly large net gainers.

California migration is large-scale even in world terms. Apparently the largest previous migration in America was to the Prairie Provinces of Canada in the early 1900's, which reached a peak of 200,000 in one or two years. The greatest *net* immigration into the whole of the United States apparently was about 800,000 in 1910 and 1913.[3] Chinese emigration to Manchuria reportedly exceeded 1,000,000 a year from 1927 to 1929, though the net ranged only from about 400,000 to 800,000. Net annual average in-migration to *all* of Asiatic Russia between 1926 and 1939 apparently was about 270,000.

All these other great migrations were induced primarily by economic opportunity. California, on the contrary, received the first large-scale in-migration to be drawn by the lure of a pleasant climate, though other factors have played a role—including war, which caused airplane production to boom and enabled thousands of servicemen to see California for the first time. War, however, in part appears to be one of the shocks precipitating changes due to other long-range trends.

In the United States as a whole, the greatest changes in distribution of population between 1940 and 1950 were: (1) the suburban flight, a 35 per cent increase in suburban population, as compared with 13 per cent inside city limits and 6 per cent elsewhere; [4] and (2) the growth of

[2] *Current Population Repts.*, Ser. P-25, Population Estimates, No. 12, U. S. Bureau of the Census, Aug. 9, 1948, p. 9. In all three periods California's net in-migration was the largest in the country, several times larger than that of the nearest competitor from 1940 to 1945. From 1945 to 1947, however, California (108,000) was barely ahead of Illinois (106,000) and New York (83,000).
[3] Calculated from "Historical Statistics of the United States, 1789–1945" (U. S. Bureau of the Census, 1949), pp. 33 and 38. See also W. F. Willcox, edit.: International Migrations, Vol. 2, Interpretations, *Publs. Natl. Bur. of Econ. Research No. 18*, New York, 1931, p. 88.
[4] Increase in population of standard metropolitan areas as a whole was 21.2 per cent, as compared with 5.7 per cent for the remainder of the country (1950 Census of Population: Preliminary Counts, Ser. PC-3, No. 3, U. S. Bureau of the Census, Nov.

California, with a 53 per cent increase, Arizona, 50 per cent, and Florida, 46 per cent, followed by Oregon, 39 per cent, and Washington, 37 per cent.[5] Undoubtedly the suburban flight has a large element of amenity seeking behind it, and was made possible by the automobile. This type of local migration will not be further considered, though it reinforces some of my later contentions on regional migration.

Climate as an Amenity

People have their violent preferences and prejudices, starting in a majority of cases with the conviction that where one was born and lives is the best place in the world, no matter how forsaken a hole it may appear to an outsider. Nevertheless, a substantial minority (millions in a country the size of the United States) have other ideas. The first requisite is a pleasant outdoor climate. The best criterion I can think of is an outdoor climate similar to the climate maintained inside our houses —a temperature of about 70° F. and no rain. Note that emphasis is on a pleasant climate, "nice" climate, not necessarily one that drives men to the greatest physical or mental efficiency, as defined by Huntington, Toynbee, Markham, and others. Since the majority of Americans live

---

5, 1950). The fact that most of the 21.2 per cent increase took place outside central cities is the basis for describing it as a "suburban flight." This, however, probably overstates the case, inasmuch as central-city boundaries were not expanded much and consequently the increase in metropolitan population had to take place outside the city (cf. Svend Riemer: Escape into Decentralization? *Land Economics,* Vol. 24, 1948, pp. 40–48). Nevertheless, population has actually decreased in places near the core of many large cities and has remained static elsewhere in some central cities, not increasing at the national rate. What is happening in cities appears to fit the amenity hypothesis; Riemer notes that the trend "is not toward 'decentralization' but toward better residential districts which—due to unfortunate circumstances—are available only at the outskirts of the city, and accessible only at the cost of long commuting distances" (p. 41).

[5] *Statistical Abstract of the United States: 1951,* U. S. Bureau of the Census, 1951, p. 31. Nevada had a 45 per cent increase, but in absolute numbers this represented an increase of only 50,000, too small to be statistically significant. Arizona's increase of 50 per cent is in somewhat the same category, since it represents only 250,000 persons. In absolute gain (rounded figures) California was far in the lead with about 3,600,000, followed by New York, 1,300,000; Michigan, 1,100,000; Ohio, 1,000,000; and Florida, 900,000 (slightly more than Illinois). If one considers estimated increases of civilian population only, up to July 1, 1951, the ranking for the 11½-year period changes slightly: Arizona, 58 per cent; California, 54; Florida, 52; Nevada, 51; Oregon, 42; Washington, 35 (*Current Population Repts.,* Ser. P-25, Population Estimates, No. 62, U. S. Bureau of the Census, Aug. 24, 1952). Estimates of net in-migration gain, 1940–1950, are: California, 38 per cent; Nevada, 31; Florida, 30; Arizona, 28; Oregon, 26; Washington, 23 (*ibid.,* No. 72, May, 1953). Percentage increases for the period April 1, 1950, to July 1, 1952, for the fastest-growing states are: Arizona, 15; Nevada, 12; Florida, 12; Maryland, 8 (suburban spillover from Washington, D. C.?); Colorado, 8; California, 8. Absolute increases in the same period by rank are: California, 804,000; Texas, 477,000; New York, 348,000; Michigan, 337,000; Florida, 329,000 (*ibid.,* No. 70, Mar. 24, 1953).

in the Northeast, in a colder, long-winter climate, this means attraction of warmer climates.

A rough but objective ranking of the regions of the United States in climatic pull puts coastal Southern California and the climatically somewhat similar protected coastal areas of Central and Northern California alone in Class I. This, the only Mediterranean-type climate in America, has relatively warm winters and relatively cool summers, coupled with low rainfall and abundant sunshine. Some might also include a small strip along the lower east coast of Florida, primarily because of its winter pull. This area, "The Florida Tropics," as demonstrated by Carson, has a unique combination of warm and relatively sunny winters, and a summer without excessively high temperatures because of ocean exposure and the cooling effect of winds. The most unpleasant feature probably is the long length of the summer. This small area of "tourist" climate is the one that has grown by far the most in Florida, just as coastal Southern California has in California.

Class II areas will not be considered in detail, because of limitations of space and variations in taste and local climates. These areas might include a thin coastal strip along the Gulf and South Atlantic (a winter resort for the North and a summer resort for the South), parts of Arizona and New Mexico, protected parts of the remainder of the Pacific Coast, and other local areas with more benign climates than their neighbors, such as the Colorado Piedmont or Cape Cod.

Climate is probably the most important regional amenity, because it can be combined with other amenities, especially within the continental United States, where there is a fairly even spread of culture, education, sanitation, and creature comforts of all sorts. The best scenery and bathing in the world are useless unless one can get out in them. Furthermore, climate has an important effect on the health of many sufferers, warm, dry regions outside storm-track zones (southwestern United States), according to Mills, apparently doing the greatest good for the greatest number of ailments, though Winslow and Herrington state: "Thus, considering all the evidence at hand, we can only predicate with certainty that extremes of heat and cold are definitely harmful; and that even moderately hot conditions increase susceptibility to intestinal diseases, and moderately cold conditions increase susceptibility to respiratory diseases."

Other amenities, however, do exert a pull; mountains and beaches, hunting, fishing, and other sports, beautiful New England towns, all come to mind. Even if the Great Plains had a near-perfect climate, they probably would not lure as many people as the same climate in a region with mountains and water. This is a subjective matter: some people seem to like flat country, but most residents of the Pacific Coast (since most of them are refugees from the Middle West) would probably gain solace from the fact "that no matter what may happen to them, no matter what their lot in life may be, they do not live in Kansas."

The rest of the world will not be considered except to note the two types of areas with "ideal" climates: (1) parts of the other "Mediterranean" climatic regions, and some ocean-tempered trade-wind islands such as Hawaii; and (2), potentially the best in the world, high altitudes in low latitudes—parts of tablelands in Latin America and other tropical mountain zones.

Outside the United States, the population generally is less wealthy and foot-loose, and no growth related to climate comparable with that in California has taken place, with two possible exceptions, both in countries somewhat similar to the United States in wealth, and each with a "nicer" place within its borders to go to. In Canada, Vancouver is the most rapidly growing city. The Vancouver region is no California, but compared with the rest of Canada, it has the best climate and scenery as well as other attractions. In France, Nice, on the Riviera, was the fastest-growing city before the war.

If, for the first time in the world's history, the population of "nice" areas in some countries is growing more rapidly than that in the remainder of those countries, the fundamental question is: What has happened to the economy to make this possible? Following are some factors, many of which need further research to establish their quantitative contribution.

Retirement and Tourist Factors

The growth of early, paid retirement, coupled with longer life expectancy for the population as a whole, is one factor. Even in the high-birthrate period from 1940 to 1950, the number of persons over 65 years of age increased from 6.9 percent of the total United States population to 8.2 percent. Industrial unions have been obtaining retirement provisions so generally that the number of retired workers will increase enormously in the future; so also will the number aided from expanding Social Security.[6] Furthermore, old people seem to like a warmer climate, and, as noted, most of the workers now live in the colder cli-

[6] "By mid-1950 practically every major union in the country . . . had to some extent negotiated pension or health and welfare programs" (E. K. Rowe: Employee-Benefit Plans under Collective Bargaining, Mid-1950, *U. S. Dept. of Labor, Bur. of Labor Statistics Bull. 1017*, 1951 [reprinted from *Monthly Labor Rev.*, Vol. 72, 1951 pp. 156–162]. At least seven million industrial workers now have pension plans, most of them only a few years old; government old-age insurance is also increasing. However, as a counterbalance, the effects of inflation have cut into these benefits enormously and have also reduced the return from savings. Lower interest rates have had the same result (Proceedings of the Governors' Conference on the Problems of the Aging, Sacramento, Calif., Oct. 15–16, 1951, p. 282). Note, as a further counterbalance, the obvious fact that old people do not live as long as younger people and hence a given number are not as long-lasting a gain in population.

mates of the Northeast or Midwest. The net effect of the removal of a number of these people to places such as Florida or California is a subsidy from one region to another.[7] However, only a portion of amenity-induced growth can be attributed to this factor, since people over 65 are merely a small part of the United States population. The National Planning Association estimates that in 25 years they will number 20 million, of whom 14 million will not be working.

Related to retirement is the well-known growth of the tourist industry, partly a response to the spreading practice of paid vacations, even for industrial workers. In 1940, only one-fourth of all labor contracts called for paid vacations; now almost all do. Altogether, 42 million workers are eligible, many of them for increasingly long vacations, up to three weeks or more. Florida and California derive substantial incomes from this trade, as do amenity regions closer to home for the majority of workers, such as New England.

Increase in Foot-loose Workers

Increase in number of foot-loose workers is related to war production, but particularly to the long-range trends established by Colin Clark: a decrease in the number of primary workers (agriculture, fishing, and forestry), because of increasing mechanization and agricultural efficiency; a static or, in some cases, declining level of secondary workers (manufacturing, mining, and construction) except perhaps in wartime; and a great increase in tertiary employment (trade and services).[8]

Logically, the increase in tertiary employment should occur in areas of primary and secondary employment; up to now this paper has established only an increased base of retired people and tourists to support this increased number of tertiary workers in benign areas. However, it seems reasonable that a growing but unknown number of tertiary workers are also nationally foot-loose. Many specialized services can meet the needs of a national market from anywhere in the country, such as the movie, radio, and TV industry in California. The cinema appreciates the same climate and scenery as humans (as also, to a certain extent, does California and Florida agriculture). Clear weather

[7] When wealthy people are involved, this may introduce a large amount of capital and start off a chain reaction. Carey McWilliams (California: The Great Exception [New York, 1949], pp. 257 and 260) notes the effect of Pasadena retired millionaires in building and endowing Mt. Wilson Observatory and the California Institute of Technology.

[8] In 1850 primary employment amounted to 65 per cent, secondary to 18 per cent, and tertiary to 18 per cent; in 1920, the percentages were 27, 33, and 40 respectively; and by 1950, 17, 34, and 49 respectively (1950 figures calculated from 1950 Census of Population: Preliminary Reports, Ser. PC-7, No. 2, U. S. Bureau of the Census, April, 1951, pp. 31–33; figures for 1920 and 1850 taken from P. K. Whelpton: Occupational Groups in the United States, Journ. Amer. Statist. Assn., Vol. 21, 1926, p. 340).

for shooting pictures, particularly in the industry's initial outdoor period, plus a variety of scenery, was a factor in locating the motion-picture industry in Hollywood, along with the specific flight of independents from business troubles in New York.

In the business world also, there are indications of at least a partial effect of amenities on the location of activities, though whether they overbalance the presumed agglomerative benefits of an eastern, closer-to-market headquarters is unknown. The Carnation Milk Company, for example, has recently centralized its headquarters in Los Angeles. Part of the reason given (other than the need for centralizing operations and the relatively important market position of the company in the West) was better living conditions; another part was the professed "dynamic" quality of Los Angeles. National control from Los Angeles is considered feasible now because of the speed of traveling to, or communicating with, the whole country.[9]

In industry, evidence, again not yet as quantitative as desirable, indicates some pull of amenities. High-value products such as calculating machines or advanced electronic products can afford shipping costs all over the country from California. On the other hand, some companies producing a bulkier product that started in California have moved east to get efficient national distribution. Likewise, some other industries benefit somewhat from a benign climate just as motion pictures do. This is one of the location factors for the otherwise mobile, somewhat outdoor industry of airframe assembly, the largest industry in California.

In assessing the pull of amenities on foot-loose industries one runs into a reluctance of executives to admit that personal-comfort considerations motivate them, "seeming to feel that the location of the firm ought to be justified on more objective grounds." [10] This reluctance, noted in Arizona, seemed to prevail also in the aircraft industry in California, according to personal conversation I have had with Glenn Cunningham, an authority on location of the industry, though he had no way of proving the point. Nevertheless, for 34 small industries studied by Casaday in Tucson, Ariz., climate was found to be the overwhelming attraction, not only to executives, but even more to labor, because of its

---

[9] Address, "The Los Angeles Opportunity," by P. H. Willis, general advertising manager, Carnation Milk Company, to the Advertising Club of Los Angeles, Sept. 7, 1948. According to *Fortune* ("Industrial Los Angeles," June, 1949, p. 154), Vice-President Alfred M. Ghormley of Carnation noted that Los Angeles was the company's largest single market and was stimulating to management because it generated so many new grocery techniques, but "the most important factor" was that "while money means a lot to all of us, it certainly is not everything today, and we felt that we could attract better executive material if we could bring some of these men into a climate they might enjoy more."

[10] L. W. Casaday: Tucson as a Location for Small Industry, *Univ. of Arizona, Bur. of Business Research Special Studies No. 4*, 1952, p. 23. The other quotations in this paragraph are from the same source, pp. 23 and 24.

favorable effect on labor availability, satisfaction, and efficiency. A representative comment of those interviewed is as follows:

. . . a shortage of labor will never develop here. Thousands of families in the east and midwest who have health problems or who have always wanted to move to Arizona would come at the drop of a hat if they were sure of steady employment and adequate housing. At the worst, a little direct advertising in the eastern part of the country would solve any labor supply problem Tucson is likely to have.

Still another, referring to a rapidly growing, relatively foot-loose phase of industry:

. . . It would take a helluva lot to get me to leave Tucson but even if I did have to go back east I would see to it that the laboratory operations remain right here. There couldn't be a better location for that type of work.

Market-Orientation Factor

The shift of industry to greater market orientation has apparently over-balanced the movement to raw materials in recent years and means a larger amount of industry supported by the increased population of the newly expanding areas.[11] Much of California's postwar manufacturing growth is market-oriented. Three long-range factors help explain the shift: changes in technology, in transportation, and in economies of scale.

In heavy industry, for example, economies in use of fuel have re-duced raw-material requirements per ton of finished products; this, along with other factors, has made it possible for Kaiser to produce steel in Fontana for the California market even though coal has to move more than 500 miles by rail from Utah. Apparently, also, the cost of transporting bulky raw materials, which can be handled mechanically in volume, has decreased more than that of shipping finished products requiring more hand labor, an increasing cost item. Thus an increasing percentage of fuel requirements are obtained from oil or gas, much of which now moves by pipeline longer distances than coal could afford to move by rail.

Finally, as a market increases in size, new economies of scale are possible and an additional number of new specialties can be supported on the increased base established. This has happened for manufactur-ing to some extent in California. The state has had a real increase in percentage of population employed in manufacturing. However, as

[11] Even in the South; note the conclusions in G. E. McLaughlin and Stefan Robock: Why Industry Moves South, *National Planning Assn. Committee of the South Rept. No. 3*, 1949. About 45 per cent of the new plants (and a larger percentage of employment) moved to serve southern markets, 30 per cent to raw materials, and 25 per cent to cheap labor (pp. 26–27).

compared with national growth, manufacturing has not expanded as rapidly in California as population has. Thus the deviation of the percentage of California population employed in manufacturing from the national percentage was −1.6 in 1929 and −3.2 in 1947.[12] On the basis of these trends, economies of scale, both external (regional) and internal (single industry or plant), apparently have abundant scope for still greater application in the future.[13]

Other New Factors

Still other new factors, mostly social but partly technological, bear on the thesis that pleasanter places are due for an increase in population.

1. The greatly increased mobility of the American people, because of universal auto ownership and good roads, makes transcontinental moves reasonably commonplace and permits Americans to discover amenable regions during longer vacations.

2. As more people settle in pleasant areas, they themselves will exert an agglomerative pull, bringing in still more newcomers. As is well known, firsthand reports from friends and relatives are one of the strongest means of advertising for immigrants.

3. One of the results of these two factors is to bring to light a minor economic incentive to live in warmer climates: the lower cost of fuel, housing, and some other items.

4. The prospects for widespread air conditioning will make warm regions more attractive, especially in the United States, where income levels will be sufficient to cover costs.[14] Theoretically, this should relatively favor Florida and Arizona, with warm summers, rather than coastal California, with cool summers.

5. The present high birthrate is resulting in larger families and thus creating more mothers who wish they could let their youngsters run outdoor in winter and hope (probably in vain) that they would thereby escape the high and gloomy incidence of winter colds and flu. Anyone

[12] In 1929, 6.3 per cent of California's population was employed in manufacturing, 7.9 per cent in the United States as a whole; in 1947 the percentages were 6.8 and 10.0 respectively (1947 Census of Manufactures, Vol. 1, U. S. Bureau of the Census, 1950, pp. 35 and 39).

[13] We do not yet know at what thresholds of population various increases in industry are likely to occur, except in general terms. In practice, lag and speculation are involved, as well as absorption pricing policies of plants elsewhere in the country, and other factors.

[14] *Business Week*, Mar. 7, 1953. Some authorities indicate that costs for household air conditioning can be as low as $12 a month throughout the year to cover both operation and amortization. In a dry area such as southern Arizona simple evaporation systems, which work well except during infrequent humid periods, are even cheaper (personal communication from Mr. A. W. Wilson, University of Arizona, Tucson).

who has spent a winter in New England or the Midwest must have heard mothers wish that they could move to California or Florida (many do, probably a reflection of our matriarchal society! As many have noted, "the really fundamental economic decisions are made in bedrooms not board rooms."

6. In our society today the conviction apparently has grown up, along with heavy taxation, that it is difficult to make a lot of money and consequently one might as well enjoy life—the reverse of the earlier emphasis on the hereafter. A pleasant place to live is given more consideration, other things being equal. Likewise, "mass leisure" is now a feature of the United States. Reduction in the industrial work week from 64 hours in 1860 to an average of 42 in 1930 (and a further drop since then) has given the worker more leisure time to appreciate outdoor and other amenities.[15]

Most state planning and development agencies, and public utilities, recognize the lure of amenities, some of them with reason. Officials of a large utility in Chicago have told me that one of their biggest problems in luring industry to Chicago is the unwillingness of executives to live in the city. As a result the company has gone all out in advertising the presumed cultural and recreational advantages of its city. North Carolina advertises, "There is profit in pleasure"; New Hampshire, "There's a Plus in every pay envelope"; Colorado offers, as a minor inducement, the "magic" of the Colorado climate; and finally, British Columbia advertises itself as the "California of Canada"! [16]

Underlying this thesis is the apparent hedonistic goal of the American people and of much of the rest of mankind; this goal may represent a new emphasis—but I doubt it—on tangible physical pleasure rather

---

[15] Reuel Denney and David Riesman: Leisure in Industrial America, in Creating an Industrial Civilization: A Report on the Corning Conference, Held under the Auspices of the American Council of Learned Societies and Corning Glass Works . . . , edited by Eugene Staley and others (New York, 1952), pp. 245–246.

[16] Others have also recognized the contribution of amenities, as witness the following statement: "Although, historically, migration within the United States was always associated with improved economic opportunities, the permanency of war migration to this region was apparently strongly influenced by the psychological factor of taste for the region and its climate and other preference imponderables. This unpredictable permanent increase of people in the Columbia Valley region has also been affected by the remarkable postwar expansion of commercial, industrial, and construction activity, which has easily absorbed the large number of migrants choosing to stay, as well as most of the returning veterans . . ." (Charles McKinley: Uncle Sam in the Pacific Northwest, *Univ. of California, Bur. of Business and Econ. Research Pub.*, 1952, p. 9). And still another, typical of an intermediate locality and bringing in home ties: "Consideration of climate and recreational facilities, or the fact that the owner has grown up in Michigan appear to determine in not a few cases the choice between a Michigan location and one in Ohio, Indiana, or Illinois" (James Morgan and Harold Guthrie: What Michigan Manufacturers Think of Michigan, *Michigan Business Rev.*, Vol. 3, 1951, pp. 18–20).

than on psychic pleasure from religion or prestige,[17] or a puritanical glow derived from hard work and acquisition of wealth, or a humane stimulation from learning, culture, and the growth of the inner man.

Forces are also working in the opposite direction. These will not be treated here, nor do I feel that they counterbalance the forces allowing population to move to amenities. At most, they represent another pole pulling simultaneously, such as the growth of West Virginia and Texas, based on natural, chemical resources, along with that of California and Florida, based largely on climate.

Conclusion

Discovery of the spark starting regional development is crucial in view of the increasing number of service workers and industries dependent on the initial base. In singling out amenities for analysis, I have deliberately concentrated on a new, speculative force, whose workings are not yet understood and whose influence may be greater in the future. Nor is it my intention to explain in terms of a single cause so large a phenomenon as the growth of California or the recent migration of peoples.

Before definite conclusions can be drawn, further research and testing are required. Basic to this testing is analysis of the trends and probable degree of future foot-loose orientation of services and industries in terms of national location. This probably means a detailed and exhaustive analysis of growth of individual industrial products and services based on stage of process, which census classifications do not give.

As was noted before, the continental limits of the United States rather sharply contain the area within which amenities for Americans can operate on a large scale today, not only because of uniformly widespread culture and comfort, but mainly because linkages with the rest of the economy are easiest, and in many cases, only possible, within the continental United States. Because of the small area of subtropical climate within the country, California and Florida largely escape competition. Their amenity pulling power is reinforced by the relative uniqueness of their environment, which enables them to exert a pull even across half a continent. Thus Carson notes that southeastern Florida is probably the only "place on earth where middle latitude progressiveness meets the exuberance and livability of the tropics . . . Inhabitants of other tropical regions may enjoy complete freedom from frost but are less likely to acquire a car, a mail order catalog, or a

---

[17] Note, for example, the increasing popularity of various house, garden, and living magazines of national and regional circulation. To mention one from the West, there is the popular and attractive *Sunset* magazine. Note also Ghormley's statement in footnote 9, above.

legacy of intellectual curiosity.[18] Migration to amenities and pleasanter climates appears to be one of the more reasonable results of what the economist Galbraith calls the "unseemly economics of opulence," a more rewarding way of spending effort than in advertising cigarettes or degrading flour and then re-enriching it to make bread, or any of the countless other ways in which money is thrown around in our wealthy economy. Even Aristotle noted, "Men seek after a better notion of riches . . . than the mere accumulation of coin and they are right."

It looks as if America, given half a chance, might become a nation of sybarites. We now have this half chance. Oscar Handlin observes, for example, that the American laborer who once hesitated to risk merely shifting from one factory to another is now willing "to move from one section of the country to another, confident he will anywhere find a demand for his services."

Even if our ends have not changed, our means have. And these changes seem to be just beginning so far as the predictable future is concerned. Even the unpredictable future indicates the same: really cheap atomic or solar energy will make men still more foot-loose. Thus the climate of California and Florida takes its place as a population magnet along with the coal of Pittsburgh and the soil of Iowa.[19]

Assuming that we have proved our case, what is the moral? There are at least three:

1. The amenity factor should be kept in mind in predicting future regional population and development; the predictor, however, is under

---

[18] R. B. Carson: The Florida Tropics, *Econ. Geogr.*, Vol. 27, 1951, pp. 338–339. Note also Ackerman's conclusion that citrus fruits are grown in California and Florida, even though they are slightly colder than the optimum, because they are in the United States (E. A. Ackerman: Influences of Climate on the Cultivation of Citrus Fruits, *Geogr. Rev.*, Vol. 28, 1938, pp. 289–302).

[19] This is somewhat of a reversal of Ellsworth Huntington's optimum-climate hypothesis that the slightly cooler climates are more stimulating and therefore Northern Europe and the northern United States are the most "advanced" regions in the world. To me, this appears to be a reasoning after the fact, a fact for which coal and iron ore, strongly localized in these regions, and an earlier start were more important causes. (Huntington does, however, include coastal California in his optimum climate along with the Northeast; see his "Civilization and Climate" or "Mainsprings of Civilization," cited in footnote 12, above). Toynbee, in his challenge-and-response theory of history, advances a slightly different argument, though not limiting his environment to climate. McWilliams, *op. cit.* [see footnote 7, above], employs Toynbee's thesis with a new twist in noting the different nature of California's environment and its consequent (?) stimulation to invention and growth. S. F. Markham: Climate and Energy of Nations (London, New York, Toronto, 1944), indicates much the same optimum climate as Huntington does and emphasizes the development of indoor heating based on coal in these areas as a way of overcoming the cold winters. He also notes that future air conditioning in wealthy countries (notably the United States) may well minimize some of the handicaps of the warm climates.

special obligation to be objective, because most of mankind thinks his own region is best, and indeed may even be paid to think so.

2. Improvement of amenities of a city or region may actually pay off in the long run, something no planner has ever been able to prove. Here care should be taken not to kill the goose that lays the golden egg by crowding population and industry into a place in an unplanned and unpleasant manner and creating intolerable traffic, smog, and other conditions, as has happened in some cases, but need not.[20]

3. No matter how much man tries, he cannot compete with Nature in regard to some of the most important amenities, such as climate, though air conditioning will make warm climates more attractive in countries that can afford it, just as central house heating improved cold climates in the past.

[20] Note the following opinion of a West Coast city manufacturer (quoted from the January 24, 1952, issue of *Direction Finding*, a service published by Industrial Survey Associates, 605 Market Street, San Francisco 5, Calif., and reprinted in *Area and Industrial Development Publications No. 18*, Area Development Division, U. S. Dept. of Commerce, March, 1952, p. 8).

"In response to your letter regarding an increase in our subscription to the chamber of commerce for the specific purpose of bringing in more industry, new people, and new payrolls, including greater quantities of sewage pollution on our beaches and rivers, greater congestion in living quarters and in our temporary school buildings, greater congestion of traffic and carbon dioxide gas pollution in our streets, and general destruction of our natural resources wherever increased population can spoil and destroy them—if these are the things you want, I certainly am not for them.

"Since we are in the manufacturing business we are naturally interested in payrolls, transportation, housing, schools, etc. We are considering plant expansion ourselves, but it certainly will not be in this city under present conditions. In fact, we are moving as far away from these congested conditions as we possibly can get, to a small town where we will have room to breathe and happy home-owning employees, far removed from the mess we have here. Until these conditions are cured, I am against bringing any more people to this area. . . ."

18. Some Theoretical Considerations for Manufacturing Geography

John H. Thompson

The search for meaningful generalizations and theory has become increasingly important in manufacturing geography research. Concepts developed by economists such as Lösch, Hoover, and Weber have been adopted and adapted by

*geographers, but the search continues for ideas that will
further and foster the theoretical framework for spatial
analysis. Thompson indicates some of the theoretical considerations that have been deduced from manufacturing studies
in various parts of the world. They provide a good conceptual basis for the specific manufacturing articles that
follow. The cycle, differential growth, concentration, agglomeration, and changing role theories are illustrated by the
articles on automobile and paper manufacturing.*

*Figures 1 and 2 in this article show, in convincing fashion,
the increasing importance of the tertiary sector of the
United States economy, in terms of employment over a
period of time, the gradual rise of the secondary sector, and
the rapid decline of the primary sector. This accents the
dynamic character of economic geography in a given country.
Changes are also rapid when countries and parts within a
country are compared. As Thompson makes clear, we need
improved theory and generalization to understand change in
the spatial structure of economic activity.*

It has been argued repeatedly in recent years that if *geography* is to
make as significant a contribution to the understanding of the functional
organization of space as *economics* has to the understanding of economic processes and systems the field must develop concepts at reasonably
high levels of abstraction. It follows that more geographic studies need
to be conceived and designed as parts of a larger whole rather than as
entities in themselves; that more researchers, at the outset of their investigations, should be interested in the possible role of their conclusions in the overall geographical system of which their work is presumably a part. It follows, too, that more geography theses, disserta-
tions, and scholarly books ought to be concept oriented and that more
geography courses should be built around generalizations.

There is a body of theory in manufacturing geography but most of
it has been contributed by economists such as Weber, Lösch, Hoover,
Greenhut, and Isard,[1] and it has been related primarily to *least cost* and
maximum profit questions. More recently the geographer D. M. Smith
has attempted to approach industrial location in theoretical terms by

SOURCE: *Economic Geography*, XLII (October, 1966), 356–64. Reprinted with
permission of the author and the editor. The author is professor of geography at
Syracuse University.
[1] A. Weber: Theory of the Location of Industries (1909), trans. by C. J. Friedrich,
Chicago, 1929; A. Lösch: The Economics of Location (2nd rev. ed.), trans. Wolfgang F. Stolper (New Haven, Conn., 1954); E. M. Hoover: The Location of Economic Activity (New York, 1948); M. L. Greenhut: Plant Location in Theory and
Practice (Chapel Hill, N.C., 1956); and W. Isard: Location and Space Economy
(Cambridge, Mass., 1956).

constructing a series of models which are intended to demonstrate the influences of various factors on factory locations.[2] Smith admits to be concerned fundamentally with least cost matters too. Least cost theory is both important and very complex, and probably is in some way tied up with almost every conceivable notion concerning manufacturing geography. Certainly it should be looked upon as a fruitful area for continued research.

The purpose of the following comments, however, is not to inquire further into matters specifically related to traditional least cost theory but instead to present some notions concerning regional impact, spatial structure, and the general role of manufacturing. These notions have accrued largely from investigations of manufacturing trends and characteristics in Northeastern United States, but from observations in Japan, U.S.S.R., and other parts of the world as well. They are presented here as five theories: (1) cycle theory, (2) differential growth theory, (3) concentration theory, (4) agglomeration theory, and (5) changing role theory. All are to some degree interrelated, and hopefully contribute something toward the understanding of the functional organization of manufacturing in a spatial context. Before arguments are raised that these constructs appear to be of lesser order than theories, let it be agreed they might be called something else such as hypotheses, concepts, generalizations, or principles. In this short treatment, defense of their designation seems less important than their presentation.

Cycle Theory

The cycle theory stipulates that a manufacturing area, once established, goes through a predictable sequence of change with an attendant changing set of problems. Its competitive position and the likely success of various types of manufacturing are strongly affected by the changing set of problems.

In analyzing individual manufacturing establishments it is apparent that some are young and vigorous, some are mature and stable, and others are old and declining. Although each is changing at a particular rate of increase or decrease, most tend to exhibit a common course of development involving a period of experimentation, a period of rapid growth, a period of diminished rate of growth, and a period of stability or decline. This growth cycle has been called the *law of industrial growth*. Among the factors responsible are: changes in technical progress, market demand competition, regional and local cost advantages, and management vigor.

Manufacturing *areas* commonly exhibit a growth curve similar to that

[2] D. M. Smith: A Theoretical Framework for Geographical Studies of Industrial Location, *Econ. Geog.*, Vol. 42, 1966, pp. 95–113.

expressed by the law of industrial growth for individual establishments. Although growth might be measured in terms of revenue, profit, or many other criteria, it is thought of here as being identified by employment changes. The causes of growth trends are regional or locality-wide in nature rather than internal to an enterprise, but they often are quite similar. The idea that areas go through a predictable evolutionary process and as a result experience a particular sequence of problems is bound to be useful to the understanding of industrial history, as well as to programming for adequate development work.

Northeastern United States serves as a good example for illustrating the industrial cycle. Manufacturing had its start in New England. A rapidly growing new country crowded against the east coast, and the demands of the War of 1812 as well as the Civil War made manufacturing prosper in the Northeast in general. No part of the United States could as yet compete with this vigorous industrial region. Even Europe, with distance and tariffs as disadvantages, had difficulty selling manufactured goods in the United States. The most favorable localities in the Northeast experienced unusual manufacturing growth and large cities began to evolve. Transport nets into the Midwest and South were being established, but up to 1880 a manufacturer in Woonsocket, Lowell, or Troy did not have to contend much with competition from the Midwest or South. The wave of industrial spread was moving forward, but hadn't reached these areas. They were still largely beyond what might be termed the industrial frontier. Few places had the locational advantages of the Northeast. It might be said to have been at that time in the stage of vigorous *industrial youth*. Analogy to the life cycle may not be ideal but it is used because a better alternative has not been identified.

In the ensuing years as manufacturing continued to grow rapidly in the Northeast, entrepreneurs, management people, and even foremen, who had learned their business there, began to be "exported." Northeastern companies moved or established branches elsewhere and new industrial areas began to open up in other parts of the country. Population shifts also occurred and accompanying these shifts was a change in the geography of markets. World War I found the Northeast a strong, successful manufacturing area, but one which was in the midst of a competition battle with other more rapidly expanding industrial regions. It had industrial inertia, traditional managerial know-how, the country's most skilled labor force, and still reasonably good access to national markets. It was in a competitive struggle all right, but it was doing well industrially. It might be said to have been in the stage of industrial *maturity*.

By the 1920's and 1930's population and market shifts had been extensive, the transportation net was efficiently serving the entire nation, and new sources of industrial raw and processed materials became available. Many of the Northeast's earlier locational advantages in the geography of markets, labor, transportation, and power, too, had disappeared. To stay with the life cycle analogy, the Northeast was at that time taking on the symptoms of industrial *old age* and the following major problems appeared: (1) Labor costs became relatively high. Older experienced individuals who made up a large part of the factory payrolls demanded more pay, shorter working hours, and less input of work. Union pressures were greater than in more youthful competing areas. (2) Land occupied by factories became surrounded by the urban land uses of cities. It cost more and there was little available space for expansion. (3) Taxes, including real estate, state income, and workers' compensation, were high by comparative standards. (4) Buildings and equipment had grown old and obsolescent. (5) Many products, long manufactured and in demand in the national market, were by this time difficult to sell in competition with new products developed elsewhere. (6) In some instances, most often among the smaller establishments owned and operated by local families, management quality and know-how had not kept pace with those of younger industrial areas elsewhere.

These kinds of problems are serious enough but they usually will not, as the life cycle analogy suggests, result in eventual "death" or complete disappearance of manufacturing from an area although this may in fact occur. More likely the manufacturing activity will experience a combination of decline, a change in type structure, and a loss of relative position in the national economy. In some instances an emergence of new locational advantages, improved technologies, or unusual management skills may cause rejuvenation. Government policies, particularly in countries or situations where manufacturing is government owned, certainly can be presumed to have at least temporary effect on the cycle. It is possible even that the concept of industrial renewal, like urban renewal, will be employed as a means of combating the impact of industrial old age. It may be reasonable to assume also that some areas, like some concerns, might remain highly successful indefinitely, but to do so they must adequately deal with the problems of industrial old age in some manner or another. An important aim of regional development efforts in an old age industrial region would seem to be, therefore, to effect a satisfactory manufacturing economy within the framework of the problems at hand.

Certain kinds of manufacturing are especially subject to difficulties arising from problems of industrial aging and therefore are least able to survive in old age areas. In general these include the soft goods industries, especially certain kinds of textiles, shoes, and to lesser degree, carpets, furniture, and ceramics. These are generally "low value added" types where high percentages of jobs are of the unskilled variety. The kinds of manufacturing which do best in old age areas—in fact in some cases may do better there than any place else—are those which require maximum skills and are "high value added" types. These include establishments which turn out electrical machinery and appliances, precision instruments and computers, complex parts for transportation equipment, printing and publishing, etc. Often they produce the things that society buys more of as it becomes increasingly complex and its supply of money becomes larger. Research and development divisions of large nationwide manufacturing concerns do especially well.

As implied above, big inter-regional waves of industrial aging spread across regions and whole nations, but smaller intra-regional waves of metropolitan scale also are usually simultaneously moving outward from urban centers. The problems of industrial old age show up most sharply in the oldest manufacturing areas of old age regions, but may even appear in older centers within regions that are generally still in earlier stages. The result is that factories normally are an important part of the rapidly expanding "donut" ring which is to be found in different localities at different times around most large urban systems. A factory, forced to move from a congested city center, has two choices: (1) to move to the periphery of the city or (2) to move outside the general region—say from New England to the South. Developers often negotiate in favor of the former choice and "save" the industry for the local area even though it is lost to the city center.

Differential Growth Theory

The differential growth theory holds that as an industrial society advances and the population becomes more affluent the growth in demand for certain maufactured products will greatly exceed that for others. This notion is really an expansion of Engel's law and compatible with what some economists refer to as the idea of transformation.

It is clearly demonstrable, for example, that recent demand in the United States for such types of things as electrical machinery, appliances, and transportation equipment has risen much more than has the demand for textile products, underwear, and shoes. As a family's income increases from $3000 to $15,000 per year, proportionate increases in expenditures for shoes, underwear, or window curtains are not made. Instead, more is spent on automobiles, T.V. sets, refrigerators, and other high-cost items.

The point that is important here is that an area which is dominated by fast-growth types of manufacturing, everything else being equal, can expect more favorable employment trends than an area whose industrial base is largely tied to slow-growth types. In nineteenth century America, textiles and shoes were fast-growth types. But, in the first half of the twentieth century, they became slow-growth types, and, thus, areas specializing in these products such as eastern New England or the Mohawk Valley in New York have been adversely affected. Syracuse, New York, on the other hand, which never emphasized soft goods production, has had a much more successful recent manufacturing history.

Concentration Theory

The concentration theory stipulates that, because of strong locational affinities, manufacturing activities group together in such a way as to form a hierarchy of concentrations. The hierarchy contains at least six classes of concentrations differentiatable in terms of amount and density, and probably in terms of function and linkage as well. Suggested names of the classes are: (1) plant or individual factory, (2) district, (3) central place, (4) urban system, (5) zone, and (6) belt. Although the classes are presented here without specific quantitative definition, it is probable that further study could establish perfectly suitable definitions. A major step would be taken toward establishing an overall classification system for industrial areas if students of manufacturing geography would work on the question of definitions.

The *plant,* including buildings and grounds used by a given manufacturing enterprise at one site, is the elemental unit in the classification. The entire land area in this class is considered used for manufacturing, and employment may be small or large. Although all of the classes in the hierarchy might conceivably be discussed within significance frames such as community growth potential, nuisance factors, labor market, or military objectives, only one aspect of the latter, air or strategic missile attack orientation, will be speculated upon here. In this connection, the plant class would be clearly the target of small-scale conventional weapons delivered hopefully with pinpoint precision.

A *district* typically contains a fairly large number of plants, and, within it, manufacturing usually utilizes from 25 to 100 percent of the land. Predominance of factory buildings, storage yards, loading and unloading facilities and the general overall appearance permits even the most casual observer to perceive the approximate boundaries. The threshold for district status probably has to be based on amount or function rather than on the existence of two, or any specified number of plants in juxtaposition. In other words it is quite evident that two closely spaced factories employing 25 workers each might not justifiably constitute a district.

A district's affinity for transportation and low, level land is usually evident. Although, as the importance of highway traffic has increased, the locational characteristics of new industrial districts are markedly different from those of old railroad- or water-tied districts. Districts are of such size that they would probably be the target of large-scale bombing attacks with conventional weapons or the objective of a single small nuclear weapon.

The *central place* class contains a minimum of two concentrations of district class. Both would be functionally tied largely to a single central place. Manufacturing is no longer the principal user of land. In fact it is likely to utilize less than 5 percent of the area enclosed by any one line which delineates the districts and the built-up portions of the urban place to which they are tied. Typically, at least several thousand factory workers are involved. New districts may be emerging beyond the political boundaries of the urban place making this class not confinable to areas within city boundaries. Individual districts within the city might be singled out for attack as described above or the whole central place class would have to be the target of saturation bombing with conventional weapons or the target of a single medium- to large-scale nuclear weapon.

The *urban system* class contains two or more concentrations of central place class. For example, central place classes found associated with the political cities of Albany, Schenectady, and Troy are a part of a larger spatially associated urban system in Upstate New York usually called the Capital District. Although it may be difficult to identify a magnitude threshold for this class it ordinarily supports several tens of thousands of factory workers. Manufacturing in the urban system class is likely to exhibit considerable diversity and linkage. The great number and variety of establishments are attracted to each other as well as to the diverse and special tertiary functions which the urban system provides. Only a fraction of 1 per cent of the land will be devoted directly to manufacturing use. Militarists, at the present time, might think of attacking manufacturing concentrations of the urban system class through use of multi-megaton nuclear weapons, although in World War II repeated massive attacks with conventional bombs were partially successful.

The *zone* contains two or more concentrations of urban system class. For example, in Upstate New York, the Capital District, Utica-Rome, Syracuse, Rochester, and Buffalo Urban Systems form what has been termed the Mohawk-Lake Plain Zone. The Pittsburgh, Cleveland, Youngstown, and Akron Urban Systems comprise what might be referred to as the Pittsburgh-Cleveland Zone. In essence the zone as used here approximates the areas usually designated in textbooks as principal concentrations or districts within the American Manufacturing Belt.

Although very important in the spatial structure of any manufacturing nation and containing hundreds of thousands of manufacturing workers, the zone has such a low overall density of manufacturing that it presumably could not be thought of as a single military target. Nevertheless, its manufacturing might be destroyed through use of a carefully coordinated multimissile attack on urban systems and districts. It is doubtful that .01 percent of the land is used by factories. As economic development proceeds, the very large urban systems within zones increase their percentage of total manufacturing at the expense of the smaller cities and rural locations also within the zones.

The *belt* class, at the top of the hierarchy, characteristically involves a very large area and contains a substantial percentage of a nation's manufacturing. It can be presumed to be composed of at least two, but typically a larger number of zones. In the United States the commonly called American Manufacturing Belt between Boston and Baltimore on the east and Milwaukee and St. Louis on the west accounts for 70 percent of the United States' manufacturing as measured by employment. Belts of almost identical relative significance have been described in the U.S.S.R. and Japan and probably occur in Canada, the Common Market area of Europe, and other localities as well.

Belt status probably must be reserved for *the* great manufacturing area of a nation. Often the Belt corresponds geographically to what has been called the *national core* or *principal economic axis*. In places like western Europe because of the small sizes of national states and recent economic cooperation perhaps a belt can be meaningfully identified only as an international feature. Military destruction of a belt implies all of the coordinated efforts needed for destruction of a zone multiplied many times over. In this case one is in essence almost talking about destruction of a nation.

In addition to the above classes there may be a need in the hierarchy for some sort of a sub-belt designation. This situation occurs where two or more zones, rather closely spaced, result in an important concentration but one of far less importance than the belt as described above. Portions of the South may be cases in point.

Agglomeration Theory

The agglomeration theory is of a similar nature to the concentration theory but carries the idea of concentration further and associates it with economic development. It stipulates that manufacturing increases its affinity for the very large urban system as the stage of economic development advances.[3] This means that, more commonly than not, least cost and maximum profit points are found in or near the larger urban places in the later stages of economic development. Actually, the best sites are those close enough to the large city to benefit from the market and service facilities it provides, but far enough away to escape con-

[3] This idea has been elaborated upon in many places, but perhaps most relevant is Eric E. Lampard: The History of Cities in the Economically Advanced Areas, *Econ. Development and Cultural Change*, Vol. 3, 1954–1955, pp. 81–136.

gestion and excessive land costs. Thus the "donut ring" or the periphery of cities gets the lion's share of new industrial units; units which may have migrated either from the center of the old cities or from distant points, or which may be entirely new. In the Northeast it appears there is an urban threshold size of at least 100,000 population for substantial manufacturing success. Further investigations with more samples and better definitions of success may show the threshold to be even higher, perhaps 300,000. Of course, some shipbuilding yards, furniture factories, apparel concerns, and paper plants, using local raw materials and plentiful water supplies, may select new sites in smaller cities, but the smaller urban systems and rural areas seem to have very real difficulty in competing for most kinds of manufacturing establishments with the newly emerging industrial districts at the peripheries of the large urban systems.

For both market and material reasons factories attract factories and large urban systems have many factories. Furthermore, as equipment and processes become more complicated, advanced service facilities are most likely to be available in the big cities where they are in greater demand. These may range from repair to educational services. Too, air connections and other transport facilities between large urban systems are superior to those offered by smaller centers. Finally, there has been a "brain" drain away from smaller places and rural areas toward the large cities for years, and the peripheries of the large urban systems provide plenty of space at reasonable cost close enough to the city to take advantage of the brain power there. Manufacturing congregating in the large urban systems of course in turn attracts service and transportation activities and people. The result: the very large urban systems will get very much larger.

Changing Role Theory

The changing role theory states that the importance of manufacturing to the overall economy of an area changes as economic development advances. This idea appeared in the economics literature some time ago and has more recently been elaborated upon by the writer. Using employment by economic sector as a guide, it may be demonstrated that the three sectors perform quite differently through time and that the secondary sector (dominated by manufacturing) experiences a distinct leveling in the later stages of development. The important point here is that substantial growth in manufacturing employment in advanced societies apparently cannot be expected. Even manufacturing areas which have experienced fairly good growth trends in the past probably cannot expect to expand indefinitely, not as least as far as employment is concerned. Certainly, with only limited total growth likely, none but the best locations can expect a spectacular future.

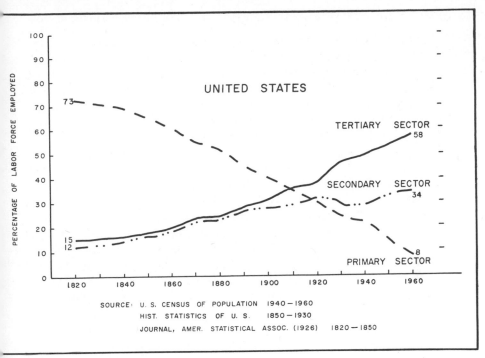

FIGURE 1: Economic sector—employment relationships for the United States.

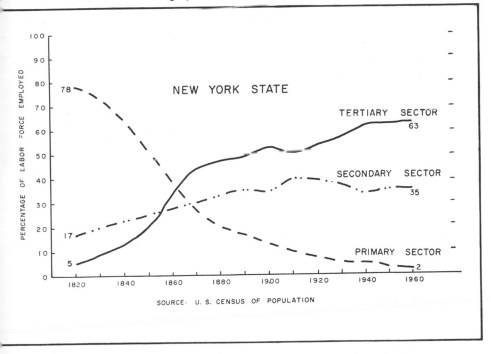

FIGURE 2: Economic sector—employment relationships for New York State.

309

Figure 1 shows the percentage of the labor force associated with the primary (agriculture, forestry, fishing and mining), the secondary (largely manufacturing but including construction), and the tertiary (sales and service) sectors through time for the United States. It is in a sense a model of economic development based on employment. It ranges from a preindustrial situation to what W. W. Rostow has called "Age of High Mass Consummation." Perhaps our present situation might better be referred to as the *High Service Consumption Stage*.

Figure 2 showing employment trends for New York State differs little from Figure 1. As part of the older Northeast, however, New York experienced the characteristic drop in the importance of the primary sector and rise in the secondary and tertiary sectors some 50 or 60 years earlier than the United States as a whole. The relative importance of the secondary sector in the United States and New York today is remarkably similar. Of special interest is the high level of the tertiary sector in New York, a level which the United States as a whole probably will attain in the decades ahead. In both the United States and New York the secondary sector has barely maintained its significance since early in the twentieth century. Mechanization and automation of factories permit a continuing rise of output without additions to the labor force.

The above theories are not unrelated, nor do they seem to be relevant only in the milieu of the United States. In this writer's mind they help explain a good deal about the evolving manufacturing geography of many areas and shed light on the industrial problems these areas seem to have. It is hoped they may not only help others think more effectively about manufacturing geography, but that they also will be tested and refined. If they are found wanting by some readers, then may those readers offer improvements or substitutes so that the body of geographic constructs can move forward.

19. The Automotive Industry: A Study in Industrial Location

Neil P. Hurley

The United States and Western Europe—and increasingly other parts of the world as well—are automobile-dependent · societies. Mass-production methods and dispersed parts and assembly plants have made the automotive industry directly significant to many parts of the United States. Indirectly, of course, the entire economy of the United States is automobile-dependent. This is illustrated by the crippling effect of a major auto-manufacturing strike on the whole United States economy, even though southern Michigan, and Detroit in particular, is still the hub of the industry. The total United States output projected for 1970 is over nine million vehicles. The manufacturing of automobiles illustrates the principles developed by Thompson in the preceding selection.

Automobile production is a good example of manufacturing based on heavy industry (iron and steel) but utilizing a large variety of materials in the final product. The owning of an automobile is almost a necessity in our society, and the health of this industry is essential to the economic well-being of the country. Interrelated to most primary, secondary, and tertiary economic activity, automobile manufacture is a key to the economic geography of the United States and also of Western Europe.

The geographical patterns which characterize different industries are a compound of economic considerations, socio-historical factors and happenstance. Especially true is this of the geography of automotive manufacturing in the United States. This study will attempt to dissociate the myriad threads in the intricate web of causal factors which have shaped, and are now re-shaping, the locational profile of America's automotive production.

The development of the industry in Detroit is a classic instance of how historical accident and socio-economic factors combine to determine industrial sites. The fact that Henry Ford, Ransom E. Olds, Elwood Haynes and Charles Durvea lived in Michigan undoubtedly had much to do with the state of Michigan, and particularly Detroit, becoming the cradle of auto manufacturing.[1] This accords with Piquet's observation in 1925: "A recent canvass of a 100 leading industries has disclosed the fact that in almost all cases the location of the plant was the founder's home town. That, and not industrial factors, was the reason for the location."

There were nevertheless sound commercial reasons why automotive manufacturing succeeded in thriving in the Detroit area. First, the

SOURCE: *Land Economics*, XXXV (February, 1959), 1–14. Reprinted by permission. The author was on the staff of Jesuitenkolleg, Innsbruck, Austria, when this article was written.

[1] For early locational influences in the auto industry, see E. M. Hoover, Jr., *Locational Theory and the Shoe and Leather Industries* (Cambridge: Harvard University Press, 1937), p. 247; Allan Nevins and F. E. Hill, *Ford: The Times, the Man, the Company* (New York: Charles Scribner's Sons, 1954), pp. 20–35; Alfred P. Sloan and Sparkes Boyden, *Adventures of A White Collar Man* (New York: Doubleday Doran & Company, 1941).

vigor of such industries as machine shops, tool and die makers, and parts manufacturing exercised an unmistakable attraction on car producers. Bankers in the east were less willing to furnish short-term credit to the infant industry's promoters than were the more progressive Middle West financiers. An additional factor in favor of locating in and around Detroit was that gas engines were preferred in Michigan as opposed to the steam engine (favored in Massachusetts) and the electric motor (in Connecticut); Ohio had been experimenting with all three. Naturally Michigan had a decided advantage over the other states when the gas engine proved to be the most efficacious way to power an auto. Otherwise New England could have easily become the motor region of the world.[2]

Other factors of varying weight played their part, too. Thus the importance of motor boats and commercial vessels on the Great Lakes resulted in an important marine-engine industry developing in the area; this lent impetus to the production of all types of engines, including those for autos as well. The horseless carriage, a hybrid product developed by crossing a buggy with a marine engine, would naturally be manufactured in a region such as that of the Great Lakes.[3] Moreover, Detroit, Cleveland and satellite cities were specialists in pressed steel, malleable iron, brass parts, springs, rubber tires, paints and varnishes, materials which were indispensable for the assembly of a horseless carriage.

The Midwest, with its sprawling land expanses and scattered trade centers, was more transport-conscious than was the East. Its flatland surfaces were ideal for experimentation inasmuch as the first autos lacked the extra horsepower to navigate hilly terrain. Besides, glacial gravels were sufficiently plentiful in the region to make road-building an easy matter. Lastly, an intense spirit of resourcefulness and enterprise, so characteristic of pioneer groups, flourished in the Midwest in contrast with the more conservative, tradition-bound East.

So much then for historical background. To understand the subsequent maturing of the industry it is necessary to recall some basic principles of locational economic theory. Every fabricating industry, such as auto manufacturing, lends itself to the combined pull of five vector forces: raw materials, fuel and power sources, market availability, the proximity of labor and capital pools, and transport arteries. Using these five rubrics, an attempt will be made to explain the geographical patterns which the American auto industry has historically assumed.

[2] For further details consult Paul M. Banner, *Competition in the Automobile Industry* (Unpublished Doctoral Thesis, Cambridge: Harvard University, 1952), pp. 22–27.
[3] Since an abundance of the supply of hardwoods was present in the area at the turn of the century, the Midwest attracted more than 60 percent of the total carriage production in the United States at that time. *Loc. cit.*

Locational Factors Peculiar to the Automotive Industry

The assembly-line nature of the industry rules out its being oriented to raw materials; it does not consume raw materials directly but in the form of semi-finished and finished components such as steering shafts, cylinder blocks, bearings, axles, etc. The auto industry is so dependent on diverse material sources that when its assembly lines stop for lack of sales "a tide of secondary idleness washes through hundreds of other cities across the nation." A Ford chemist stated before World War II that Ford cars used cotton from 433,000 acres, wool from 800,000 sheep, hair from 87,500 goats, 11,200 acres of corn, 12,500 acres of sugar cane, 61,500 acres of soy beans not to mention a fifth of the nation's steel and staggering quantities of rubber, glass and textiles.

The auto industry is not linked to any invariable factor such as land in the case of agriculture, or climate and flat land in the case of aircraft plants, or raw materials as in the extractive industries. Extractive industries, such as mining, lumber and whaling, have little locational freedom; reproductive industries, such as tobacco, cotton and fruit growing, must conform strictly to the natural conditions of soil, climate and topography, while service industries, such as retailers, brokers and barbers, are predominantly market- and therefore urban-oriented. Fabricating industries, such as auto producing, generally seek that site which affords optimum access to all the materials ingredient in the final product. This necessitates a compromise location.

Essential to an understanding of the locational policies in the auto industry is its oligopolistic and highly competitive nature. There are three giant producers (General Motors, Ford and Chrysler) and three smaller independent producers of note (American Motors, Kaiser-Willys and Packard-Studebaker).[4] Entry into the field is extremely difficult, if not virtually impossible, due to the large capital investments required to maintain a vertically integrated productive process, a nation-wide dealer system and the exorbitant costs attendant upon advertising and establishing company prestige and goodwill. Indicative of the difficulty involved in offering more than negligible competition to General Motors, Ford and Chrysler is the fact that together these three firms control about 93 percent of the market.[5] The fact that within a

---

[4] All three firms were the product of mergers. As of 1953 there were six independent auto producing firms: Nash and Hudson (which later merged into the American Motors Company), Kaiser and Willys (later combined into Kaiser-Willys) and Packard and Studebaker (subsequently merged into Packard-Studebaker).

[5] From 1946 to 1954 the share of the market that went into the so-called "Big Three" (General Motors, Chrysler and Ford Motor Company) rose from 85.5 percent to 95.6 percent. General Motors' proportion has been as high as 55 percent; in 1957 it fell to 45 percent but in 1958 rose again to 50 percent. Ford's share of the

span of a few years six independent companies merged into three companies indicates the oligopolistic nature of the American auto industry. Because of the sensitivity of their product to the business cycle and because of the huge investment requirements in the annual model change-over, the auto producers are quick to exploit any advantages which sound plant site decisions may yield. Such advantages are linked with: (a) the assembly-line nature of the industry; (b) freight-rate practices; (c) the economies of specialization; (d) labor volatility; (e) the process of technical maturing; (f) the pyramidal nature of large-scale production in the auto industry; (g) managerial decentralization policies among the "Big Three"; and (h) the multiplier effect in regional expansion.

The Assembly-Line Nature of the Automotive Industry

It is a well-known fact that the auto industry pioneered in mass-production techniques and spawned the assembly line, which today can turn out a finished car every minute. The refined subdivision of labor, the endlessly moving belt, the concourse of subassembly lines feeding into the main belt, the logistical wizardry required to supply basic items without, however, maintaining large plant inventories, the minute detailing of "lead-time" production plans to harmonize a process extending from the blue-print stage to the display floor—all have captured the imagination of the world and elicited the laments of sociologists and industrial psychologists the world over.

The creation of the "Model T" Ford added to the two fundamental principles of standardization and inter-changeability three other steps: (1) the orderly progression of the product through the shop in a series of planned operations arranged so that the right part always arrives at the right place at the right time; (2) the mechanical delivery of these and of the assembled product to and from the operators; and (3) a breakdown of operations into their simple constituent motions.

The assembly line permits larger integrated firms with annual sales volumes of tens of thousands of autos to offset the costly investment for machines, jigs, dies and tool fixtures by means of volume production of standardized parts. Only the "Big Three" can afford the burdens of a heavy automation program and the yearly re-tooling which accompanies model re-design. The assembly-line operation, in permitting a divorce among parts-manufacture, subassembly and final assembly, enables

---

automobile market hovers between 22 and 28 percent, while Chrysler's proportion ranges from 15 to 20 percent. "New Hands at the Wheel of an Auto Empire," *U.S. News & World Report*, September 5, 1958, p. 63. Also *cf.*, Banner, *op. cit.*, Chapter II. Another characteristic of oligopoly in the industry is General Motors' traditional role as the price leader. "Has GM Lost Price Leadership?", *Business Week*, November 9, 1957, p. 171.

centralization of operations where component and semi-finished parts are concerned and a decentralization of regional assembly plants. Consequently, the "Big Three" have centralized the assembly of component parts and units (e.g., chassis, pistons, transmissions) in and around Detroit, to take advantage of nearness to Midwestern suppliers and then have arranged to ship these assembled units to regional assembly plants for final assembly in order to reap the economies of proximity to local markets. This divorce between the parts manufacture and the final assembly phase enables sizeable economies; however, it leads to vulnerability in the event of civil or military disaster. This was demonstrated in 1953 when one of the nation's greatest industrial fires struck the General Motors hydromatic-transmission plant at Livonia Michigan, and crippled some 20 percent of the industry's auto production.

One sees how geographically strategic is the location of Detroit, equidistant between both coasts and advantageously situated for shipment of parts to regional assembly plants in any part of the nation. The economies which attach to the centralization of facilities manufacturing auto parts and accessories become obvious when one considers how dependent the early phases of auto production are on nearby industries. In the Great Lakes area are concentrated such vital industries as electric generating stations, electrical machine producers, foundry shops. Besides, the iron ore resources of the Lake Superior region and the proximity of steel centers such as the Chicago-Gary area, Pittsburgh-Cleveland area, not to mention Akron's rubber supplies and the area's rail and water transport facilities, are location factors of great moment. The early phase of parts manufacture and primary assembling is then distinctly materials-oriented and labor-oriented and as such seeks out urban locations near basic suppliers and pools of semi-skilled and skilled workers. The later phase of final assembly is market-oriented and is therefore decentralized to reduce transport costs to the dealer.

Freight-Rate Practices in the Automotive Industry

Prior to 1936 the industry's advertised price differed markedly from delivered price because of accessories, state and local taxes, and carrying charges on sales-financing contracts. In that year the Automotive Manufacturing Association published a list of agreed-price quotations. This led to the practice of including freight charges from the home plant (Detroit in the case of the "Big Three" and most independents) to the regional assembly plant in the final selling price. This meant that the customer paid freight on a fully assembled car shipped from Detroit even though the car was actually shipped unassembled from Detroit to a plant near the dealer. Whereas only four assembled cars can be loaded into a freight car, some twelve "knocked-down" (unassembled) cars can be shipped from Detroit and later assembled into final form for distribution.[6] In any event the customer pays the freight bill— f.o.b. Detroit. Supposing the car were assembled in New Jersey and marketed in New York, using 1955 prices, the differential between the shipping costs incurred by the producer and the freight bill paid by the customer would be $50 a model.[7]

By applying modern techniques of linear programming to determine the most profitable location of regional assembly plants in relation to earlier assembling phases and later marketing operations,[8] companies such as Ford and General Motors can, because of their nation-wide network of assembly plants, operate their own basing point system. The only difference between the method employed in the auto industry and basing point is that the customer absorbs the freight charge, not Ford or General Motors. The transportation charge, with its element of "phantom freight," has in the past swelled the profits of those auto producers who could avail themselves of the practice.[9]

The more common practice in American industry (e.g., steel) is freight absorption by the manufacturer even to the point of quoting a lower delivered price in more remote markets than in the home market. In the case of General Motors and Ford, however, there is the anomalous situation in which a seller has less competition from producers in a remote market than in the home market.[10] The apparently inflationary nature of freight policies of Ford and General Motors are understandable in the light of the industry's concentration in the Michigan area, the vertical structure of the industry's production process and the

---

[6] This figure is based on the estimate of industry experts who insist that it is unthinkable to give a figure of 40 "knocked-down" autos per freight car. The number 40 is the figure found in the 1950 edition of E. B. Alderfer and H. E. Michl, *The Economics of American Industry, op. cit.*, p. 165.

[7] Further savings are possible, obviously, when cars are transported from the assembly plant to the local dealers on specially designed two-story motor carriers. *Ibid.*, p. 165.

[8] The use of computers and linear programming are becoming widespread management tools in determining the most profitable distribution arrangements in the auto industry. The author is indebted to a pilot study done by John F. Kain, *Linear Programming—An Answer to the Automobile Distribution Problem* (Mimeographed Copy, Bowling Green College, 1957).

[9] It has been estimated that General Motors made $33 million in 1938 on "phantom freight"; the Federal Trade Commission announced that the corporation's profits for that year were $77 million. If the "phantom freight" profits were accurately gauged, then 42 percent of General Motor's profits in 1938 were from this single source. "Chevrolet," *Fortune,* January 1939, p. 108.

[10] Naturally, Chrysler and the independent auto firms sought to have the Interstate Commerce Commission stabilize the situation by lowering the Detroit freight rate and by increasing rates from branch assembly plants. "Auto Freight Row," *Business Week,* December 2, 1950, pp. 20–21; also, *Hearings Before the Subcommittee on Automobile Marketing Practice of the United States Senate Interstate and Foreign Commerce Committee. Statement of Mr. Frederic G. Donner, Vice-President of General Motors, 1956.*

assembly-line nature of its operations. Other industries with different structures must follow other freight pricing policies; one should not forget that dealerships play a critical role in the auto business. As members of the service or tertiary segment of our economy, auto dealers are urban-oriented. Where population density is heaviest, there are the dealers and where the dealers are close by will be found the regional assembly plants. At this phase of operations decentralization brings the greatest rewards.

The Economies of Specialization in the Automotive Industry [11]

In the earlier stages connected with manufacturing parts and accessories the auto industry reveals a nucleated pattern designed to reap the competitive advantages associated with (1) the principle of multiples, (2) the principle of the massing of reserves, and (3) the principle of bulk transactions.

The principle of multiples offers a major producer the opportunity to offset what is known as the imperfect divisibility of units of equipment and labor. An example will make this clear. In the Detroit Plymouth plant there are, say, four key pieces of equipment: (1) a 6-spindle boring machine which rough-bores cylinder blocks two at a time; (2) a multiple spindle drill press which drills 110 holes simultaneously; (3) a special automatic 6-spindle grinder which faces the hand valve seats at the rate of 90 motor blocks per hour; and (4) a milling machine which cuts pistons to specified dimensions. Assuming that these machines are used in successive steps and that daily unit capacities for these machines are respectively 1000, 1250, 1500, and 3000, then the plant's daily output should be 15,000 or some multiple of 3000 higher than 15,000 if all the machines are to be used at full capacity. It is this principle of multiples which is continually at work in auto centers such as Saginaw, Lansing, Pontiac and Detroit, where large scale economic concentration insures a minimum of waste, curtailed production and "down-time" for heavy equipment.

How does the principle of the massing of reserves operate in large auto producing units? A giant car manufacturer is in a position to dispense with the larger margin of inventory resources which smaller operators must maintain against demand fluctuations, production interruptions, accidents, etc. With a far-flung system of branch assembly plants the "Big Three" can readily estimate the individual requirements of each brand more closely than a smaller competitor might since they know statistically that the fluctuations of requirements in each branch

---

[11] Henry Ford once said: "There is no point in centralizing manufacture unless it results in economies. If we, for instance, centered our entire production in Detroit we should have to employ about 6 million people." Cited in Lewis Mumford, *Technics and Civilization* (New York: Harcourt, Brace & Company, 1934).

will cancel out. This is an obvious advantage at the concentrated stage of automotive operations where production is geared for a national demand and not just for a local demand as is the case with regional assembly plants.

As for the principle of "bulk transactions," it is fairly obvious that large manufacturers enjoy considerable bargaining power in closing contracts for material purchases, advertising and dealer arrangements. A company such as Kaiser-Willys, with average annual output of some 100,000 cars, could not possibly sustain the tremendous overhead burdens which a General Motors must carry as a condition for its extensive plant expansion, automation programs, annual model change-overs and "hippodrome" advertising campaigns. Not only are important items such as gas, electricity and water sold to industrial consumers at graduated rates, but a predictable and sizeable volume of business furnishes a safe margin for capital investment and bulk buying at propitious fluctuations of the market and the business cycle.

Geared to volume production in order to avail itself of the triple advantages of the principle of multiples, the massing of reserves and bulk transactions, the industry seeks an expanding market. In doing so its aim is "to create both consumer satisfaction and consumer desire, and at the same time." In executing its program of planned obsolescence, the auto manufacturers employ classy dealers' showrooms, mass-advertising and the annual model change to create consumer dissatisfaction within a relatively short time. The fact that some degree of success has been attained in this respect is borne out by statistics: more than 35 million families own almost 50 million cars; 35 million of these cars are postwar vintage and some 12 percent of all car owners in America own two or more vehicles. Thus it becomes relatively clear how specialization and volume production go hand in hand. The result has been the entrenchment of three companies as production leaders with negligible rivalry from other producers, the geographic concentration of the early phases of manufacture in Michigan and the diffusion of assembly plants to handle regional demands of a national market.

Labor Volatility in the Automotive Industry

The most unpredictable labor market in the entire economy is to be found in the automotive industry and the most mercurial labor center is unquestionably Detroit. Consider some essential facts. Work is seasonal; mass lay-offs invariably occur during the model change-over period. The greater part of the working force is not skilled; reliable estimates claim that 65 percent of the industry's total force of 900,000 is made up of assemblers, janitors, sweepers, stock shipping clerks, receivers, checkers and sundry unskilled employees. The instability of the industry is further aggravated by the fact that the product marketed is one whose purchase can be deferred if signs of recession set in.[12] Consequently, both dealers and personnel lead uncertain lives.[13]

This uncertainty has led to the creation of the powerful United Automobile Workers' Union which has secured high wage scales for its members to offset the disincentives of assembly-line monotony and seasonal lay-offs. Few industries have had labor-management relations which have been so marred by mutual bitterness and class antagonism. The nature of operations in the automotive industry is such that the union is ever seeking new claims; the "guaranteed annual wage" demand was a counterweight to the adoption of automation programs by car producers. Critically dependent upon a large urban pool of unskilled, semi-skilled and skilled employees, the industry has reluctantly yielded to union requests.[14]

The auto industry's labor situation has serious locational implications: it is a general principle of locational theory that a less costly center of labor diverts the industrial process from its cheapest transportation point at that moment when labor savings at a new site exceed the additional transportation costs. Detroit labor costs are very high due to a combination of factors; the concentration of the industry in a single area making it vulnerable to strikes and work stoppages; the strength and quality of the union and its leadership; the uncertainty of income payments; the high cost of living in Detroit and environs; the repetitive nature of the industry's operations with concomitant psychic dissatisfaction which must be compensated for in a monetary manner.

The result is a tendency to seek plant sites in areas where labor is cheaper, less troublesome and free from a tradition of hostile labor-management relations. Although industry-wide bargaining insures equality of payment throughout the nation, definite advantages nevertheless accrue to, say, a southern location rather than one in the Midwest. Workers there will be much more satisfied with wage rates than those in a city with a high living standard. Secondly, no tradition of labor strife exists. Thirdly, management can install labor-saving ma-

[12] The industry is regarded by its representatives as being income elastic and not price elastic. Thus, it is believed, that annual income levels of the average American consumer affect car sales more than the price fixed by producers. Within limits, this is undoubtedly true.

[13] This was dramatically seen in the sharply curtailed payrolls, shortened work schedules and skip-weeks which the recession in early 1958 caused in the motor city of Detroit. A. H. Raskin, "Detroit: Focus of the Basic Duel," *The New York Times Magazine*, May 4, 1958, p. 7 ff.

[14] Here the principle of the "massing of reserves" applies in reverse inasmuch as labor, by use of the ritual strike, can force management's hand. The auto union, for example, protested in the winter of 1951 when Ford decided to decentralize the River Rouge plant in the name of national security without, at the same time, refusing to divert any of its billion dollar defense contract to its Iron Mountain-Kingston plant in upper Michigan, a site well outside the defined target area for urban localities. "Union Protests Sale of Ford Plant," *The Wage Earner*, December 1951, p. 6.

chinery and automatic equipment more readily in such a branch plant than in an established one. This is not to say that automation eliminates workers over the long run but merely to assert an undeniable fact— namely, the resistance of workers and the union to automation. There has been a real decentralizing force at work in the industry; management cherishes harmonious relations with its labor force and will go to great expense to achieve this ideal. One manufacturer moved his plant 400 miles to insure continuous production, free from the frequent and violent labor disturbances he experienced at his original site.[15] The deviation in the industry from traditional patterns of nucleation is due in large measure to the desire to mitigate as much as possible the volatility and antagonism found historically in the Detroit region.

The Process of Technical Maturing in the Automotive Industry

Discussion of the auto industry's labor problems leads naturally into the question of technological advance. The working staff, which is trained for highly specialized operations even of an unskilled nature, has been highly paid as we have seen. The labor pool has had a monopoly position due to the extreme degree of concentration of production in and around Detroit. However, with increasing scatter the industry's dependence on a central labor pool becomes concomitantly relaxed. The locational histories of most individual industries have typically involved an early stage of increasing concentration followed by a stage of redispersion. The auto industry reflects this characteristic. As an infant industry with peculiar problems it succeeds in combining appropriate basic skills with managerial resourcefulness, financial support and enterprising engineers. With the introduction of standardization of parts and mass-production techniques the industry became rooted in the Detroit area where it could be close to independent suppliers.

Since 1940, however, the industry has been in a maturing stage. The war led to many government contracts and served as a catalytic agent in expanding the industry and in dispersing it geographically. The application of automatic controls and electronic devices, the new methods of marketing and distribution, the refinement of advertising techniques have all cooperated to bring the industry out of its period of industrial adolescence.[16] Competition and scientific advances have eliminated

[15] An incentive to plant re-location also exists where labor and tax policies are influenced by local or state legislation. For instance, one Wisconsin firm, with an annual tax charge of $68,000, moved to another state where its tax liability was $16,000 (or 75 percent) less. Ralph L. Woods, *America Reborn* (London: Longman's Green & Co., 1939), pp. 341–343.

[16] An excellent treatment of the influence of automation on geographical patterns in industry is to be found in, David G. Osborn, *Geographical Features of the Automation of Industry* (Chicago: University of Chicago Press, 1953). "Detroit automation" (the mechanical counterpart of electronic feedback control) is explained

many of the crudities and accidental elements in car production. The overhauling of the monolithic Ford Empire in the mid-1950's has been dramatic proof of this fact.

Maturity of the industry has brought with it what might be called an "hourglass pattern." Flowing down from some 25,000 suppliers of independent parts and accessories through the concentrated plants of Ford, Chrysler, General Motors corporations and independent producers, America's autos gradually take shape and move outward toward the regional assembly plants and finally to some 45,000-odd dealers. The top half of the hourglass is materials- and labor-oriented; the assembly plants in the early stages are dependent upon the basic suppliers in the Michigan area. These plants represent the stem of the hourglass. From these Detroit-clustered plants are diffused the component parts and subassemblies which reach the decentralized branch assembly plants. These assembly plants, located near regional dealers, finish the assembly and send the finished product on to the 45,000-odd dealers, who represent the lower half of the hourglass pattern. This pattern has been the result of years of integration, both vertical and horizontal as well as forward and backward. A brief history of the auto industry's integration reveals a stress on engineering and production in the early history of car production. Later, marketing became important and caused the disappearance of auto wholesaling. Forward vertical integration took place in the form of factory branches and dealerships controlled by the company. It was only to be expected that auto producers would want to exercise surveillance over car dealers where it concerned problems of financing, maintaining customer goodwill, "repeat" sales and institutional brand advertising. Vertical backward integration arose when Ford bought coal and iron-ore mines, built and purchased steel plants, glass factories, rubber plantations, etc. In time, General Motors developed a refined system of horizontal integration, manufacturing such diverse products as diesel locomotives, electric fans, Frigidaires, Allison engines, AC spark plugs, Delco radios and a host of other products (numbering in all over 40).[17] Over the years both Ford and General Motors have extended themselves forward, backward and laterally until the "hourglass pattern" has emerged. Seeking to minimize costs and to maximize profits the large-scale auto manufacturers have concentrated where economic advantages dictated and decentralized to

in John Diebold, *Automation—The Advent of the Automatic Factory* (New York: D. Van Nostrand Company, 1952); also, Hans Roeper, *Die Automatisierung* (Stuttgart-Degerloch: Verlag Dr. Heinrich Seewald, 1958).
[17] Ford's vertical integration and its historical origins are treated in Garet Garret, *The Wild Wheel* (New York: Pantheon Books, Inc., 1952), pp. 96 ff. Ford's tapering integration is described in Alderfer and Michl, *op. cit.*, pp. 162–163. For a brief, popular discussion of General Motor's horizontal integration, *see*, "The Battle of Detroit," *Time*, November 1, 1954, p. 90.

take advantage of market proximity at the final assembly stage. Since the finished product is bulky and susceptible to the weight-gain interpretation of locational economics, the market will always exert a strong locational pull on final assembly plants. The f.o.b. Detroit pricing practice made this pull even stronger by making the consumer pay the all-rail-freight charge for a fully assembled car even when it is shipped more cheaply as a so-called "knocked-down" car.

Managerial Decentralization Policies Among the "Big Three"

Although managerial decentralization is a radically different concept from plant decentralization, both are not completely unrelated. It is common to find progressive firms with avowed managerial decentralization policies constructing modern one-story country plants away from congested urban areas. Divisionalization, as managerial decentralization is called in the auto industry, is a common practice among the "Big Three," Alfred P. Sloan first initiated the policy in his tenure as president of General Motors from 1923 to 1937. Both Ford and Chrysler, after many long years of remaining centralized in all levels of operations, followed General Motors' divisionalization program in the mid-1950's.[18] At the head of each division (e.g., Buick, Pontiac, Chevrolet in the case of General Motors) is a divisional chief who directs the affairs of the entire division as if it were an autonomous company in production and sales; moreover, a controller is charged with the financial supervision of each unit so that a closer check on costs may be maintained. Autonomy is so complete that divisions really compete with one another.

The significance of divisionalization for location, however, is that autonomy in divisional operations enables segments of the company's activities to seek sites outside of Detroit and away from the traditionally congested loci of auto production. Managerial decentralization reduces impersonal human relationships and as such enhances personnel satisfaction. Job satisfaction is difficult to measure empirically but it is a

---

[18] The rapid growth of the American economy and its bellwether industry of auto production together with close competition among the "Big Three" have caused successive changes in organization structure in General Motors, Ford Motor Company and the Chrysler Corporation. General Motors' organizational development can be traced in Peter Drucker, *Concept of the Corporation* (New York: The John Day Company, 1946); "New Hands at the Wheel of an Auto Empire," *op. cit.*, p. 60 ff. Ford's re-organization is described in: "An Auto Empire Decentralizes and Reorganizes," *Business Week*, October 17, 1953, pp. 130–4; "Ford's Fight for First," *Fortune*, September 1954, p. 123 ff; James C. Jones, "The New Ford Drive," *The American Legion Magazine*, January 1955, p. 22 ff.; "Co-Captains in Ford's Battle for Supremacy," *Life*, February 28, 1955, p. 84 ff; "Ford Gets Full Line at Last," *Business Week*, June 22, 1957, p. 45 ff.; Chrysler's managerial posture has been set forth in "The Chrysler Situation," *Fortune*, April, 1954 and "Chrysler Restyles Its Executive Structure," *Business Week*, November 3, 1956, p. 85 ff.

parameter which all management experts accept today for increasing plant efficiency. A moderate-sized community plant within an autonomous divisional unit can be placed in a semi-rural area, enabling an employee to ride from his bungalow-type home to a spacious parking lot near the plant, free from all the inconveniences of commuting. In addition, auto plants generally have high land-extensive requirements for in-line productive processes which cannot ordinarily be accommodated by city lofts or a crowded urban site. Detroit has consequently experienced the migration of many types of businesses, including automotive production, which are land-extensive. Divisionalization serves to flatten out the organization chart and to dispose of a company's operations for that degree of physical plant decentralization which has been a notable phenomenon in the auto industry in the decade after the end of World War II.

The Multiplier Effect in the Regional Expansion of the Industry

Probably the greatest single force in mitigating the historical centripetal tendencies of the American auto industry is the growth of the broad middle-class suburban market. Constituting only 19 percent of the nation's population in 1953, America's suburban families accounted for 20 percent of the nation's spendable income. The automobile is not only a sought-after item in suburbia (with not a few families owning two cars) but the auto has made suburban and rural habitation possible.[19] With the establishment of new communities and new urban strips in the Pacific Northwest, the Old South, the Gulf Coast and the Pacific Coast, new markets will arise and prompt the auto industry to set up dealerships and regional assembly plants in the vicinity. The attraction of new, wealthy markets will likewise precipitate the building of metalworking facilities, tool and die establishments, foundries, parts and accessories manufacturers, who will seek to supply the needs of the regional plants which the industry will have introduced. A glance at the new assembly plants erected by the "Big Three" in the decade from 1945–1955 indicates a trend toward such dispersed sites as Los Angeles (General Motors, Ford and Chrysler); Atlanta (Ford and General Motors); Louisville (Ford); San Jose, California (Ford); Metuchen, New Jersey (Ford); Arlington, Texas (General Motors); Wilmington, Delaware (General Motors); and Framingham, Massachusetts (General Motors).

There are several multiplier effects at work in this regional expansion of the automotive industry. Motor vehicles are serving to accelerate

---

[19] "The Lush New Suburban Market," *Fortune*, November 1953, p. 131; Joseph C. Ingraham, "Auto, Multiplying Faster than Man, Rule, Inconvenience and Frustrate Urban Life," *The New York Times*, January 28, 1957; and Neil P. Hurley, "New Patterns in American Commuting," *Social Order*, September 1958, pp. 343–349.

the phenomenon of suburban living; as higher income levels become fixed in these non-urban locales an attractive natural market area arises for goods and services. Thus, in contributing to nation-wide decentralization the auto industry is effecting *pari passu* its own decentralization. In addition to this consumer multiplier effect there is also a consumer-goods multiplier effect noticeable. This consists in the relocation in newer regions of the United States of major industries and corporations which are large users of motor vehicles.[20] Sufficient demand on the part of newly situated customers can exercise a strong geographical magnetism on the auto industry, even at the earlier productive stages. Conversely, the relocation of basic suppliers of the auto industry is an invitation to auto producers to locate plants to be nearer to sources of capital, and to processed and unprocessed materials, thus to minimize transport costs.

Similar trigger effects are also evident in locational changes in the earlier stages of production. The gradual depletion of iron-ore sources in the Mesabi Range in the Lake Superior area is affecting a modification of traditional geographic patterns in the steel industry and less immediately on dependent consumer industries, of which the largest is the auto industry. Take the example of the Fairless Works which United States Steel Corporation put up in 1952 at Morrisville, Pennsylvania, in order to be close to imported Venezuela ore and Eastern markets.[21] In the wake of further decentralization of the steel industry a production-multiplier effect will influence the auto industry to locate near the relocated steel mills and the metalworking shops which spring up around them.

Capital equipment multiplier effects should also be mentioned since budding industrial opportunities in new regions such as Dallas, Texas, and Los Angeles, California, attract investors and financial interests. Mention has already been made of the readiness of Midwest financiers to invest in the infant auto industry as contrasted with the conservative eastern banking houses. Certainly the postwar boom made it relatively easy to float reasonably sound business ventures. The experience of the Kaiser Company in attempting to achieve entry in the automotive field proved the availability of capital in an expanding market economy.

Obviously, the multiplier effects can cooperate toward centralization equally as effectively as toward decentralization just as it can confirm the economic anemia of "stranded areas" (e.g., mill towns in New England and coal towns in Pennsylvania). However, the postwar trend in

[20] This was undoubtedly one of the significant locational pulls in General Motors' selection of a plant site at Arlington, Texas, to fulfill government defense contracts during the Korean episode.
[21] The long-standing basing point system gave way in 1948 to the f.o.b. ("free-on-board") mill freight pricing policy. Under the latter system, proximity to markets exercises a strong locational pull.

the auto industry has been toward scatter, and the multiplier effects with its tandem reactions and mutual causation have helped the process to gain momentum.[22] Since 1940 the profile of American industry has undergone a marked change. Although it will be decades before the primacy of Michigan as the nation's auto state will be seriously challenged, there seems little doubt that Michigan is losing its historic position of dominance. To mention but one highly significant factor, automation is working a revolution in the auto industry as profound as that of Ford's assembly-line techniques. Automation effects the locational factors of space and labor suchwise that the industry is growing more "footloose" than it was formerly. The "Big Three" of the auto industry are in a position to keep astride of the tide of expanding markets, technological advance, managerial decentralization and geographic de-concentration which has swept the entire American economy in the years following World War II. Nor is there any portent that these trends will reverse themselves.

So much for the economic factors in the locational policies of auto manufacturers. Just a word about the attempts of the national government and private industry to minimize atomic vulnerability in the age of the hydrogen bomb by a conscious strategy of dispersal. The inauguration of the National Industrial Dispersion Program by President Truman in 1951 sought to use accelerated tax amortization privileges as part of the defense contract program to encourage industry to locate new plants outside of defined target zones. The significance of the auto industry as a prime defense industry and its highly vulnerable nature have led the industry's executives to consider industrial dispersal as good business insurance where dispersal does not openly conflict with predominating economic goals.

Summary and Conclusions

While substantially sound economic reasons existed for the birth and growth of the auto industry in and around Detroit, certain happenstance factors such as the local presence of inventors and men gifted with engineering genius also played a role. With the development of highways and such dependent industries as petroleum and steel, the industry grew into an "hourglass pattern" whereby the manufacture and assembly of component parts became decidedly centralized in and about

---

[22] Input-output analysis studies can contribute to a better understanding of the causal interactions involved in the multiplier effect. "Considered from the point of view of the input-output scheme any national economy can be described as a system of mutually interrelated industries or . . . interdependent economic activities." Wassily Leontiff, *Studies in the Structure of the American Economy* (New York: Oxford University Press, 1953), p. 9; also, Walter Isard, "Distance Inputs and the Space Economy," *The Quarterly Journal of Economics*, May and June 1951, pp. 181–198; 373–399 of Volume LXV.

Detroit while the later operations of final assembly and distribution were scattered in order to reduce transport costs on a product which gained substantially in bulk and weight in the ultimate assembly phase.

Mass-production methods have led to widespread division of labor and specialization of function in all phases of the productive process. This together with dependence upon a large supply of skilled and unskilled labor and ready access to semi-fabricated materials, parts and accessories dictated the nucleated patterns of the industry in the productive stages leading up to final assembly. The policy of charging the customer f.o.b. Detroit freight rates on a fully assembled car while shipping "knocked-down" cars to regional assembly plants confirmed General Motors and Ford in a policy of maintaining a vast network of branch assembly plants.

Furthermore, the economies attaching to the principles of multiples, massed reserves and bulk transactions enable large-scale auto producers to reap the advantages of spreading lowered fixed costs over a great volume of finished goods. Without the economies of mass-production, concentration in the earlier production stages and oligopolistic features, it is doubtful if the industry could have succeeded in bringing the auto within the price range of the average American family. Only a giant producer can afford a policy of nation-wide branch assembly plants near regional markets, expensive automation and re-tooling programs for annual model change-overs, extravagant advertising campaigns and a vast arterial system of dealers under agreement to the factory. Helping decentralization trends in the auto industry is management's desire to settle in new regions where no tradition of labor strife exists, where workers are more content with their wages and where resistance to labor-saving devices is minimal.

Since motor vehicles render suburban living possible, the industry is contributing to its own decentralization by marketing a product which encourages industrialization and population of new regions, thus creating markets which eventually will exercise a locational pull on the industry itself. The overall maturing of the American economy in all regions, the rapid technological strides in the fields of chemical, electronic, atomic and solar energy, the radial growth of transport and communication lines all involve multiplier effects and economic chain reactions which are dissolving the traditional, deep-seated concentration of auto production in the Michigan area.

20. An Economic-Geographical Study of the Localization of the Swedish Paper Industry

Olof Lindberg

This analysis of the localization of the Swedish paper industry at various points in time illustrates the application of economic location theory in explaining the distribution of a given kind of production. In emphasizing transport costs, Lindberg indicates how economic theory must be adapted in a geographical study. The paper industry serves as an example of light manufacturing that is found in all countries. In Sweden, however, the industry assumes high relative importance in the manufacturing picture as the processing of raw materials obtained from the forests is vital in the total industrial complex. Swedish geographers are leaders in theoretical geographical research. This selection is an example of how quantitative methods are being used to facilitate economic geographic analysis.

This study attempts to analyse the transport costs of certain Swedish paper and pulp mills. The method used has been an adaptation to a geographical foundation of the theory of location as it appears in economic works at the present time.

In this investigation, the most important way of illustrating the conditions imposed by location makes use of the concepts *isovecture* and *isodapane*. An isovecture is a line joining points with equal transport costs for a certain commodity to a certain place. Isodapane is the name given to a line joining points with the same total transport costs for all the commodities entering into the production process. The relation between isovectures and isodapanes is illustrated in Fig. 1. The point B in that figure indicates a raw-material locality (for example, iron ore), and point A a consumption locality or harbour for shipping the finished good. Two tons of ore are taken to be necessary for the production of one ton of iron, and consequently, around B, the lines for transport costs (isovectures) are drawn twice as close together as they are around A.

SOURCE: *Geografiska Annaler*, XXXV, 1 (1953), 28–40. Reprinted by permission. The author is a geographer at the University of Uppsala, Sweden.

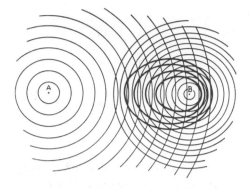

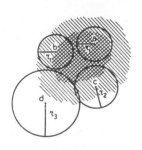

FIGURE 1: Construction of isodapanes.

FIGURE 2: Harvest circles at areal consumption.

The total cost of the transport of ore and iron may be read off at the points of intersection of the two systems of isovectures. The oval lines which join these points of intersection are the above-mentioned isodapanes.

The construction in Fig. 1 indicates the relation between isovectures and isodapanes when the raw material is supposed to come from a *point*. But if it is gathered from an *area*, the relations are somewhat different. The shaded area in Fig. 2 denotes a bounded area where a raw material is produced. The figure shows four different consumption localities: *a, b* and *c* within the "harvest" area, and *d* outside it. If the amount of consumption remains constant, at *a* and *b* a circular area of radius r_1 may be harvested. If *c* is the consumption locality, the harvest circle must be greater (radius r_2), and at point *d* outside the harvest area the radius of the harvest circle must be increased to r_3. Since the radius of the circle increases, the transport costs also increase. The more peripheral the consumption locality with respect to the harvest area, the higher the transport costs when the amount of consumption is constant. In the central parts of the harvest area the location of the consumption locality is of no importance. The cross-shaded area in Fig. 2 is an "area of ubiquity", within which the harvest circle is everywhere of radius r_1.

The increase in transport costs is illustrated in Fig. 3. For the sake of simplicity, the harvest area is taken to be circular. The variable consumption locality is taken to require a surrounding circular area of radius r_1. The average costs for transport within this area have been abstracted in the upper half of the diagram in the figure. We suppose that these costs are 8 units everywhere within the area of ubiquity, and the isovecture for this value passes through the point r_1. If the locality is moved outside the area of ubiquity, the transport costs rise, as is shown in the figure, for instance. When the distance to the harvest area is

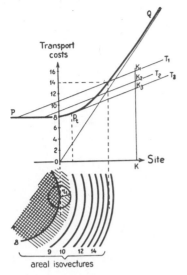

FIGURE 3: Increase of transport costs at areal consumption.

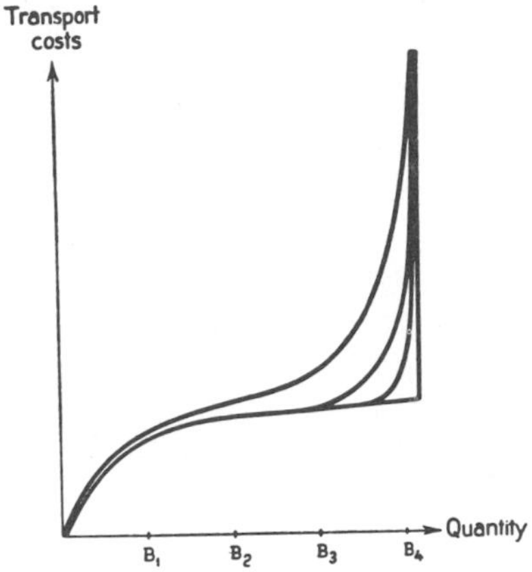

FIGURE 4: Increase of transport costs at different scale of consumption.

great, the variations of costs are similar to those for production at a point. The isovectures, which are widely spaced in the beginning, become closer as the distance from the harvest area increases. Ultimately, the distance between them becomes constant, as in Fig. 1.

The scale of consumption in Figs. 2 and 3 has been taken to be constant. The consequence of any variation would be that the area of the harvest circle would increase or decrease, and the transport costs to the consumption locality would thereby be altered. Unlike the situation when consumption is *at a point* (Fig. 1), when consumption is *over an area*, not only the position, but also the amount of consumption, affects the transport costs. The effect is illustrated in Fig. 4, which shows how transport costs increase with increasing consumption. The different curves indicate different positions of the consumption locality within the harvest area. If this latter is taken to be circular, and the consumption locality is taken to be situated at its centre, the greatest possible harvest yield at the lowest possible transport cost is obtained, since the harvest area and the harvest circle coincide. There cannot then be any further increase of the harvest, however, because the curve for transport costs rises vertically.

The reasoning from the theory of location which has been used in connection with Figs. 2, 3 and 4 is applicable to every branch of industry for which the raw material is harvested. However, in the case of the paper industry, the production process is often divided up into the manufacture of paper-pulp and the further treatment of this pulp to make the finished paper. The location circumstances for such non-integrated production may be illustrated by the upper part of Fig. 3. If the consumption locality is taken to be K, the total transport costs there may be obtained by adding the areal transport costs (the curve PQ) to the linear transport costs (T_1, T_2 etc).

When the total cost is K_1 the production locality is situated at one of the points of intersection of the line T_1 and the curve PQ. If the production locality is on the left-hand part of the curve, the total transport costs are higher because of the heavy freight charges to K for the paper. But if it is on the steeper part of the curve to the right, the total transport costs will be high because the cost of raw material increases with the distance from the place where it is obtained. The costs are lowest at K if the production locality is situated at P_t, that is, the linear transport costs touch the curve PQ.

If we suppose that there is a paper mill at K, the costs for the linear transport are equal to zero, but on the other hand the cost of raw material is very high. In such a case, the costs may be diminished by separating the pulp manufactory from the paper mill. The pulp mill ought to be at P_t, and the pulp manufactured there transported to K. If we neglect the differences which arise because of freight charges for the transport of pulp and paper, and the extra expenditure on the production process necessitated by increased drying and the like, and if we suppose that a ton of paper is obtained from a ton of pulp, the cost at K should also be K_3 in this case.

For those paper mills which lie to the right of P_t, integration with the pulp mill is not advantageous. On the other hand, to the left of P_t it is more profitable to combine the pulp and paper mills than it is to trans-

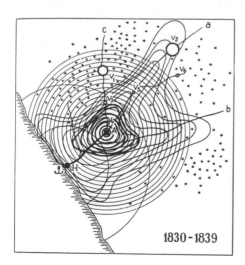

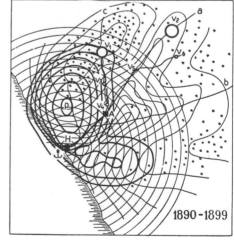

FIGURE 5: Handmill period.   FIGURE 6: Groundwood period.

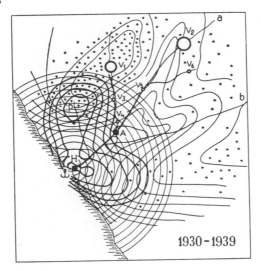

1930-1939

Figure 7: Chemical pulp period.

port the pulp from separate pulp mills. P_t is a boundary point for profitable integration.

Since the preceding investigation has dealt with a "harvesting" industry, the concept of isovectures has been used both for points and for areas when the conditions imposed by the location of various places has been described. The isovectures have also been used to describe the development of conditions during different periods, as will be seen from Figs. 5–7.

These figures show a region at three stages of the development of its location. The towns A and H lie on the river a, A being a central place with a relatively large need for paper and H is a seaport dealing with imports and exports. There are waterfalls on the tributaries b and c, and the suffices of their symbols indicate the order of their capacities. Near to the river a is the agricultural land, and farther away is the thinly populated forest region marked with forest symbols.

Fig. 5 shows an example of the conditions imposed by localisation during the first half of the nineteenth century. The raw material, straw and rags, was brought from the densely populated areas at that time. The region nearest to the river a may be regarded as an area of ubiquity but farther away the cost of transport for the raw material is much higher, and this is apparent in the increasing closeness of the areal isovectures. As far as the transport of finished paper is concerned, this must be greater the farther one goes from the main consumption locality A. It is assumed that only insignificant amounts are shipped from H, so that the point system of isovectures around A is considerably tighter around A than around H. As in Fig. 1, the total costs are given by isodapanes (the heavy lines in Fig. 5). They are almost coincident with the point isovectures around A. Not until the distance from the consumption locality is large do the isovectures for the raw material begin to have an effect on the system of isodapanes.

So the optimum place as far as transport costs are concerned is certainly at A. But during the nineteenth century it was impossible to have a paper mill there, since there was no waterfall. The paper mill had to be built at the nearest waterfall—V_4—which is taken to be capable of driving a hand-mill.

Fig. 6 shows the same region as before, but the date is now the end of the nineteenth century, and the conditions imposed by the localisation of the paper industry are now quite different. The raw material is now no longer straw and rags, but wood, and consequently the isovectures for the raw material are close to either in the more densely populated areas which are free of forest, and thinly distributed in the forest land near these areas. The area of ubiquity is now in the forest instead of the agricultural land. For the point isovectures, the seaport H has increased in importance; export has come to be of some importance, and there is also some importation of coal for instance. The hand-mill has now been replaced by machinery, and the paper industry now requires greater power. However, the most important power is water-power. The mechanical methods for the production of pulp made particularly large demands on cheap and abundant water-power. At that time it was not possible to transport power from the waterfall, and it was therefore necessary to build the paper mill by the waterfall. So, in Fig. 6 it is not p, the best place from the point of view of transport costs, which is chosen as the site of the mill, but the most favourably situated large waterfall, V_1.

Fig. 7, which shows the conditions at the present time, is not much different from Fig. 6. The configuration of the isovectures is much the same as at the end of the nineteenth century. What is different is that the large waterfalls V_1 and V_2 have been harnessed to power stations, and since technical development at the beginning of the twentieth century made it possible to carry electric power for long distances, the paper mill need no longer be at the waterfall, but can be sited at p, the optimum place from the point of view of transport costs.

In order to find out the extent to which the development of the theoretical conditions has actually been in accordance with the localisation which occurred, the development of paper mills in different parts of the country has been studied. The result has been illustrated in the diagrams Figs 8–11 and in the circle-cartograms Figs. 12–14. The investigation shows that certain forest regions in Southern Sweden (Småland) had a surprisingly large number of paper mills during the first half of the nineteenth century, which does not agree with what was to be expected from the reasoning based on location which has been advanced.

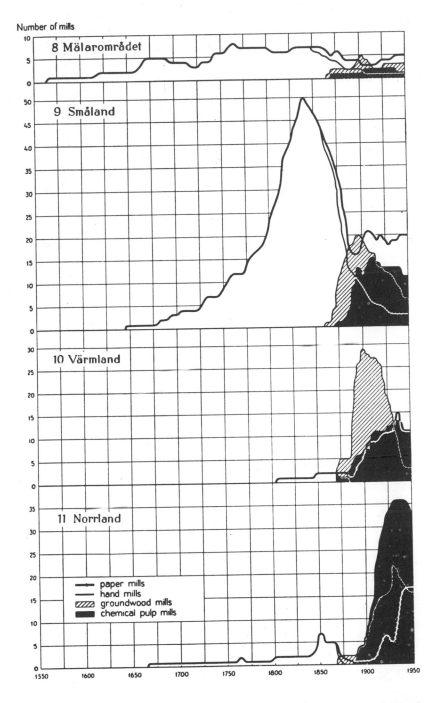

Number of mills

8 Mälarområdet

9 Småland

10 Värmland

11 Norrland

paper mills
hand mills
groundwood mills
chemical pulp mills

FIGURES 8–11: The evolution of paper industry in four regions of Sweden.

333

The reason for the rise of the paper industry in Småland at that time seems to have been the need to find outlets for the productive capacity of these poor and somewhat overpopulated districts.

However, the expansion of the paper industry in Småland was brought to a hasty stop at the end of the nineteenth century, when the machine-produced pulp began to replace rags as the raw material. The outlying forest regions west of Lake Vänern then became the main area for the paper industry. There was water-power and forest, as well as relatively good communications with the seaport of Gothenburg. Mechanical pulp-mills especially flourished there just before the end of the century. Then the transmission of electric power made it possible to choose a locality independent of water-power, and the remoteness of the forest sites became a considerable disadvantage for many of the firms in this region, and the day of the Värmland groundwood-mills came to an end as abruptly as had the period of the hand-mills in Småland (cf. Figs. 9 and 10).

So, as regards the earlier localisation of the paper industry, it may be said that the so-called *hand-mill period* was hardly at all dependent on factors concerned with transport economy. In the heyday of the *mechanical pulp-mills* the agreement of theory and reality was better, but even here in many cases other factors were of importance in determining the site of the mill. The present-day paper industry bears traces of earlier localisation, but the tendency to fit the locality to considerations of transport economy is fully apparent at the present time.

How, then, is the present transport situation of the paper industry to be measured? In the first place, in order to give some estimate of the

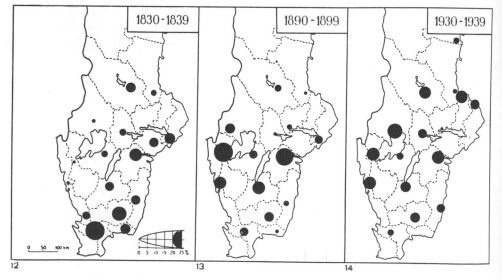

FIGURES 12–14: The value of the Swedish paper production percentually for each county.

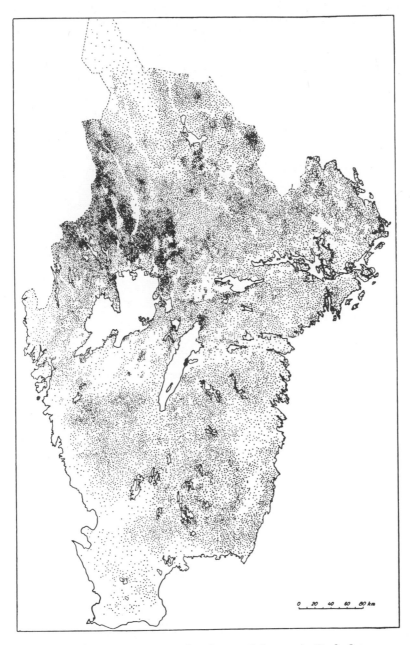

Figure 15: Potential production of pulp wood (spruce). Each dot represents a production capacity of 200 m³ (solid measure).

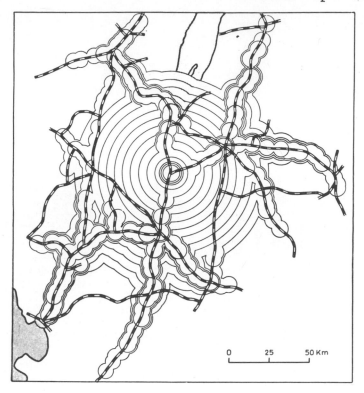

FIGURE 16: Isovectures for the Vaggeryd mill in southern Sweden. Each isovecture represents an increase of the transport costs with 20 öre/m³ pulp wood.

situation with regard to raw material, it is necessary to know the productivity of forest land in terms of wood for paper in different regions, and to be able to estimate the freight charges for different means of transport.

The first element of the analysis, the forest, is given in Fig. 15. This map has been based on a calculation of the lumber yield, which was made by the Ingeniörsvetenskapsakademi (The Academy of Engineering Science) in 1939, and the figures which were obtained from that investigation were proportioned with the help of map information from Riksskogstaxeringen (National Forest Taxation) 1923–32. The map is drawn according to the "absolute dot"-method, and each dot represents a lumber capacity of 200 m³ solid measure of spruce.

The second element, transport costs, has been illustrated by point isovectures for each firm investigated. Road transport has been taken to be upon a uniform transport surface. Where it has been possible to include rail or water freight charges, these means of transport have caused anomalies in the circular system for road transport. Fig. 16 shows an example of such isovecture maps. The distance from one isovecture to another, called "zone" here, has been calculated from available figures on freight charges. In general the railways do not give rise to big irregularities in the form of the isovectures, but water transport and ways for floating may lead to patterns which are quite complicated.

The above-mentioned elements have been combined by superimposing the isovecture map for a firm on the forest map, and the dots of the latter have been counted within each "zone." In this way we get a measurement of the amount of wood which is theoretically at the disposal of the mill, at a certain transport price. The figures used have been dealt with in such a way that the average transport costs have been computed for various magnitudes of supply. If the relation between quantity and transport costs is illustrated in a diagram in this way, the rise in costs may be given by a curve like that in Fig. 4. Since these curves give a comprehensive picture of the raw material situation at each place investigated, they have been called *characteristics*.

Usually, characteristics of two sorts have been shown, A and B curves. The A curves have been so drawn that they refer only to road transport. The isovecture map which has been used in this case has been entirely regular and made up of rings, similar for every place investigated. Thus the A curves are only different from one another in that there are local differences in the potential of the forest. The B curves show the influence which cheap transport might be supposed to

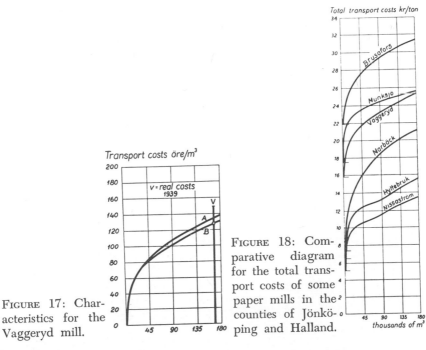

FIGURE 17: Characteristics for the Vaggeryd mill.

FIGURE 18: Comparative diagram for the total transport costs of some paper mills in the counties of Jönköping and Halland.

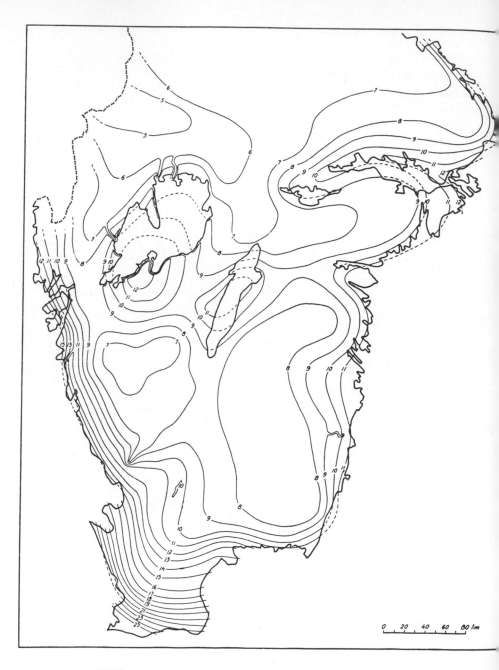

FIGURE 19: Isovecture map showing the costs of wood transport for assumed manufacturing centres in various parts of the country. Only the "A-situation" is considered, corrections having been made for certain big floating-ways but not for sea-floating. The lines connect places with the same average costs of pulp wood transport in kronor per unit of production, the yearly consumption being 120 000 m³. The unit of production 1 ton of paper equals a consumption of 7 m³ of pulp wood.

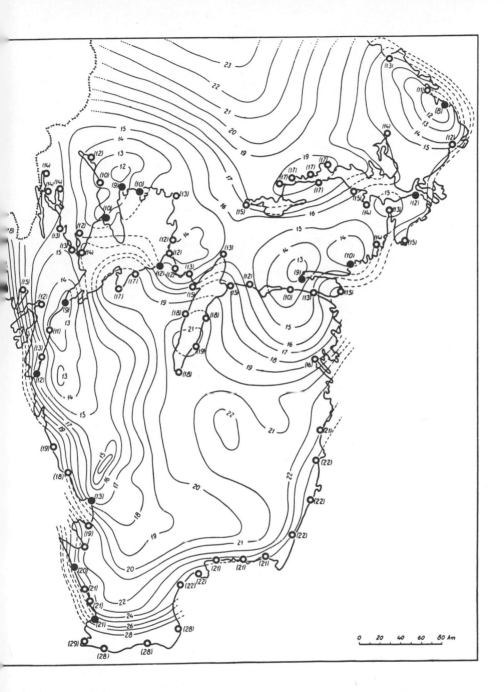

FIGURE 20: Isodapane map showing the total costs of transport with reference to assumed manufacturing centres. The ports included in the calculation are indicated by circles—open ones only for import harbours and filled ones for both export and import harbours. The transport costs for factories if situated in the ports are indicated by figures in brackets.

have on the situation. So the difference between the A and B curves at a place is an indication of the importance of floatage ways, railways, etc., with respect to the supply of wood to the firm (Fig. 17).

Since the transport costs of the paper industry do not depend only on the raw material, but also on the transport of coal, sulphur and limestone, as well as the finished paper, the transport costs for each firm examined with respect to these materials have also been computed. These costs per ton do not change with the scale of production, and the total transport costs are therefore the costs for the transport of the raw material (from the characteristics) together with the total costs for the materials just mentioned (Fig. 18).

The analysis which has been carried out for some fifty paper and pulp mills in the way described above shows that there are considerable differences with regard to the transport costs for factories in different parts of the country. Since the paper produced is mostly exported, the inland mills often have a disadvantageous position compared with those which are near the coast. The differences with regard to raw material have not in general signified so much as the differences with regard to the possibilities for easy and cheap communications for export.

Thus, for Sweden, the generally accepted idea that the paper industry is mainly dependent on its raw material does not apply. Previous opinion in this respect seems to have been based on Weber's theories on the location of industry. But since the paper industry is a "harvesting" industry, Weber's ideas are not entirely applicable to it. The raw material—wood—is ubiquitous to such a great extent that its localising effect is small, despite its low material index (3 tons of wood to one ton of paper).

In order to describe the localisation conditions for such an industry as the paper industry it is necessary to apply the same method as has already been described in connection with Figs. 5, 6 and 7. The areal isovectures in Fig. 19 have been drawn in such a way that the transport costs have been computed for a large number of points, and those with the same transport costs have been joined by isovectures.

To these areal isovectures have been added point isovectures originating from the seaports, which are marked by small circles. Some ports have only been taken as import ports (open circles), while others are counted as both import and export ports (filled circles). The result of this combination of point isovectures is the *isodapanes,* which have been constructed in Fig. 20. These isodapanes give a picture of the conditions of localisation of the Swedish paper industry at the present time.

IV. TERTIARY
ECONOMIC
ACTIVITY

Tertiary economic activities are neither extractive nor productive in character. Rather, they include the vast range of *service* activities, many of which are of substantial economic value and contribute greatly to the richness, variety, and enjoyment of living. They include wholesale and retail merchandising and sales, transportation, recreational facilities, the whole spectrum of professional occupations, including teachers, doctors, journalists, musicians, athletes, and many others, as well as a wide variety of labor services in the operation, maintenance, and repair of the complex mechanisms of contemporary life, especially in advanced technological societies.

In no case does tertiary economic activity mean the actual production of crops, minerals, or other natural products; furthermore, there is no transformation of any primary materials into other products, a fundamental characteristic of secondary economic activity.

An important characteristic of tertiary activities is their agglomerative nature; services, despite their great individual differences, tend to group together. These agglomerations are known as trade or service centers. In recent decades, considerable geographic research has been concerned with the "central place" nature of these centers, as well as with their function as "nodal" regions. Central-place analysis has become one of the important geographic tools for analyzing and understanding the character of urban places of all sizes. "Christaller's Central Place Theory" discusses this important concept as an introduction to tertiary activity.

One of the most accurate indices of the maturity of an economy is the percentage of the work force engaged in services. Worldwide tertiary activity represents less than 10 percent of the total human work force. It is clear that at subsistence levels, there would be little opportunity or scope for many of the service operations suggested above. Nevertheless, every economy at all levels must have some of its members engaged in tertiary activity, as exemplified by "The Role of Tribal Markets in Morocco."

In the most highly developed and urbanized parts of the world, tertiary activities may involve as much as 40 percent of the total work force, and elsewhere, the increase in service activities is rising rapidly. Retail-store trading areas and markets, characteristic of service activities in the United States, are examined by Applebaum and Cohen, two specialists in retail and commercial location.

It is clear that large-scale service centers functioning as central places do not and cannot consist exclusively of tertiary activities. Even the most modest trade centers are closely related to primary activities in nearby areas, and nearly all include some manufacturing establishments characteristic of secondary economic activities. A large and varied pattern of service activities is a characteristic of urban areas, and in general, the larger the city, the greater the variety; as a result, some of the larger American cities have become what Goodwin calls "management centers."

As discussed above, *services* generally, but *trade* especially, require various kinds and amounts of transportation. This section concludes with a selection examining international trade and the transportation role played by the ocean "tramp."

21. Christaller's Central Place Theory
Arthur and Judith Getis

One of the most important developments in contemporary geography is the application of the central place theory of the German geographer Walter Christaller. The central place theory has become a "classic" of geographical thought and forms the basis of much theoretical research in economic and urban geography. Even though his work was aimed primarily at explaining the arrangement of smaller places, or settlements, around a larger central place, the theory is very much concerned with the production and distribution of goods as they relate to the size and distribution of villages and towns. Christaller felt that his theory could be "designated as the theory of location of urban trade and institu-

tions." It is, therefore, fundamental to any understanding of the role and location of tertiary activities.

Much present-day research in urban geography has its roots in the work of Walter Christaller, a German scholar from Bavaria. He was attempting to find the laws which determine the number, size, and distribution of towns. He was convinced, he wrote, that just as there are economic laws which determine the life of the economy, so are there special economic-geographic laws determining the arrangement of towns.

Since 1933, when his book on central places in southern Germany was published, many writers have praised and criticized, reformulated and expanded parts of Christaller's theory. Today very few accept all aspects of his work, but they realize that it stimulated some of the most advanced scientific work in geography. The following summary of the rudiments of central place theory is included here in order to acquaint the reader with the meaning of some of the terminology prevalent in urban geography today—a terminology introduced into our literature by those dealing with Christaller's work. Hopefully this will be a reference when reading about urban geography.

No attempt is made to summarize all of Christaller's work. The emphasis is on Christaller's marketing principle or k — 3 network. Other networks were derived which had their foundation in principles of transportation and administration.

A Central Place

The chief function or characteristic of a town, Christaller said, is to be the center of a region. Settlements which are prevalently centers of regions he called *central places*. In contrast to these are dispersed places, i.e., all those places which are not centers. They might be areally-bound places (the inhabitants live from their agricultural activities), pointly-bound places, the inhabitants make their living from resources which occur at specific locations, such as mining settlements, customs places, and so on), or settlements which are indifferent with regard to their location (monastery settlements). Christaller was concerned with the central places only.

Some central places are more important than others—their central functions extend over regions in which other central places of less importance exist. Christaller devised a means of measuring the centrality of towns—their relative importance in regard to the surrounding region.

SOURCE: *Journal of Geography*, LXV (May, 1966), 220–26. Reprinted by permission of the authors and the publisher. Dr. and Mrs. Getis are on the staff, Department of Geography, Rutgers—The State University.

Central Goods and Services

Goods produced at a central place, and services offered there, are called *central goods and services*. Dispersed goods and services, in contrast, are ubiquitous; they are offered and produced everywhere. Further, an industry using raw materials imported from outside the local region and shipping its products out of the local area would not constitute a central service. The goods must be produced for the surrounding region.

The Range of a Good

This is the distance the dispersed population is willing to travel to buy a good offered at a central place. The good has both an upper and a lower limit to its *range*. The *upper limit* is the maximum radius of sales beyond which the price of the good is too high for it to be sold. The upper limit may be either an ideal or a real limit.

IDEAL LIMIT / The maximum radius results from the increase of price with distance until consumers will no longer purchase the good.

REAL LIMIT / The radius is determined by the proximity of an alternate center which can offer the good at a lower price at a certain

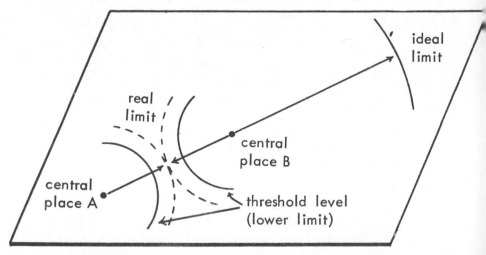

FIGURE 1: The range of a good, say a radio, offered at both A and B. Since the threshold level is less than the real limit, both central places will produce it. The real limit, halfway between the two central places, shows the trade area for radios for each place. Those living beyond the ideal limit must either do without radios or establish a new central place supplying the good.

distance from the first center. The *lower limit* of the range encloses the number of consumers necessary to provide the minimum sales volume required for the good to be produced and distributed profitably from the central place. This has been called the *threshold level* of the good. It should be noted that there is no fixed distance between the lower and upper limits of a range; sometimes the distance between the two is small, at other times it is great.

Each good will have its own range, due to the fact that the prices of various goods increase at different rates with increasing distances from the center, and to the fact that different goods have different thresholds. Further, Christaller notes that the range of any one good may be different at each central place and at each point in time.

The Complementary Region

This is the area enclosed about a central place by the range of a good. Christaller assumes that the central place has a monopoly in the supply of the good to its complementary region by virtue of the price at which it can offer the good.

Ideally, each central place would have a circular tributary (market) area, with itself at the center. However, either unserved places would exist, if this were the case, or the circles would overlap, in which case the condition of monopoly would not be fulfilled. Next to circles, hexagons are the most efficient figures both to serve an area (central places and distances traveled will be minimized) and to fill an area completely, as the figure below indicates. Therefore the complementary region of a central place assumes the form of a hexagon.

Using the terms defined above, and a set of assumptions and conditions, Christaller evolved a system of central places. The assumptions, which are listed below, tell us about the kind of landscape on which his system would be erected.

1. An unbounded plain with soil of equal fertility everywhere and an uneven distribution of resources.

2. An even distribution of population and purchasing power.

3. A uniform transportation network in all directions, so that all central places of the same type are equally accessible.

4. A constant range of any one central good, whatever the central place from which it is offered.

Given this landscape, we have to know what the desires of the people are—i.e., what constraints will exist on the system. These conditions follow:

1. A maximum number of demands for the goods and services should be satisfied.

2. The incomes of the people offering the goods and services should be maximized.

3. Distances moved by consumers to purchase the goods and services should be minimized; i.e., goods are purchased from the closest point.

4. The number of central places should be the minimum possible.

The System of Central Places:
The k = 3 Network

Under the assumptions and conditions stated above, Christaller's system of central places may be derived. Let us assume first that there are two central places, called G centers, which offer all of the goods and services, from a good or service called order 1 with the highest threshold, to a good or service of order 100, with the lowest threshold. Of neces-

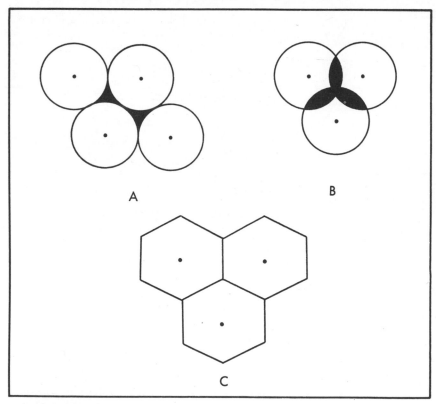

FIGURE 2: Three Arrangements of Complementary Regions.
  A. The unserved areas are shaded.
  B. Shaded areas indicate places where the condition of monopoly would not be fulfilled.
  C. Hexagons completely fill an area, with no overlap.

sity, the two G centers have the largest market areas (complementary regions) of all central places. The "real" range of the highest order good demanded, good of order 1, defines the boundary between the two G centers. Therefore, the two hexagon-shaped complementary regions have one side in common.

As was noted above, the ranges of the goods decline successively; good of order 2 has a smaller range than that of order 1. As the ranges decline, larger and larger numbers of consumers are left between the two G centers. With some good, say good of order 30, there are enough "surplus" consumers over and above the thresholds of the G centers to allow the development of alternate centers. These are called B centers.

B centers supply goods 30, 31, . . ., 100 at lower prices than the G centers *in the areas between the threshold ranges of those goods from the G centers*. B centers are located at the maximum economic distance from the G centers—i.e., on the outermost edges of the areas defined about G centers by the real range of good of order 1. In this way, consumer movements are kept to a minimum, and a maximum number of demands are satisfied from a minimum number of centers.

B centers in turn leave progressively larger numbers of surplus demands, and with some good, say good of order 50, these are large enough to permit the existence of a third rank of centers: K centers. K centers provide goods 50, 51, . . ., 100. The existence of four other types of centers is accounted for in the same manner.

Besides its definite spatial pattern two things should be noted about Christaller's system. First, a very rigid class structure has been described. That is, each central place supplies all the goods and services—the *identical* goods and services—that the centers below it provide, plus

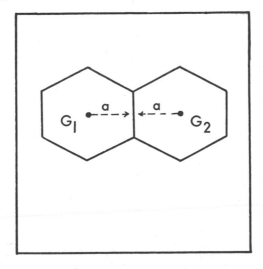

FIGURE 3: Real range of good 1 is shown by distance a.

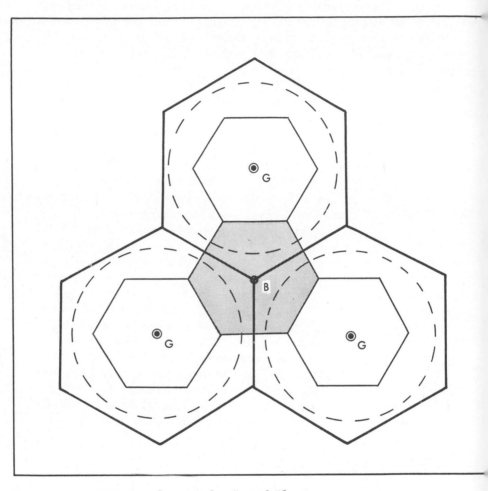

FIGURE 4: The Creation of a B Order Central Place.

Heavy Line—Each G center serves good or service 1 to its entire complementary region. All goods from 1, 2, . . . , n, are supplied by G centers.

Broken Line—Threshold of good or service 15. It encloses areas less than the real limit. However, the area between the thresholds of the three G centers is too small to allow the establishment of new central places able to supply good or service 15.

Light Line—Threshold level of good or service 30. It encloses areas small enough to allow the establishment of a new central place between the G centers.

Shaded Area—The real limit of good or service 30 supplied by a new order central place, B. B centers supply goods 30, 31, . . . , n. G centers also supply these goods and services, as well as those of higher order.

348

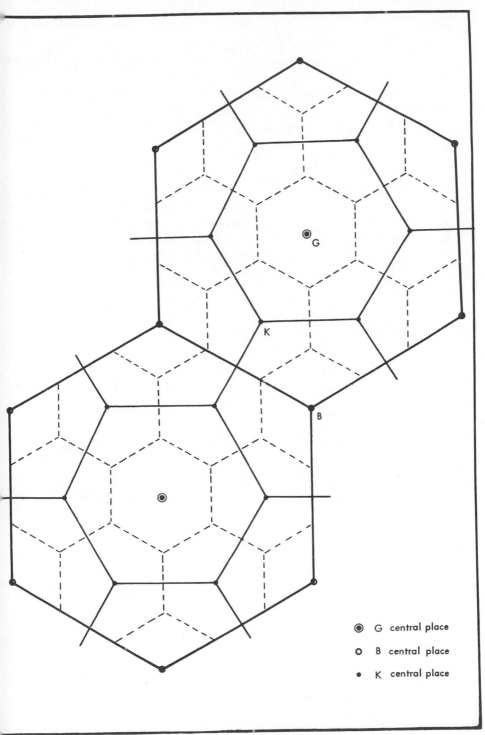

FIGURE 5: The k = 3 network.

some additional ones. It is due to this fact that Christaller was able to assume that discrete population levels could be assigned to centers of the same type. Since the population of a town depends upon the number and types of functions it performs, then centers performing similar functions will have similar populations. Further, since no centers not of the same type offer identical goods and services, the population levels will be unique.

Second, the system of central places and their complementary regions is characterized by interdependency. All centers except the smallest have other centers dependent upon them for the supply of certain goods. Thus, B centers have K centers and their complementary regions, and all centers of a lower rank than K, dependent upon them for the supply of goods 30, 31, . . ., 49. In turn, B centers and their complementary regions depend on G centers for the supply of goods 1, 2, . . . , 29. Each complementary region of a B place is served with those goods by three G centers, and Christaller assumes that one-third of its trade goes to each. Each G center thus serves its own region for the supply of goods 1, 2, . . ., 29 as well as one-third of the complementary regions of the six B centers. In all, a G center serves three total B-type regions. This is called a k = 3 network, where k equals the total number of complementary regions of next lowest order served by the central place of next highest order. Likewise, of course, three complete K-type regions are served with goods 30, 31, . . ., 49 by a B center, and so on.

In summary, the chief contribution of Christaller to central place theory is, of course, its basic formulation. More specifically, his identification of concepts relevant to the location of cities, his logically derived system of central places, and the conclusions following from it are to be noted. Further, it should once more be pointed out that there is much in the book which has not been mentioned here. Christaller recognizes certain deficiencies of his system and qualifies it whenever he deems necessary. In general, he notes that:

The strict mathematical scheme developed previously is imperfect in some respects. It is even incorrect in this strictness. The scheme should approximate reality; therefore we should study the factors under whose influence it undergoes change.

22. The Role of Tribal Markets in Morocco

Marvin W. Mikesell

However simple an economy may be, whether subsistence agriculture or nomadic herding, almost invariably, some sort of local markets have been developed to serve the people. The local trade center is one of the most important tertiary activities, whatever the scale and level of development of the economy or wherever it is located—a modern suburban shopping center surrounded by a huge parking lot serves the same function as the small market center on the fringe of the desert. Tribal markets in Morocco today have many characteristics similar to those commonly found on the desert fringes during the times of the Roman Empire some two thousand years ago.

Western observers in Morocco are astonished by the juxtaposition of modern urban districts and deeply rural tribal territories. The gleaming, up-to-date buildings of Morocco's European quarters remind one of California rather than of France. Casablanca bears a strong resemblance to Los Angeles and its suburbs; Rabat could be San Diego; Oujda has the aspect of Fresno or Bakersfield. It is possible to travel for weeks in Morocco and never leave excellent highways. But in the areas of European influence one is never far from the "real Morocco," where tribal authority is still dominant and the goals of life are independence and self-sufficiency. The generalization is often made that the tribal territories are evolving from a medieval to a modern way of life, but such a comparison does not do justice to the magnitude of the change. The economic and social environment of tribal Morocco more closely resembles that in northern Europe at the time of earliest Roman conquest. In recent years Morocco has been struggling with problems that were resolved in the West more than a thousand years ago.

The clearest expression of this "split personality" is an abrupt transition from urban to rural settlement. In the Western world we are accustomed to think of towns as links between these two modes of life. In Morocco such links are hard to find. Between one city and another are only villages, hamlets, or isolated farmsteads. Towns of the Western

SOURCE: *The Geographical Review*, XLVIII (October, 1958), 494–511. Reprinted by permission. The author is professor of geography at the University of Chicago.

type are of very recent origin, and most of them are in areas where European influence has been strong. The almost total absence of towns in Morocco can be explained by the presence of a special instrument of trade—the weekly market, or *suq* (plural, *aswaq*). These markets are held in the open, at predetermined sites, which are deserted during the rest of the week. In each tribal area one or more sites are reserved as market places and are named according to the day of the week on which the market is held. On the morning of the appointed day streams of people converge on the market place. After a few hours of brisk trading, the market begins to break up, and by nightfall the site is empty again.

The deeply rural "Northern Zone" of Morocco (until April of 1956 controlled by the Spanish as a "protectorate") is an excellent area in which to study the traditional role of the suq. This "zone," like the large area of Berber speech in the High, Middle, and Anti-Atlas, has suffered little from the obscuring effects of foreign influence. The Arabs, who first entered Morocco at the end of the seventh century, had small interest in the highlands. European colonists, largely concerned with mechanized agriculture, also preferred lands of gentle relief. All the mountain tribes have embraced Islam, some have learned to speak Arabic, and a few have adopted the Singer sewing machine. But it is only in the last two decades that their traditions of independence and self-sufficiency have been seriously disturbed.

Time and Place

Maps of Morocco show more than a thousand markets. Their presence is indicated by the following names: *El had* (Sunday), *Et tnine* (Monday), *Et tleta* (Tuesday), *El arba* (Wednesday), *El khemis* (Thursday), *El jema* (Friday), *Es sebt* (Saturday). For political as well as economic reasons each tribe holds at least one suq of its own, and a complete cycle of markets may be maintained. Six markets, for example, are held by the numerous Rifian tribe of the Beni Ouriaghel. The ideal location permits any member of the sponsoring tribe to visit the market and return home in a single day. This stipulation can be satisfied even when the distance is as much as 20 or 30 miles; for the Moroccans are great walkers, and on market day no one wants to remain at home. The suq is much more than a market in the economic sense; it is also a social and political assembly of great importance in tribal life. Market day is the time for legal transactions and all manner of negotiations. By nightfall tribal authorities have resolved most of the problems of the week. Since the suq serves as a clearinghouse for gossip and news, its attraction is overpowering. The *qadi* (Koranic judge) of the tribe of the Beni Seddat once granted a divorce to a woman whose husband had refused to allow her to visit the suq. On market days in the

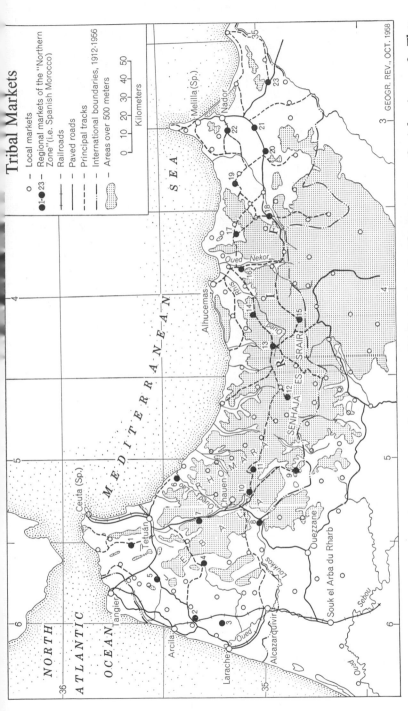

Tribal Markets

Legend:
- o – Local markets
- ●1-●23 – Regional markets of the "Northern Zone" (i.e. Spanish Morocco)
- —†— – Railroads
- — – Paved roads
- ------ – Principal tracks
- —·—·— – International boundaries, 1912–1956
- ⠿ – Areas over 500 meters

Kilometers: 0 10 20 30 40 50

3   GEOGR. REV., OCT. 1958

FIGURE 1: Tribal markets of the "Northern Zone." Key to regional markets: 1, Khemis Anjera; 2, Arba Ayasa; 3, Tleta Reisana; 4, Khemis Beni Aros; 5, Tleta Jebel Hebib; 6, Sebt Oued Lao; 7, Arba Beni Hassan; 8, Had Agadir el Kruch; 9, Tleta Beni Hamed; 10, Arba Bab Taza; 11, Had Beni Dercul; 12, Tleta Ketama; 13, Arba Targuist; 14, Tnine Beni Hadifa; 15, Tnine Beni Ammart; 16, Tbine Beni Bou Ayyash; 17, Sebt Tensaman; 18, Arba Midar; 19, Tleta Kebdani; 20, Tnine Tistutin; 21, Had Jebel Arruit; 22, Khemis Segangan, 23, Khemis Zaio.

Senhajan mountains the writer has seen people wading barefooted through snow.

Physical factors are of primary importance in the selection of market sites. The critical requirement is a reliable water supply. In the moist highlands of Jebala and Rhomara each tribe possesses dozens of potential market sites, but in the Rif perennial streams are rare and the chief markets are located where there are springs or wells. Markets are often placed close to a religious sanctuary or shrine (*murabit*), since the site is protected by sacred authority, and malediction (*tagat*) falls on anyone who disturbs the peace. This was a major consideration a generation ago when Morocco was rent by tribal warfare and markets were turbulent assemblies of armed men.

Two types of market are distinguishable (Fig. 1). The more influential is the local suq. Markets of this type draw a few hundred people from a radius of 10 to 12 miles. Their main function is to serve as foci of commerce for dispersed but sedentary populations engaged in subsistence agriculture. Differences of slope, exposure, and soil permit some specialization, but no community specializes to the point of dependence on others for staple foods. One village may try to increase its flocks beyond the level of need or, if its land is wooded, may make pitchforks or plows. Another village may have a surplus of eggs or an overabundance of fruit. In spring cereal stocks are low, and there is a brisk trade in raisins and dried figs. The local suq also serves as a place of deposit for sugar, salt, cooking oil, and kerosene—the primary commodities that must be brought in from outside.

The second type of suq, the regional market, draws a larger number

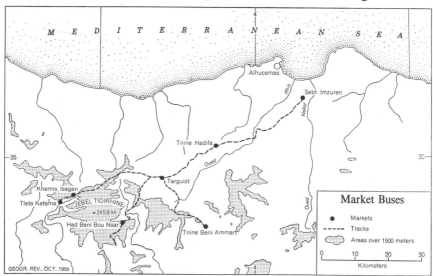

FIGURE 2: Circulation of market buses from Targuist.

of people from a radius of as much as 20 miles. Markets of this type are located at the convergence of major communication lines and on the frontiers of complementary production zones. Moroccans make a distinction between *bled seguia,* where crops can be grown under irrigation, and *bled bour,* where only dry farming is possible. The larger markets are usually on the frontiers of these two zones. The Wednesday market at Targuist, on the eastern edge of the mountains of Senhaja es-Srair, enjoys this combination of advantages (Fig. 2). The sole transportation artery between the humid Rhomara and the semiarid Rif passes nearby. Targuist is also the apex of two tracks over northern Morocco's mountainous spine. From the irrigated terraces of the highlands come summer crops of maize, beans, squash, and *kif* (hashish, *Cannabis sativa*). In the drier but warmer Rif there is in normal years a surplus of winter wheat and barley, nuts, fruit, and olive oil. The mountain tribes bring planks of cedar and pine, and the Rifian tribes make baskets, hats, and matting from cane, palmetto fibers *(Chamaerops humilis)*, and esparto grass *(Stipa tenacissima)*. The mountain tribe of Tarhzout specializes in tanning and leather work, which can be exchanged for pottery manufactured in the Rif.

Examples of Local and Regional Markets

Let us consider two markets celebrated on the same day. El had Beni Bou Nsar (Sunday [market] of the sons of the father of Nsar) is a local suq that attracts about 300 people from a narrow zone extending along the flanks of a deep valley cut by the Oued el Had (Sunday stream). This is an area of subsistence agriculture. The slopes are steep and the soils stony and thin, but a few streams are perennial, and a variety of crops can be grown under irrigation during the dry summer to supplement the winter crops of barley and rye. The suq is reached by a track from Targuist (Fig. 2), and when this is not blocked by snow or mud, a small bus filled with merchants comes to the market. They set up tents or booths and display rolls of cotton cloth, soap, sugar, salt, tea, and a variety of other goods ranging from fertility charms to ball-point pens. Artisans repair shoes and make charcoal braziers from scrap iron. There may be a truckload of fish from Alhucemas and possibly a traveling medicine man.

By noon all who are coming to the market have arrived. The suq is at its peak, "a vociferating, seething mass of human beings, quadrupeds and feathered things." [1] The women exchange gossip as well as their special property—eggs, poultry, bread, and fruit. The men gather

---

[1] This colorful phrase, written by Budgett Meakin at the turn of the century, is just as applicable to the markets of today (The Moors: A Comprehensive Description [London and New York, 1902], p. 172).

apart and besides settling the important tribal business haggle over the prices of tea, oil, sugar, and meat. Everyone has a turn with the itinerant peddlers, but few purchase anything; for in this area of subsistence economy each family guards its currency for a marriage or some other special event. A rough system of quarters (*rahba*) is recognized, and week after week the same goods are found at the same place. Butchers and blacksmiths work a short distance away from the rest of the group. When there is a load of fish, fires are kindled and part of the purchase is consumed on the spot. But most people are satisfied with a simple meal of barley bread and dried fruit. By midafternoon the load of fish has been sold, and those who live close to the road—sometimes more than 50 people—crowd on the truck for a ride. The bus stays as long as the merchants feel that there is a chance for a sale, but by nightfall the suq is abandoned and the market bus is stirring up giant clouds of dust.

Each market has four main functions: (1) distribution of local products; (2) exchange of rural surplus for urban goods; (3) circulation of articles such as pottery and millstones from special places within the country; and (4) dissemination of foreign imports. The larger, regional, markets differ from the smaller, local, markets in a greater emphasis on the last two functions. A good example of the regional type is El had Jebel Arruit, located close to the ports of Melilla and Nador (Fig. 1). In addition to the simple goods offered at Had Beni Bou Nsar, this market boasts toy ballons, firecrackers (for use on wedding days), and a myriad of other commodities of national and international origin. On a representative day at Jebel Arruit one can see cotton cloth from England, canvas shoes from Spain, flashlights and padlocks from Japan, political posters from Egypt, and spices of many varieties, mostly from India. More than a thousand people gather here on market day. Four buses bring merchants from Melilla and Nador. Trucks also come from these cities and from Alhucemas and Oujda. This suq is large enough to require the services of professional weighers and criers.[2] But at nightfall the market place is deserted, and there is little to suggest that this suq was large and the other one small. The largest trade at both markets is in the simple necessities of rural life, such as sugar, salt, and kerosene.

Uniqueness of the Suq

This system of trade has no counterpart at present in the Western world. The uniqueness of the suq derives from the fact that it is regarded as an institution, an event, and not as a feature of settlement. Merchants and peasants meet on neutral ground during a time of truce. For more

[2] The Rifian term for such people is *imazilen*, "shameless ones." Shyness and reserve are cardinal virtues to the dignified Rifi. Market criers, musicians, dancers, and others who display themselves in public are members of outcaste groups.

than a thousand years merchants in the Occident have occupied fixed positions and encouraged dispersed rural populations to come to them. Three rural trading institutions have been prominent in Europe, and none of them corresponds to the suq. The general commodity fairs of medieval time, such as those founded by the counts of Champagne, were annual or semiannual events designed to encourage wholesale exchange. Livestock fairs began either as specialized derivatives of general commodity fairs or as expressions of more ancient commercial contacts between pastoral peoples and entrepreneurs based in towns. The periodic village markets, still to be found in most of Europe, show a closer functional resemblance to the suq. But as early as the twelfth century rural markets in Europe had concrete expression as *bourg, Marktflecken,* or *market town.* Furthermore, these were imposed institutions with "market rights" and "market days" assigned by decree. In order to find a counterpart in Europe of the Moroccan suq, one must look beyond the Middle and Dark Ages to pagan time. Then, in northern Europe at least, "market" meant periodic assembly and not necessarily a feature of settlement.

Open-air markets of the Moroccan type represent an attempt to reconcile desires for security and for commercial exchange. But this system of trade can be effective only among populations of sedentary habit and dispersed settlement. Where settlement is dense, as in the Nile Valley, or widely dispersed and nomadic, as in the pre-Saharan steppe, other arrangements for trading must be made. Another prerequisite is that communications must not be too elaborate; for when transportation facilities evolve to a Western standard, markets of this type tend to lose their ephemeralness and change into trading towns.

Where are these prerequisites satisfied? And where are recurrent markets to be found? Carleton S. Coon considers that the right conditions for the existence of a "staggered series of weekly markets" are found in North Africa and along the Caspian shore of Iran. In reality, markets of this type are scattered over an area extending from Morocco to the Philippines. Patterns of rural trade in Ethiopia are similar. Stanley found market places on the banks of the Congo, where all was "animation and eager chaffer" until noon, when they became "silent again and untenanted, a prey to gloom and shade." Weekly markets play an important role in the economy of rural India. The West Bengal *hat,* for example, functions almost exactly like the suq, and a similar comparison can be made between Moroccan markets and the village fairs of Szechwan. As in most problems of culture history, it is a question of independent invention versus diffusion. Is a pattern of trade with rotating weekly markets sufficiently complex to suggest origin in one culture area? Or are we dealing with a system of exchange that could have evolved spontaneously wherever conditions of settlement and livelihood were appropriate? It may be noted that annual and weekly trade fairs also exist in parts of Latin America, and that the weekly fairs, at least, probably trace to pre-Columbian time.

Negative Role in Urban Evolution

Fortunately, ignorance of cause, in this case, does not preclude consideration of effect. The successful functioning of the suq in Morocco has had an arresting effect on urban evolution. These markets serve as links between cities and the rural countryside and render trading towns unnecessary. Indeed, there is no equivalent in Maghribi Arabic of the word "town." From *medina*, "city," the Moroccan vocabulary turns to *dechra*, "village," *douar*, "hamlet," and *azib*, "farmstead."

How could cities have evolved in Morocco without leaving traces of

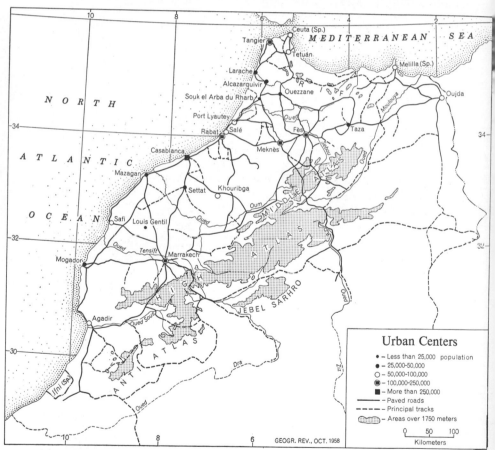

FIGURE 3: Urban centers. Source: "Maroc: Voies de communication," 1:1,500,000, Institut Geographique National (Annexe du Maroc), Rabat, 1955; population data from "Les guides bleus: Maroc," Paris, 1954.

intermediate stages of urbanization? The answer is that Moroccan cities did not evolve as trading centers for the rural countryside; they were established by decree. The Moroccan city is an imposed entity, foreign to tribal life. Some cities trace their origin to Roman time, others began during the period of Arab conquest, still others were founded by the Europeans. No Moroccan city is truly native. It is not surprising, therefore, that cities should be found only in the lowlands, where alien authority was easy to establish and maintain (Fig. 3). In the highlands Berber ideals of political independence and economic self-sufficiency acted as a check against urbanization.

Intimate relations between city and hinterland are difficult to establish when urban institutions are imposed by alien authorities. Cities thus established become parasites, drawing support from the rural countryside but offering little in exchange. The peasant population continues to look to its local markets for satisfaction of basic needs. Fès, located in a rich agricultural area and renowned for the high quality of its crafts, is the only Moroccan city intimately related to its hinterland. But the nucleus of the Fès bourgeoisie is formed by descendants of Arab immigrants from Spain, whose pronunciation of Arabic often is unintelligible to tribesmen living a few miles away.

Illustrations can again be taken from the Northern Zone. The ports of Ceuta and Melilla were used by the Portuguese and Spanish as bases of colonial and military activity and even today are governed as integral parts of Spain (*plazas de soberanía*). Larache and Arcila also reflect Iberian influence. Tetuán began as a military fort designed to protect the government route between Tangier and Fès. In the sixteenth century it was a focus of immigration for Muslims and Jews who were being expelled from Spain. Chauen, established in 1471 as a base for campaigns against the Portuguese, served also as a refuge for Andalusian Moors. Alcazarquivir (Ksar el-Kebir) served a similar function in the eleventh century. Tangier has been the headquarters of a whole series of foreign interests—Carthaginian, Roman, Portuguese, Spanish, English, and lately, even "international." Most of the Moroccan residents of Tangier are immigrants from the Rif, who have little in common with the Jebalan tribesmen of the nearby hills. There are only two other settlements in the Northern Zone that deserve to be called towns, Alhucemas and Nador, and they owe their origin to the establishment of the Spanish protectorate.

The same pattern exists in the French zone. Casablanca, Port Lyautey, and the mining communities of Khouribga and Louis Gentil reflect European planning and investment. The name of Casablanca's tiny ancestor, Anfa, is no longer remembered; Moroccans know their bustling economic capital as Dar el-Beida, which also means "white house." The important native cities likewise began as planned communities. Oujda, Rabat, Salé, and Marrakech owe their origin to governmental decree.

Taza and Meknès began as military outposts. Even the maritime trading centers of Mazagan, Safi, Mogador, and Agadir were established as centers of political control. The economic function of these cities was a consequence of their urban function rather than a cause.

Recent Trends

At the beginning of the twentieth century there was not a single kilometer of road in Morocco suitable for wheeled vehicles. In fact, the only vehicles known were decorative carriages used by the Sultan for ceremonies. The French, realizing the need for good communications if they were to pacify the country and remain in power, promptly began work on an extensive network of roads. The Spanish made similar, though less successful, efforts in their zone, In 1955 there were 10,000 kilometers of primary or secondary roads (mostly macadam) and 35,000 kilometers of tracks open to buses and trucks during the dry season. With the advent of roads and motorized transport, the traditional role of the suq began to change. The markets located on natural communication routes grew in size and influence, whereas the more isolated markets either remained local or simply faded away. Elderly Moroccans everywhere speak of markets unknown to their children. The site of an abandoned market can be established by suq terminology in a local place name; for example, a name such as *Bab et-tleta* (Tuesday Pass) or *Ain et-tleta* (Tuesday Spring) in areas where no Tuesday market remains.

Before the establishment of the European protectorates, not only were communications primitive but they were disrupted by tribal warfare. One of the main themes of Moroccan history is the distinction between *bled el-makhzen* (the land of government) and *bled es-siba* (the land of dissidence). The *bled es-siba* corresponded to the Rif and the Atlas Mountains, where communications were difficult to establish and maintain. Travel was possible only under the approval and protection of local authorities. Since intertribal feuds were common, long-range travel involved great risk. Merchants and travelers assembled in the cities until they were numerous enough to pay for protection. In parts of the Rif the tradition of market truce broke down, and a special system of women's markets had to be established so that noncombatant members of the feuding tribes could carry on a rudimentary trade.

Primitive communications and tribal strife not only prevented the evolution of towns; they even discouraged the growth of the regional suq. The modern trend has been different. The more accessible markets have grown in size, and some have evolved into permanent establishments. In short, the suq, which for centuries acted as a substitute for the trading town, is now evolving into the very thing it had militated against. This trend ceases to be paradoxical when it is viewed against the background of Morocco's expanding network of roads.

The changes that have taken place at Tleta Ketama are indicative of this trend. Thirty years ago this was a local suq patronized mainly by members of a single tribe. Today the market easily qualifies as a regional suq. During the warm months of spring and summer more than a thousand people assemble here. Today's market has one advantage over its predecessor—it is reached by a road (Fig. 2). The presence of the road does not mean that the market is more accessible to the tribesmen who gather there, but it does mean that the site is more accessible to merchants from Targuist, Alhucemas, and Tetuán. Before the road was completed, the suq was no more attractive than several others in the area. Now everyone who possibly can goes there, even if it means neglect of markets closer to home. The simple charms of the local suq lose their appeal when larger markets with a wider range of goods are accessible.

The principal expression of the new trend is the overcrowded market bus. These buses carry a simple notation in Arabic script, *aswaq* (markets), which is perfectly understood by the merchants and shoppers who board a bus at its terminal or flag one on the road. On Monday they are going to *suq et-tnine*, on Tuesday to *suq-et-tleta*, and so on through the week.

The circulation from Targuist, in northern Morocco, is representative of the whole country. Two buses of 1935 vintage start from here (Fig. 2). On Monday one goes to the market of the Beni Hadifa and the other to the market of the Beni Ammart. On Tuesday they both go to the mountain suq at Ketama. Wednesday is market day at Targuist, and not enough bus tickets can be sold to justify a trip. On Thursday the buses go back into the mountains to the small market at Isagan (Spanish, Llano Amarillo). Friday is a day of rest, and the buses again stay at their base. On Saturday there is a large market at Imzuren, in the territory of the Beni Ouriaghel. On Sunday the attraction is the small suq of the Beni Bou Nsar, described above. There is not a single kilometer of surfaced road in this whole area, and by American standards the buses are long overdue for the junkyard. Yet day after day, year after year, they lumber on.

The buses are also used by tribesmen who take advantage of the market circulation to get close to their homes. Most villages in Morocco are within a day's walk of a bus route at least once in the week. But most of the tickets are sold to merchants who follow the complete circuit to sell their array of goods. The prices current at Targuist give an idea of the weekly volume of trade. Each round trip costs about one dollar. In order to recover this investment, pay for his goods, and make a small profit, the itinerant merchant must earn about twenty dollars during the week. By Western standards this seems a small sum. But it must be remembered that rural Morocco is still a region of subsistence agriculture, and that barter usually has priority over cash transactions. By Moroccan standards the Targuist merchants are doing well.

The influx of a larger number of people from farther away necessitates a more elaborate establishment at the market place. Inns are necessary, and also permanent storehouses and shops. Some structures were built by the Europeans. The officers of Affaires Indigènes in the French zone and of Asuntos Indígenas in the area of Spanish influence functioned as overseers of the native government, and this function required that they be present on market day. The practical procedure was to establish headquarters at the larger markets, and this led to the erection of buildings to serve as offices and dwelling places. Walls and gates were added, since the suq was the best place to collect taxes. At the larger markets the services of veterinarians and physicians were provided, and they too needed places of consultation and residence. As often as not the suq also served as headquarters of a military detachment. Almost all the regional markets now have structures built by Europeans, and many of the local markets have been enhanced in some way. A few markets have been moved from their original locations or shifted from one day to another. For example, the market at Targuist was moved from the valley of the Oued Rhis to the center of a small garrison town built by the Spanish after the end of Abd el-Krim's rebellion. These innovations seem likely to persist. The local officials of the Moroccan government function independently of the old tribal authorities, and for the most part they have simply taken over the offices and houses used by the Europeans before Moroccan independence.

As a result of these trends many markets now have an appearance of permanence and solidity. In time trading may be spread throughout the week. Merchants may elect to stay put instead of moving their goods from place to place. Perhaps the shifting suq will continue as an instrument of barter, and permanent markets will develop as centers of retail trade. It is not yet possible to predict the outcome of these trends. In fact, it cannot be taken for granted that they will persist. The principal cause of change has been Morocco's expanding network of roads, and it remains to be seen whether the new government will be able to continue this work. Here is the key to the problem; for it seems to be a principle of economic geography that improvement of communications encourages centralization of trading facilities.

23. The Dynamics of Store Trading Areas and Market Equilibrium

William Applebaum and Saul B. Cohen

Modern retail stores, supermarkets, and shopping centers are at the opposite end of the market scale from the simple Moroccan tribal markets in the preceding selection. Marketing geography, a highly empirical and sophisticated discipline, is attracting an increasing number of professional geographers. They are engaged chiefly in selecting locations for commercial and manufacturing activities, often working for large manufacturing corporations or serving as professional real-estate consultants. The geographer's spatial approach to economic problems and distributions is particularly useful in this kind of locational analysis. This selection is concerned with the characteristics of retail markets as areas of economic demand, and with the role of these factors in determining commercial locations.

Businessmen and marketing geographers are interested in the trading areas of retail stores. Businessmen are interested in store trading areas because these areas contain the source of business—customers, current and potential. Knowledge of a store's trading area is essential for judicious investment in facilities, merchandise, and promotional activities to attract and serve customers.

Marketing geographers are interested in store trading areas because they are complex areal phenomena. In studying these areas, marketing geographers seek to provide scientific knowledge and specific assistance to businessmen in evaluating market area potentials. A market area is an area of demand—it includes existing or potential buyers of goods and services within clearly defined geographical limits. These areas may be trading centers and their hinterlands or metropolitan districts; or, they may represent the administrative units of business firms.

This paper deals with:

SOURCE: *Annals* of the Association of American Geographers, LI (March, 1961), 73–101. Reprinted with permission of the authors and the publisher. Dr. Applebaum is professor at the College of Social Science, Harvard University, and Professor Cohen is director of the School of Geography, Clark University.

1. Store trading-area features and the conditions under which changes in these features occur.

2. The networks formed by store trading areas of different sizes and ranks in a given market area, and the conditions under which regroupings occur.

3. Stores of market-area saturation in relation to the dynamics of trading-area features and trading-area networks.

These topics are not individual and separate, but are interconnected. A market usually contains stores of different types and sizes. Each store has its trading area. When the market area is served by stores so located, physically planned, and merchandized that customer needs are met adequately, and use of store facilities is efficient, then the market is in balance, or saturated.

Trading areas of stores do not remain fixed in time because of a multitude of dynamic changes. Likewise, store facilities become outmoded. As new store facilities, merchandising methods, or services are introduced, new trading-area patterns emerge, resulting, in time, in new trading-area networks within a market area. This process leads to a new state of balance between retail facilities and their use.

The concepts presented here are derived and broadly generalized from retailing experience in the United States and Canada, particularly in the post-World War II era. The presentation is a description of what is currently taking place. These concepts should have special relevance to store development in other parts of the world as they too adopt mass retailing methods, achieve widespread use of the automobile, and create planned shopping centers.

Marketing geography is a highly empirical discipline, with those who work in the field acting as practical engineers. A greater number and variety of samplings will have to be made of retail store trading-area patterns and networks, in the United States and Canada and elsewhere, before clear-cut theories can be offered for universal application.

Trading Areas

A store meets the needs and wants of customers who move about within a spatially ordered framework. This movement may be related to the place of residence, work, recreation, or other activities, but the movement occurs within a specific area. The economic function of the store is to sell goods, services, or both. The store's trading area is determined by what the store sells, the manner in which it sells, the shopping habits of customers, existing competition, and type of location.

Store trading areas are phenomena that are fixed in space for recognizable periods of time. Their boundaries are zones, not lines; the boundaries are flexible, not rigid. These boundaries change with changes in shopping-habit patterns and with changes in merchandising practices.

Store trading areas are the joint product of many simultaneously interacting factors, so numerous that they almost defy generalization. To overcome this dilemma, those who attempt to define store trading areas must either offer a specialized definition that applies to a particular store trading area, or a broad generalization that may not be very applicable to any specific store trading area.

Some of the specialized definitions use as major criteria such factors as drawing power, per capita sales, share of market, movement, population, and competition.[1] *Drawing power* refers to the percent of sales that a store obtains from a specific area in relation to its total sales. *Per capita sales* refers to sales per unit of population. *Share of market* refers to percent of total available sales that a particular store obtains. *Movement* refers to transportation in terms of travel time or distance. *Population* refers to the number of people required to support a specific store. Competition refers to the location of competitive facilities and the power exerted by each in securing sales.

Various difficulties are encountered in applying these criteria. The delineation of the boundary of a store trading area to correspond to a fixed drawing-power standard requires much detailed data as well as practical skill in interpreting the effect of numerous geographic and other factors on the extent and shape of a store trading area.

Per capita sales and share of market criteria vary according to the

---

[1] The following are examples:
A. *Drawing power.*
    1. The trading area is "that area from which the community receives approximately 90 percent of its total retail patronage." Isadore V. Fine, *Retail Trade Analysis*, University of Wisconsin, Bureau of Business Research and Service (Madison, 1954), p. 11.
    2. "The area of influence from which a shopping center could expect to derive as much as 85% of its total sales volume is defined here as the trade area of the center." Victor Gruen and Larry Smith, *Shopping Towns U.S.A.* (New York: Reinhold Publishing Co., 1960), p. 278.
B. *Per capita sales.* The trading area is "that area which will provide [a general merchandise store] a minimum annual per capita sale of one dollar." Howard L. Green, Montgomery Ward Co., correspondence with the authors, April, 1959.
C. *Movement.* "Generally speaking . . . a large majority of customers are willing to travel 12–15 minutes, and a maximum of 25 minutes to reach a regional shopping center." Gruen and Smith, *op. cit.*, p. 33.
D. *Population.* "2,000 families would spend $2,000,000 for food annually, or enough to support a large supermarket—if all families were to patronize one store." Max S. Wehrly and J. Ross McKeever, eds., *The Community Builders Handbook*, Community Builders' Council of the Urban Land Institute (Washington, D.C., 1954), p. 134.
E. *Competition.* "The actual trading area is entirely determined by the operation of attraction and resistance of competitive trading areas . . . the trading area is not a permanent geographical fact but is created entirely by the response and behavior of individuals." Richard L. Nelson, *The Selection of Retail Locations*, F. W. Dodge Corp. (New York, 1958), p. 183.

types, sizes, and locations of stores and with the policies and capabilities of each firm. One general merchandise store company considers as within its trading area all areas from which it obtains $1.00 per capita per year or a 0.5 percent share of the market. One supermarket chain considers as within its trading area all areas from which it obtains $5.00 per capita per year or a 1.5 percent share of the market. Should the population within the trading area thus defined increase considerably and should additional competition be established in the process, a decreased per capita sales and/or share of the market might not alter the store's total sales obtained from the trading area, but the definition would no longer be valid. Actually, a thickly populated core will lower the minimum per capita sales necessary to support a store, and a thinly populated core will raise them.

Trading-area criteria based upon movement, such as distance or travel time, might be useful if it were possible to develop a valid formula that would allow for differences in competition, traffic friction,[2] and frequently of customer shopping.

Population can be a useful trading-area criterion if the number is weighted for competition. The trading area of a full-scale department store would require and include 100,000 persons if *all* expenditures of these 100,000 persons for department store goods were made at the store. If this were only one of five equal competing stores, then an area with a population of 500,000 would be needed to constitute the trading area.

Location of competition as a criterion of store trading area is difficult to apply in metropolitan areas, where competition exists not only among stores of approximately equal rank, but also with stores of much greater and lesser rank.

Broad definitions of trading areas suffer from vagueness. Nonetheless, generalizations are useful guides. Some of these definitions stress movement; others, spheres of influence; still others, people.[3] As a broad definition, we suggest that the trading area is the area from which a

---

[2] Traffic friction results from such disconcerting elements as turning against traffic flow, heavy truck or bus movement, and stops and starts due to street lights, pedestrians, or access lanes.

[3] Examples of such definitions are:

A. *Movement.* "In this study, a market or trading area is thought of as being composed of an area provided with means for the movement of persons and commodities, and occupied by people who have common and daily economic interests." John Paver and Miller McClintock, *Traffic and Trade* (New York: McGraw-Hill, 1935), p. 5.

B. *Sphere of influence.* "A trade center region, i.e., a trade center and its continuous hinterland, is one in which spheres of influence should be exerted by the former upon the latter." Eugene Van Cleef, *Trade Centers and Trade Routes* (New York: Appleton–Century Co., 1937), p. 38.

C. *People.* "A store does not obtain business from any area. It obtains its business from people." Reavis Cox, correspondence, December, 1959.

store gets its business within a given span of time. This does not exclude the reality of overlap. It also emphasizes the "area" in trading area. People must come to a store from a specific area. If other stores offer equal attractions, then the trading area of a given store will be related to this store's distance and convenience of access from the origin and destination of the potential customers.

Because a store's trading area frames the lines of customer movement, the impact of changing shopping-habit patterns upon the channels of this movement is of major importance. Customers today originate the bulk of their shopping trips from home. Their mode of travel, with some rare exceptions, is by automobile, public transportation, or on foot. In the future, they may relate more of their shopping habits to places of work or recreation. There may also be shifts and changes in mode of travel. Regardless of whether the origin of the trip or an intermediate or final destination is the more important, the fact that every shopping trip is linked to a *place* gives a geographical character to the trading area. The mode of travel affects the distance that people will travel readily to shop.

Finally, a generalization of a store trading area must take into account the fluctuations in and somewhat amorphous nature of the boundaries arising from the day-to-day actions of the retailer, his competitors, and the customers. This is discussed more fully later.

Features of Trading Areas

A store trading area is a nodal region (i.e., it contains a focus—the store —which is the node of organization and the surrounding area is tied to the focus by lines of transportation). Its features include: (1) cores, (2) morphology—shape, size, and arteries of movement, (3) competing stores, (4) internal components, and (5) external boundaries.

The Core

The core consists of the point at which the store is located. Characterizing the core are (a) type of location, (b) size of store, (c) retail structure, and (d) store associations.

LOCATION TYPES / We find the following classification useful in analyzing store trading areas in relation to location types:[4]

A. Unplanned business districts
    1. Central business district

---

[4] This is not a quantified classification; therefore, it lacks precision of definition. However, it is a classification which can be readily applied. For an approach to a quantified, functional classification, see *Shopping Center Report* (preliminary report), Cleveland Regional Planning Commission, Cleveland, Ohio, 1958, p. 26.

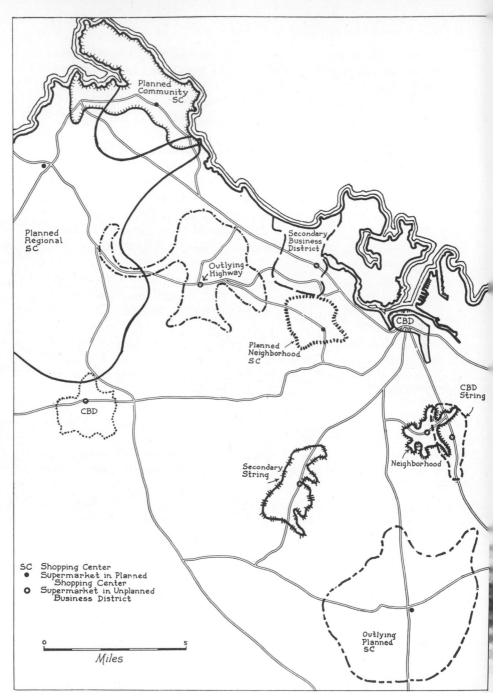

FIGURE 1: Effect of location on size of trading area. The map is based on a study of modern supermarkets similar in size, age, and quality, and owned by one corporate chain. Supermarkets located within planned shopping centers have more extensive trading areas than those located in unplanned business districts of comparable size.

2. CBD string stores. Adjoin the CBD
3. Secondary business district. Serves portions of a central city, or a suburb
4. Secondary string stores. Adjoin secondary business districts
5. Neighborhood stores. Occur in small clusters or in isolation
6. Outlying highway stores. Occur in strings or in isolation

B. Planned shopping centers
1. CBD planned shopping center. Arises through urban renewal
2. Regional planned shopping center. In strong competition with the CBD
3. Community planned shopping center. In competition mainly with secondary business districts, or with the CBD in smaller cities
4. Neighborhood planned shopping center. Frequently called neighborhood "strip"
5. Outlying planned shopping center. Draws, in part, upon the passing parade of highway traffic

In towns and small cities where the CBD is generally the only important business district, the size and other characteristics of a store are more important than type of location, since, in order to obtain a significant amount of trade, a store must draw its business from the same trading area as the CBD. Therefore, the location types presented in this classification, except for the CBD, are of practical significance only in metropolitan areas and larger cities.

Figure 1 presents examples of store trading areas in these types of locations, based on a number of supermarkets, similar in size, age, and quality and located within a relatively evenly populated metropolitan area.

STORE SIZE / Store size has a bearing upon trading area insofar as size of facility reflects the amount and variety of goods and services that can be provided for customers. However, trading-area extent does not increase proportionately with increasing store size.

A supermarket with 8,000 square feet of sales area can carry a selection of items to compete in trading-area extent with a store very substantially larger in size. A supermarket of 25,000 square feet of sales area, however, has a significantly larger trading area. A discount house with 40,000 square feet can command as extensive a trading area as one 50 percent larger. Smaller discount houses, however, have smaller trading areas. Branch department stores may range in selling area from 60,000 to 100,000 square feet without appreciable change in their trading-area extent. A full-line department store of 250,000 square feet creates a far different trading area.

RETAIL STRUCTURE / A store's trading area is affected by (1) the retail-gravitation power of the city in which the store is located and (2) its proximity to other stores.

The retail-gravitation power of a city derives from the number and type of stores it has. This number and size is usually related to the size and function of the city. Large cities have more extensive trading hinterlands than small cities. So do cities whose factories reach out to distant towns and villages for additional labor forces. When factories extend their employment base rapidly and as retailers recognize and take advantage of the changes in market potential, store trading areas are extended.

In general, the larger the population of a city or metropolitan area, the more extensive is the trading area of the CBD. Similarly, the larger the suburbs in metropolitan areas, the more extensive are the trading areas of their stores dealing in shopping goods and even convenience goods.

The decentralization of retail facilities via large planned shopping centers in suburban areas is increasing the extent of metropolitan areas into urban and rural hinterlands.

As the size of a city increases, the share of the available retail business secured by stores located outside the CBD increases also. Larger cities present more traffic friction to shoppers in getting to and from the CBD. This traffic friction creates greater opportunity for suburban stores. As cities grow, therefore, the CBD stores receive a smaller share of the retail business of suburban and rural portions of the trading area.

Table 1 presents data on the trading areas of department stores in 13

TABLE 1. Department Store Drawing Power, by Size of City and Extent of Trading Area

Size of City (Population)	Trading Area Extent (Miles)	PERCENT OF DEPARTMENT STORE SALES	
		Outside City	In City
15,000	15	45	55
40,000	20	30	70
50,000	40	35	65
60,000	15	40	60
60,000	20	50	50
150,000	25	30	70
200,000	20	35	65
225,000	15	25	75
350,000	15	10	90
350,000	50	20	80
450,000	50	25	75
750,000	60	10	90
1,000,000	50	10	90

cities of different size. These data show an inverse relationship between the drawing power of a store and the extent of its trading area. When these statistics are weighted by the proximity of competing cities and by traffic friction outside the city, the inverse relationship between drawing power and trading-area extent is more pronounced than indicated by the table.

A study of supermarkets in or near the CBD's of 40 towns and small cities affirms that as the size of a city increases, store drawing power beyond the city decreases, even though trading-area extent increases with city size (see Table 2). Because of greater frequency of trips to supermarkets than to department stores, traffic friction and competitive opportunities play a stronger role in affecting the drawing power of supermarkets than of department stores.

As stated previously, increased size of metropolitan areas, as well as of cities, increases the extent of their CBD store trading areas. However, increased size of the metropolitan area does not appear to result in decreased drawing power beyond the metropolitan area. An indication of this comes from an examination of the retail sales of standard metropolitan areas in relation to their populations. If drawing power to the hinterland increased with a decrease in size of metropolitan area, then per capita sales—calculated by dividing total retail sales of all stores in the metropolitan area by the population residing within the metropolitan area—would increase accordingly. However, this is not the case.

An analysis of the 1954 *U.S. Census of Business* data of annual per capita retail sales by metropolitan areas in the United States indicates a wide range, with no correlation with increased size. Among the first

TABLE 2. Drawing Power of Supermarkets, by Size of Cities

Size of City (Population)	Supermarket Sales Outside City	(Percent) In City
Under 2,500	50	50
2,500 to 10,000	40	60
10,000 to 20,000	35	65
20,000 to 40,000	25	75
40,000 to 60,000	15	85
Over 60,000	10	90

40 Standard Metropolitan Areas, the range of annual per capita retail sales is from $900 to $1,500. The figure for the largest Standard Metropolitan Area, New York, is $1,150; for the 40th, Fort Worth, it is $1,270. The median is $1,230. There appears to be no discernible order in the figures in relation to size of metropolitan areas.

While these data are inadequate for more than a tentative conclusion, the authors conjecture that highest per capita sales for the

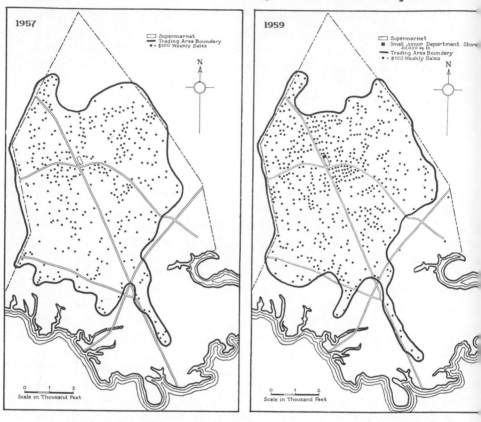

FIGURE 2: Effect of a small junior department store upon the trading area of a super market. Built as a free-standing unit in 1957, the supermarket shown on the map was joined in 1959 by a small junior department store. While the supermarket's trading area boundary has remained unchanged, per capita sales have increased by 15 percent

metropolitan area as a whole occur in metropolitan areas which have the largest number of planned regional shopping centers.[5] The occurrence of such shopping centers is not directly related to the size of metropolitan areas. Most of these planned regional shopping centers are on the fringes of metropolitan areas. They have extended their retailing influence much farther than ever before. Because most of these planned regional shopping centers are still surrounded by relatively sparse populations, and because their strongest pull is away from the CBD, their trading areas are extensive and their drawing power to the hinterland is high.

[5] Verification of this conjecture will be possible by studying the latest available data on planned shopping centers, the 1958 *Census of Business* data by metropolitan areas, and the 1960 population data, when published.

In the long run, as population density builds up around these planned regional shopping centers, drawing power can be anticipated to increase close to the center and to decrease in the hinterlands.

STORE ASSOCIATIONS / When a site is occupied by a combination of stores, the trading area of each store is affected by the trading area of its neighbors. In theory, the most extensive boundary of the most powerful store will also serve as the boundary of all other stores. In practice, however, the percentage of business that many stores obtain from the outermost portion of a retail district's trading area tends to be only slightly greater than if these stores were free-standing. The association of one store with another either helps to extend its drawing power or increases its per capita sales, or both. Where the drawing power of two stores is different, there is no assurance that the more powerful store will significantly affect the drawing power of the weaker store. Differences in customer shopping habits in patronizing the various stores concerned, as well as the location of stores that are competitive to the less powerful store, must be taken into account.

A study of the trading areas of 32 modern supermarkets, half in planned shopping centers containing department stores or large variety goods stores and half on free-standing highway sites, indicates that associated stores with considerably greater trading-area extent do expand the trading-area boundaries of the supermarkets; in many cases, a mile or so more than normal. Furthermore, by this association the drawing power of the supermarkets in the large planned shopping centers was 15 percent from beyond 3 miles, compared with 10 percent for the supermarkets on the free-standing sites. On the other hand, while small junior department stores may contribute to an increase in a supermarket's per capita sales they have little impact upon a supermarket's trading area (see Fig. 2).

Trading-Area Morphology

The size and shape of store trading areas are determined by location, population density, accessibility, natural and cultural features, competition, and store "personality."

TABLE 3. Effect of Population Density on Trading Area Extent and Drawing Power of Neighborhood-type Supermarkets

| | | | SUPERMARKET SALES (PERCENT) | |
Number of Stores	*Population Within One Mile of Store*	*Trading Area Extent (Miles)*	*Beyond One Mile*	*Within One Mile*
25	7,000	1½	75	25
20	17,000	1¾	60	40
20	27,000	2	50	50

SIZE OF TRADING AREA / As discussed in the sections devoted to store size and retail structure, the size of the trading area of a store (or of a group of stores) increases with the size of the store and with the size of the urbanized area, and the percentage of sales obtained from the more distant portions of the trading area varies inversely with the size of the city. In relating the latter phenomenon to specific stores, we find that population density affects a store's drawing power. This is demonstrated by the experiences of 65 neighborhood-type supermarkets, as presented in Table 3.

Dense populations attract larger and greater numbers of the same type of store to one focal point. The effect of such multiplication of store facilities is to extend the trading area for each store. Traffic friction, on the other hand, acts as a counterforce and serves to reduce the share of business that is obtained from more distant parts of this trading area.

Another observation that can be made is that the higher the income of the tributary population, the more extensive is the store's trading area and the greater the drawing power to the more distant parts of the trading area. Also, the more densely populated the rural parts of the trading area, the greater the drawing power of a store.

The role that accessibility plays in determining a store's trading area can be seen from mapping the trading areas of stores that lie close to

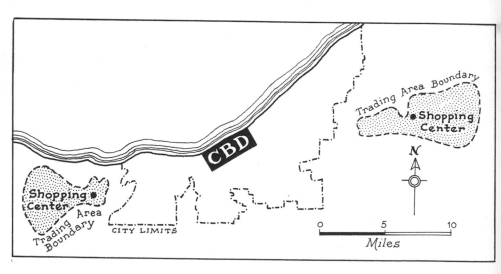

FIGURE 3: Shape of trading areas of suburban stores. Trading areas of suburban stores tend to be elliptical, with the longer axis trending away from the CBD. Customer-spotting maps of two medium-size suburban planned shopping centers are the basis for this figure.

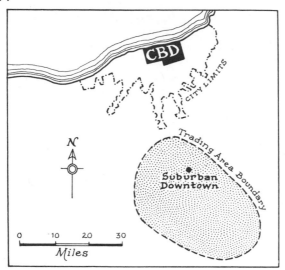

FIGURE 4: Impact of the CBD of a large city upon the shape of a suburban downtown trading area. This elliptical trading area presents the trading area of a downtown in a suburb of 60,000 population; the suburb is located within a large metropolitan area.

major intersections. Thus, differences in accessibility for two shopping strips on opposite sides of a rotary helped to account for a difference in trading-area extent of one and one-half miles.

SHAPE OF TRADING AREA / Theoretically, the hexagonal, triangular, or square trading areas offer the best possibilities for covering a market. In practice, however, street patterns play the most significant role in moulding such shapes, and frequently they run counter to what would be theoretically desirable. In cities with grid-type street patterns, store trading areas tend to be rectangular with amoeba-like extensions, and adequate coverage with least overlap is obtained. Natural and cultural features, such as rivers, railroads, greenbelts, escarpments, unpaved roads, and differences in population characteristics, can abort the shape of store trading areas at distances that vary with location types. Numerous examples can be cited. Caution should be exercised in evaluating such barriers. Where rivers are crossed by wide, toll-free bridges, where railroad tracks are in use at infrequent intervals, where well-maintained highways cut escarpments, there the barrier qualities of such features are nullified. Certain cultural features are more lasting barriers than physical features. For example, a political and cultural break between a fashionable suburb and a slum area tends to form a sharper trading area boundary than does a river. Also, such trading area boundaries occur in border zones between the white and Negro populaces of large northern U.S. cities. On the other hand, the general rise in living standards acts as a counterweight in blurring these distinctions.

The effects of competition upon the shapes of store trading areas can be seen most clearly from the relation of the trading areas of suburban stores to the CBD. Usually, the trading-area shapes of suburban stores are elliptical, with the longer axis trending away from tthe CBD. The trading-area shapes of suburban CBD's are similarly affected by the central-city CBD (see Figs. 3 and 4). In some instances, the competition of the CBD may create a hole within the shape of a large suburban store's trading area. This occurs when the CBD is in competition with large suburban department stores (see Fig. 5).

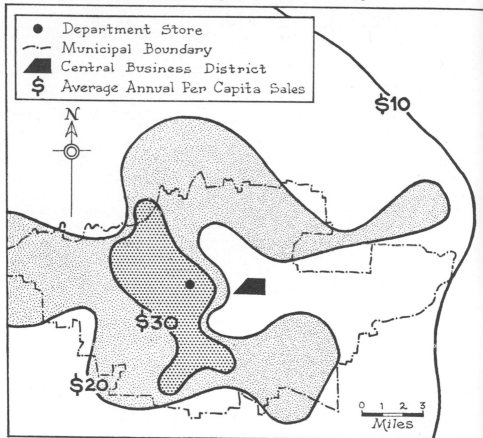

FIGURE 5: Effect of CBD as competitor of a large suburban department store illustrated by per capita sales contour map. Per capita sales contours are "pinched in" by the CBD; only $10 and $20 in annual per capita sales are being realized by the department store from the areas surrounding and east of the CBD.

Store "personality" refers to the customer's image of a store, formed on the basis of merchandise, price, services, and physical facilities. Store "personality" affects the trading area, even though this effect

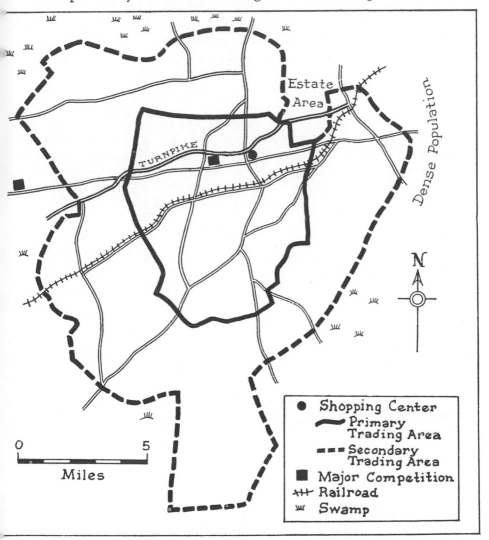

FIGURE 6: Effect of population, accessibility, physical and cultural features, and competition on shape of store trading area. The trading area shown is that of an outlying highway planned shopping center with moderately priced goods. Swamps, dense population to the east, and style-conscious estate dwellers to the northeast abort the secondary trading area. Major competition two miles to the west is too near to affect the boundary of the primary trading area. However, the location of a major shopping area 12 miles to the west does affect the western boundary of the planned shopping center's primary trading area—the boundary follows the breaking point between the two business centers.

eludes measurement. Marked uniqueness of store personality is likely to extend the trading area significantly. This is the case, for example, where a mill discount outlet carries the same broad lines of merchandise as a junior department store of the same size. The former features lower prices, frequently on lower quality merchandise.

While it is possible to isolate the specific effects of population, accessibility, physical and cultural features, and competition, usually a combination of these elements is involved. This is demonstrated through the mapping of a planned shopping center of medium size (see Fig. 6).

ARTERIES OF MOVEMENT / In general, store trading areas are elongated in the direction of customer movement (see Fig. 1). This tendency is qualified, however, by the distribution of population and competition, by access to and traffic friction along the artery. If the population tributary to a major highway is sparse, then, despite heavy traffic flow along the highway, the store does not draw much trade from this traffic flow.

Competing Stores

The effect of competing stores upon each other's trading area should be considered in a time dimension. The initial trading area of a store will be related to the location of existing competing facilities. A store's trading-area boundaries lie within a zone that forms the "trading divide" between this store and competing stores. Only when there is little or no population between two competing stores, or when the stores are very close together, do we find that competing stores exercise no impact upon each other's trading-area boundaries. Our studies of 15 large urbanized areas show that supermarkets which are within a half mile of one another serve the same general trading area and do not influence significantly each other's trading-area boundaries. The same applies to department stores within five miles of each other.

Once the trading-area boundaries of a store have been established, then these boundaries are not affected greatly by additional nearby competing stores. However, the store's market penetration is very likely to be affected adversely. This is not to say that new, nearby competing facilities do not abort, bend in, or create a gap within certain portions of the trading area of an existing store. But in broad, meaningful terms, the boundaries remain fairly constant (see Fig. 7).

What has been said above refers to competing stores that belong to different companies. The competitive impact of a store belonging to the same company is quite different. A store's strongest competitor is a sister store with similar facilities. The trading-area boundaries of a store that is confronted with competition by a new store of the same company tend to shift and seek a trading divide. Figure 8 shows how the trading-area boundaries of a CBD supermarket changed as a second

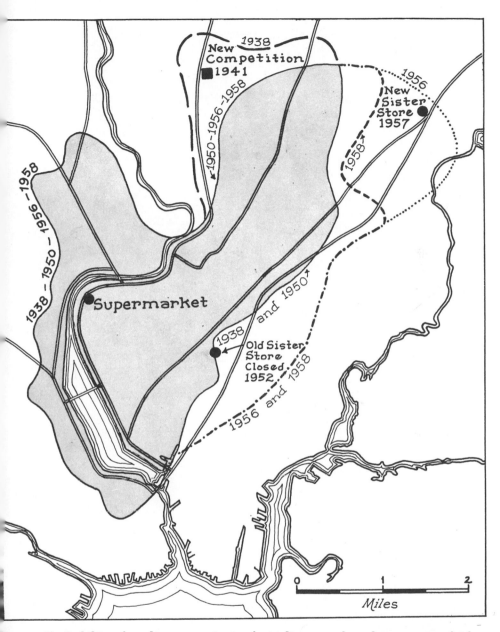

FIGURE 7: Stability of trading area. A store's trading area boundary remains fairly constant over long periods of time. Customer-spotting studies in 1938, 1950, 1956, and 1958 are the basis for this map. The supermarket was built in 1938. Significant boundary changes have occurred only in the areas affected by the 1957 opening and the 1952 closing of sister stores, and by the construction in 1941 of a considerably larger competitive store with better facilities.

379

and then a third supermarket were built in the town by the same company.

Internal Components

A store trading area contains within it individual houses, city blocks, neighborhoods, large urban areas, a metropolitan region, and sometimes even larger geographic units. These parts of a store's trading area are the internal components. They have different sales values to a store

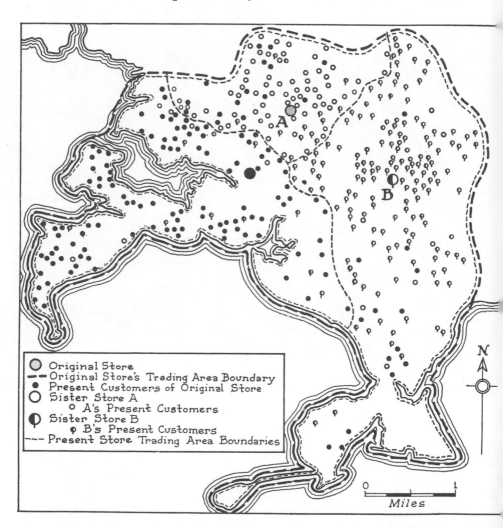

FIGURE 8: Impact of competition on a store's trading area. A store's strongest competitors are its sister stores. With the building of sister stores A and B, the trading area boundary of the original supermarket shown has shrunk to one-fourth of its original extent.

and must be studied to understand the complex nature of a store's trading area.

To differentiate these different components, various criteria are employed: share of market, driving time, traffic flow, location of competition, and drawing power.[6]

A major share of the market is often used to mark off one part of the trading area from another. While a retail district may obtain more than half of the available business of a given area, individual stores rarely secure a major share of the available business of any substantial part of the trading area.

Driving time (determined by mode of travel, traffic friction, individual driving habits, weather, accessibility, and parking) can be a useful criterion if the values of the units of time used as measurements are related to actual sales experience.

Breaks in traffic-flow density can be useful as a rough guide in differentiating trading-area components; however, total traffic density may not be a good indicator of traffic density for shopping purposes.

Location of competition as reference points in establishing the components of a store's trading area is useful only for broad generalizations which do not give due consideration to the element of overlap of store trading areas.

[6] Examples of various criteria for differentiating the internal components of a store's trading area are:
A. *Share of the market.* "The uncontested trading area is that part of the trading area in which the great majority of business goes to the retail center." August Lösch, *The Economics of Location,* transl. by William H. Woglom (New Haven: Yale University Press, 1954), map p. 418.
B. *Driving time.* "The critical point at which the maximum effectiveness [of the shopping center] decreases varies less than might be expected in terms of driving distance and driving time for regional shopping centers regardless of size. The primary trade area is the area of strongest influence, normally three to six miles [12 to 15 minutes] from the site." Gruen and Smith, *op. cit.,* pp. 33 and 278.
C. *Traffic flow.* "The Traffic Stabilization boundary is that portion of the Urban Market that lies at the center of the Trading Area in which there is from the center of the city . . . a relatively high and continuous density of population. This can be marked by the traffic stabilization point . . . the point outward from which there is no further rapid decrease of traffic volume." Paver and McClintock, *op. cit.,* p. 52.
D. *Drawing power.* "Normally, the trade area is divided into zones which indicate variations in the drawing power and strength of the development in different portions of its tributary areas. These zones are usually called the primary, secondary and tertiary zones of the trade area." *Definitions of Terms* (Washington, D.C.: Larry Smith & Co., 1960), p. 2.
E. *Location of competition.* "The primary trade area—the close, walk-in area that has daily convenience stores closer than a site under investigation; the secondary trade area—the area which has . . . no important soft line and hard line stores or shopping goods stores with more convenient access than the site; the country or fringe trade area—the area which may be closer to department and apparel stores, but from which customers might be drawn because of greater parking conveniences and better merchandise to be offered." Wehrly and McKeever, *op. cit.,* p. 136.

Drawing power is a useful criterion in differentiating trading-area components. However, its usefulness depends on giving proper weights to differences in population density and purchasing power.

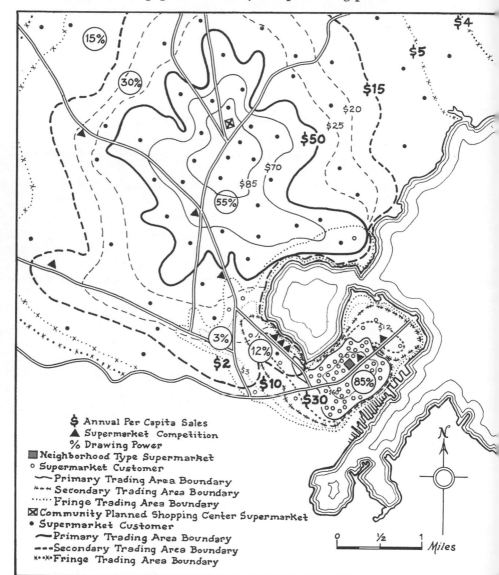

FIGURE 9: Sales penetration and drawing power of two supermarkets, one in a planned shopping center, the other in an older neighborhood business district. Per capita sales of the neighborhood store are lower and drawing power is more intensive, because of the greater competition and traffic friction encountered in the neighborhood location. The store in the planned shopping center, on the other hand, encounters a minimum of competition and traffic friction.

Various terms are used to describe trading-area components. *Primary, secondary,* and *fringe* are perhaps the most common. These terms are often used ambiguously. For a large retail district, say a CBD, "primary" may be used to designate that part of the trading area from which a major share of the total market potential is obtained. For individual stores, "primary" usually means the largest single share of only a fraction of the total market potential.

We suggest that the components of the trading area be differentiated on the basis of the sales penetration and drawing power of a store (or group of stores) within the trading area. This combination of judiciously selected measurements offers a sound, practical method for evaluating and mapping the internal components.

The per capita sales of a store, i.e., a store's retail sales per person (per week or per annum), measure the extent of a store's sales penetration of a trading area. This measurement represents differences in the store's influence upon customers in different parts of the trading area. Per capita sales can be weighted for differences in purchasing power for more meaningful comparisons, and can be adjusted for price index changes, where comparisons over time are needed. Such weightings and adjustments are essential to arrive at sales penetration in terms of share of market. Drawing power quantifies the relative sales value of that component to the store. Thus the selected drawing-power criterion designates the proportionate value of the component, and the selected per capita sales contour outlines the boundary of the component (see Fig. 9).

Customer-spotting maps, which show the varying density of customer distribution, can serve as the guides to the selection of drawing-power criteria for establishing internal components of a trading area. Customer-distribution density varies for different types of stores and for different locations. Our experience leads us to designate the primary trading area of supermarkets in large planned shopping centers as that area which contains somewhat more than half of all the customers; for neighborhood supermarkets the primary trading area is designated to contain up to 85 percent of all the customers. For department stores and large planned shopping centers, we would designate the primary trading area as that component which embraces 50 to 70 percent of all customers; the secondary trading area, 30 to 20 percent; the fringe, 20 to 10 percent.

In mapping store trading areas, we have found it practical to include in the primary trading area the area in which per capita sales are at least twice those of the secondary trading area. Similarly, the per capita sales in the secondary trading area are at least three times those of the fringe trading area, and, usually, much more. If customers are so thinly diffused in the fringe trading area that meaningful measurement of per capita sales cannot be made, then the fringe trading area is described only in terms of drawing power—i.e., percent of sales obtained from beyond the secondary trading area. The inclusion of the fringe-area sales in the total is essential to bring the measurements up to 100 percent.

Per capita sales vary by type of store and type of location. Therefore, in differentiating between primary, secondary, and fringe trading areas, it is necessary to select different per capita sales as units of measurement for each store type and location type. In general, greatest sales penetration can be expected for those types of stores which are most specialized and least numerous, with high-priced and slow-turnover goods. In the fringe trading areas, however, per capita sales as measures of penetration are likely to be more nearly equal for various types of stores. Studies of fringe areas of both supermarkets and department stores indicate that per capita sales account for 1 to 2 percent of the market.[7] This fact is probably due to relatively less frequent customer visits from the fringe trading areas to department stores than from the fringe trading area to supermarkets.

The boundary between primary trading area and secondary trading area appears to be affected by the location of competition, but not the boundary between the secondary and fringe trading areas.

We have found that for supermarkets in neighborhood locations, the boundary lines of the supermarket's primary trading area were unaffected by the location of competition within a half mile of the store. Where competition was located from three fourths of a mile to one and one-half miles away, the location of these competing stores marked the edge of the primary trading-area boundary. Where competition was located beyond one and one-half miles, the boundary of the primary trading area lay midway between the supermarket and the competing store. For supermarkets located within large planned shopping centers, the location of competing stores within one and one-half to two miles (along the routes of major highways) did not affect the boundary of the former's primary trading areas.

External Boundaries

Store trading-area boundaries tend to remain fixed. Changes occur mainly because of the impact of competition from new stores belonging to the same company. A radical change in transportation can also change the boundary.

By fixed boundaries, however, is not meant complete rigidity. Store trading-area boundaries shift within a zone. In certain instances, these shifts take place over a relatively brief period. Customer-shopping hab-

[7] This share of the market is obtained by relating a store's actual per capita sales to estimated available business. Available department store and supermarket business is estimated on the basis of $100 per capita per annum for the former and $325 for the latter.

its in the United States are such that persons living a considerable distance from supermarkets tend to concentrate their shopping towards the
end of the week, while those living close by spread their more frequent shopping trips throughout the week. Thus, there is a measurable
difference in the trading area of a supermarket at the beginning versus
the end of the week.

Store trading areas also vary according to changes in seasonal population. A store that serves an area with a large influx of summer residents experiences an "extended" trading area in serving these people.
This does not necessarily mean a blanket extension of the trading area.
While adding close-by summer resort sections, the influx of seasonal
population, increased traffic friction, and more (seasonal) competition
at other points may exclude certain distant parts of the store's winter
trading area. (See Fig. 10 for examples of seasonal fluctuations in a

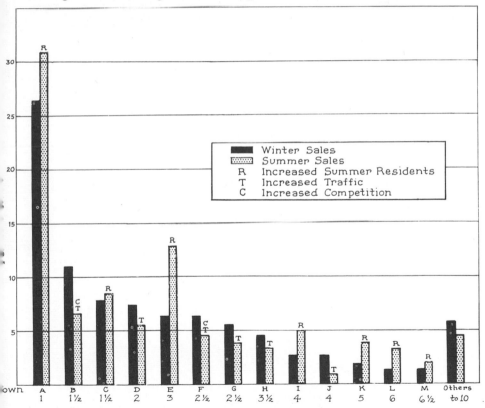

FIGURE 10: Seasonal fluctuations in a store's drawing power as influenced by competition and traffic friction. This large supermarket's sales are twice as high in summer as
in winter. In general, the drawing power of this store is more extensive during the
summer because of an increase in population in the outlying areas. However, competition and traffic friction decrease the drawing power in much of the 1½- to 3½-mile zones.

supermarket's drawing power.) A special events sale, with extraordinary advertising power, also may extend a store's trading area, albeit for a very brief time.

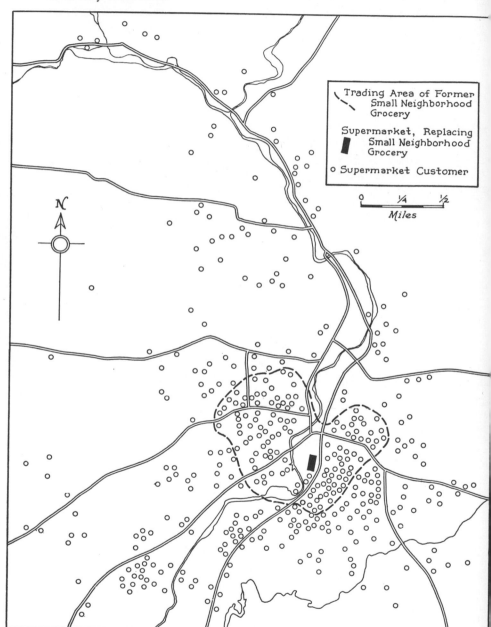

FIGURE 11: Effect of change in functions of a store on trading area boundaries. This change is illustrated by the replacement of a small grocery store by a modern supermarket.

The permanence of a store's trading area lasts only so long as the store carries out the same functions. If, for example, a store is replaced by the same type of store with improved merchandising facilities only, then the trading area may remain unchanged, although the market penetration may improve. This point is illustrated by Figure 7. The original store was one of the early self-service supermarkets located on a highway. When replaced a decade later by a new, more modern unit, its trading area did not appreciably change, but its penetration did change very markedly.

If the functions of a store change significantly, as reflected by changes in the merchandise mix and in service, trading area boundaries tend to change. Figure 11 illustrates this point by comparing the boundary of a CBD service food store that was replaced by a modern supermarket. Similarly, where a modern supermarket was replaced by a very large, combination supermarket-general merchandise store, a marked change in trading area occurred (see Fig. 12, stage 3).

Hierarchical Networks of Trading Areas

Within a given market, each store acts as the focus for a particular trading area. The pattern of the network formed by the trading areas of all stores serving a market is intricate, both because of the overlap of trading areas of stores of the same type and because of the superposition of different orderings of trading areas.

Two forces in particular influence the pattern of store trading-area networks. One force is the central-place role of each store. Lösch and others have stated that market areas for the same branches of business resemble even-meshed nets of hexagons, and that stores serving these networks tend to be as close to their population centers as possible.[8]

The second force—in a sense a counterforce—is the competing facilities. While enterprises seek to find in the existing trading-area network a "gap" large enough for successful investment, such "gaps" cannot always be found. Therefore, a forward-looking enterprise may endeavor to create a new arrangement of networks in the market area. This is done by seeking new locations on modern transportation arteries, more frequently focal, but at times eccentric, to the existing population. The site requirements generally can be found only on highway locations and

---

[8] August Lösch writes, "The market networks for nonagricultural enterprises are widely spread out in space . . . 'belts' disturb our theoretical economic geometry much less than districts do, for example." Lösch, *op. cit.*, p. 372.

Edgar M. Hoover states: "There is an internal contradiction in Lösch's theory. The hexagonal market (or supply) areas that he made assume a uniform density of demand (or supply); but once he has established his concentrations of production, demand and supply are thenceforth not uniformly distributed any more and the hexagons ought to be of different sizes and shapes." Correspondence, December, 1959.

large tracts of land suitable for the new type of store, with its superior facilities and merchandising techniques. This new type of store generates enough merchandising power to create a new trading area of considerable magnitude. As the number of such new store trading areas is multiplied, a new network of trading areas is created.

As stated, the problem of finding "gaps" in the existing arrangement is complex. One company may consider a gap to exist when 20 percent of an entire market area is not served adequately by existing store facilities. Another company, however, with a policy of building high-volume stores, may not consider that a gap exists in this market, because the available "surplus" (potential) is insufficient to meet this company's store-volume needs.

What compounds the problem is that a company with a number of established stores in a given market is certain to lose ground in some of its locations, as competitive conditions change. Hence, it must be growing elsewhere or it faces decline, and even possible disaster. A business enterprise must be able to sustain dynamic growth from its own resour-

TABLE 4. Generalized Example of Trading Area Components by Per Capita Sales

| | | ANNUAL PER CAPITA SALES BOUNDARIES | | |
Store Type	Annual Sales Volume	Primary Trading Area	Secondary Trading Area	Fringe Trading Area
Department store	$12,000,000	$30	$15	$3
Discount store	8,000,000	20	8	2
Supermarket (in large shopping center)	2,500,000	50	15	4
Junior department store	2,000,000	13	5	2

ces, by generating profits. Without dynamic growth, there can be no survival. Dynamic growth means keeping pace with market opportunity changes; it also means changing physical facilities to keep pace with competition. A business, therefore, must rejuvenate itself by replacing its outmoded facilities and must increase in size through building additional facilities.

The growth of a business enterprise can take place by expansion into completely new territories, and by filling existing gaps or rearranging trading-area networks. There is a distinction, however, between, on the one hand, creating new store trading areas that mesh in with existing trading areas, and, on the other hand, creating new store trading areas that overlap or lie completely within existing store trading areas. Under

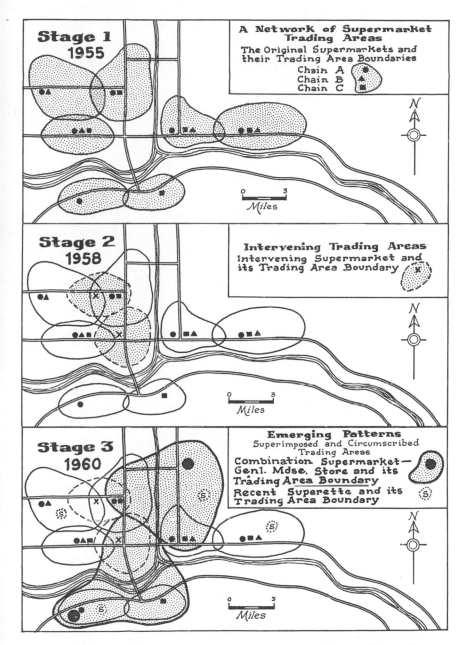

FIGURE 12: Rearrangement of store trading area networks as additional stores enter market area. Stage 1 represents the trading area networks formed by groups of supermarkets in a small metropolitan area in 1955. Stage 2 shows that in 1958 new supermarkets found room within the market area by taking up intermediate locations. Stage 3 shows that in 1960 new stores were opened, designed to perform radically different functions, reflected by their superimposed or circumscribed trading areas.

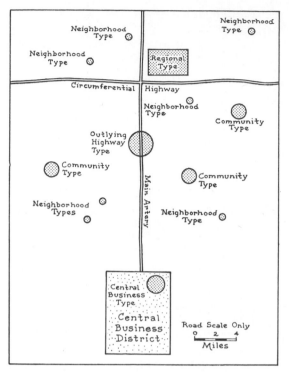

FIGURE 13: Schematic presentation of the location of planned shopping centers in metropolitan areas. In examining existing planned shopping center patterns, it was found that the outward side of regional shopping centers generally supports only small, not medium-size centers.

the former condition, store trading-area networks are filled in "harmoniously"; under the latter, complete "surgical" rearrangements occur.

Where, for example, a store is built at the juncture of two separate store trading areas, and this store is comparable to its surrounding competitors, the new store adds a third, intervening, trading area which overlaps segments of the other two trading areas and becomes part of the existing network. Figure 12 illustrates examples of both complementary store trading-area networks and new ones that rearrange the network. This map shows how a city of 100,000 population has been divided into a number of discrete store trading areas by 30 supermarkets. The most recently built supermarkets have not moved into gaps within existing trading areas; nor have they complemented the trading-area network by taking up intervening locations. Instead, they have quadrupled their size, have introduced in some instances a complete line of nonfoods, and are in the process of rearranging the trading-area network.

Another type of rearrangement occurs in smaller cities and towns when important new retail facilities are developed at the periphery of the town. Thus, whereas formerly the town had only one trading area tributary to the CBD, the new arrangement results in additional and overlapping trading areas.

New sets of small trading areas are created within existing larger trading areas by establishing stores with modern facilities to capitalize on special customer demand for convenience of location (see Fig. 12, stage 3).

The hierarchy of store trading-area networks in the Anglo-American city has been made more complex by the spectacular post-World War II growth of suburbia and the advent of the planned shopping center. Utilizing the classification presented earlier, Figure 13 presents this hierarchy schematically. This diagram indicates that while community and neighborhood planned shopping centers are found between regional shopping centers and the CBD, usually only neighborhood planned shopping centers are found on the outward-facing side of the regional shopping center. This development results from the sparser population density on the outward-side of the regional shopping center and, correspondingly, also fewer "interceptor" locations.

Two remarkable facts about planned shopping centers are: (1) the ease and speed of their emergence within the market area, and (2) their impact upon new and existing shopping facilities. Either real estate developers or retailer-owned real estate enterprises are the prime movers responsible for the planned shopping center. These are men and firms with force and determination who have promoted and effected concentrations of modern shopping facilities almost overnight.

These new shopping-facility concentrations may have, depending perhaps on one's point of view, either good or bad effects upon the retail structure of a city, but certainly the effects are profound. The impact of new planned shopping centers on older store facilities, particularly the CBD, varies considerably with three factors: (1) growth of population and the corresponding need for new store facilities, (2) relative amount and kind of new store facilities provided by planned shopping centers, and (3) response and countermeasures taken by merchants operating existing older store facilities to meet the new competition. The relative importance of the CBD's share of the total retail sales in metropolitan areas is adversely affected by the competition of the planned shopping centers.

Many of the planned shopping centers house stores with higher- and medium-priced goods, which appeal mainly to the middle and higher income groups of their trading areas. In these instances, lower-priced stores or strips of stores tend to locate near these planned shopping centers to tap essentially the lower income group of the same trading area.

The planned shopping center can upset equilibrium as it competes with older facilities. But it can also upset equilibrium by forcing retailers to concentrate new facilities rather than to spread them uniformly. In smaller cities, in particular, leading retailers may not be enthusiastic about a planned shopping center, but they also may not dare to stay out of the development. Furthermore, if a developer insists on having two stores of the same type in a shopping center, then even though an operator may prefer another location or may desire to wait for further population growth, he may nonetheless enter the shopping center to keep a competitor out. Thus, overbuilding of stores or poor distribution of retail facilities within the market may result.

In general, the larger the retail district, the greater the percent of retail sales to total sales obtained by shopping-goods establishments in that district; the smaller the retail district, the greater the percent of sales obtained by convenience-goods stores. The pattern of store trading-area networks is one in which the CBD trading area has been superimposed upon the entire metropolitan area. Secondary business districts attempt to compete with the CBD, and their smaller trading areas lie within that of the CBD. The string developments that adjoin the CBD, with their heavy emphasis on automotive and furniture stores, duplicate the CBD in the total coverage of the metropolitan area, just as strips adjoining the secondary business districts duplicate the latter.

Within this framework are the convenience neighborhood or isolated stores whose small trading areas form islands within the trading areas of greater magnitude.

While planned shopping centers of various sizes generally exhibit the same hierarchical patterns of trading areas as do unplanned business districts, there are important deviations. Essentially these deviations result from the types of stores found in the planned shopping centers.

Planned shopping centers offer advantages of proximity to home, ease of parking, minimum traffic friction, and space for large stores. Here the customer can shop comfortably not only for food and other convenience goods but also for a wide selection of general merchandise. Thus, food stores may account for only 5 percent of the total sales within a large CBD, but for as much as 20 percent of the total sales of a regional planned shopping center. Shopping-goods stores, on the other hand, may account for only 10 percent of the total sales of a neighborhood business district and 20 percent of total sales of a neighborhood shopping center.

The trend to a higher percentage of convenience-goods sales in large planned shopping centers and to a higher percentage of shopping-goods sales in small planned shopping centers can result in a more uniform distribution of planned shopping centers than now exists. Furthermore, the altered association of stores in the planned shopping centers may effect a greater coincidence of individual store trading areas for the different stores within a given shopping center.

Few planned shopping centers have been built in association with other business activities—large numbers of offices, wholesaling and manufacturing plants. Consequently, even the largest of the regional planned shopping centers cannot exert a power of penetration commensurate with that exerted by the competing CBD, in superimposing its

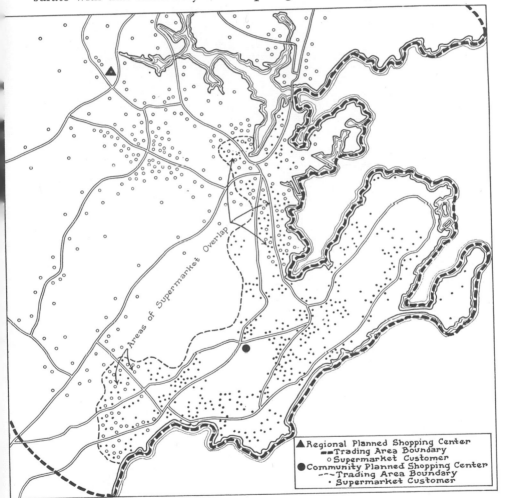

FIGURE 14: Variation in overlap of store trading areas. While there is trading area overlap for planned shopping centers of differing sizes and functions, this overlap does not apply to all stores within the centers. Two modern sister supermarkets, one located in a regional planned shopping center and the other in a smaller center show a very limited overlap in their respective trading areas.

trading area upon the trading areas of other planned shopping centers of lesser magnitude. Thus, while the trading area of a large planned shopping center is superimposed upon that of a smaller planned shopping center, there is not a complete overlap for all stores. Figure 14 shows this. Here a full-line department store exists in the former but not in the latter shopping center. For the supermarket of the larger shopping center, however, the existence within the smaller shopping center of another modern supermarket belonging to the same company limits its power to superimpose its trading area.

Store Saturation and Market Equilibrium

Store Saturation

Store saturation of a market is a condition under which existing store facilities are utilized efficiently and meet customer needs adequately. When a market has just enough store facilities of a given type to serve the population of the market satisfactorily and yield a fair return to the owners on their investments, without raising prices to the customer to achieve this return, then saturation exists for the given type of store. When a market has too few stores to provide satisfactorily the needs of the customer, it is *understored*. When a market area has too many stores to yield a fair return on investment, it is *overstored*.

Static and Dynamic Equilibrium

Store saturation is an ephemeral condition, for balance between facilities and their use cannot be rigidly maintained in an inherently dynamic situation. Additional facilities or changes in merchandising techniques or in the geographical environment will upset the balance.

The tendency is for stores of the same type to equal each other in size insofar as market opportunities permit. Such equality in size becomes a competitive offensive and defensive necessity to satisfy customers and achieve optimum operation and/or merchandising efficiencies in a given marketing environment. If all companies expand store facilities beyond the needs of the market, then a situation is created where all have lowered their productivity in terms of sales per square foot of selling area.

Disturbance in equilibrium may occur if anticipated population increases fail to materialize or if an area is depopulated. It may take place if there is a basic change in the transportation pattern, opening the existing trading area to outside competition. It may occur if customer shopping habits, affected by mode and frequency of travel, alter radically.

If the balance between need and availability of store facilities is restored without appreciably altering the existing trading-area pattern, then the period of imbalance can be described as one of "short-run disequilibrium." Such a restoration of balance occurs in situations when understoring is corrected through the building of additional store facilities to keep pace with population growth. This type of restoration may take place in fast-growing suburban areas where subdivisions of a few thousand homes may spring up overnight. It may also take place in mature areas, such as the inner portions of central cities which become engulfed by the immigration of younger persons with large families, for example, in cities in the northern United States which receive annually thousands of immigrants from the South. Such restoration can occur under conditions of overstoring through growth of population, or through the elimination of some unprofitable facilities.

At times, however, the balance between the availability of and need for store facilities can only be restored through innovations in facilities, through vastly improved uses of existing facilities, or through changes in merchandising techniques. These revolutionary changes usually seek lower operating costs, and/or greater customer satisfactions—in the form of lower prices, a more pleasing shopping environment, or increased services. The period of imbalance that marks such changes is one of "long-run disequilibrium."

As innovations in facilities and merchandising techniques are made (see Fig. 12), networks of new trading-area patterns are introduced. This process was set in motion as: (1) grocery stores gave way to supermarkets, movie houses to drive-in theaters, corner gasoline stations to super-service stations, dry goods stores to self-service general merchandise stores, and drug stores to super-drug stores, and (2) planned shopping centers emerged in competition with older business districts.

When saturation or balance is restored under short-run conditions, the equilibrium that is established might be described as "static equilibrium." When balance is restored under long-run conditions, the equilibrium might be described as "dynamic equilibrium."

In viewing the pattern of the location of retail facilities through a system of equilibrium, we consider the following among the disturbing factors that constantly operate within the environment to upset equilibrium: changes in population, accessibility, merchandise assortment, purchasing power, demand, retail facilities, shopping and buying habits, and concepts of profitability margin or return on investment. These changes bring about conditions representing either a lack or an excess of needed store facilities. The periods of imbalance, or disequilibrium, are lengthy and saturation, the point of equilibrium, is brief in time and in space. Yet it is equilibrium which is the basis for an orderly arrangement of patterns of retailing facilities, for it is the constant goal (see Fig. 15).

How to Measure Saturation

Measurement of saturation is a matter of professional interest to economists, geographers, and city planners, and of practical concern to businessmen. Several approaches may be taken:

1. Number of persons per retail establishment. The national or regional norm of the number of persons per specific type of store is calculated from available census or other statistical data. Similarly, the number of people for the same type of store is calculable for the given market; the figure thus obtained is compared with the national or regional norm to measure saturation.

2. Available retail expenditures per retail establishment. The number of persons times per capita retail expenditures for specific types of goods is calculated for the given market. The figure obtained is compared with national or regional averages. There are many difficulties in using this measurement: No allowance is made for differences in store size. Average purchasing power disguises too many relevant factors. Different income groups may buy different things or in different amounts. People buy different goods at different times in their lives; thus the same number of toy stores serving a youthful population will provide an excess of facilities to this population as it ages.

3. Number of persons per store-front footage. The data for a given market are compared with averages determined in other studies, made mostly by city planners. This does not take into account multiple-story

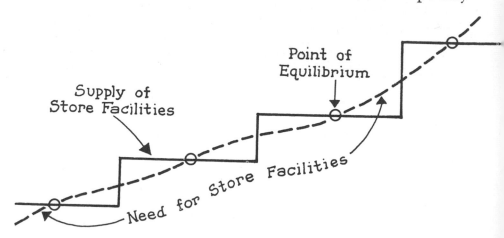

FIGURE 15: Schematic presentation of store equilibrium. Equilibrium is the basis for an orderly arrangement of patterns of retailing facilities, for it is the constant goal. Here equilibrium is presented schematically as the point of balance between the need for store facilities and the supply of store facilities.

facilities. Store frontage without store depth is not a true index of store area, and city blocks differ in depth. Frequently, in older areas stores expand their frontage but do not expand their depth correspondingly; whereas in newer areas buildings can be extended in depth more readily.

4. Ratio of store vacancies to total stores. This ratio can be measured on the basis of number of vacant store or vacant floor area. Many vacancies imply overstoring. However, lack of vacancies may not mean the converse, because many stores do not use their space fully or effectively.

5. Sales per square foot of selling area. This, in our opinion, does measure productivity and efficiency of use of space. Therefore it is suggested as the basic measure of saturation. (The use of sales per square foot of total store area gives lesser comparability than sales per square foot of selling area.)

There are capacity norms of selling-area productivity for various types of retail business. Related to these sales-capacity norms are rentals and other operating costs. For example, supermarket operators are not likely to establish a store at a given location if estimated annual potential sales per square foot of selling area are not likely to exceed $150 or even more. Many department-store operators are not likely to build new facilities if these facilities cannot generate estimated annual sales of at least $100 per square foot of selling area.

As with all standards, there are difficulties in using the measure of sales per square foot of selling area. Some of these difficulties are:

1. Differences in company policies, among enterprises within the same type of retailing, result in variations in the percentage of total store area devoted to selling area. For various operating reasons, some companies devote more store space than others to storage, preparation of goods, office use, etc.

2. Changes in price index require statistical adjustments of per capita sales figures for comparability.

3. Differences and changes in the merchandise mix (i.e., variety and quality of type of goods) handled also require weighting of measurement standards. If one store devotes 15 percent of its space to slow-moving merchandise, and a second store only 5 percent, then sales per square foot of selling area are not strictly comparable unless adjustment is made for the difference. Quality differences present a similar problem. In any case available information may not be adequate to avoid some margin of error.

4. Because of differences in number of hours per week that stores are open for business, some stores use their selling facilities more inten-

sively than other stores. While sales productivity per square foot is stepped up by such more intensive use of store facilities, normal sales become more spread out or diffused and the additional operating expenses incurred may exceed the gains from higher sales per square foot. To make meaningful measurement adjustments for these differences is a complicated task.

5. Finally, there are differences in merchandising methods. Self-service merchandising generally means a more rapid turnover of goods and higher sales per square foot of selling area than does service merchandising. Mail order business can be done from a desk with little or no merchandise on the premises. Similarly, sales to customers over the telephone require little selling area. Judicious allowances must be made for these complicating factors in using sales per square foot of selling area as a measurement of store saturation.

In spite of these difficulties, sales per square foot of selling area is the most significant broad guide to store productivity that we can find. The smaller the sales area in relation to sales:

1. The less the investment in land, building, and fixtures.
2. The less the inventory on display and hence the greater the turnover.
3. The fewer the steps for employees.
4. The less the time that is consumed by customers in completing their purchases.

Thus, higher sales per square foot of sales area means greater return on investment. If sales per square foot of selling area are unusually high, and where customers are inconvenienced in travel to shop (too far) and while shopping (too crowded and slow), then a situation of understoring exists. Where the reverse is the case, overstoring exists. Thus, while supermarkets with annual sales of $150 per square foot of selling area represent the norm for new stores, sales of $300 per square foot would indicate understoring and sales of $100 per square foot, overstoring.

Attempts have been made to measure productivity on the basis of profits per square foot of selling area, or on the basis of potential sales per square foot of selling area. The former, however, requires too many adjustments to make the measure meaningful for comparative analysis; the latter is unrealistic for practical application.

Store Saturation at Various Organization Levels and for Various Market Areas

Understoring, saturation, and overstoring for a given type of store occur on two levels: for the group as a whole, and for specific companies within the group. Thus, in a given self-contained market area of 500,000 persons, there might be 400,000 square feet of department store selling area, and annual sales might average $125 per square foot. Since $100 per square foot of selling area is the generally accepted capacity norm for department stores, the market area could be regarded as under-stored.

If, however, within this market area one company already accounts for one-quarter of the total department store sales, then the company might consider the market saturated with respect to itself. Few department store companies seek more than 30 percent of the total market in metropolitan areas of this size.

For each company, there is a diminishing return on investment if it seeks to obtain too great a share of the market. When this occurs, competition reacts through expansion of facilities or stronger merchandising. The company in question, then, to hold its share of the market, must increase services or lower prices, thus reducing its return on investment.

Saturation, as expressed by share of market goals for individual companies, varies with the strength and philosophy of the company and with the general market area served. In larger metropolitan areas, some chain department-store companies set 20 percent of the market as saturation, while in smaller metropolitan areas saturation is set at 30 percent. Similarly, chain supermarket companies set their saturation goals for nonmetropolitan areas at 25 to 30 percent of the market, and at 10 to 15 percent of the market in large urbanized areas. This difference springs from two considerations: (1) The amount of sales needed to support a modern store facility in nonmetropolitan areas can be achieved only by getting large per capita sales. (2) In metropolitan areas there are usually a number of strong companies competing with each other and the sales are divided more evenly among them.

Within a given market, saturation for individual companies can vary with company policy. In some cases, saturation is established by set minimum goals of store-sales for new stores. If the gaps between or within existing trading areas do not promise such minimum sales, then the market is overstored for this company. One national chain in the United States does not establish a new supermarket unless estimated sales are at least $1,000,000. A leading regional chain has set $2,000,000 as its minimum of new supermarket annual sales. An aggressive local chain seeks minimum sales of $3,000,000 for its new supermarkets. Thus, areas that are overstored for the last company may not be overstored for the first two. Furthermore, if the local chain decides to change its policy on store sales goals, the market may offer it opportunities for opening smaller supermarkets. On the other hand, the store "personality" of the aggressive local chain may be powerful enough to attract $3,000,000 annual sales, in part from existing stores operated by the national chain and by the regional chain, in spite of the overstoring.

A supermarket company may be willing, because of a desire to add store facilities, to lower its yardsticks for saturation in another way: it may set saturation at $125 per square foot of selling area, rather than the industry's capacity norm of $150. This desire may be based upon a number of considerations:

1. To gain better purchasing terms.
2. To provide or make better use of warehousing facilities.
3. To provide more retail outlets for its own processed goods.
4. To reduce relative costs of advertising or store supervision.
5. To anticipate future store space requirements for handling additional lines of goods.

Scrambling of Merchandise

If all retail stores sold the same goods in the same manner, the conditions for market equilibrium would be met by small, compact trading areas surrounding each store. The stores would be uniformly spread, insofar as the distribution of population and lines of transportation would permit. Of course, instead of a more or less uniform spread of stores, all of these general retail facilities could be clustered in a compact belt. But this has not happened. Rather than serving as general stores for all goods, retail stores have specialized along particular lines, benefiting from specialized facilities, merchandising skills, and operational techniques.

The customer's choice of specialized offerings of goods versus generalized offerings is the basis for store trading area differentiation. The fewer the number of stores that carry the same item, the more extensive are their trading areas. The less frequent the number of visits needed to replace an item, the more extensive is the trading area from which these customers come. Conversely, the greater the number of stores that carry the same item, and the more frequent customer visits are needed to replace these items, the less extensive is the trading area.

For a number of years now there has been a tendency in the United States for the specialized retail outlets to scramble their merchandise mix by taking on lines traditionally sold by other types of store. Thus self-service dry goods stores have taken on appliances; super-drugstores have extended lines to include variety, hardware, and general merchandise; supermarkets have added health and beauty aids, housewares, and garden supplies, and are now expanding into soft goods.

In some instances, stores do extend their trading areas by scrambling their goods. On the other hand, by scrambling goods, stores may concentrate more of their sales in nearby areas and decrease their drawing power to the more distant parts of the trading area.

Two forces intensify the scrambling of merchandise: (1) economy of scale derived from larger buildings, larger parking lots, and a wider variety of goods that can be sold under one roof, and (2) the planned shopping center, which stimulates other stores to try to duplicate all of the one-stop shopping offered by the shopping center. The granting of "monopoly" positions to national and regional chains by American shopping-center developers, at the expense of independent merchants or small chains, has speeded the development of large combination food and general merchandise stores and all-purpose discount stores adjacent to shopping centers or on the fringes of their trading areas. This is quite different from parts of Europe where independent merchants are so firmly entrenched as to restrain the development of large chains.

Scrambling of merchandise occurs also in stores located within planned shopping centers through duplication of lines carried. There are many instances where half a dozen stores within a shopping center will devote space to the same types of goods, frequently of the same brands or varying little, if any, in quality and price. The element of association with successful neighbors, and the desire to secure a larger share of the customer's expendable income are reasons for this.

There are, of course, such limitations to scrambling as cost of operation, space, merchandise knowledge, and restriction or other means of regulation (liquor permits, zoning ordinances, lease restrictions to the sale of goods).

Scrambling of merchandise also leads to wider selection, more attractive pricing and better presentation than does specializing. But in the long run, if scrambling is to lead stores outside shopping centers to duplicate shopping centers, or shopping centers to try to duplicate one another by appealing to the same types of customers through the same lines of medium- to high-priced merchandise, then store locations, as a whole, will take on a more uniform distribution pattern.

Competition and Market Equilibrium

A competitor who miscalculates and overbuilds can create disequilibrium. A powerful competitor who overbuilds can ruin others. A weak competitor who miscalculates can ruin himself. However, it is not necessary to have new store facilities built to touch off conditions leading to disequilibrium. A change in store ownership, and with it in store personality, can stimulate others to add new facilities. The absorption of a strong local chain by a larger company can result in a weakening of the personality and performance of the absorbed stores, giving competitors an incentive to expand.

Mergers are frequently considered a vehicle for resolving or averting problems of overstoring in a market area. Merging works well if the store facilities added by the acquiring firm can be used efficiently or partly disposed of; otherwise, a merger, rather than restoring equilibrium, can heighten a condition of disequilibrium.

A change in ownership may disrupt equilibrium, not because the new owner is weak, but because some of the added facilities cannot be used effectively. Because competitive stores are being located within shopping centers, and close to each other on highways, or because bigger stores are being built with more extensive trading areas (and more overlap with competition), it becomes increasingly difficult for one chain to absorb a second without acquiring duplicatory or otherwise inefficient store facilities.

New building programs and/or reshuffling of store ownership result in a change in the balance between available store facilities and their use. Building programs can be either boons or detriments, and there is never a perfect merger.

Conclusion

Changes in store facilities, merchandising, and services are the means by which dynamic equilibrium is maintained by a retailing society. Addition to existing facilities is the method by which static equilibrium is maintained.

In general, the more regulated the retailing society, the greater the possibilities of freezing store facilities and trading areas. The more competitive the society, the more likely it is for change to be introduced, shaking up the equilibrium and hastening the process of store adjustments.

Government and political influences can be put to positive use. They can serve to induce or anticipate change. In the United States, zoning and licensing may prevent builders from bringing about changes, but they can also serve as vehicles for encouraging the development of additional shopping facilities where needed. In the English "new towns," the planning process is used to anticipate changing needs.

Acting as regulators or breaks are capital limitations and the high investment cost in modern retail facilities. On the other hand, the basic value of land, particularly in inflationary periods, as compared to the more ephemeral value of buildings, makes it easier to shift retail store facilities to new sites and use older sites for other purposes.

To prevent run-away changes in store facilities within a competitive society, sound planning by individual companies is essential. Such planning must undertake to evaluate the potential needs of the market area as well as anticipate store location moves by competitors. Under rational behavior of retail society, strong and well-informed competition is the best agent for maintaining dynamic equilibrium within market areas.

24. The Management Center in the United States

William Goodwin

The growth of cities and the consequent growth in the complexity of business, manufacturing, and trade in the twentieth century have necessitated a like increase in managerial capacity to handle these large-scale activities. Management has almost become a separate service activity; certainly it has an increasingly important economic role.

By definition, management is an "idea-handling, not a materials-handling, function," and management centers are cities in which there is a "concentration of headquarters offices of nationally important companies," a center that may be widely separated from areas or centers of production. This selection identifies the characteristics and functions of management centers as an important tertiary activity in major American cities.

In the literature on the classification of cities little or no attention has been given to management per se or to management centers. A recent bibliography of central-place studies, which lists the significant studies of tertiary activities, does not contain among its more than five hundred entries a single reference explicitly to management centers; and neither this work nor the extensive bibliographies in Isard's "Methods of Regional Analysis" make any mention of management functions.

Among the better-known functional classifications of cities, none appears to regard management as a separate function. Harris states that this classification "is based on the activity of greatest importance in each city." Functional importance, in the Harris classification, is measured mainly by the number of people employed in each industry. Harris recognizes nine classes of cities but does not include management among their activities.

More recently, Nelson has also presented a functional classification of American cities, based, like Harris's, on United States census categories. Although Nelson includes a wider range of activities than Harris, he makes no mention of management as a separate category. Alexanders-

SOURCE: *The Geographical Review*, LV (January, 1965), 1–16. Reprinted by permission. The author is professor of geography, University of Wisconsin, Milwaukee.

son, in his comprehensive analysis of the functional role of American cities, which utilizes the concepts of "city forming" and "city serving," evidently does not regard management as either and therefore does not include it in the classification. Hart's study of the cities of the American South follows the general pattern set by Harris; it likewise makes no mention of the importance of management and fails to identify any city as a management center.

"In "Metropolis and Region" Duncan and his associates classify standard metropolitan areas with 300,000 inhabitants or more in 1950 into seven categories according to "metropolitan functions and regional relationships." [1] Although these investigators did not consider management as such, their grouping of the SMA's appears to correspond closely with the grouping resulting from the work presented in this paper.

The omission of management in the classifications reviewed above is readily explained by the fact that their basis was the most important "function" as measured by employment. By this criterion the number of people engaged in management is not large enough to be of significance. Moreover, although it is possible to extract "managers" from the census data, the category is too inclusive to be satisfactory. In any case, it is questionable whether or not employment is a proper measure of management activities.

It is hoped that the present paper may contribute toward filling the gap in the literature by identifying the cities in which management is important. Admittedly, the methods used are not wholly satisfactory, but it is believed that they are a step in the right direction.

Management and Management Centers

Management is an idea-handling, not a materials-handling, function, and as such it is somewhat intangible. Vernon points out that "whereas manufacturing, transportation, retail trade, and wholesale trade are economic activities whose existence is easily recognized and catalogued, many aspects of office activity are more difficult to classify." Managerial operations are office activities if nothing else. As part of the national and local urban scene, managers, the offices they occupy, and the distribution of these offices invite investigation.

Vernon also observes: "To the extent that the office function grows,

---

[1] Otis Dudley Duncan and others: Metropolis and Region (Baltimore, 1960), pp. 259–275. The seven categories are as follows: National Metropolis (N); Regional Metropolis (R); Regional Capital, Submetropolitan (C); Manufacturing, three classes (D, D–, and M); and Special Cases (S). These are based on a scattergram that plots per capita value added by manufacture against per capita wholesale sales; the third dimension of population is indicated by the size of the circle (pp. 264 and 271).

therefore, the growth may well occur to a disproportionate extent in the office districts of the *larger central cities,* at the expense of the regional centers. The possibility [is] that only the largest cities may be the principal beneficiaries of continued office growth—indeed, . . . they may be the only beneficiaries." If, as it appears, office functions and, particularly, the headquarters offices of nationally important companies are to continue to gravitate to the already existing office centers, it is pertinent to establish which are the presently important cities.

In the past twenty years the electronic computer has grown from a curiosity to a much-used tool of management. Many routine decisions are programmed for electronic computers; many data are processed by punch cards rather than by pencil, paper, and desk calculators. This "revolution" has reduced the number of clerks needed to prepare the raw materials for decision making. The change now taking place in the mechanics of decision making may have either of two opposite results with respect to the location of management centers. On the one hand, the reduction in the number of employees needed to staff a headquarters office may hasten the concentration of decision making in a few locations; on the other hand, it may well mean dispersion of headquarters because of the flexibility of data flows through a computer. At the moment it is not clear just what effect the rapid introduction of electronic data processing will have on the concentration of office functions, but one must be aware of its great potential for changing the pattern of "office" cities.

Although the making of decisions is the function of only a very small part of the American labor force, the influence of the decision makers on the social and economic welfare of the nation is enormous. The day-to-day decisions of the executives of the largest businesses, together with the decisions made in Washington, D.C., determine the course of economic events in the country—and, to no small degree, in the rest of the world as well.

A management center may therefore be defined as a city in which there is a *concentration of headquarters offices of nationally important companies.* It is a place apart from the production centers. The people identified as "managers" are those who sell their managerial talents irrespective of the nature of the company that employs them. A management center is a reservoir of managerial talent available for hire.

Management and Population

New York City would unquestionably be accorded the position of prime management center of the United States, but which other cities exhibit the same general characteristics as New York?

Intuitively, and probably by common assumption, the relative importance of a city as a business-management center is considered to have a more or less positive linear relation to the size of its population. The most readily available measure of management would be the count of managers and clerks made by the census. Figure 1 plots the total number of managers and clerks for the twenty largest (according to population) urbanized areas of the United States against the populations. Clearly a straight-line relationship exists.

However, when the relation of managers and clerks to all other workers is calculated and the result plotted against the population (Fig. 2), no such straight-line relationship emerges. Rather, a distribution of cities can be observed from left to right across the graph, from the industrial centers of Detroit, Pittsburgh, and Buffalo to the purely administrative center of Washington, D.C. Thus it would seem that the intuitive view is both confirmed and questioned, and one is led to further consideration of the question.

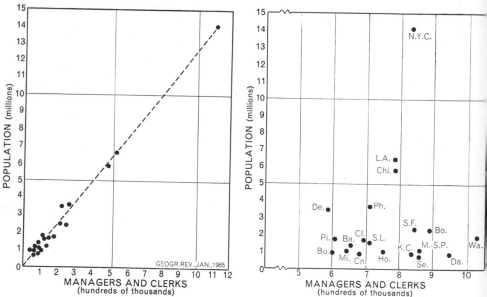

FIGURE 1: Managers (except farm managers) and clerks in relation to total population for the twenty largest urbanized areas in the United States. Source: 1960 Census of Population and 1958 Census of Manufactures.

FIGURE 2: Managers (except farm managers) and clerks per 100,000 workers in relation to population for the twenty largest urbanized areas in the United States. Key: N.Y.C., New York City; L.A., Los Angeles; Chi., Chicago; De., Detroit; Ph., Philadelphia; Pi., Pittsburgh; Bu., Buffalo; Mi., Milwaukee; Ba., Baltimore; Cn., Cincinnati; Cl., Cleveland; S.L., St. Louis; Ho., Houston; K.C., Kansas City; Se., Seattle; M.-St.P., Minneapolis-St. Paul; S.F., San Francisco; Bo., Boston; Da., Dallas; Wa., Washington, D.C. The horizontal scale has been expanded to permit clarity in reading the graph. Sources: 1960 Census of Population; 1958 Census of Manufactures.

Sources of Data

It can be assumed that large companies require a large managerial personnel, and therefore the concentration of large companies in a city is indicative of managerial concentration also. Relevant information about individual companies was assembled and summarized, city by city. Publicly owned companies are required to publish annual reports of their financial status, and these reports carry a wealth of additional information. The business publications, such as *Moody's*, and the *Standard and Poor* investors reference manuals publish annually the information available about companies. *Fortune* has made a survey of America's largest companies, both industrial and nonindustrial, and for the past nine years has published annually (July and August) a list of America's five hundred largest industrial companies, and for the last five years a list of the fifty largest commercial banks, insurance, transportation, utility, and merchandising companies respectively.

Since it is presumed that only companies of national importance can collectively create a management center of national importance, the 750 companies listed in the *Fortune* survey served as a base. Each company was checked against one or both of the standard investors manuals and also against *Thomas' Register of American Manufacturers*, 1961 edition, for accuracy and to determine the location of the production facilities of the company. The data used in this study refer to the 1962 status of the companies. This list, published in 1963, was first compared with the lists published in earlier years to determine whether there had been significant shifts in the composition. Only the companies in the lower ranks appear to have changed completely, though naturally there has been some shifting of relative importance over the years. It was felt, however, that changes over the last ten years had not been sufficient to warrant taking earlier years into account, because the appearance or disappearance of companies from the list did not modify substantially the relative importance of a city as a management center. Also, comparison of the two years 1954 and 1963 did not reveal any substantial geographical shift in management centers.

Results of the Analysis

The results of this investigation are most easily presented in a series of tables. Because of the limited scope of the data, these results are certainly neither final nor conclusive, and undoubtedly other means of attacking the problem need exploration.

Table I presents data concerning the 500 leading industrial companies of America aggregated according to the locations of their headquarters cities. Three reasonable, if arbitrarily chosen, criteria served to determine the cities that seemed to meet the test of national importance as management centers: (1) at least ten headquarters offices, (2) at least two billion dollars in assets or sales in 1962 (about 1 percent of the total assets and sales of the 500 companies), and (3) at least 100,000 employees (about 1 percent of the total employment of the 500 companies). Centers included in the original compilation but eliminated from the table are Akron, Minneapolis-St. Paul, Wilmington, Bethlehem-Allentown, Seattle, Cincinnati, Dallas, Toledo, Milwaukee, and Bartlesville (Oklahoma). Although these cities had one or both of the other qualifications, each failed to have more than ten offices.

It is not enough that a city has a large concentration of offices; these offices should represent widespread control, both spatially and industrially, and separation from production facilities. To determine the extent of the "empire" controlled from each city, a tabulation was made of the states in which each company with headquarters in that city had located one or more plants, and the totals were summed. For example, 83 companies with headquarters in New York City had one or more plants in California. However, for determining the extent of geographical control of a city the total number of plants was not considered necessary, merely the number of companies with branch plants in the various states. A city whose control did not extend to at least twenty-four states and Canada was not regarded as a management center. Only New York City and Chicago companies are represented in all forty-eight states of the conterminous United States and in Canada; the most poorly represented is Cleveland, with twenty-nine states and Canada. Table II summarizes this information.

A more satisfactory view of the extent of the control of a city can be gained from a map on which have been plotted the basic data from

TABLE I. Concentration of Industrial Headquarters Offices

City	Number of Offices	Sales (In Thousands of Dollars)	Assets (In Thousands of Dollars)	Number of Employees
New York	163	84,355,806	124,477,751	3,650,089
Detroit	13	28,801,564	19,319,678	1,594,487
Chicago	51	19,798,326	14,300,775	717,541
Pittsburgh	21	10,760,815	12,031,841	439,313
Los Angeles	16	8,361,378	5,698,259	307,056
San Francisco	14	5,690,201	6,973,327	206,227
Philadelphia	16	4,423,190	4,372,831	171,613
St. Louis	12	4,229,250	3,177,712	185,734
Cleveland	15	4,172,215	3,512,877	188,902
Boston	12	2,140,787	1,503,882	118,358

Compiled from *Fortune*, July, 1963, and *Moody's Industrials*, 1962 edition.

TABLE II. Extent of "Empire" by City of Control, Conterminous United States and Canada *

Head-quarters City	No. of States With Branch Plants	Total No. of Plants	Head-quarters City	No. of States With Branch Plants	Total No. of Plants
New York City	48	1,455	San Francisco	34	97
Chicago	48	528	Wilmington*a*	34	51
Minneapolis–			Detroit	30	112
St. Paul*a*	43	128	Philadelphia	30	82
Pittsburgh	40	212	Cleveland	29	99
St. Louis	38	125	Boston*b*	21	48
Los Angeles	38	98			

* All cities listed have a plant or plants in Canada.
a Not included in Table I because of failure to meet requirements, but included here for completeness and the fact that it is industrially significant.
b The small extent of its industrial empire eliminates Boston as an industrial management center, in accordance with the criterion.
SOURCE: *Moody's Industrials,* 1962 edition; *Thomas' Register of American Manufacturers,* 1961.

which Table II was constructed. Six such maps are presented, for New York, Chicago, Los Angeles, San Francisco, Detroit, and Pittsburgh (Figs. 3–8). The importance of New York and Chicago as headquarters cities emerges clearly from these maps and contrasts strongly with that of the West Coast centers of Los Angeles and San Francisco. Detroit and Pittsburgh, notable manufacturing centers, appear to have their control principally in the industrial sections of the country.

Although a city need not necessarily have a diversity of industries to qualify as a management center, undoubtedly a large pool of broader managerial talents would be available in a city with many different industries than in a one-industry city. Other things being equal, a city with a wide range of nationally important companies is better qualified to claim a position of rank among managerial centers. An attempt was made to classify all companies studied according to the United States Standard Industrial Classification (Table III), but only at the two-digit level.[2] The internal diversity of many companies makes it impossible to use a more detailed category, and for a few it was not possible to use even the two-digit categories; these companies are listed as unknown. Where possible, the company was assigned to a class according to its principal product. A summary appears in Table III. Clearly, certain cities that rank high in Tables I and II have little diversity in production, and consequently little diversity in management talent.

[2] In the Standard Industrial Classification (SIC) all industries are divided into 9 major groups at the one digit level, into 99 groups at the two-digit level, and into 999 groups at the three-digit level.

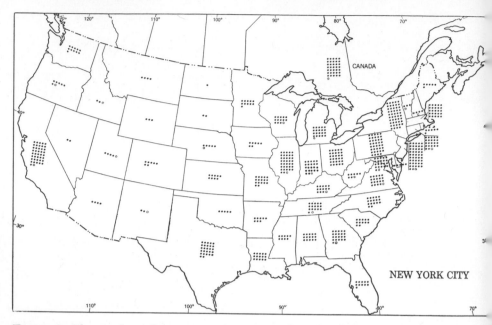

FIGURE 3: The number of companies, by states, whose headquarters offices are located in New York. A solid dot represents two plants; a circle, one plant. Sources: *Moody's Industrials*, 1962; *Thomas' Register of American Manufacturers*, 1961.

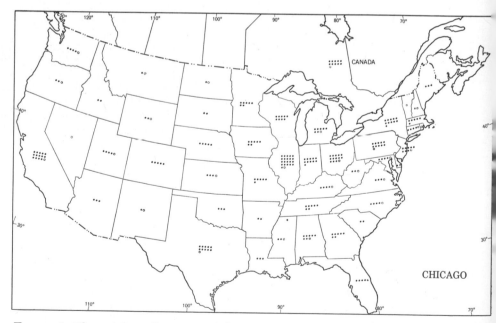

FIGURE 4: The number of companies, by states, whose headquarters offices are located in Chicago. A solid dot represents two plants; a circle, one plant. Sources: *Moody's Industrials*, 1962; *Thomas' Register of American Manufacturers*, 1961.

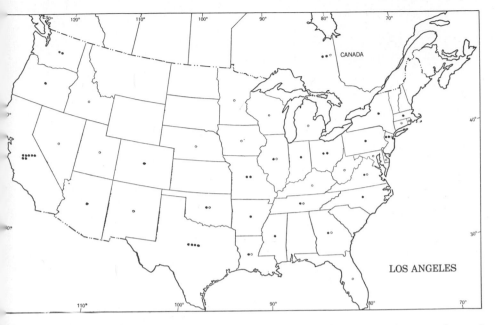

FIGURE 5: The number of companies, by states, whose headquarters offices are located in Los Angeles. A solid dot represents two plants; a circle, one plant. Sources: *Moody's Industrials*, 1962; *Thomas' Register of American Manufacturers*, 1961.

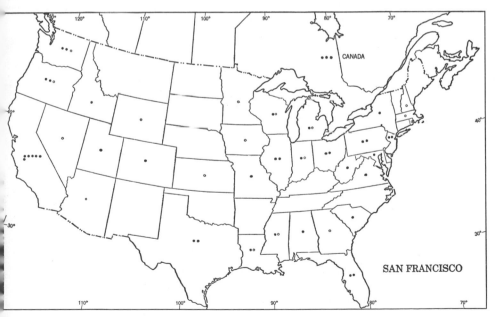

FIGURE 6: The number of companies, by states, whose headquarters offices are located in San Francisco. A solid dot represents two plants; a circle, one plant. Sources: *Moody's Industrials*, 1962; *Thomas' Register of American Manufacturers*, 1961.

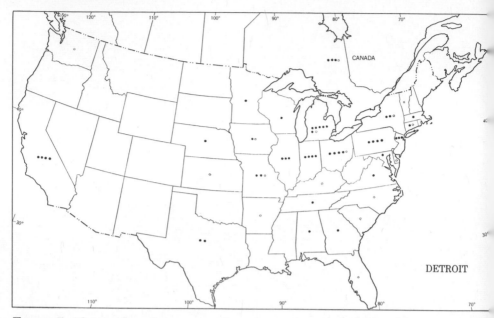

FIGURE 7: The number of companies, by states, whose headquarters offices are located in Detroit. A solid dot represents two plants; a circle, one plant. Sources: *Moody's Industrials*, 1962; *Thomas' Register of American Manufacturers*, 1961.

FIGURE 8: The number of companies, by states, whose headquarters offices are located in Pittsburgh. A solid dot represents two plants; a circle one plant. Sources: *Moody's Industrials*, 1962; *Thomas' Register of American Manufacturers*, 1961.

TABLE III. Number of Companies According to United States Standard Industrial Classification

Management Center	SIC NUMBER																				
	20	21	22	23	24	25	26	27	28	29	30	31	32	33	34	35	36	37	38	39	U[a]
New York	19	5	9	2	1	1	10	5	30	6	4	0	2	13	12	11	12	7	5	0	9
Chicago	14	0	0	1	0	0	2	0	4	1	1	0	1	2	5	4	9	3	1	0	3
Pittsburgh	1	0	0	0	0	0	0	0	1	2	0	0	1	6	2	3	2	0	0	0	3
Los Angeles	2	0	0	0	0	0	0	1	2	4	0	0	0	0	0	1	0	4	0	0	2
Philadelphia	0	0	1	0	0	0	2	0	2	2	0	0	1	0	0	1	2	2	0	0	3
Cleveland	0	0	0	0	0	0	0	0	4	1	0	0	0	4	1	4	0	1	0	0	0
San Francisco	3	0	0	0	2	0	1	0	1	0	0	0	0	1	1	1	2	0	0	0	2
Detroit	1	0	0	0	0	0	0	0	0	0	0	0	0	2	1	2	1	5	0	0	0
St. Louis	4	0	0	0	0	0	0	0	3	0	0	2	0	0	0	0	2	1	0	0	0
Boston	1	0	1	1	0	0	0	0	2	0	1	0	1	0	1	1	1	0	2	2	1
Minneapolis–St. Paul	3	0	0	0	0	0	1	0	0	0	0	0	0	0	1	1	1	0	0	1	0

Ranking of Industrial Management Centers

If it can be assumed that the four criteria of Table I have equal value as measures of management concentration and that the extent of areal control and diversity are also of about the same value, the cities can be tentatively ranked (Table IV) by a simple averaging of the total rankings of each city. Akron, Wilmington, and Bethlehem-Allentown, with small "empires" and little diversity but important for particular products, are not general management centers, even industrially.

Nonindustrial Position

The importance of a city as a management center has so far been confined to its importance as a center of industrial management, but this is inadequate, for it does not take into account other business activities. For example, the large commercial banks and the insurance companies exercise an all-pervasive influence as major sources of funds that recognize no visible bounds. Legal restrictions and banking and insurance laws place limits on the tangible evidence of control, but the size of assets alone is indicative of relative importance. Few transportation

TABLE IV. Ranking of Cities as Industrial Management Centers

	RANK						
City	No. of Offices	Sales	Assets	No. of Employees	No. of Plants	Diversity	Av. Rank
New York	1	1	1	1	1	1	1
Chicago	2	3	3	3	2	2	2
Pittsburgh	3	4	4	4	3	4	3
Detroit	8	2	2	2	5	6	4
San Francisco	7	6	5	6	8	4	5
Los Angeles	4½	5	6	5	7	9	6
Philadelphia	4½	7	7	9	9	4	7
Cleveland	6	9	8	7	6	7	8
St. Louis	9	8	9	8	4	9	9

companies are national in scope, but the larger airlines and railroads serve large sections of the country and may therefore be considered of national importance. Utility companies, with the exception of American Telephone and Telegraph and Western Union, are commonly local, both in service area and in outlook; therefore only the national service utilities were included in the computations. Inasmuch as the sole common denominator among the various kinds of business activity is assets, this criterion was used, though "policies in force" or "policyholders"

TABLE V. Nonindustrial Assets, Fifteen Largest Centers *(In billions of dollars)*

City	Bank	Insurance	Transport	Utility	Total
			ASSETS		
New York	49.0	63.6	4.9	36.0	153.5
San Francisco	19.9	–	2.8	–	22.7
Chicago	9.9	0.9	6.0	0.7	17.5
Hartford	–	13.5	–	–	13.5
Boston	2.0	9.2	–	–	11.2
Los Angeles	8.8	1.6	0.1	–	10.5
Philadelphia	3.6	3.3	3.2	–	10.1
Cleveland	3.5	–	2.2	–	5.7
Milwaukee	0.9	4.5	–	–	5.4
Houston	0.9	–	–	3.9	4.8
Detroit	4.6	–	–	–	4.6
Pittsburgh	3.6	–	–	–	3.6
Dallas	2.5	0.9	0.1	–	3.5
Minneapolis– St. Paul	0.7	0.4	2.4	–	3.5
St. Louis	1.5	–	1.9	–	3.4

SOURCE: *Fortune*, August, 1963; *Moody's Financials*, 1962 edition.

TABLE VI. Total Assets Controlled by Companies in Management Centers *
(In billions of dollars)

Rank	City	Assets	Rank	City	Assets
1	New York	283.3	17	Wilmington	3.5
2	Chicago	36.5	18	Cincinnati	3.3
3	San Francisco	30.2	19	Akron	3.1
4	Detroit	24.7	20	Springfield (Mass.)	2.7
5	Los Angeles	16.4	21	Bethlehem–	
6	Pittsburgh	15.7		Allentown	2.4
7	Philadelphia	14.4	22	Winston-Salem	2.0
8	Hartford	13.5	23	Des Moines	1.9
9	Boston	13.0	24	Bartlesville	1.7
10	Cleveland	9.2	25	Fort Wayne	1.6
11	St. Louis	7.0	26	Richmond	1.5
12	Houston	6.7	27	Toledo	1.2
13	Milwaukee	6.6	28	Rochester	1.2
14	Minneapolis–St. Paul	5.4	29	Peoria	1.14
15	Dallas	4.5	30	Baltimore	1.12
16	Seattle	3.8	31	Nashville	1.0

Compiled from *Fortune, Moody's, Standard and Poor.*
* Includes assets held by national merchandising companies but not used in previous calculations. Their inclusion here is to indicate full economic power and thus the magnitude of management control centered in each city.

might have provided a better measure for insurance companies. Table V presents a compilation of the nonindustrial assets of the cities in the same fashion that the industrial data were summarized.

Many of the important industrial cities are also important non-

TABLE VII. Ration of Nonindustrial to Industrial Assets

City	Ratio	City	Ratio
Akron	0.16[a]	Los Angeles	1.89
Toledo	0.16[a]	Minneapolis–St. Paul	1.98
Bethlehem-Allentown	0.21[a]	Philadelphia	2.35
Detroit	0.26	Houston	3.00
Pittsburgh	0.31	San Francisco	3.34
St. Louis	1.06	Milwaukee	3.86
Cleveland	1.48	Dallas	4.00
Cincinnati	1.54	Boston	7.35
Chicago	1.58	Hartford	13.50
New York	1.82		

[a] Estimate based on assignment of nonindustrial assets as determined by summing the assets of banks and the like within these as recorded in *Moody's*. Nonindustrial assets include assets of nationally important merchandising companies.

industrial centers, but Hartford, Milwaukee, Houston, and Dallas, as measured by assets, are obviously more important as financial centers than as industrial centers. Thus a second criterion of rank is suggested, namely the total of nonindustrial assets. In addition to repeated proof of the importance of New York City and Chicago as control centers, the great banking wealth of San Francisco is pointed up, together with the insurance centers noted above.

With the two rankings of importance before us, it is now necessary to attempt to combine them into a single measure. The one set of data common to all economic activities and to all cities is assets. Assets, whether of a business firm or of a bank, are commonly recognized as a measure of importance. Table VI combines all assets, industrial and non-industrial, for each city with assets of more than one billion dollars and ranks the cities accordingly.

The relation between the industrial and nonindustrial assets can be analyzed both arithmetically and graphically. The simple ratio of nonindustrial to industrial assets was computed (Table VII), and the relative importance of the cities was graphed (Fig. 9). The graph serves as a basis for qualifying the cities as balanced in management control or more important industrially or financially. If the graph is read clockwise from the vertical axis, the cities are seen to be arrayed in order from those dominated by industry to those which are primarily financial centers. In addition, the graph shows the relative importance of each city, at least with regard to assets held by its major companies, and thus, if assets of large companies are a reliable measure of management, their importance as management centers. A similarity is apparent between Figures 2 and 9. It would seem that the relation of managers and clerks to all workers is indicative of a management center—an assumption confirmed by the analysis in this paper.

Types of Management Centers

Three distinct groups of cities emerge: (1) general management centers of two sizes, regional and national, called by Gottmann *quaternary centers;* (2) financial cities of regional and national importance. here

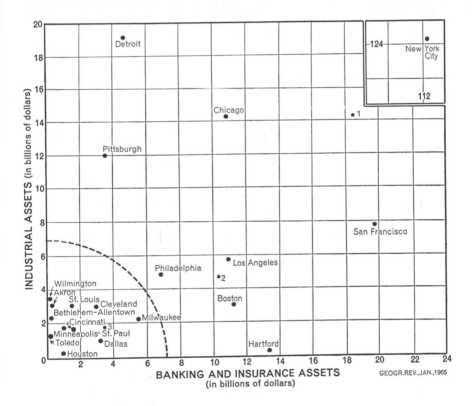

FIGURE 9: Industrial assets plotted against banking and insurance assets. The numerals 1, 2, and 3 represent the positions that Chicago, Philadelphia, and Minneapolis-St. Paul respectively would have had if the assets of transportation companies had been included in the nonindustrial assets. The arc in the lower left corner roughly delimits the nationally important centers from the centers whose influence is more restricted.

labeled *tertiary centers;* and (3) industrial cities, in which the bulk of
the wealth and control is in industry, here called *secondary centers.*

Figure 10 identifies all cities with assets of one billion dollars or
more held by nationally important companies (Table VI). The twenty-
one largest are identified according to their relative importance as
quaternary, tertiary, or secondary. It is clear that few cities can be called
national management centers. The dominance of New York is overwhelming; its total assets are nearly eight times those of its nearest rival,
Chicago. No other city can approach the diversity of operations performed, and it must be remembered that using only the five hundred
largest industrial companies and the fifty largest of each kind of major
nonindustrial company has not revealed the full importance of the city.
In the quaternary group, New York, Chicago, Los Angeles, and Philadelphia can be considered national management centers (though the case
for Los Angeles is weakened by its heavy dependence on the aircraft
industry for the bulk of its industrial assets), and Cleveland, St. Louis,
Minneapolis–St. Paul, and Cincinnati regional management centers. In
the tertiary group, San Francisco, Hartford, and Boston must be classed

GEOGR.REV.,JAN.,1965

FIGURE 10: Headquarters cities. This map is based on the total assets held by major
companies in the 31 cities shown. The cities have been differentiated into three major
categories according to the source of their power.

as nationally important; Milwaukee, Dallas, and Springfield (Massachusetts), all with important insurance companies dominating the pattern, are of lower rank, as is Seattle. The secondary centers are Detroit, Pittsburgh, Akron, Bethlehem-Allentown, and Wilmington.

25. The Independent Transport Carrier in Ocean Tramp Trades

Douglas K. Fleming

The transportation of people and commodities in all kinds of carriers is an important tertiary economic activity, and trade at all economic levels and in all areas is also a significant service activity. Much of the transoceanic and long-distance transport of people in and between the more developed areas of the world has been taken over by airlines. A significant portion of the world's surplus production, however, continues to be transported to diverse markets by the independent tramp cargo vessel. Fleming indicates in a detailed manner the factors important to the success of such trade from both the user's and the carrier's points of view. These factors indicate that the ocean tramp will continue to be the chief carrier of products traded between the nations of the world.

A "user bias" frequently affects attitudes toward transportation services. There is an understandable tendency to regard transport costs as an obstacle to be controlled, reduced, even eliminated in the satisfaction of personal needs. The owner of an automobile might pause to consider the economic activity of vehicular movement since he is both operator *and* user. The same individual is not as likely to apply similar analysis from the carrier's viewpoint to the many other transport services he requires. Perspectives may therefore be unconsciously predetermined when evaluating general economic and geographic theory pertaining to movements of goods and people. Impressions and interpretations may be slanted whether or not the theorists' premises and analyses are

SOURCE: *Economic Geography*, XLIV (January, 1968), 21–36. Reprinted with permission of the author and the editor. The author is assistant professor of geography at the University of Washington.

valid. Above all, the "user bias" appears to obscure the dynamism of the transport factor and the reasons behind its variability.[1]

In a brilliant study of ocean shipping in the early twentieth century, A. J. Sargent, a British commercial geographer, brought the transport variable into particularly sharp focus. Sargent viewed the economic activity of ocean cargo movement from the ship operator's perspective. He observed that the operations of shipowners as applied to the various commodities of commerce shaped the character and direction of great world trade routes and, bluntly, that ocean lines were not usually worked for purposes of philanthropy but to pay dividends. This was not a denial of the effects of regional geographical conditions which represent the "ultimate determining element in the employment of shipping." It was, however, a clear recognition of the *active* role of the transport carrier and the profound effects of this activity in shaping the routes and costs of transportation.

This paper is concerned with contemporary *independent* ocean carrier operations in world tramp trades, particularly with the complex interplay of economics and geography which characterizes these operations. To investigate the respective roles of carrier and user in establishing the costs, strengths, and spatial arrangements of tramp connections requires shifting perspectives. In recognition of the carrier's unusual dynamism in tramp trades, the steamship operator's viewpoint will frequently be adopted.

A large segment of today's world commerce is serviced by the independent carrier—independent in the sense of not belonging exclusively to or not being used exclusively by *one* user of its services. In the relationship between commodity producers and commodity consumers the introduction of a foreign wedge in the form of the independent carrier has practical and theoretical consequence, whether the carrier is owned by one man or by an entire government, whether operations are unfettered or rigidly regulated. The foreign wedge destroys the integrated producer/carrier relationship which exists in the case of farmers hauling produce to market in their own trucks or oil companies connecting their own supply and market areas with their own tanker fleets.[2] The independent carrier's operations are not likely to be dictated by one user's requirements. Significantly, also, transport costs (to the

---

[1] Economist Walter Isard has sharply criticized early trade, production and location theorists for a "neglect of the distance variable and the role of space." Actually the criticism is directed more against geographically misleading premises than against subsequent analysis which may have significant general validity. See, particularly, W. Isard: *Location and Space-Economy* (New York, 1956), pp. xi, 24–26. However, in his consideration of the variability of transport prices, Isard's viewpoint is essentially that of the user of "transport inputs." The distinction between costs to the carrier and costs to the user is not very clearly made. (*Ibid.*, pp. 86–88.)

[2] But is an integrated relationship, which implies a *passive* role for the carrier, one which we unthinkingly assume in our consideration of transport links? The conceptual difference between the controlled and the independent carrier is briefly

carrier) and charges (to the users) need not be identical. Economies achieved by or diseconomies experienced by the carrier are not immediately and automatically passed on to the user. In short, the carrier has assumed a dynamic (though not necessarily controlling) role in the determination of his own operating costs and of the charges for his services.

In a traditional classification according to service, the tramp vessel, in contrast to the liner, has no regular schedule or fixed routes. Both are usually *common* carriers in contrast to the industrial carrier which is owned by *one* manufacturing or business firm for the transport of the firm's own raw materials and products.[3] In commercial usage, the adjective "tramp" has been affixed to owners, vessels, cargoes and trade routes. It is not a precise term. For the writer's purpose, tramp trade shall be defined to include only those full cargoes, primarily commodities in bulk, which move internationally under freely-negotiable freight rates. In the nineteenth and twentieth centuries ocean tramp trades have provided a wide arena for independent carrier operations, despite the rise of "controlled" bulk commodity flows serviced at cost rates by industrial carriers, or sometimes at fixed rates by liners. Heavy volumes of grain, oil, ores, coal, sugar, scrap, lumber, etc., move under rates negotiated in a decided "free market" atmosphere.[4] Vessels compete with one another for cargo, shippers with one another for vessel space. Normally, the individual steamship firm—frequently including the industrial carrier which strays from its "captive" route—has numerous cargo, port, and trade route alternatives and a considerable freedom in voyage negotiations in spite of periodic political, economic, and physical obstruction.

Commodity and Freight Rate Transactions

Tramp trade flows directly involve commodity producer, transport carrier, and commodity consumer.[5] *Each* has the potential of making, strengthening, weakening, or breaking tramp connections.

Suppose that free market conditions prevail for export sales of wheat.

noted by P. Haggett: *Locational Analysis in Human Geography* (New York, 1966), p. 169.

[3] L. A. Bryan: *Principles of Water Transportation* (New York, 1939), pp. 70–77; G. Alexandersson and G. Norström: *World Shipping* (Stockholm, 1963), pp. 34–36. Alexandersson and Norström quote estimates of tramp vessel tonnage for 1914 as 46 per cent of world fleet tonnage, declining to 16 per cent in 1951 but rising again to 19 per cent in 1957. These writers are plagued with the problem of defining "tramp," recognizing that there is no firm dividing line between tramp, liner, and industrial carrier services.

[4] A long but only partial record of bulk commodity fixtures is listed in *Chartering Annual* issued annually by Maritime Research, Inc., New York. Many freighting arrangements are not recorded because of their confidential nature.

[5] In the hypothetical example which follows, for simplification the commodity producer will be synonymous with cargo shipper, and commodity consumer synonymous with cargo receiver.

Assume that a wheat producer has a shipload quantity of a particular quality stored in a dockside grain elevator and that a foreign grain buyer requires this quality and quantity at his overseas port storage facility. There is, then, a specific supply and demand which may provide the basis for initiating negotiations.

Suppose now that free market conditions exist for freighting negotiations and that export sales of wheat are customarily "c.i.f." (cost, insurance, and freight) so that the wheat producer will be responsible for freighting arrangements. The producer is immediately concerned with the transport factor since it will directly affect his price quotation to the consumer.

Now assume that an independent vessel operator owns a vessel, properly positioned in time and space, uncommitted and suitable in all technical respects for this commodity movement. There might now exist another supply/demand situation in terms of cargo (producer's supply, vessel's demand) or of vessel space (vessel's supply, producer's demand).

Presumably, the stage is set for sales and freight rate negotiations. In all probability, however, there will be alternative markets for producer, alternative supply sources for consumer, alternative cargoes or trade routes for vessel operator, and alternative vessel space available to producer. Each alternative affects the bargaining strengths of producer, carrier, and consumer, quite possibly precluding the specific commodity sale and movement.

If transactions ensue between producer and consumer there may well be a *range of prices* which will be mutually tolerable if not mutually desirable. Alternative opportunities limit this range. Similarly, for producer and transport carrier, there may be a range of mutually tolerable freight rates, also limited by alternative opportunities. Producer, carrier, consumer, and their respective negotiating representatives will have evaluated their own immediate and future objectives, costs, and alternatives, based on an imperfect knowledge of these factors. Their evaluation of one another's bargaining strengths will be based on even more imperfect knowledge. In most instances, negotiators are individuals, not groups. Normally they are given free bargaining discretion within tolerable ranges. The outcome of negotiations will, therefore, depend not only upon objective situational evaluations but upon momentary personal inclinations, strengths, and weaknesses of the negotiators.

If negotiations are successfully consummated, the geographer might claim that specific complementarity between areas has been translated into an actual cargo flow through the provision of suitable transferability in the absence of overriding intervening opportunity. Such a generalization may, in fact, provide a valid "raison d'être" for long-term, well-established material flows; however, its impression of economic and geographic inevitability hides the significant role of the individual negotiator, the possible volatility of transport prices, and the short-term variability of tramp connections.

Carrier's Negotiating Scope

The carrier's part in the construction of a freight rate, which defines transport cost to shipper or receiver, has been briefly considered. In actual fact, the carrier's negotiating scope generally extends far beyond an agreement on freight rate levels. The benefits of high freight rates to the carrier evaporate if brokerage commissions or stevedoring rates are excessive or if dispatch and demurrage terms are unfavorable.[6] Each of these items directly affects net revenues to the carrier; therefore, each must be considered in close conjunction with freight rates. At times there are standard commissions, standard stevedoring rates and dispatch/demurrage terms, but frequently these items are negotiable in the voyage charter.

Additionally, the tramp operator is often in position to demand considerable freedom in dates of loading, an option of substituting alternative vessels and as much as 20 percent leeway in cargo quantity. Quite often he may negotiate the selection of loading or discharge ports for the voyage, if alternative routings for interior shippers or receivers are feasible. Moreover, the carrier usually retains operational flexibility in cargo stowage, manning, provisioning, repairing, and fueling schedules. Finally, there are virtually no restrictions imposed on navigational discretion en route.

The vast scope of negotiable items is best illustrated by the length and complexity of voyage charter documents which cover full cargo negotiations. To understand the tramp carrier's need for and use of this flexibility and negotiating scope, it is necessary to analyze his own estimated costs and expectations.

Carrier's Perspective: Voyage
Costs and Their Effects

The division of costs which follows is arbitrary.[7]

[6] Demurrage is payable to the carrier by the shipper or receiver upon vessel delays in loading and discharging operations. Dispatch is payable to the charterer (shipper or receiver) by the carrier in the event cargo operations are accomplished more rapidly than originally stipulated.

[7] However, daily operating costs are computed by the U.S. Maritime Administration as described below except office overhead expenses are not included.

Daily Operating Costs

On all but the shortest tramp cargo voyages the vessel's daily operating costs multiplied by voyage length in days represent a preponderant portion of total voyage expenses. Crew wages often constitute more than half the daily operating expenses. Crew subsistence, vessel maintenance and repair, vessel insurance and vessel depreciation, all calculated on a daily basis, are also significant. Many shipowners will include an estimated daily allocation of home office overhead expenses in this general category as well.

From day to day, at sea or in port, loaded or empty, vessel operating expenses are estimated at a constant daily figure, adjusted as necessary over long intervals.[8] Clearly *time-saving* economies are vital, perhaps the ruling consideration in tramp operations. Since the freight rate, once negotiated, also remains constant, a major opportunity to reduce voyage costs lies in voyage time minimization.

Vessel routings, therefore, tend to take maximum advantage of tide, current, and wind conditions and to avoid adverse weather or climatic conditions. This is illustrated by general comparison of summer and winter transoceanic tracks; or by comparison of easterly and westerly tracks; or by the use of "weather routing" services to avoid storms.[9]

Advances in transport technology also reflect the operator's desire for time economies—for example, faster steaming speeds, rapid automated cargo handling, and larger vessel capacities without fully concomitant increases in crew complement, fuel consumption, etc.

Individual tramp operators often display a preference for certain types of cargoes and trade routes which, by experience, are known to afford time economies. Thus, vessels with very high daily operating costs—for example, United States flag vessels—will seldom if ever be found on the British Columbia/United Kingdom lumber route. Even a temporarily high freight rate will not counterbalance the costs of time consumed in lengthy loading and discharging operations. On the other hand, there are a number of coal, ore, and grain runs which often attract higher-priced (in terms of daily operating costs) ships despite seemingly low freight rate levels. The popularity of these runs derives from minimal experienced voyage delays. Tramp carriers may value

---

[8] Obviously, crew wages and other items change over time, but not continuously. It may be argued that fuel consumption (to be considered later) represents a daily expense, but fuel consumption and expenses are operationally and areally *inconstant*.
[9] In an analysis of historical sailing ship patterns, actual physical capabilities are probably more significant than voyage time considerations. The southwesterly track from Northwestern Europe to the West Indies derived maximum benefit from the northeast trade winds; the trip up the North American Coast was expedited by the Gulf Stream; the northeastward return passage across the North Atlantic was speeded by prevailing westerlies and the North Atlantic Drift. Fortunately cargo flows in colonial days fitted this pattern rather neatly.

time conservation sufficiently to negotiate for *consecutive* voyages ballasting back each time to cargo source. This is common practice on several transatlantic and transpacific coal and grain routes. The diseconomies of emptiness are partially balanced by economies of time. The attractiveness of speedy voyages to the carrier often tends to be reflected in surprisingly low freight rate levels on steady one-way cargo flows. These rate levels, if commodity demand is rather elastic and if transport charges constitute a goodly portion of delivered commodity price, tend to stimulate commodity transactions.

The tramp operator also displays aversion to congested ports and to those ports with notoriously slow cargo-handling reputation. For each voyage, there is continual incentive to reduce the number of necessary ports of call (and berths visited within each port).[10] Shifting operations are time-consuming and cost-increasing. Occasionally, the tramp operator is willing to absorb cargo transshipment expenses if allowed to restrict cargo discharge to a desirable port. If the voyage can be expedited he is frequently amenable to payment of stevedoring overtime and dispatch charges to charterer.

There are many "exogenous influences" which may result in vessel port delays. Some of these, for example holidays, may be anticipated by the carrier. Others—for example, labor disturbances, strikes, storms, equipment failure, catastrophies—are generally unpredictable. Impressions gained through unfortunate experience often shape the carrier's future behavior. An American tramp operator whose vessel was forced to wait 28 days for a particular African ore berth while 12 later-arriving vessels were loaded is not likely to forget this apparent discrimination, nor is he likely to select this specific port or trade route again.[11]

It is reasonable to conclude that time savings are most important to vessel operators with the highest daily operating costs. Variations in the latter attributable to type of vessel or nationality of the crew do, therefore, affect individual vessel orientations toward certain routes, cargoes, and ports. Vessels with *low* daily operating costs will find lengthy voyages, perhaps in lumber and scrap trades, relatively more remunerative.

Vessel Port Expenses

There are other port expenses (in addition to the "costs of time") which accentuate the carrier's port minimization urge. Pilotage, tug charges, port dues, wharfage and dockage fees, line handling, agency fees, and

[10] Of course, there are limits to carriers' bargaining powers and cargo owners' capabilities in this regard. If congested or numerous ports are *required* this will often be reflected in higher freight rate levels and more generous demurrage terms.
[11] This incident was revealed and verified in personal conversation with an official of an unsubsidized American independent steamship line.

many other minor charges are applicable to virtually all vessel calls.[12]

Through past experience or hearsay, the tramp operator is generally familiar with port conditions and expenses on a worldwide basis. Existing physical limitations such as insufficient water depth, inadequate berthing facilities, insufficient bridge, lock, or turning basin clearance, seasonal ice conditions, etc., may remove all possibility of particular vessel calls. Difficult physical conditions—for example unusually high tidal ranges, awkward climatic conditions, strong currents, tortuous harbor entrances, silting tendencies, etc.—often result in unusually high port dues, towing and pilotage charges and in vessel delays. The tramp operator is tempted to avoid these ports or pad his revenue to cover these expenses.

Canal tolls might be considered a special variety of vessel port expenses. The dramatic effect of canal building upon both tramp and liner trade routes has been carefully considered by several geographers.[13] Despite enormous mileage savings in certain trades, it should be noted that the tramp operator frequently has a choice upon which physical characteristics of vessels and cost comparisons of alternative routes have bearing. On U.S. Gulf/India grain movements, perhaps the alternatives are using either the Panama or Suez Canal.[14] On Persian Gulf/U.S. East Coast oil movements, perhaps the choice is either steaming extra thousands of miles around the Cape of Good Hope or paying very sizable Suez Canal tolls. In "borderline" cases, factors such as proper positioning of vessels for the next voyage must be considered.

Vessel Cargo Expenses

All cargo storage, stevedoring, vessel fitting (for cargo), vessel hold cleaning, cargo inspection, cargo insurance, and other cargo handling expenses, *borne by the carrier,* may be termed vessel cargo expenses.[15]

The tramp operator sometimes is able to negotiate an "F.I.O." (free in

[12] Agency fees in many instances might be considered a combined vessel/cargo port expense. Often the carrier is charged a lump sum fee which covers vessel and cargo handling (documentation, etc.) expenses.

[13] For example: A. J. Sargent: *Seaways of the Empire* (2nd edit.; London, 1930), pp. 80–96; and André Siegfried: *Suez and Panama* (New York, 1940). The rather recent opening of the St. Lawrence Seaway canal system has stimulated an entire new series of ocean grain and ore movements as may be seen in any modern recording of tramp cargo charter fixtures.

[14] Neither the Suez nor the Panama Canals will accommodate the largest, modern supercarriers. The Suez Crisis in 1956, resulting in a temporary canal closure, opened the eyes of some carriers to unexpectedly interesting alternatives both in vessel construction and routing.

[15] Brokerage commissions and dispatch payments to charterers, previously mentioned in connection with freight rate negotiations, are really in this same cargo expense category. That part of the port agency fees applicable to cargo booking, tracing, expediting and documentation is also a cargo expense.

and out) agreement so that the major cargo loading and discharging expenses are borne by the shipper or receiver, not by the vessel operator. Moreover, on relatively low-value bulk commodities, stevedoring expenses, even if covered by the vessel operator, may not constitute a great proportion of total voyage costs. Automatic cargo-handling equipment tends to keep the costs per ton low, particularly on oil, coal, ore, and grain movements.

However, there are two factors to be weighed by the carrier: the actual cost of cargo-handling and the vessel time expended. Usually commodity shipper and receiver are concerned with these factors also, since the penalties of inefficiency will often be reflected in higher freight rate levels or heavy demurrage payments.

Again through experience, the tramp operator is usually well aware of the advantages and disadvantages of cargo handling in various ports. While the hourly wages of longshoremen may be equal over a large geographic range of ports, their productivity measured in tons handled per hour may vary considerably. The carrier may also be faced with a multitude of variable fringe charges and fringe benefits offered by different ports in connection with cargo handling.

These factors may strongly influence the carrier's selection of cargoes and choice of ports, if he can bargain. It also has affected transport technology by inducing vessel operators to adopt more advanced ship's gear and design for utmost cargo-handling economy and efficiency.

Fuel Expenses

Particularly on long tramp voyages, fuel costs are a major component of total voyage expenses. For two reasons this is a variable cost. First, daily fuel consumption is a great deal higher steaming than in port—another strong incentive to reduce vessel steaming time. Second, the costs of fuel vary markedly between bunkering depots in different parts of the world. This variation bears relation to the economic distance of depots from their fuel sources.[16]

Sargent recognized the remarkable port activity of Las Palmas and Tenerife (in the Canary Islands) as coal depots in 1912. Today, oil has replaced coal as the major steamship fuel but the strategic location of the Canary Islands near important ocean great circle routes is still significant. Las Palmas remains an active oil bunkering port. Similarly, St. Vincent (Cape Verde Islands), Curaçao, Aruba, Colombo, Aden,

---

[16] In the modern supertanker era, with recent increases in proven oil reserves and with vigorous oil company competition for markets, these differentials have decreased. Still, according to Shell Oil Company's *"Marine Bunker Prices Schedule No. 1/1966,"* the price of marine fuel oil (bunker "C") varies from $2.00 per barrel in Curaçao to $5.40 per barrel in Valparaiso, from 85 shillings per long ton in Abadan (Persian Gulf) to 153 shillings in Auckland.

Singapore, San Pedro (California), Gibraltar, Ceuta, Port Said, Suez, Cristobal, Balboa, and several other marine oil bunkering depots capitalize either upon locational advantage or upon low price fuel to attract vessel calls. Although vessel diversion from the "straight path" may not be tremendous, the fueling factor has a definite shaping effect upon ocean tracks.[17]

Most bulk commodities in full cargo lots put vessels down to their "marks" without filling them cubically. In this event, the tramp operator is often faced with an ultimate choice between cargo and fuel oil; that is, if he bunkers to capacity, his cargo capacity is reduced. If there is no opportunity of bunkering en route, he must compare the fuel price differential between loading and discharge port with the cargo freight rate. Logically, if fuel price at loading port is $8.00 per ton cheaper than at port of discharge and cargo freight rate is only $6.00 per ton (stevedoring unconsidered), he will probably bunker to absolute capacity at loading port, reducing cargo lifting accordingly.

Vessels must also abide by freeboard regulations which vary zonally and seasonally over the globe. Essentially, these are regulations for vessels' steaming safety. Thus, for a ten thousand deadweight ton vessel there may be a 350-ton lifting capacity difference between "tropical zone" and "summer zone," and a similar difference between "summer zone" and "winter zone." The seasonal aspect of these zones often results in markedly different summer and winter tracks. Furthermore, cargo freight rate levels tend to vary slightly from one part of the year to another to compensate for variations in total vessel lifting capacity.[18]

With these many variations, the fueling program necessitates intricate calculations. The zones in which vessels operate, the necessary fuel safety margins, possibilities of diversion to enroute bunkering ports, vessel time expended, port charges, finally the comparison of fuel price differentials with cargo freight rates are necessary considerations. Usually, the ultimate decision on these matters rests with the carrier. His decisions affect tramp vessel tracks, port activity, and individual cargo liftings.

---

[17] The effect is variable depending upon the fuel prices and cargo freight rate levels at the time. It is the writer's belief that the availability of cheap bunkers at San Pedro (Long Beach/Los Angeles area) close to the "effective" great circle ocean route from Panama Canal to Japan has redounded to the benefit of California ports in general. The attraction of low fuel costs reduces the necessary cargo incentive for a vessel call. The number of vessel calls increases sailing frequencies to the Orient, thus stimulating cargo routings via West Coast United States ports. This effect has more relevance to liner than to tramp activity, however.

[18] In the 1950's the United States East Coast/Western Europe coal and grain freight rates showed this tendency. For late fall and winter movements the "winter zone" regulations reduce cargo liftings, making the voyage slightly less profitable for the carrier. To compensate, the freight rates tend to climb slightly for these seasons.

Carrier's Expectations and Their Effects

The behavior of the independent carrier is strongly affected by future expectations as well as by immediate voyage costs.

Future vessel employment plays a vital part in the carrier's selection of cargoes, trade routes, and ports. These selections cumulatively affect the nature of tramp cargo movements. The tramp owner is constantly analyzing worldwide cargo movement prospects and freight rate trends, attempting to anticipate *regional* abundances or shortages of shipping space. Temporary dislocations of world tramp shipping space—e.g., a clustering along certain unusually active routes—often has marked impact upon freight rate levels. The mere anticipation of these dislocations, arising, for example, from an official announcement of heavy relief grain shipments, has similar effects upon freight rates. The tramp operator continually searches for *profitable patterns of operation.* However, immediate profit maximization motivation must be tempered by evaluation of his own long-term relationships with shippers and brokers.

A vital consideration for the carrier is the proper positioning of vessels in time and space. Thus, if freighting arrangements have been made for a particular cargo movement three months hence—or if the tramp operator merely anticipates participation in this movement—his choice of vessel employment in the interim is affected. This might lead to acceptance of normally unacceptable cargo or unusually long ballast legs provided timing and positioning are perfect with respect to subsequent employment.

One advantage of negotiating consecutive voyages on the same trade route—for example, successive Hampton Roads/Western Europe coal voyages—is the promise of *steady future employment.* For this perhaps the carrier is willing to accept barely compensatory freight rates.[19] Freight revenues on these one-way cargo flows must cover ballast return voyages. On many, if not most, tramp runs there is no equivalent volume of direct return cargo; therefore, these sizeable return ballasts are often a characteristic of the tramp connections between areas. Because of carrier time economies, as noted previously, the ballast leg is *not* an unmitigated evil. Tramp operators with large fleets of vessels often hedge their total operating position with a few long-term contracts or consecutive voyage fixtures. Usually, the operator secures options of vessel substitutions and sizeable variations in individual voyage cargo liftings. Thus he obtains valuable operational flexibility.

[19] There is special inducement for consecutive grain voyages. Often the initial cost of fitting a vessel for grain is high, therefore it may be advantageous to defray this cost over several consecutive grain voyages.

Moreover, at any time one of his vessels may "disappear" from this particular trade route and another vessel appear.

Theoretically, a two-way cargo flow between areas implies the most efficient utilization of vessel space. Presumably the attractiveness of such an operation to the carrier should be reflected in relatively low freight rate levels in both directions. Consider relief movements of grain from the east coast of the United States (e.g., Baltimore) to the west coast of India (e.g., Bombay). Were the tramp operator confronted with a return in ballast *all* the way from India to the United States plus required Suez Canal tolls, a compensatory grain cargo freight rate might be unobtainable. However, if an iron or manganese ore movement were available (or could be stimulated by a reasonably low ore freight rate quotation) from Bombay or Marmagoa to Baltimore at any freight rate which *improves upon returning empty*, the tramp operator could afford to accept a lower rate on grain. Or suppose the carrier is considering coal from Norfolk to Rio de Janeiro. If a return cargo of iron ore were available from Victoria (Brazil) to Baltimore, the carrier could offer a lower coal rate. Two-way patterns are seldom perfect—that is, they seldom involve only two ports in two areas. Usually, at least a small ballast leg is necessary. Moreover, cargo flows in each direction often vary considerably in volume and timing. Two-way patterns reflect one phenomenon which is characteristic of tramp connections. The actual economics of vessel operations tie together otherwise unrelated cargo movements. Although the commodities involved, perhaps grain and ore as illustrated above, are entirely different and the shippers and receivers of each totally different, the carriers are the same, therefore the freight rate levels interrelated. Furthermore, the volumes of the separate flows may be indirectly related through the freight rate "pricing mechanism." Thus, an urgent grain movement to India may result in a clustering of vessels seeking return cargo. Competition for this cargo may drive ore freight rates down, *stimulating* ore movements when demand is elastic. Generally, the highest relative freight rate levels apply to that portion of the two-way movement which has the most urgent shipping requirements. Urgency is easily detected by the carrier or his broker.

Most vessels engaged in tramp shipping operations are adaptable to the carriage of various types of cargo in geographically diverse trades. Thus there are elaborate patterns of operation considerably more complex than the consecutive voyage shuttle runs or the two-way cargo movements. Return cargo is not essential but future employment is a constant consideration. Even in the Baltimore/Bombay/Baltimore example above, the India/Baltimore ore cargo is only one of many possibilities. There may be India/Japan or India/Europe cargoes available as well. Using another illustration, a vessel might carry coal from

Hampton Roads to Japan, ballast transpacific, load a full cargo of lumber from British Columbia to South Africa, then ballast a short distance to Lourenço Marques for an ore cargo to Baltimore. Admittedly, there must be fundamental and specific areal complementarities for those movements to take place. In this instance, however, a sudden surge in Japanese demand for United States coal may key off a chain reaction. Urgent shipping requirements tend to boost freight rate levels on the coal movement (and, probably, on other tramp cargo movements from the U.S. East Coast). There results a later clustering of vessels free of cargo in Japan and seeking onward cargo. The abundance of shipping space available in British Columbia (after transpacific ballast) has a depressing effect upon freight rates in this area. Thus, transferability for Canadian lumber (and other Canadian tramp cargoes) is improved. If there is latent demand for lumber in South Africa, a movement may be activated. Similarly, if this occurs, another clustering of vessels later appears in South Africa, enhancing the transferability of Rhodesian ore moving out of Lourenço Marques for the U.S. East Coast.[20]

There are numerous possible worldwide combinations for the versatile tramp operator. Orientations of shipping space may be temporary, but there is a tendency toward consolidation of certain tramp patterns when areal complementarities and economics for the transport carrier combine to mutual benefit. When this occurs, the transport function itself, embodied in the tramp shipping operation, *ties together otherwise unrelated cargo movements*.

Trends in Transport Technology

Historically, it is apparent that size, speed, cargo capacity, navigational equipment, motive power, and other vessel characteristics have had significant impact upon trade route morphology and upon port geography. At times, physical limitations exist over which the strongest potentials for trade between two areas cannot immediately prevail. Moreover, those ocean movements which occur have often been physically restricted in direction, volume, and speed.[21] The revolutionary introduction of the steamship eliminated some of these physical constraints but imposed new operational requirements in the form of fueling programs. The latter accentuated the importance of strategically located bunkering depots. Additionally, movement of fuels to these depots represented important new tramp cargo flows.

[20] *The Chartering Annual* (see Footnote 4) records similar movements. It is possible to trace one vessel over several successive tramp voyages (although the carrier's option of vessel substitution tends to complicate detective work).
[21] As suggested in Footnote 9.

The impact of greater size, speed, and cargo capacity is well illustrated by the supercarrier developments of the last two decades. With giant carriers, economies of scale are achieved by transporting unusually large volumes of bulk cargo in fast, highly-automated vessels. Large quantities of cargo are transported in less time at reduced cost per ton mile.[22] One implication of this trend is a less frequent activity (number of vessels) along a given trade route (and in ports at each end) but more concentration of cargo volume in single liftings. Another curious result is a decline in the relative advantages of Suez and Panama Canal routes. As single vessel size and cargo liftings have risen, canal tolls have tended to rise at a much faster rate than daily operating costs and fuel consumption; therefore, the longer way around becomes more feasible—imperative in case of the largest bulk carriers which the canals cannot physically accommodate.

Frequently oil, ore, coal, steel, and grain companies have proprietary interest in supercarrier fleets and in terminal facilities. On "captive" routes this would not then represent an independent tramp operation. The freight rates and service are "controlled" by the cargo owner so that transfer costs and transfer charges are identical. Often bulk carrier services are "hired" by the cargo owner on long-term charter basis. This practice also eliminates some of the uncertainties of freight rates and transport service. Additionally, there are instances of government or institutional rate and service regulation. However, there is still a large segment of the supercarrier fleet engaged in giant-scale tramp operations under competitive freight market conditions. Most of the bulk carriers, for operational flexibility, are adaptable to the carriage of different commodities. Therefore, even proprietary carriers constantly seek profitable trading patterns in or out of their captive trades.[23] Oil tankers are often convertible to grain carriers. Certain bulk carriers are designed for alternative carriage of ore, ore concentrates, grain, coal, and oil. Finally, there are a number of total independent supercarrier fleets. These vessels will seek the most lucrative or dependable employment.

[22] Two somewhat different opinons of these economies are found in Dr. F. Ferraro's "Italian Developments in Iron Ore Shipping," The Shipping World, August 9, 1961, and Mr. Peter Wilsher's "Ports and Ore Carriers," Steel Review, Vol. 38, April, 1965. Both writers recognize that a valid analysis of the merits of supercarriers must take into account the capital expense of necessary port and cargo-handling improvements.

[23] For example, Sidermar, the Italian state shipping agency under Finsider (a state-controlled steel combine) operate their own bulk carriers in various patterns. Perhaps the foremost consideration is the procurement of U.S. coking coal and various ores for the Italian steel industry but the vessels also participate in other bulk commodity movements for foreign interests. In this way the shipping operation itself is more flexible and profitable. (D. K. Fleming: Coastal Steel Production in the European Coal and Steel Community—1953 to 1963, unpublished Ph.D. dissertation, University of Washington, 1965, Appendix B.)

New vessel construction in the last two decades has created a general world surplus of shipping space. To be sure, there have been vast volume increases in oil and ore movements worldwide which take up part of the slack. As previously observed, an oversupply of shipping space has a depressing effect upon freight rate levels; moreover, the economies of modern transport operations are reflected in lower freight rates. The major effects of "overtonnage" on a worldwide scale began to be felt after the Suez Crisis in the late 1950's. One indication was the rapid increase of "lay-up" fleets—both temporary and permanent. Although supercarrier operations are restricted to large volume movements between selected ports with adequate water depths and berthing facilities, declining freight rate trends extend beyond these particular bulk commodity flows. Older, smaller vessels are pushed into other trades including former liner trades so that freight rates in general have declined on bulk *and* general cargo.[24] Despite the general downward freight rate trend there are still significant fluctuations arising from periodic dislocations of shipping space and changing shipping requirements.

Advancing technology in marine transport has usually had the ultimate effect of reducing transport costs to shipper as well as to carrier. It has also changed the physical restrictions which affect the exact directions, speed, and volume of cargo movement. For many modern vessels, ocean tracks may be less restricted but port accessibility possibly more restricted. It should be remembered, however, that the world fleet, in its entirety, and the fleet engaged in tramp shipping, more specifically, include a wide variety of vessel types. Different conditions and different operational considerations apply.

Port Geography: The Carrier's View

In his port preferences, the tramp operator must weigh actual vessel capabilities, daily operating expenses, vessel port and cargo expenses, and future expectations against anticipated freight revenues. Some ports are physically inaccessible to certain vessels at all times. Others are accessible only on high tides or during certain seasons of the year. Others are temporarily blocked or "useless" because of strikes, holidays, or major physical, economic, or political disturbances. Some of these obstacles may be anticipated and avoided by proper voyage timing. Others may be avoided by a simple refusal of the carrier to enter voyage negotiations which involve these ports. Through past experience the carrier is usually aware of the comparative advantages of certain

[24] L. A. Bryan (*op. cit.*, p. 205) observes that ocean shipping is constantly changing; tramp service may give way to liner operations or liners abandon routes to tramps."

ports and certain terminals. This knowledge vitally affects his negotiating and operating decisions.

Generally, a combination of factors shape the carrier's attitude toward specific ports. Certainly the time factor has been significant in temporary avoidance of such geographically diverse ports as Haifa, Buenos Aires, Bombay, Beira, and Saigon when port congestion has resulted in excessive delays. Even the imposition of freight surcharges to protect delayed carriers may not be fully compensatory. Such conditions are usually temporary but often they stimulate port improvements, or else avoidance of these ports by carriers and diversion of cargo elsewhere.

Excessive vessel port expenses may dampen the vessel operator's enthusiasm. Certain tramp operators have assiduously avoided United Kingdom and Northeastern United States ports largely for this reason. Often these port charges reflect difficult physical conditions. Considering pilotage and tug charges alone, it is obvious that a vessel call at Astoria, Oregon, is less expensive to the tramp operator than a call at Portland, far up the Columbia-Williamette River; or a call at the island port, Galveston, is cheaper than a call at Houston, an inland channel port. The time factor (extra vessel steaming) is also significant here. The development of "outports" is one direct reflection of these considerations. This has particular relevance in the movement of large volumes of bulk cargo in large vessels.[25] The hypothesis that ports should be situated as far inland as "low-cost" ocean navigation allows tends to assume a shipper/receiver *not an ocean carrier viewpoint.*

Although stevedoring expenses are quite carefully considered in conjunction with freight rate negotiations, the availability and productivity of shore labor is not easy to gauge. The comparative efficiencies of certain ports are not fully reflected in freight rate, demurrage, or other differentials. The viewpoint of the carrier is not always (or immediately) shared by the shipper and receiver who have made elaborate terminal arrangements, nor always shared by local port authorities and local labor. The carrier's attitude, however, is shaped by past costs and past experience.

Even for the tramp operator, the attractiveness of a port extends beyond the immediate harbor and terminal area where cargo-handling, provisioning, fueling, and repairing operations occur. Banking facilities, transportation connections, customs and immigration cooperation, freight forwarding services, and a multitude of other factors may enhance a port's image in the carrier's eyes.

A combination of costly labor, slow cargo-handling, port congestion, inadequate facilities, excessive port charges, and other elements which

[25] The bulk terminals at Europoort and Weserport, outports of Rotterdam and Bremen, respectively, are particularly good examples.

increase total voyage expenses may price certain ports out of the market from the individual carrier's standpoint. If enough carriers adopt similar attitudes, a port's general activity can be profoundly affected, unless port improvements are forthcoming.

In the long run, at least, the carrier's reaction to port delays is usually shared by commodity shipper or receiver and inland transport carrier, each anxious to expedite cargo movements and economize on storage, cargo-handling, and demurrage expenses. Occasionally, when steady commodity flows are anticipated, ocean carriers, shippers, receivers, port authorities, inland transport carriers, labor, and the local business community are sufficiently interested in port activities to take concerted remedial action. Usually one or a few of these parties are much more directly concerned than the others.[26]

New terminal construction, modernization and enlargement of old terminal and port facilities, installation of automatic loading equipment, supplementation of local labor supplies, and new transport technology all may be solutions to the problems of moving heavier cargo volumes without increased vessel port delays. In each case, vessel time economies should be achieved.

Theoretically, port delays might be eliminated either through new construction of single, large-capacity terminals or through a proliferation of several smaller ones. The former is much more effective in the supercarrier era, and considerably more attractive to the vessel operator if costly vessel shifts are thereby avoided. The huge new Hampton Roads coal facilities and the Europoort bulk terminals represent more efficient accommodation of previously established bulk cargo traffic. Yet, in the case of the booming ore and oil trades, there has also been a development of large coastal bulk terminals in *new*, geographically dispersed, supply and market areas worldwide.[27] It cannot reasonably be contended that the independent bulk cargo carrier actively promotes or capitalizes large new automated terminal construction but his economies must at least be indirectly considered. The general impact of the supercarrier operation upon port developments and port activity has been profound. Many older ports and terminals have observed declining activity, often through failure to keep pace with modern transport technology. The net effect appears to be a growth in the actual

[26] Unfortunately, the interests of these various parties may often conflict. For example, desirably low labor costs for shipper, receiver or carrier may not be entirely consistent with labor's demands; or the construction of a large efficient bulk terminal may not appeal to local air-pollution and city beautification authorities or to competitive terminal operators.

[27] For example, there are a multitude of new ore-loading terminals in Africa, South America, Canada, Australia, and India and ore-receiving terminals (often integrated with coastal steelworks) in Europe, Japan, and the United States.

number of ports and port facilities, a concomitant growth in number of different ocean tracks, and a shift in heaviest volume movements from "older" to "newer" ports.

A seaport functions as a transfer point between sea and land (or inland waterway).[28] Since many of the costs of this transfer are borne by the vessel operator, he is understandably inclined to pass them on to the commodity shipper or receiver. Thus the costs of port time, the actual vessel port charges, and cargo expenses will often be reflected in freight rate levels, surcharges, demurrage payments, etc. The latter, in turn, enhance or detract from the port's attractiveness from the shipper's or receiver's standpoint.

The extent to which the ocean carrier has been instrumental in the rise or downfall of ports is debatable. Quite obviously, however, the individual independent operator has the prerogative of shunning a port, a cargo, or a trade route simply by refusing to enter rate negotiations. Even ports with completely captive hinterlands (from a physical standpoint) cannot afford complacency. Excessive freight rate levels to attract reluctant carriers may eventually block trade entirely.

From the Shipper's Perspective

The preceding emphasis upon the carrier's role in geographical tramp shipping connections must not obscure fundamental supply/demand relationships between commodity producers and consumers. Without this complementarity, movement would not occur. Transfer costs cannot be eliminated but in some instances constitute only a small portion of delivered commodity costs. Moreover, the strength of the supply/ demand (producer/consumer) relationship may override large fluctuations in transfer costs. When supply is geographically restricted and demand in one area strong or inelastic enough, tramp flows may continue unabated despite very high freight rate levels. Thus, 1956 and 1957 were peak years for Western European imports of United States coal—*also* peak years for average transatlantic coal freight rates.[29]

The commodity producer and consumer quite logically view the transport connection as a necessary service but a necessary evil, whether the performing vessels are under proprietary or independent ownership. Over long periods of time, fluctuations in cargo volume on most active

[28] A seaport, as defined by Alexandersson (*op. cit.*, p. 118), is also "a coastal point acting as a focus of one or more shipping lanes."
[29] More or less the same conditions existed in several other bulk commodity trades at this time. A combination of pressing raw material demands, the Suez Crisis and a worldwide shortage of vessel space resulted in astronomically high freight rates. At times during this period the delivered price of United States coal in Rotterdam was more than double the f.o.b. (free on board vessel) price at Norfolk. (See *ECSC, High Authority, 11th General Report*, May 1963, Table 17, p. 608.)

tramp routes certainly reflect basic changes or shifts in commodity supply and demand. These shifts have temporal and spatial aspects. However, when commodity demand is elastic, when supply is not geographically restricted, and when transport charges do constitute a large part of delivered commodity costs, flows of cargo can be significantly changed by altered transferability.

Exogenous Influences

There are many important factors beyond control of shipper, carrier, or receiver which shape tramp connections. Physical considerations relevant to tramp operations have been mentioned. Physical conditions may strongly affect producer and consumer as well. Crop failure may slow a customarily heavy grain flow to a mere trickle. Severe winters may increase oil and coal requirements. Regional depletion of mineral resources or the proving of new reserves have obvious implications. A variety of catastrophies—physical, economic, and political—may interrupt or change commodity flows.

On an even higher plateau of generalization, regional, national, and international economic and political climates have significant impact. Moreover, freight rate levels are unusually sensitive to anticipated changes in these conditions. Not least, the morass of regulation affecting trade and transportation must be considered. Tariffs, quotas, exchange controls, blocked currencies, required export or import permits, and prohibitive laws present unsurmountable obstacles to certain tramp flows. Perfect competition and perfectly unfettered market conditions do not exist, even though they may be approximated in certain tramp trades.

Visualization of Tramp Conditions

Statistical record is not a particularly vivid depiction of geographical tramp connections. The vessel and cargo carried are tangible phenomena providing a real connection along a momentary and changeable ocean track. The vessel in ballast provides a different type of connection equally vital in the total shipping operation.

Were we to focus momentarily upon tramp routes of the world, a multitude of dots representing vessels in port and underway could be cartographically depicted.[30] An alignment of dots along certain routes

---

[30] E. L. Ullman: "Mapping the World's Ocean Trade: A Research Proposal," *The Professional Geographer*, Vol. 1, No. 2 (May, 1949), pp. 19–22, suggests this instantaneous approach for "taking the pulse" of world trade activity. A very useful source for such information might be *Lloyd's Shipping Index*, a confidential weekly record of names, owners, flag, age, tonnage and *approximate position* of all registered merchant vessels over a certain size with a few specified exceptions.

might suggest the significance of major cargo flows and major ballast runs. Were it possible to indicate steaming direction and cargo aboard, the realism of this image would be enhanced. On certain longer transoceanic tramp cargo routes, there might also be a suggestion of clustering, characteristic of shipping activity when urgent shipping requirements cause sizeable fluctuations in freight rate levels. Conceptually, the geographic connection between areas on single commodity tramp flows might be likened to an unconsolidated snake which has swallowed new meals before digesting previous ones. The head and tail (port activity) might be unusually large.

Greatly expanding the time scope, annual flows can be symbolized by solid lines, the width of which represent cargo weight (or value). An enormous generalization is involved. The impression of a solid connection is given, with no suggestion of daily, weekly, monthly, or seasonal variations in strength. The unfixed nature of ocean paths is obscured. Vital ballast legs of tramp voyages have vanished. However, the selection of an annual time interval does facilitate a significant general comparison of world tramp route cargo movements.

Whichever technique or time interval is used, the characteristic spatial segmentation and temporal variability of tramp connections should be remembered. Deviation from the straightest path, predominance of cargo movement in one direction, long ballast runs and irregularity of vessel spacing, reflect a number of previously mentioned conditions affecting world tramp trades.

Conclusion

The independent ocean carrier engaged in worldwide bulk commodity trades still occupies an important place in world commerce. In a sense, he represents a foreign wedge between commodity producer and consumer. Transport costs to the carrier and charges to the shipper are not necessarily identical. The carrier's *active* role is capable of influencing the cost, speed, direction, and volume of commerce.

Both physical limitations and the actual economies of tramp cargo movement affect geographical links between areas and the geography of ports. Diseconomies of certain tramp operations and certain ports of call may weaken, even break, connections. The carrier's urge to reduce total voyage costs, particularly through time conservation, guides his selection of cargoes, routes, and ports.[31] His negotiating scope frequently extends far beyond freight rate agreements. Expectations of future employment profoundly affect the tramp operator's negotiating and operating decisions. The search for profitable patterns of operation is continual. Ballast legs are essential components in these patterns.

[31] It also partially explains modern innovation in ocean transport technology.

Through the tramp shipping operation, geographically dispersed, otherwise unrelated commodity trades are tied together, resulting in a complex interrelationship of shipping space availabilities, freight rate levels, and cargo volume.

The importance of the transport user's requirements should not, of course, be minimized. The independent carrier's profit maximization urge at a point in time must be tempered by his desire for future steady employment. Certainly, in the long run, part of his operating economies is usually passed on to the user in the form of lower freight rates and better service. Often, commodity producers and consumers strive to eliminate the uncertainties of transportation through ownership or control of transportation facilities and through the establishment of rate and service regulation. These attempts to standardize the transport function or integrate the service within a controlled producer/consumer relationship may stabilize transport charges and set rather firm trade patterns. However, the comparatively unregulated, profit-seeking, competitive, independent carrier still has vital impact in ocean tramp trades. For a balanced view of these variable trade patterns, the costs, objectives, and alternatives of both user and carrier must be considered.

V. ECONOMIC REGIONS

The regional concept has a role in economic geography just as it has in all other subdivisions of the field. Similarly, there is a duality of regionalization and regional types in economic geography. Economic regions can be determined as "uniform" regions where the pattern of economic activity is relatively homogeneous throughout, and represents in this homogeneity, a significant division on the surface of the earth. Agricultural regions, such as the "Corn Belt" for example, represent a uniform region of primary economic activity.

But the great dynamics of economic activity, as well as the diversity represented by primary, secondary, and tertiary activity, can best be expressed by the "nodal" region—the regional concept functionally related to central place theory—which demonstrates the variety, complexity, and interdependence of all activity in the technologically advanced and urbanizing contemporary world. Lösch examines "The Nature of Economic Regions" using central place theory as a means of delimiting and analyzing the economic region.

Many of the earlier selections in this volume have, both directly and indirectly, been concerned with economic regions and regionalization. The final two articles in this section are specifically concerned with the problem of defining various kinds of economic regions from empirical data. Sommers uses "economic intensity" as a method for determining regions in Norway, whereas Johnson and Teufner seek boundaries of economic regions by examining "Industry Combinations in the Central United States."

26. The Nature of Economic Regions

August Lösch

*Economic regions can be constructed as theoretical models
and then applied to the reality of the landscape, or they
may be determined by field and/or statistical analysis of
empirical data. In this selection, Lösch examines first the
ideal or theoretical region, then attempts to determine
whether this model conforms to actual conditions in the
field. He uses the Christaller central place hexagonal model
discussed in an earlier selection as the base for theoretical
regions. In the conclusion, however, he points out the limita-
tion of theory when analyzing the realities of economic
activity and states, "a region is a system of various areas,
an organism rather than just an organ."*

Impressed by the accidental way in which states are created and
smashed, we are looking out for a more natural and lasting spatial order of things. Geographical and cultural regions, however, are from an
economic point of view just as artificial, units of reference as states are.
True enough, they all are of some economic relevance, but this does
not alter their essentially non-economic nature. Important as their balance of payments, their price levels, their barter terms of trade may be
for them, to *us* these averages and aggregates are entirely arbitrary and
accidental. It is independent economic regions that we here discuss,
regions not derived from but equivalent to those political, cultural geographical units.

Even if we already knew the characteristics of economic regions—
which we do not—their counterparts in the world of reality would be
likely to differ more from each other than from an ideal picture. Hence
studying the ideal region is both the only way to learn about the *essential,* and the first step towards investigating the *actual* structure of any
real economic region. So we shall deal first with the theoretical nature
of such regions, and second with their actual existence.

SOURCE: *Southern Economic Journal,* V (July, 1938), 107–15. Reprinted by permission. The late Dr. Lösch was a German economist and geographer.

I

Let us start from very radical assumptions in order to prevent any spatial differences of an uneconomic origin from hiding in our starting points. We assume a vast plain with an equal distribution of raw materials, and a complete absence of any other inequalities, either political or geographical. We further assume that nothing but self-sufficient farmyards are regularly dispersed over that plain. How can any spatial differences possibly result from this initial situation?

Supposing one of those farmers tries to produce a certain commodity beyond his needs, will he be able to sell the surplus? He will be helped by the economies of large scale production, and handicapped by costs of transportation. Will the balance be in his favor? If his neighbors all have a similar way of living, the demand curve of one of them will be typical for the others as well. Let us assume d in Figure 1 to be such an individual demand curve for beer. OP being the price at the center of production P, the demand of the people living there will be PQ. PR being the freight from P to R, the demand of each of the people living in R is RS. Farther out, at F, where the freight is PF, no more beer will be sold. Hence PF is the maximum shipping radius for beer, and the total demand within that radius is equal to the volume of the cone which we get by rotating the triangle PQF around PQ as axis. Figure 2 shows that cone. To repeat: its volume, corrected for the density of population, is equal to the total possible demand if the price at the factory is OP. For other prices at the mill we get other cones of demand, and as a final result the curve Δ of Figure 3, that represents the total demand as a function of the price at the mill. π of Figure 3 is a so-called "planning curve," showing the minimum costs at which a given output could be produced if a new factory had to be built for that purpose. Only if the planning curve π intersects or is to the left of the total demand curve Δ, is it possible for our farmer to run a brewery. Otherwise he would produce at a loss.

The shape of a trading area, however, is not a circle, as we have so far assumed. For even if the whole country were filled up with such circular areas that are close enough to just touch each other, a number of people could still successfully try to enter the brewing business. For all the black corners in Figure 4 are left unused, and moreover, as has been shown by Chamberlin,[1] the size of the individual firm will be re-

---

[1] For those not acquainted with Chamberlin's theory it may be worthwhile to point out that his argument is based mainly on two facts: (1) Due to product differentiation, of which differentiation of the seller's location is just a special case, the demand curve facing the individual seller is not horizontal (as in pure competition where the product is perfectly uniform) but has a negative slope. If, e.g., the seller raises his price, not all his customers will buy from his competitors as in a perfect market.

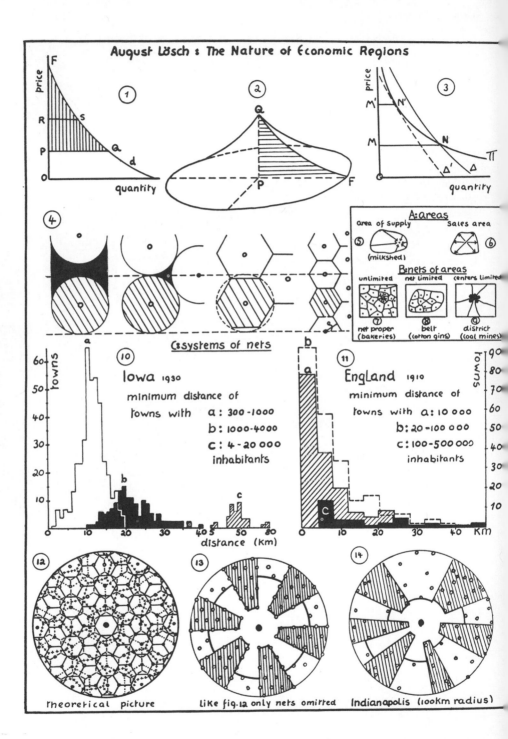

August Lösch : The Nature of Economic Regions

1 price / quantity
F, R, S, P, O, a, d

2 Q / P, F

3 price / quantity
M', N', M, N, Δ', Δ, Π

4

A: areas
⑤ Area of supply ... Sales area **⑥**
(milkshed)

B: nets of areas
unlimited | net limited | centers limited
⑦ net proper (bakeries) | **⑧** belt (cotton gins) | **⑨** district (coal mines)

C: systems of nets

10 Iowa 1930
minimum distance of towns with a: 300-1000
b: 1000-4000
c: 4-20 000
inhabitants

towns — distance (km)

11 England 1910
minimum distance of towns with a: 10 000
b: 20-100 000
c: 100-500 000
inhabitants

towns — Km

12 theoretical picture

13 like fig. 12 only nets omitted

14 Indianapolis (100km radius)

duced from *MN* to *M'N'* (in Figure 3) without rendering it unprofitable. The way to make use of the corners is to change the shape of the area into a regular hexagon. This will shift the curve Δ slightly to the left, as the hexagon is somewhat smaller than the circle that circumscribes it. Moreover, by Chamberlin's operation the size of the hexagon will be reduced until it is so small that the corresponding demand curve Δ' just touches the offer curve in *N'*. Now apparently no more people can enter the brewing business.[2] As the largest possible shipping radius results in a total demand *MN*, so the necessary minimum radius must yield the demand *M'N'*. Figure 4 shows the development from the largest to the smallest possible shipping range.

Two other possibilities of avoiding black corners are conceivable, namely the square and the triangle. But it can be shown [3] that the hexagon has an economic advantage over both: it affords the larger demand per square mile, provided the total area is the same in all cases. *The hexagon is, therefore, the most economical shape for trading areas.* For every commodity, a trading area in the form of a hexagon with a characteristic inner radius ρ is necessary and sufficient to render the production of this commodity profitable.

The trading areas of the various products look like nets of such hexagons, from very small ones to very large ones, depending upon the product. We can throw these nets over our plain at random. In spite of the resulting disorder, every place on the plain would have access to every product. Several considerations, however, which can only be mentioned here, suggest a more orderly and at the same time more economical arrangement. In the first place, we lay our nets in such a way that all of them have one center of production in common. This point will enjoy all the advantages of a large local demand. Secondly, we turn the nets around this center so that we get six sectors where centers of production are frequent, and six others where they are scarce, as is shown on Figures 12 and 13. This arrangement does not deprive any place of its access to every product, and at the same time provides for the best lines of transportation. It can be shown that the aggregate

---

To a number of them the special advantages (e.g., of convenient location) offered by him will be worth the higher price. (2) As long as the demand curve is to the right of the cost curve the extra profits thus possible will attract new competitors. They will sell products slightly different from those already in the market, or, as in our case, locate their businesses at places more convenient for part of the buyers. This will shift the demand curves of the old establishments to the left until they just touch the cost curves and all extra profits are wiped out. (See E. Chamberlin, *The Theory of Monopolistic Competition.*)

[2] We disregard here the possibility of reducing the area even more through spatial price discrimination.

[3] Whilst a more accurate and detailed proof is too lengthy for this short paper, the plausibility of our assertion can readily be seen from the fact that the regular hexagon has the advantage over the circle of using up all the territory, without departing as far from the ideal circular shape as either square or triangle.

of freights is a minimum,[4] and the final result is a complicated but orderly system of market areas. How many of these self-sufficient systems will come into existence on our plain depends merely upon the commodity which has the largest necessary shipping radius, as long as there are no economic limits to the size of the central city.

More striking about our result than any particulars is the fact that we suddenly have crowds of economic areas on a plain which we deprived of all spatial inequalities at the outset. We first have the hexagonal market area surrounding every center of production or consumption. Second, we have a net of such areas for every commodity. And third we have a systematic arrangement of the nets of market areas of the various commodities. It is the latter, the self-sufficient system of market areas as shown in Figure 12, that I should like to call the ideal economic region. How much of it we find in reality will be discussed in the second part of the paper.

II

As soon as we drop the assumption of a uniform plain, the size and shape of our market areas evidently become irregular. Moreover, if we no longer stick to the supposition of a uniform product, the individual areas for the same line of production overlap, and may consequently be full of holes particularly near the periphery. Yet there are numerous instances left where our assumptions are roughly fulfilled and where our results, therefore, must hold true without much modification, as factual investigations indeed seem to indicate.

Actually it is not quite accurate to compare the numerous market areas of commodity to a net. Due to the overlapping just mentioned they often rather resemble fish scales or an irregular layer of slabs of slate. In spite of this modification the essential characteristics of a net are mostly retained, and as a matter of fact most of the maps showing trading areas that were prepared either by scholars or by businessmen do not give any consideration to the overlapping at all. Far more important than this modification of the structure of our nets are the changes in their extension. In some instances, for which bakeries may serve as an example (Figure 7), the nets still cover the whole territory under consideration. In fact, a survey made by the author of about half the American industry would seem to indicate that the importance of this type of production is rather underrated. Nevertheless, the very nets or at least their centers are often compressed on a relatively small

[4] As more centers of production coincide more consumers are able to buy from local mills than under any other arrangement of the nets. Not only the mileage of transports but the mileage of lines of transportation as well is reduced.

space, and we may speak then of belts and districts respectively. The former case may be exemplified by the net of the areas of supply of the cotton gins that is naturally limited by the cotton belt. And an illustration of the concentration of the centers of production only are the mines in a coal district (see Figures 8 and 9 respectively). Instead of tracing out the areas, which is a very difficult task, we can show their character just as clearly by measuring the minimum distance of their centers from each other. This is done in Figures 10 and 11, not for centers of a single production but for towns of a supposedly similar economic function. In Iowa, with its rather equal distribution of production, the distances between towns increase with their size, just as in our theoretical picture based on assumptions approximately fulfilled in Iowa. In England, on the other hand, the cities cluster in the coal districts and show the same distance from each other irrespective of size. Such concentrations of the nets or their centers may have purely economic reasons such as the advantages due to the proximity of many establishments of the same branch. But it may also be a reflection of the limited geographical extension of factors of economic consequence although not of economic nature. It is worth noting, however, that these non-economic factors and their economic reflections are not co-extensive. For instance, the area where cotton *could* be grown is larger than the actual cotton belt.

In addition to the limited size of the nets, and the overlapping of the individual market areas, a third deviation from the ideal pattern is worth mentioning. In our theoretical deduction we had to cope with the problem of how the various nets should be located, while the distribution of the centers of production within a net was conspicuous for its regularity. Actually this too is a problem, and a very difficult one at that. Neither of the two traditional instruments of determining the geographical distribution of production can solve it: the theory of location proper cannot because it is applicable only to a single establishment, not to a whole industry; and the theory of comparative costs fails because it is applicable only to trade between men, not between countries. The only adequate solution of the location of all the interdependent centers of production is a system of locational equations which the author hopes to present later.

The systems of nets come off worse in the real world than either the nets or the individual market areas. It is simply impossible to arrange all the irregular nets in such a way that they have at least one point in common. There exists nowhere either a city with a complete set of industries or a self-sufficient region. But this is not the worst. We could at least imagine and probably find a few actual cases where regions trade their specialties with each other through their central cities, and through them alone. In such an instance a systematic arrangement of towns as in our ideal region would still be conceivable. Actually, however, small places which in every other respect entirely depend upon neighboring cities are the centers of large market areas. As far as their particular products are concerned, even metropolitan cities or the whole nation may be tributary to those little places, the industries of which neither need nor attract a large local market. Furthermore, while the regional system of nets of market areas centers in a large city, not every big city dominates such a system. Many mining towns, for instance, have not much of an economic function towards their hinterland. In contrast with such specialized cities, a regional center is characterized by a variety of production and trade that links it to the surrounding country. If, now, we disregard all the market areas of the type just described, a substructure of economic regions is left. They *differ* from the ideal pattern in the important respect that they are not self-sufficient; they *correspond* to the ideal inasmuch as they too are based (1) on the advantages of a large local concentration of production, consumption or trade; (2) on the most economical layout of lines of communication.

This regional substructure can be discovered almost everywhere but it is not everywhere of equal importance. Its importance can be measured by comparison with those market areas that have to be eliminated from a regional analysis as was just pointed out. To give some examples: regionalism prevails in southern Germany. The distribution of the undisputed regional centers: Frankfurt, Nürnberg, München, Zürich, Strassburg, with Stuttgart in the middle is very regular. There should be one more center to the south of München but the Alps make this obviously impossible. The rise of München over Augsburg that had the advantage of an earlier start is worth noting. München has the better location from the point of view of our theory. It is right in the middle of the region, and at the proper distance from the neighboring centers. The German Ruhr district, on the other hand, hardly displays any regional pattern whatever. According as the systematic or the chaotic distribution of the nets of market areas prevails in a given case, we may stress or disregard the regional substructure. From this it follows that while the regional concept will be most realistic with respect to some parts of a country, it would be difficult and not very useful to divide a state up into its regions.

Finally, as to the relation between economic and other regions, it is essential for the regional system of market areas to have a center. In rare and particularly fortunate cases these economic centers are at the same time cultural and political ones, thus becoming the true heart of their region, as Paris is for France.

III

To summarize, we found three main types of economic areas: simple market areas, nets of such areas, and systems of nets. Or, if we want to give a popular name to each, we may speak of markets, belts, and regions. In this sequence they become more complex, more self-sufficient, and unfortunately less real. On the one end there are the individual market areas, most simple, most real, and most dependent upon trade. The systems of market areas, or regions, on the other hand, are very complex; in an ideal case quite self-sufficient, but harder to find in reality. Many commodities are produced and traded outside of any system. And whatever systems we do find, overlap even more than the market areas of a single commodity. A clear economic region is a fortunate accident rather than a natural subdivision of states. Still, beneath a sphere of irregular market areas, we find a regional substructure of varying importance almost everywhere. Between the simple area of sale or supply and the full regional system is the net. The geographical extension of these nets or of their centers is often small. In this case these belts or districts of production or consumption are very conspicuous, but should still be distinguished from regions. A region is a system of *various* areas, an organism rather than just an organ.

27. Distribution of Manufacturing in Norway: An Approach to the Delimitation of Economic Intensity Regions

Lawrence M. Sommers

In the world today, economic development is proceeding at unprecedented rates in some areas and lagging badly in others, but a measure of various levels of economic intensity produces significant regional patterns. As one measure— and for a well-developed country such as Norway, a very suitable measure—the author uses the amount of employment in manufacturing as the principal index of intensity. This results in well-defined, useful, and understandable regions.

*Other criteria could be more suitable and revealing in other
areas, depending on the nature of economic development
in that country. It is essential that the economic geographer
be selective in determining the most significant elements
of an economy when attempting to delimit economic regions.
Therefore, regionalization often is the final product of analysis
in economic geography.*

Geographers have established various kinds of regions to aid them in
characterizing and analyzing the areal differentiation of all or portions
of the earth's surface. Treatises of the geography of any given country
may delimit regions such as physiographic, mineral, agricultural, and
geographic. These often fail to portray the relative economic importance of various parts of a country. This paper suggests intensity regions as a method of summarizing the varying economic significance of
areas within a country. Norway has been selected to illustrate this concept as the distribution patterns of economic development are relatively
simple and reliable statistics are available.

In the nineteenth and early twentieth centuries, thousands of people
migrated from Norway due to lack of employment. The traditional occupations of agriculture, forestry, fishing, and commerce failed to provide sufficient opportunity for a growing population. Without domestic
coal and petroleum, Norway lacked a natural basis for powering large
factories. Industrialization had to await the early 1900's when technical
ability was developed to allow utilization of the abundant water power
resources. Inexpensive plentiful hydroelectric power was the major key
to the rapid development of industry after 1910. In 1910 agriculture and forestry contributed 20 per cent of the total national product
as compared to only 10 per cent in 1950. Industry, including manufacturing, mining, construction and power, provided 25 per cent in 1910
compared to nearly 50 per cent in 1950. Industry employed about one-
third of the labor force in 1950 compared to 26 per cent in 1900. Capital
investment in new and expanded industry has been especially heavy in
the post-World War II period, at the expense of other sectors of the
economy, and labor shortages have been characteristic.

The location of the bulk of Norway's manufacturing is closely related
to the availability of hydroelectric power and inexpensive water transportation necessary to import and export raw materials, semi-finished
and finished products. The result is overwhelming concentrations on or
near the coast (Fig. 1). The preponderance of industrial growth has
occurred in the southeast with Oslo as the principal focus (Fig. 2). Oslo
alone has 22 per cent of the nation's manufacturing labor force. The

SOURCE: *The Journal of Geography,* LXI (May, 1962), 196–204. Reprinted with
permission of the author and the publisher. The author is professor and chairman,
Department of Geography, Michigan State University.

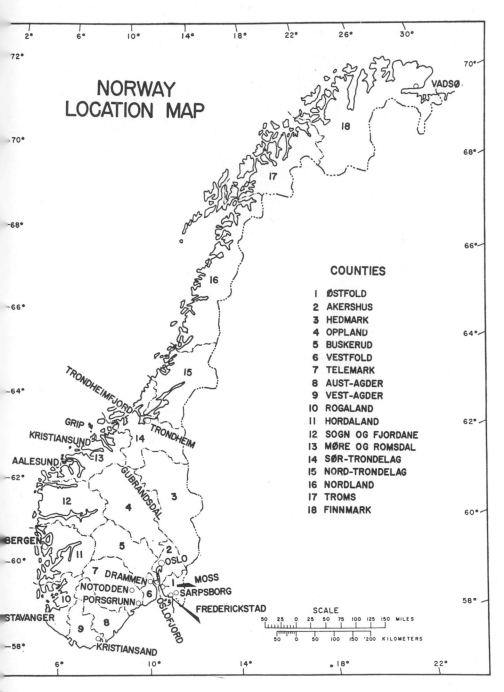

FIGURE 1.

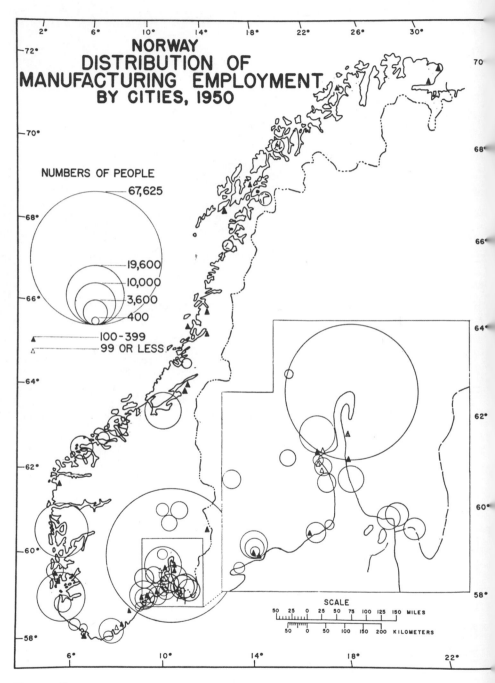

FIGURE 2.

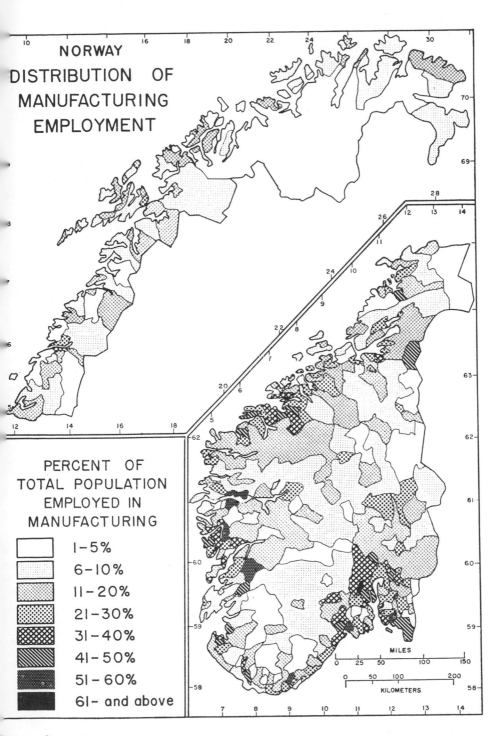

NORWAY
DISTRIBUTION OF MANUFACTURING EMPLOYMENT

PERCENT OF TOTAL POPULATION EMPLOYED IN MANUFACTURING

	1-5%
	6-10%
	11-20%
	21-30%
	31-40%
	41-50%
	51-60%
	61- and above

MILES
0   25   50   100   150

0   50   100   200
KILOMETERS

FIGURE 3.

453

eight southeastern counties have 63 per cent of the value added by manufacturing, 58 per cent of the labor force employed in manufacturing, 56 per cent of the number of manufacturing establishments, and 58 per cent of the total investment.[1] The south and west coasts possess most of the remainder of Norway's manufacturing as North Norway provides only 5 per cent (Fig. 3). Concerted attempts by the government to place new industry in the "economic problem area" of northern Norway have met with limited success; the government owned and operated integrated iron steel plant at Mo i Rana is a notable exception.

The evaluation of manufacturing intensity differentiation within a country is of prime import in determining variations in the degree of economic intensity. The mapping of the following criteria would be useful in establishing such regions and degrees of economic intensity: agricultural yields per acre, distribution of value of imports and exports, population distribution, value added by manufacturing, the number and total production value of manufacturing establishments, and employment in manufacturing. Distribution of the gainfully employed population in manufacturing by counties, herreds,[2] and cities is used in this paper as a possible meaningful criterion in delimiting varying intensities of manufacturing. As manufacturing is the principal segment of the economy of Norway, it should be possible to make certain valid inferences concerning the distribution of economic development from an analysis of the distribution of employment in manufacturing.

Manufacturing Distribution: By Counties

In 12 of the 20 Norwegian counties, manufacturing enterprises employ the largest percentage of the gainfully employed (Fig. 4). These counties, including the two principal cities of Oslo and Bergen which also have county governmental status, possess 66 per cent of the labor force of Norway, and 80 per cent of the economically active engaged in manufacturing. Agriculture leads in only the two interior counties of Hedmark and Oppland, a west coast county of Sogn og Fjordane and the five northern counties beginning with Sør Trondelag. Sør Trondelag has almost an equal dependence upon agriculture and manufacturing with 21 per cent in the former and 20 per cent in the latter. Sogn og Fjordane has the greatest dependence upon agriculture with 42 per cent. Fishing and whaling are predominant in Finnmark with 25 per cent.

The percentage of people employed in manufacturing varies from 9

[1] "Norges Industri," *Norges Offisielle Statistikk*, Statistisk Sentralbyraa, Oslo, 1958. (Industrial production statistics do not include curing and simple preparing of fish, publishing, and manufacture of dairy products.)
[2] Minor civil divisions similar to United States townships.

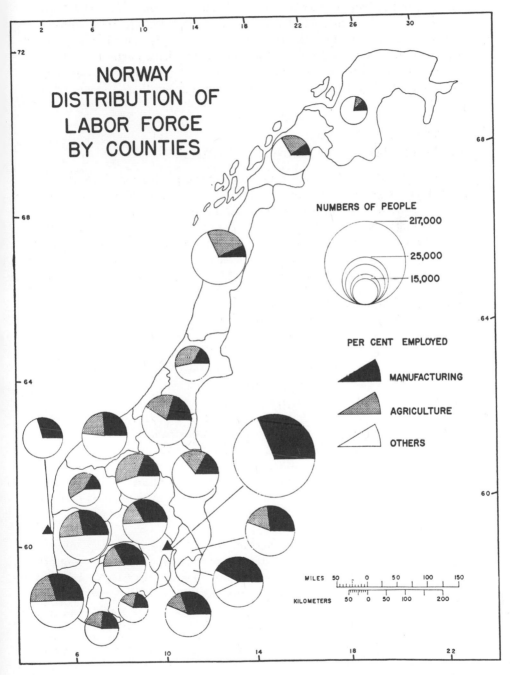

NORWAY
DISTRIBUTION OF
LABOR FORCE
BY COUNTIES

NUMBERS OF PEOPLE
217,000
25,000
15,000

PER CENT EMPLOYED

MANUFACTURING

AGRICULTURE

OTHERS

MILES 50 0 50 100 150

KILOMETERS 50 0 50 100 200

FIGURE 4.

455

per cent in Finnmark to 42 per cent in Østfold. The greatest dependence upon manufacturing occurs in the southeastern counties near Oslo and in other coastal counties as far north as Trondheimfjord with the exception of Sogn og Fjordane as indicated previously. This is too gross a picture, however, as much of the interior highland portions of these counties contain little or no manufacturing. An analysis of the distribution by herreds and cities gives a much more accurate and meaningful pattern.

Distribution of Employment in Manufacturing: By Herreds and Cities[3]

According to the 1950 census, 5 per cent of the population employed in manufacturing was in rural herreds and 45 per cent in cities.[4] The maximum variation is from none on the island of Grip near Kristiansund to 71 per cent southeast of Oslo and by cities from 9 per cent in Vadsø in the extreme north to 58 per cent in Notodden, southwest of Oslo (Fig. 3).

Those cities and herreds with more than 20 per cent of their labor force employed in manufacturing are most significant in outlining the manufacturing regions of Norway. When the percentage in manufacturing falls below 20 per cent, agriculture, forestry, or some other occupation is usually foremost. North of Trondheimfjord only six herreds and one city exceed the 20 per cent figure (Fig. 3).

About 94 per cent of the population in Norway employed in manufacturing is found south of Trondheimfjord or Sør Trondelag county. This includes 91 per cent of those in manufacturing pursuits in herreds and 95 per cent of those in cities or towns. Most of Norway's urban centers are on or near the coast with the major concentration found in southeastern Norway. The distribution of manufacturing exhibits a similar pattern. Fjords such as Sognfjord and productive river valleys such as Gubrandsdal result in some interior manufacturing centers. Four major manufacturing concentrations can be identified in Norway: 1) the dominant southeast core, 2) the south coast, 3) the west coast, and 4) the northwest coast (Fig. 3).

The southeast core region focusing on Oslo and extending inland from Oslofjord is by far the most important as it contains 49 per cent of Norway's manufacturing using the employment criteria. Nearly 50 per cent of the total population is found in the capital city and seven

[3] Cities as here defined are those urban areas in Norway that have a separate governmental status or are small coastal seaports with a customs station.
[4] Statistical data concerning employment in counties, cities, and herreds was obtained from, "Folketellingen, 1 Desember 1950, Tredje hefte," *Statistisk Sentralbyraa*, Oslo, 1956. The data for the maps in this paper were procured from this same source.

surrounding counties with the associated labor force, domestic market, export ports, and capital for industrial and commercial investment. The road and railway network of this region, complemented by easy coastwise and foreign trade connections, provide the necessary means to tie the manufacturing centers together. The transportation facilities also allow the assemblage of Norway's agricultural and forestry raw materials for processing. The rivers provide the necessary power as well as a transportation medium for timber and timber products.

Consumer goods manufacturing predominates in Oslo which is also the chief port with 33 per cent of Norway's foreign trade. Food and raw material processing such as wood and paper products are concentrated in the coastal ports at mouths of rivers where water power is available as at Sarpsborg, Fredrikstad, Moss, and Drammen. Electrometallurgical and electrochemical production such as in Porsgrunn is also noteworthy.

Along the south coast is a narrow fringe accounting for 10 per cent of Norway's employment in manufacturing. Kristiansand and Stavanger are the major foci along with a number of smaller coastal centers. The short, fast-flowing rivers provide power but offer little in the way of inland valleys and hinterlands for the coastal cities. Leading industries are base metals in Kristiansand, shipbuilding in Stavanger, and in other centers paper and paper products and food processing. A coastal highway and railway provide transportation connections, but coastal and foreign shipping connections are also significant.

The west coast region contained 11 per cent of the manufacturing labor force of Norway in 1950. Bergen is the outstanding center with shipbuilding, textile manufacturing and food processing. Smaller centers along the sides or heads of fjords, often involved in electrometallurgical manufacturing, are also significant. Coastwise and foreign shipping routes are essential in the interconnections within this region, and with other parts of Norway and foreign countries. A railway and highway connects Bergen with Oslo and the southeast core and there are local highway networks. This area has been developing rapidly since World War II.

The manufacturing in the northwest coast region, the largest in area, is more unevenly distributed than in the previous three regions. About 11 per cent of Norway's manufacturing labor force is located here. The cities of Trondheim, Kristiansand, and Aalesund are the major focal centers. Diversified manufacturing is characteristic with food processing, textiles and clothing, and furniture of importance. This area is connected by rail, highway, and ship with southeast Norway but coastal shipping takes on principal significance for connections between manufacturing centers within the area. Fjord rather than outer coast locations are predominant in this region.

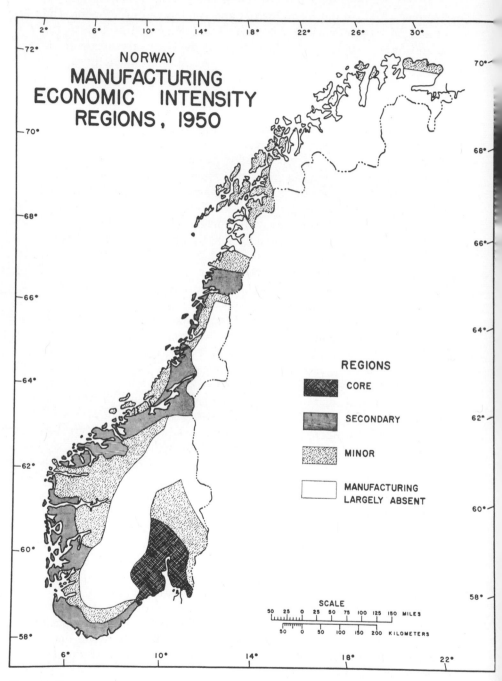

FIGURE 5.

Manufacturing Intensity Regions
for Norway

The maps showing distribution of the labor force employed in manufacturing help to regionalize the various degrees of dependence upon and
intensity of manufacturing in Norway (Fig. 5). Four scales of intensity
are identified. (1) The southeast Norway core which contains the largest city and 49 per cent of the total manufacturing labor force of Norway; 63 per cent of these are employed in manufacturing in cities and
37 per cent of these, in herreds. A large proportion of this area has more
than 31 per cent of its labor force in manufacturing with an extreme of
71 per cent in one area southeast of Oslo. (2) The secondary areas of
manufacturing intensity include most of the remainder of coastal Norway south of Trondheimfjord. The larger portion of this area falls into
the 21 to 30 per cent employed in the manufacturing category. Concentrations show a marked attraction to the coast and available hydroelectric power. This region is narrow in the south and broadens along
the west coast where fjords allow penetration into the interior. In this
region are employed 31 per cent of the total manufacturing workers of
Norway; 34 per cent of the country's laborers living in herreds and 29
per cent of all the factory workers living in cities. (3) The minor areas
include much of north Norway and the areas of south Norway interior
from the secondary regions as outlined above. Most of this region has
between 11 and 20 per cent of its labor force in manufacturing. Agriculture, forestry, and fishing are predominant with scattered industrial
establishments emphasizing the processing of raw materials. (4) Those
regions largely devoid of manufacturing are located in the plateau and
mountainous sections of Norway. Less than 10 per cent of the labor
force is employed in manufacturing and, in large areas, under 5 per
cent. Economic activity is limited to marginal agriculture and forestry
with only wide scattered home handicraft and small manufacturing or
processing plants.

It is proposed that manufacturing intensity is a valuable indicator of
the over-all economic intensity in Norway as well as many other parts
of the world. Other criteria such as value added by manufacturing
should be evaluated to further substantiate and refine the degree of
economic intensity in various parts of Norway. In other parts of the
world criteria such as measuring agricultural or some other form of
intensity perhaps would be more successful. Such economic intensity
regions are highly meaningful, perhaps more so than most other types
of regions that could be delimited, in the summary evaluation of the
relative importance to man of the areal differentiation within the political boundaries of a country or even a larger unit.

28. Industry Combinations in the Central United States: An Application of Weaver's Method

Lane J. Johnson and Waltraud E. Teufner

Many economic regions have been delimited by the use of a carefully selected combination of significant criteria. This has been particularly true in analyzing patterns in agriculture where crop combinations have been used to develop useful agricultural regions in the American Middle West. This method of using a combination of criteria can also be applied to other economic activities, such as manufacturing. In this selection the combination method is used to determine industrial patterns and regions. As is made clear, the important element in this, as in all, regionalization is a careful selection of criteria.

Several years ago, John C. Weaver identified agricultural combinations by treating local complexes of relevant phenomena.[1] Those geographers following his lead have continued to investigate agricultural combinations, but Weaver's method is not by nature limited to agricultural studies. The present authors propose to illustrate its generality for investigating complexes of elements by applying it to local (county) economies. More specifically, the purpose of the present study is to determine industry combinations and to designate industry-combination

SOURCE: *The Professional Geographer*, XX (September, 1968), 297–301. Reprinted with permission of the publisher and the authors. Dr. Johnson is professor, Department of Geography, Temple University. Miss Teufner is continuing graduate work at the University of Chicago.

[1] The basic article is by Weaver, J. C., "Crop-Combination Regions in the Middle West," *Geographical Review*, Vol. 44, 1954, pp. 175–200. Other articles, involving the same author and including the combination idea, are: Weaver, J. C., "Changing Patterns of Cropland Use in the Middle West," *Economic Geography*, Vol. 30, 1954, pp. 1–47; Weaver, J. C., "Crop-Combination Regions for 1919 and 1929 in the Middle West," *Geographical Review*, Vol. 44, 1954, pp. 560–72; Weaver, J. C., "The County as a Spatial Average in Agricultural Geography," *Geographical Review*, Vol. 46, 1956, pp. 536–65; and Weaver, J. C., Hoag, L. P., and Fenton, B. L., Livestock Units in the Middle West," *Economic Geography*, Vol. 32, 1956, pp. 237–59.

regions. The area selected as large and varied enough for this purpose includes the states of Illinois, Iowa, Missouri, Nebraska, Kansas, and Colorado.

Data and Technique

Data for the study are 1960 figures for "industry group of employed persons." Based on a 25 per cent sample of all employed persons by place of residence, these are good data considering the study's areal scope and county framework. They have a high degree of completeness with only 4.4 per cent of the employed persons in the study area in the "industries not reported" category. Moreover, they get directly at the employment mix, a matter of primary economic and social significance within a local area. For the study, the data are grouped into seven major industry classes—(A) agriculture, (C) transportation and communication, (E) mining, (F) forestry and fishing, (M) manufacturing, (S) service, and (T) trade (Table 1).

The technique applied to the complex of industries in each county is the variance formula:

$$\sigma^2 = \frac{\Sigma d^3}{n}$$

where:
d is the difference between an industry's percentage of the total employed in all seven industry groups and an ideal percentage;
and n is the number of industries in a combination.

Rounded ideal percentages are 100 per cent of the employed in a single industry group for a 1-industry economy, 50 per cent of the employed in each of two industry groups for a 2-industry economy, through to 14 per cent of the employed in each of seven industry groups for a 7-industry economy.

The industry combination having the smallest variance within a county is selected as typifying that county. For example, the combination determined for Calhoun County, Illinois, is AST (Table 2).

In order to further clarify the technique, two additional points should be noted. (1) No account is taken of the rank of an industry within the combination for a county, e.g., AST also designates the permutations ATS, SAT, STA, TAS, and TSA. (2) No computations are made for combinations which would include an industry having less than 5 per cent of the employed persons in a county.

Industry Combinations

With seven industry groups, 127 different economies are possible. Twenty of these economies appear in the six states investigated (Fig. 1).

AST, usually representing an agricultural economic base accompanied by largely ubiquitous service and trade facilities, is the most prominent economic type, occuping 233 counties and the greatest area. This local economy is dominant in the central section of the study area. There also are a few AST extensions and exclaves beyond the central section. In most counties in which this type is found, agriculture ranks first among the industry groups.

The AMST type is second in number of counties, 183, and area occupied. This more diversified local economy dominates the eastern part of the six-state area and is found in scattered counties as far west as central Colorado. Manufacturing is of major importance in many counties having this kind of economy.

The 54 MST counties do not characterize any large area. Though found mainly in the eastern half of the six-state area, MST in fact represents many urban counties which, sometimes singly and sometimes jointly, function as massive centers of manufacturing, service, and trade.

The three local economies just noted account for over 80 per cent of the area's 577 counties. If one disregards their common components, S and T, the symbols indicate a progression from agriculture, to agriculture and manufacturing, to manufacturing (rural predominance, to mixed rural and urban, to urban). There also is a progression by type in total numbers of people employed. For this reason, while AST does not describe any of the states taken as a whole, AMST is the symbol for the states of Iowa, Kansas, and Nebraska, and MST is the symbol for Colorado, Illinois, and Missouri, as well as for the United States.

The remaining 17 types of economies range from specialized to diversified and together involve all industry groups, except forestry and fishing. The 107 counties having these various economies are distributed through the study area, although certain types concentrate significantly in the mountains and plateaus of Colorado.

Industry-Combination Regions

On the basis of the industry combinations, three general regions have been designated within the study area. These are outlined approximately in Figure 1.

The eastern region is typified by AMST counties and a large number of counties having MST economies. This region might be characterized as having achieved a blending of urban and rural activities. Local diversification is the rule, with 4-industry combinations predominating; in addition, several counties have 3-industry or 5-industry combinations.

The central region is composed mainly of AST counties. Other types found here detract little from the region's agricultural emphasis, as they as often as not also are basically agricultural. Local diversification

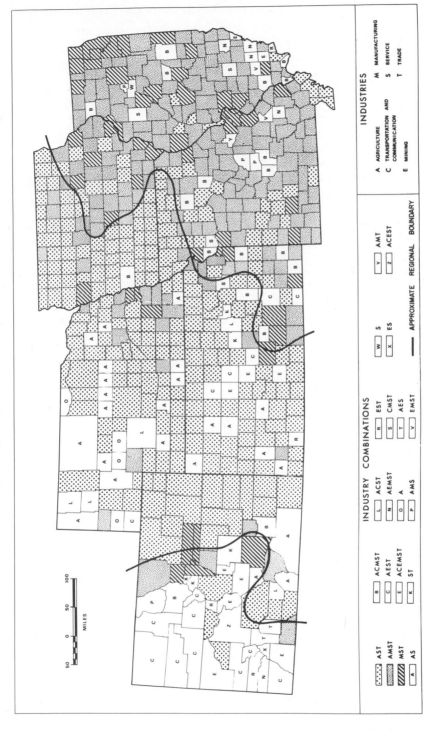

INDUSTRY COMBINATIONS
CENTRAL UNITED STATES   1960

MILES

INDUSTRY COMBINATIONS

AST	B	ACMST
AMST	C	AEST
MST	E	ACEMST
AS	K	ST

L	ACST	R	EST	W	S
N	AEMST	T	CMST	X	ES
O	A	V	AES		
P	AMS		EMST		

Y	AMT
Z	ACEST

—— APPROXIMATE REGIONAL BOUNDARY

INDUSTRIES

A AGRICULTURE   M MANUFACTURING
C TRANSPORTATION AND   S SERVICE
   COMMUNICATION   T TRADE
E MINING

TABLE 1. Employees in Major Industry Groups, Six Central States, 1960

		Number of Employees
(A)	Agriculture	794,462
(C)	Transportation & Communication[a]	544,257
(E)	Mining	62,680
(F)	Forestry and Fishing	3,704
(M)	Manufacturing	2,111,451
(S)	Service[b]	2,953,136
(T)	Trade[c]	1,584,904
	TOTAL	8,054,594

[a] Railroad and railway express service; trucking service and warehousing; other transportation; communication.
[b] Construction; utilities and sanitary services; finance, insurance, and real estate; business services; repair services; private households; other personal services; entertainment and recreation services; hospitals; educational services: government and private welfare, religious, and nonprofit membership organizations; other professional and related services; public administration.
[c] Wholesale trade; food and dairy product stores; eating and drinking places; other retail trade.

is relatively weak. The region is dominated by counties having 3-industry combinations; some have more, but several are marked by 1-industry or 2-industry combinations.

The western region contains a great variety of local economies; indeed, this variety is what sets it apart from the other regions most strikingly. The region is further distinguished by the common appearance of mining within combinations. However, service, trade, and agriculture figure even more prominently, and manufacturing and transportation and communication also are present. The western region, like the eastern, tends towards local diversification with 4-, 5-, and 6-industry combinations predominating.

Individual Industry Groups

Industry combinations are relative descriptions which ultimately depend upon the distributional characteristics and total employment of each industry in comparison with those of other industries. The presence or absence of industries in combinations does not reflect accurately either absolute or relative magnitudes from place to place. Rather, individual industry distributions, as they appear within the combination context, reflect only relative industry importance on the local scene (Table 3). The pattern of an industry's presence is one indication of its value for areal differentiation within the combination framework; the strength of its presence also indicates broad economic differences.

TABLE 2. Industry Combination Determination, Calhoun County, Illinois, 1960

Industry	Number of Employees	Per cent of Employees	DEVIATION (D) IN PER CENT FROM IDEAL				d^2			
			1ᵃ	2ᵃ	3ᵃ	4ᵃ	1ᵃ	2ᵃ	3ᵃ	4ᵃ
A	710	37	63	13	4	12	4149	169	16	144
S	593	31		19	2	6		361	4	36
T	293	16			17	9			289	81
M	186	10				15				225
C	65	3								
F	36	2								
E	27	1								
TOTAL	1,910	100					4149	530	309	486
σ^2							4149	265	103	122
Combination										AST

ᵃ Number of industry groups in the combination.

Service is almost everywhere. It commonly ranks high and is represented in all but five counties. Therefore, the service industry has little value as a differentiating element in this study.

Trade is a poor industry for differentiating purposes for the same reason. Only 35 counties, mainly in the Great Plains area, do not include this function within their industry combinations. Trade generally rank lower than service throughout the six states, frequently ranking as low as fourth in the three eastern states.

Agriculture's importance for differentiation rests primarily on certain common associations with other industries. For, although a weak fourth among the industries in total employment, agriculture is widely distributed on a county basis. It also is locally powerful in less populated counties, particularly in the central region. Agriculture is not included in the combinations of 71 counties, mainly in the eastern half of the study area.

Manufacturing is of basic importance as a differentiating industry. Although employing almost three times as many workers as agriculture, manufacturing is much more concentrated on a county basis. Its presence is characteristic of the eastern region where it ranks particularly high in northern Illinois and in an area including southeastern Missouri and part of southwestern Illinois. Manufacturing is less important in the western region, both in rank and areal coverage, but it is weakest in the central region where few counties contain manufacturing and then generally as a low ranking function.

Mining shows up in only a few places—mining counties of southern Illinois and southeastern Missouri, petroleum producing counties of the Great Plains, and the Rocky Mountain mining counties. Mining commonly does not appear within combinations, even in counties where mineral production is large, because of the small number of people employed in the industry. Only the concentration of mining in the Rocky Mountain area is of regional differentiating value at the scale of this study.

The transportation and communication industry appears in the combinations of only a few scattered counties, and it never ranks higher than third. While employing two-thirds as many people as agriculture (nine times as many as mining), transportation and communication is concentrated in strategically dispersed, heavily populated counties where it often is overwhelmed by other industries. Therefore, this industry is of little use for areal differentiation within the combination construct.

Forestry and fishing is of no use for either place descriptions or regional differentiation within the study area. This industry group employs so few people that it does not enter into any combinations.

TABLE 3. Industry Ranks in Counties, Six Central States, 1960

Industry	NUMBER OF COUNTIES BY RANK						TOTAL
	1	*2*	*3*	*4*	*5*	*6*	
Agriculture	235	137	70	58	5	1	506
Transportation & Communication	0	0	3	13	21	2	39
Mining	6	4	10	15	2	4	41
Forestry & Fishing	0	0	0	0	0	0	0
Manufacturing	33	75	75	90	6	3	282
Service	300	260	12	0	0	0	572
Trade	3	96	373	69	1	0	542

Conclusion

John C. Weaver's method of determining agricultural combinations clearly may be extended to other phenomena. Application of the method to county economies in six central states distinguishes 20 economic types. These types describe related elements of local economic structures; to a degree, they identify economic ways-of-life. Moreover, certain industry-combination descriptions characterize large areas and thus allow the designation of regions whose general significance is enhanced by the method's emphasis upon related elements. Regions so designated would seem to have utility as a framework for broadly based regional treatments and for some aspects of national planning. Finally, although it is not touched upon in this paper, Weaver's approach also might be used for noting changes over time for economic complexes, individual industries, and the broader regions.

Classifying complexes of all kinds appears to be increasing among geographers. Although more inclusive than systems in that relationships among their elements may be more broadly defined, complexes still provide for regions and place descriptions based on meaningfully related and meaningfully limited criteria. Therefore, they offer one workable solution to the problem of accommodating several elements within a single organizing theme. Focusing in unified fashion upon complexes, instead of successively upon element after element, can add to the value of uniform regions for certain purposes. Weaver's method, which unites considerable comprehensiveness and discrimination with ease of understanding and application, is one of the means available for deriving such regions.

Correlation of This Book with Representative Texts

Text chs.	ALEXANDER *Economic Geography* Prentice-Hall, 1963	BOESCH *A Geography of World Economy* Van Nostrand, 1964	FRYER *World Economic Development* McGraw-Hill, 1965
	Related Selections in *Economic Geography*		
1	*1, 2, 4*	*1, 2, 4, 18*	*5, 15, 22, 28*
2		*3-12*	*24*
3	*5, 6*	*3, 9, 10*	*3*
4	*5, 6*	*4-7*	*4-8*
5	*10, 15*	*5-8*	
6	*9*	*1, 2, 4, 18, 21*	
7		*16, 18*	*8*
8	*8*	*11-13*	*9*
9	*3*	*19, 20*	*10*
10	*7*	*21-25*	*16-18, 26-28*
11		*23, 24*	*12*
12			*11*
13		*16, 25-28*	*13*
14	*11, 13*		
15	*12*		
16			
17			*19*
18			
19			*20*
20	*19*		*21-24*
21			*14, 25*
22			
23	*16, 17, 28*		
24	*27*		
25	*26*		
26	*14, 25*		
27	*25*		
28	*21, 22*		
29	*21-24*		
30	*22, 23*		
31	*16, 20*		
32	*2, 4, 18*		
33	*26-28*		
34			
35			
36			

	HIGHSMITH AND NORTHAM *World Economic Activities: A Geo-graphic Analysis* Harcourt Brace & World, 1968	HOFFMAN *Economic Geography* Ronald, 1965	JONES AND DARKENWALD *Economic Geography* Macmillan, 1965
Text chs.	Related Selections in *Economic Geography*		
1	*1, 5*	*1*	*1*
2	*3*	*26*	*2*
3	*4*	*2*	
4	*6*	*3*	*10*
5		*4*	*10*
6		*5, 6*	*15*
7		*7*	*9*
8	*8*	*8*	*20*
9	*10*		
10	*9*	*9*	*22*
11		*10*	
12	*11, 12*	*18, 28*	*5*
13	*2, 18, 28*	*11, 12, 26*	*6, 7*
14	*14, 15*	*15, 17-19*	
15	*19, 27*	*20, 27*	*6*
16	*21-23*	*21, 24, 25*	
17	*25*		*7*
18			*3*
19	*26, 27*		*4*
20	*3*		*8*
21			
22			
23			
24			
25			
26			
27			
28			*11*
29			*12*
30			*13*
31			*14*
32			*16, 17*
33			*15*
34			
35			*19*
36			
37			
38			*14*
39			
40			*25*

4